GCSE
Combined Science
Physics

The Complete Course for AQA

St Leonards Physics Department Book Issues

This book is loaned to you for the duration of your studies. Please keep the book clean and free from damage at all times. Please look after you book and refrain from graffiti. Books not returned in a reusable condition will incur charges that will be levied against your school account for a replacement. This book must be returned along with the protective cover by the 30th of May, prior to you completing your studies to avoid charges. The replacement cost is £30.00. Thank you.

Name (Print Name)	Date of Issue	Date Returned
Alice Dunstan	31/8/17	
Brodar as well		

How to get your free Online Edition

Go to **cgpbooks.co.uk/extras** and enter this code...

4303 6202 3794 8541

This code will only work once. If someone has used this book before you, they may have already claimed the Online Edition.

Contents

Published by CGP

Editors:
Robin Flello, Emily Garrett, Sharon Keeley-Holden, Duncan Lindsay, Frances Rooney,
Charlotte Whiteley, Sarah Williams and Jonathan Wray.

From original material by Paddy Gannon.

ISBN: 978 1 78294 640 3

With thanks to Glenn Rogers for the proofreading.
With thanks to Ana Pungartnik for the copyright research.

Data used to construct stopping distance diagram on page 177 from the Highway Code.
Contains public sector information licensed under the Open Government Licence v3.0.
http://www.nationalarchives.gov.uk/doc/open-government-licence/version/3/

Printed by Elanders Ltd, Newcastle upon Tyne.
Clipart from Corel®

How to use this book

Learning Objectives

- These tell you exactly what you need to learn, or be able to do, for the exam.

- There's a specification reference at the bottom that links to the AQA specification.

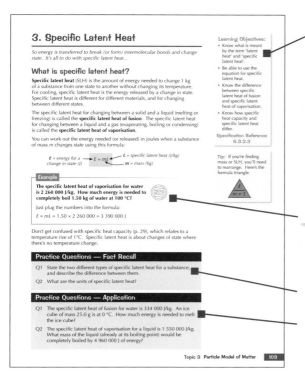

Maths Skills

- There's a range of maths skills you could be expected to apply in your exams. The section on pages 237-246 is packed with plenty of maths that you'll need to be familiar with.

- Examples that show these maths skills in action are marked up with this symbol.

Practice Questions

- Fact recall questions test that you know the facts needed for the physics part of GCSE Combined Science.

- Annoyingly, the examiners also expect you to be able to apply your knowledge to new situations — application questions give you plenty of practice at doing this.

- All the answers are in the back of the book.

Examples

These are here to help you understand the theory.

Required Practical Activities

There are some Required Practical Activities that you'll be expected to do throughout your course. You need to know all about them for the exams. They're all marked with stamps like this:

REQUIRED PRACTICAL 14

They're numbered 14-21 for physics to match the AQA specification.

Practical Skills

There's also a whole section on pages 231-236 with extra details on practical skills you'll be expected to use in the Required Practical Activities, and apply knowledge of in the exams.

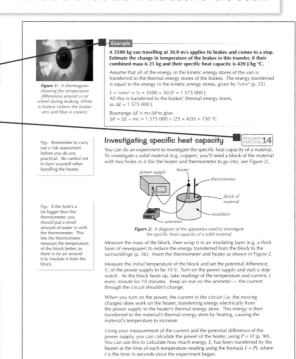

i

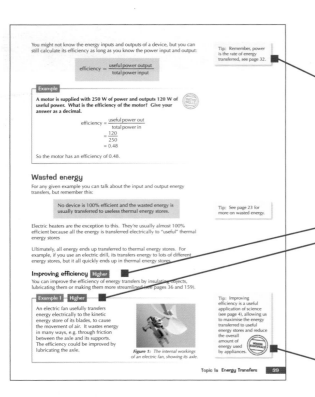

Tips and Exam Tips

- There are tips throughout this book to help you understand the theory.

- There are also exam tips to help you with answering exam questions.

Higher Exam Material

- Some of the material in this book will only come up in the exam if you're sitting the higher exam papers.

- This material is clearly marked with boxes that look like this:

  Higher   **H**   **Q1**

Working Scientifically

- Working Scientifically is a big part of GCSE Combined Science. There's a whole section on it at the front of the book.

- Working Scientifically is also covered throughout this book wherever you see this symbol.

Exam-style Questions

- Practising exam-style questions is really important — this book has some at the end of every topic to test you.

- They're the same style as the ones you'll get in the real exams.

- All the answers are in the back of the book, along with a mark scheme to show you how you get the marks.

- Higher-only questions are marked like this: **1.2**

Topic Checklist

Each topic has a checklist at the end with boxes that let you tick off what you've learnt.

Glossary

There's a glossary at the back of the book full of definitions you need to know for the exam, plus loads of other useful words.

Exam Help

There's a section at the back of the book stuffed full of things to help you with the exams.

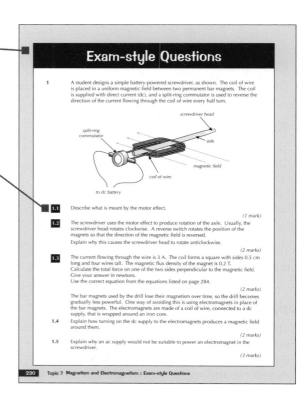

1. The Scientific Method

Science is all about finding things out and learning things about the world we live in. This section is all about the scientific process — how a scientist's initial idea turns into a theory that is accepted by the wider scientific community.

Hypotheses

Scientists try to explain things. Everything. They start by observing something they don't understand — it could be anything, e.g. planets in the sky, a person suffering from an illness, what matter is made of... anything.

Then, they come up with a **hypothesis** — a possible explanation for what they've observed. (Scientists can also sometimes form a model — a description or a representation of what's physically going on — see page 2).

The next step is to test whether the hypothesis might be right or not. This involves making a **prediction** based on the hypothesis and testing it by gathering evidence (i.e. data) from investigations. If evidence from experiments backs up a prediction, you're a step closer to figuring out if the hypothesis is true.

> **Tip:** Investigations include lab experiments and studies.

Testing a hypothesis

Normally, scientists share their findings in peer-reviewed journals, or at conferences. **Peer-review** is where other scientists check results and scientific explanations to make sure they're 'scientific' (e.g. that experiments have been done in a sensible way) before they're published. It helps to detect false claims, but it doesn't mean that findings are correct — just that they're not wrong in any obvious way.

Once other scientists have found out about a hypothesis, they'll start basing their own predictions on it and carry out their own experiments. They'll also try to reproduce the original experiments to check the results — and if all the experiments in the world back up the hypothesis, then scientists start to think the hypothesis is true.

However, if a scientist somewhere in the world does an experiment that doesn't fit with the hypothesis (and other scientists can reproduce these results), then the hypothesis is in trouble. When this happens, scientists have to come up with a new hypothesis (maybe a modification of the old hypothesis, or maybe a completely new one).

> **Tip:** Sometimes it can take a really long time for a hypothesis to be accepted.

Accepting a hypothesis

If pretty much every scientist in the world believes a hypothesis to be true because experiments back it up, then it usually goes in the textbooks for students to learn. Accepted hypotheses are often referred to as **theories**.

Our currently accepted theories are the ones that have survived this 'trial by evidence' — they've been tested many, many times over the years and survived (while the less good ones have been ditched). However... they never, never become hard and fast, totally indisputable fact. You can never know... it'd only take one odd, totally inexplicable result, and the hypothesising and testing would start all over again.

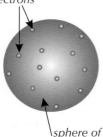

negatively-charged electrons

sphere of positive charge

Figure 1: *The plum pudding model of the atom.*

> ### Example
>
> - About 200 years ago, John Dalton proposed that atoms were tiny bits of matter which could never be split up.
>
> - About 100 years later, the electron was discovered. This meant our hypothesis of atoms was revised, and we began to think of atoms as lumps of positive charge with negative electrons sat inside them (see Figure 1) — this was the plum pudding model (see page 108).
>
> - After more evidence was gathered, the hypothesis was changed again and we developed the nuclear model of the atom — a tiny positive nucleus, orbited by negative electrons (see p. 110).

Tip: Like hypotheses, models have to be tested before they're accepted by other scientists. You can test models by using them to make a prediction, and then carrying out an investigation to see whether the results match the prediction.

Models

Models are used to describe or display how an object or system behaves in reality. They're often based on evidence collected from experiments, and should be able to accurately predict what will happen in other, similar experiments. There are different types of models that scientists can use to describe the world around them. Here are just a few:

- A **descriptive model** describes what's happening in a certain situation, without explaining why. It won't necessarily include details that could be used to predict the outcome of a different scenario. For example, a graph showing the measured resistance of a device at different temperatures would be a descriptive model.

- A **representational model** is a simplified description or picture of what's going on in real life. It can be used to explain observations and make predictions. E.g. the nuclear model is a simplified way of showing the arrangement of electrons in an atom (see p. 110). It can be used to explain how electrons move between different energy levels.

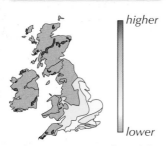

higher

lower

Figure 2: *A spatial model showing radiation from rocks in the United Kingdom. The scale shows how the level of radiation from rocks in different areas varies.*

- **Spatial models** are used to summarise how data is arranged within space. For example, a map showing where high levels of radiation from rocks is found would be a spatial model.

- **Computational models** use computers to make simulations of complex real-life processes, such as climate change. They're used when there are a lot of different variables (factors that change) to consider, and because you can easily change their design to take into account new data.

Tip: Mathematical models are made using patterns found in data and also using information about known relationships between variables.

- **Mathematical models** can be used to describe the relationship between variables in numerical form (e.g. as an equation), and therefore predict outcomes of a scenario. For example, an equation can be written to predict the energy transferred to or from a material's thermal energy stores when it changes temperature. This is dependent on the change in temperature of the material, its mass and its specific heat capacity (see page 29).

All models have limitations on what they can explain or predict. The Big Bang model (a model used to describe the beginning of the universe) can be used to explain why everything in the universe is moving away from us. One of its limitations is that is doesn't explain the moments before the Big Bang.

Tip: Like hypotheses, models are constantly being revised and modified, based on new data.

Communicating results

Some scientific discoveries show that people should change their habits, or they might provide ideas that could be developed into new technology. So scientists need to tell the world about their discoveries.

Example

Radioactive materials are used widely in medicine for imaging and treatment. Information about these materials needs to be communicated to doctors so they can make use of them. The patients also need to be told of the risks involved so they can make informed decisions about their treatment.

Tip: New scientific discoveries are usually communicated to the public in the news or via the internet. They might be communicated to governments and large organisations via reports or meetings.

Reports about scientific discoveries in the media (e.g. newspapers or television) aren't peer-reviewed. This means that, even though news stories are often based on data that has been peer-reviewed, the data might be presented in a way that is over-simplified or inaccurate, leaving it open to misinterpretation.

It's important that the evidence isn't presented in a **biased** way. This can sometimes happen when people want to make a point, e.g. they overemphasise a relationship in the data. (Sometimes without knowing they're doing it.) There are all sorts of reasons why people might want to do this.

Tip: If you're reading an article about a new scientific discovery, always think about how the study was carried out. It may be that the sample size was very small, and so the results aren't representative (see page 10 for more on sample sizes).

Examples

- They want to keep the organisation or company that's funding the research happy. (If the results aren't what they'd like they might not give them any more money to fund further research.)
- Governments might want to persuade voters, other governments or journalists to agree with their policies about a certain issue.
- Companies might want to 'big up' their products, or make impressive safety claims.
- Environmental campaigners might want to persuade people to behave differently.

Tip: An example of bias is a newspaper article describing details of data supporting an idea without giving any of the evidence against it.

There's also a risk that if an investigation is done by a team of highly-regarded scientists it'll be taken more seriously than evidence from less well known scientists. But having experience, authority or a fancy qualification doesn't necessarily mean the evidence is good — the only way to tell is to look at the evidence scientifically (e.g. is it repeatable, valid, etc. — see page 8).

2. Scientific Applications and Issues

New scientific discoveries can lead to lots of exciting new ways of using science in our everyday lives. Unfortunately, these developments may also come with problems that need to be considered.

Using scientific developments

Lots of scientific developments go on to have useful applications.

Examples

- The discovery of the generator effect (which turns movement into potential difference) allowed people to develop machines to easily generate electricity. This is the basis for the widespread electricity supplies we have today.

- As scientists investigated the effects of radiation, they found they had damaging effects on the body, which could be used to kill cancer cells.

Issues created by science

Scientific knowledge is increased by doing experiments. And this knowledge leads to scientific developments, e.g. new technologies or new advice. These developments can create issues though. For example, they could create political issues, which could lead to developments being ignored, or governments being slow to act if they think responding to the developments could affect their popularity with voters.

Example

Some governments were pretty slow to accept the fact that human activities are causing global warming, despite all the evidence. This is because accepting it means they've got to do something about it, which costs money and could hurt their economy. This could lose them a lot of votes.

Scientific developments can cause a whole host of other issues too.

Tip: See page 54 for more on global warming.

Examples

- **Economic issues**: Society can't always afford to do things scientists recommend (e.g. investing heavily in alternative energy sources) without cutting back elsewhere.

- **Social issues**: Decisions based on scientific evidence affect people — e.g. should fossil fuels be taxed more highly (to encourage investment in alternative energy)? Should alcohol be banned (to prevent health problems)? Would the effect on people's lifestyles be acceptable?

- **Environmental issues**: Human activity often affects the natural environment — e.g. burning fossil fuels may be cheaper than using alternative energy resources, but it has a large impact on the environment.

- **Personal issues**: Some decisions will affect individuals. For example, someone might support alternative energy, but object if a wind farm is built next to their house.

Figure 1: *The ATLAS detector at CERN, part of the Large Hadron Collider (LHC). The LHC has greatly advanced our knowledge of subatomic particles, but it also cost a lot of money to build and run.*

3. Limitations of Science

Science has taught us an awful lot about the world we live in and how things work — but science doesn't have the answer for everything.

Questions science hasn't answered yet

We don't understand everything. And we never will. We'll find out more, for sure — as more hypotheses are suggested, and more experiments are done. But there'll always be stuff we don't know.

Examples

- Today we don't know as much as we'd like about the impacts of global warming. How much will sea levels rise? And to what extent will weather patterns change?

- We also don't know anywhere near as much as we'd like about the universe. Are there other life forms out there? And what is most of the universe made of?

In order to answer scientific questions, scientists need data to provide evidence for their hypotheses. Some questions can't be answered yet because the data can't currently be collected, or because there's not enough data to support a theory. But eventually, as we get more evidence, we probably will be able to answer these questions. By then there'll be loads of new questions to answer though.

Figure 1: *The night sky. We can use high powered telescopes to observe some of the universe but we still have little idea what most of it is made of or how it was formed.*

Questions science can't answer

There are some questions that all the experiments in the world won't help us answer — for example, the "should we be doing this at all?" type questions.

Example

Take the idea of space exploration and the search for alien life — some people think it's a good idea. It increases our knowledge of the universe and the new technologies developed to explore space can be useful on Earth too. For example, a lot of developments within space exploration has led to improvements of MRI machines — these are used in hospitals to image the inside of the body. It also inspires young people to get into science.

Other people say it's a bad idea. They think we should concentrate on understanding our own planet better first, or spend the vast amounts of money on solving more urgent problems here on Earth — things like providing clean drinking water and curing diseases in poor countries.

The question of whether something is morally or ethically right or wrong can't be answered by more experiments — there is no "right" or "wrong" answer. The best we can do is get a consensus from society — a judgement that most people are more or less happy to live by. Science can provide more information to help people make this judgement, and the judgement might change over time. But in the end it's up to people and their conscience.

Tip: Some experiments have to be approved by ethics committees before scientists are allowed to carry them out. This stops scientists from getting wrapped up in whether they <u>can</u> do something, before anyone stops to think about whether they <u>should</u> do it.

4. Risks and Hazards

A lot of things we do could cause us harm. But some things are more hazardous than they at first seem, whereas other things are less hazardous than they at first seem. This may sound confusing, but it'll all become clear...

What are risks and hazards?

A **hazard** is something that could potentially cause harm. All hazards have a **risk** attached to them — this is the chance that the hazard will cause harm.

The risks of some things seem pretty obvious, or we've known about them for a while, like the risk of causing acid rain by polluting the atmosphere, or of having a car accident when you're travelling in a car.

New technology arising from scientific advances can bring new risks. These risks need to be thought about alongside the potential benefits of the technology, in order to make a decision about whether it should be made available to the general public.

Tip: A CT (computerised tomography) scan uses X-rays to form an image of the inside of a patient (see page 208).

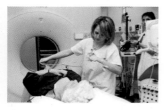

Figure 1: *A patient being prepared for a CT scan.*

> ### Example
>
> There are now a number of imaging technologies, like CT scans, that can be used to see inside the human body. These can allow doctors to diagnose medical conditions in order to treat them.
>
> However, these scans use ionising radiation, and so carry with them the risk of causing cancer in the patient. The risk of dying from cancer caused by the scans has to be weighed against the risk of dying from the medical condition that needs to be diagnosed. Often the risk from the medical condition far outweighs the risk from the scan, so the scan will go ahead.

Estimating risk

You can estimate the risk based on how many times something happens in a big sample (e.g. 100 000 people) over a given period (e.g. a year). For example, you could assess the risk of a driver crashing by recording how many people in a group of 100 000 drivers crashed their cars over a year.

To make a decision about an activity that involves a hazardous event, we don't just need to take into account the chance of the event causing harm, but also how serious the consequences would be if it did.

The general rule is that, if an activity involves a hazard that's very likely to cause harm, with serious consequences if it does, that activity is considered high-risk.

> ### Example 1
>
> If you go for a run, you may sprain an ankle. But most small sprains recover within a few days if they're rested, so going for a run would be considered a low-risk activity.

Example 2

If you go skiing, you may fall and break a bone. This would take many weeks to heal, and may cause further complications later on in life. So skiing would be considered higher risk than running.

Perceptions of risk

Not all risks have the same consequences, e.g. if you chop veg with a sharp knife you risk cutting your finger, but if you go scuba-diving you risk death. You're much more likely to cut your finger during half an hour of chopping than to die during half an hour of scuba-diving. But most people are happier to accept a higher probability of an accident if the consequences are short-lived and fairly minor.

People tend to be more willing to accept a risk if they choose to do something (e.g. go scuba diving), compared to having the risk imposed on them (e.g. having a nuclear power station built next door).

People's perception of risk (how risky they think something is) isn't always accurate. They tend to view familiar activities as low-risk and unfamiliar activities as high-risk — even if that's not the case. For example, cycling on roads is often high-risk, but many people are happy to do it because it's a familiar activity. Air travel is actually pretty safe, but a lot of people perceive it as high-risk. People may under-estimate the risk of things with long-term or invisible negative effects, e.g. using tanning beds.

Tip: Risks people choose to take are called 'voluntary risks'. Risks that people are forced to take are called 'imposed risks'.

Reducing risk in investigations

Part of planning an investigation is making sure that it's safe. To make sure your experiment is safe you must identify all the hazards. Hazards include:

- Lasers: e.g. if a laser is directed into the eye, this can cause blindness.

- Gamma radiation: e.g. gamma-emitting radioactive sources can cause cancer.

- Fire: e.g. an unattended Bunsen burner is a fire hazard.

- Electricity: e.g. faulty electrical equipment could give you a shock.

Once you've identified the hazards you might encounter, you should think of ways of reducing the risks from the hazards.

Tip: You can find out about potential hazards by looking in textbooks, doing some internet research, or asking your teacher.

Figure 2: A scientist wearing safety goggles to protect her eyes during an experiment.

Examples

- If you're working with springs, always wear safety goggles. This will reduce the risk of the spring (or a fragment of it) hitting your eye if the spring snaps.

- If you're using a Bunsen burner, stand it on a heat proof mat. This will reduce the risk of starting a fire.

5. Designing Investigations

To be a good scientist you need to know how to design a good experiment, including how to make sure you get good quality results.

Making predictions from a hypothesis

Scientists observe things and come up with hypotheses to explain them. To decide whether a **hypothesis** might be correct you need to do an investigation to gather evidence, which will help support or disprove the hypothesis. The first step is to use the hypothesis to come up with a **prediction** — a statement about what you think will happen that you can test.

> **Example**
>
> If your hypothesis is "aluminium foil is a better thermal insulator than newspaper", then your prediction might be "a cup of hot water wrapped in newspaper will cool down to a lower temperature than a cup of hot water wrapped in aluminium foil will over a period of five minutes".

Once a scientist has come up with a prediction, they'll design an investigation to see if there are patterns or relationships between two variables. For example, to see if there's a pattern or relationship between the variables 'insulating material used' and 'change in temperature'.

Tip: A variable is just something in the experiment that can change.

Repeatable and reproducible results

Results need to be **repeatable** and **reproducible**. Repeatable means that if the same person does an experiment again using the same methods and equipment, they'll get similar results. Reproducible means that if someone else does the experiment, or a different method or piece of equipment is used, the results will be similar.

Tip: Data that's repeatable and reproducible is <u>reliable</u> and scientists are more likely to have confidence in it.

> **Example**
>
> In 1989, two scientists claimed that they'd produced 'cold fusion' (the energy source of the Sun but without the high temperatures). If it was true, it would have meant free energy for the world forever. However, other scientists just couldn't reproduce the results, so 'cold fusion' wasn't accepted as a theory.

Figure 1: Stanley Pons and Martin Fleischmann — the scientists who allegedly discovered cold fusion.

Ensuring the test is valid

Valid results are repeatable, reproducible and answer the original question.

Tip: Peer review (see page 1) is used to make sure that results are valid before they're published.

> **Example**
>
> **Do power lines cause cancer?**
>
> Some studies have found that children who live near overhead power lines are more likely to develop cancer. What they'd actually found was a **correlation** (relationship) between the variables "presence of power lines" and "incidence of cancer". They found that as one changed, so did the other.
>
> But this data isn't enough to say that the power lines cause cancer, as there might be other explanations. For example, power lines are often near busy roads, so the areas tested could contain different levels of pollution. As the studies don't show a definite link they don't answer the original question.

Tip: See page 16 for more on correlation.

Ensuring it's a fair test

In a lab experiment you usually change one variable and measure how it affects another variable. To make it a fair test, everything else that could affect the results should stay the same (otherwise you can't tell if the thing you're changing is causing the results or not — the data won't be valid).

Tip: For the results of an investigation to be <u>valid</u> the investigation must be a <u>fair test</u>.

> **Example**
>
> To investigate how the length of a wire affects its resistance, you must only change the wire length. You need to keep, for example, the temperature the same, otherwise you won't know if any change in the resistance was caused by the change in length, or the change in temperature.

The variable you change is called the **independent variable**. The variable you measure when you change the independent variable is called the **dependent variable**. The variables that you keep the same are called **control variables**.

> **Example**
>
> In the resistance experiment above, the length of the wire is the independent variable, the resistance is the dependent variable, and the control variables are the temperature, supplied potential difference, wire thickness, etc.

Control experiments and control groups

In some investigations it's useful to have a **control experiment** — an experiment that's kept under the same conditions as the rest of the investigation, but doesn't have anything done to it. This allows you to see exactly what effect changing the independent variable has in the investigation.

Tip: Control experiments let you see what happens when you don't change anything at all.

> **Example**
>
> You can investigate how different materials act as thermal insulators by wrapping each material round a beaker of hot water and recording how much the temperature of the water has dropped by after a given time period. However, you would also carry out the experiment without any insulating material — the control experiment. This gives you a point of comparison, so you can evaluate by how much a thermal insulator has slowed down the cooling process. Without it, you wouldn't know if the insulators were actually slowing down the cooling rate.

Tip: The control experiment in this example could also account for any systematic errors (see page 12) that may be affecting all of your results.

It's important that a study (an investigation that doesn't take place in a lab) is a fair test, just like a lab experiment. It's a lot trickier to control the variables in a study than it is in a lab experiment though. Sometimes you can't control them all, but you can use a **control group** to help. This is a group of whatever you're studying (e.g. people) that's kept under the same conditions as the group in the experiment, but doesn't have anything done to it.

> **Example**
>
> If you were studying the link between CT scans and thyroid cancer, you'd take one group of people who have had CT scans, and another group (the control group) who haven't. Both groups should be of roughly the same age, live in the same area, have similar lifestyles, etc.
>
> The control group will help you try to account for other variables like people's diet, which could affect the results.

Sample size

Tip: It's hard to spot anomalies if your sample size is too small.

Data based on small samples isn't as good as data based on large samples. A sample should be representative of the whole population (i.e. it should share as many of the various characteristics in the population as possible) — a small sample can't do that as well.

The bigger the sample size the better, but scientists have to be realistic when choosing how big.

Example

If you were studying how exposure to sunlight affects people's risk of skin cancer it'd be great to study everyone in the UK (a huge sample), but it'd take ages and cost a bomb. Studying a thousand people with a mixture of ages, gender and race would be more realistic.

Trial runs

Tip: If you don't have time to do a trial run, you could always look at the data other people have got doing a similar experiment and use a range and interval values similar to theirs.

It's a good idea to do a **trial run** (a quick version of your experiment) before you do the proper experiment. Trial runs are used to figure out the range (the upper and lower limits) of independent variable values used in the proper experiment. If there was no change in the dependent variable between your upper and lower values in the trial run, then you might increase the range until there was an observable change. Or if there was a large change, you might want to make your higher and lower values closer together.

Example

In the experiment on p. 143, masses are added to a spring to find how the force acting on the spring is related to its extension. Enough data points need to be collected before the spring stretches beyond its limit of proportionality. Doing a trial run on the spring (or an identical one) ensures that your lower independent variable value (the smallest total mass) doesn't stretch the spring too far, but is also large enough to cause a notable extension. A trial run could also be used to check that your upper independent value (the largest mass) will tell you what the spring's limit of proportionality is.

Trial runs can be used to figure out the appropriate intervals (gaps) between the values too. The intervals can't be too small (otherwise the experiment would take ages), or too big (otherwise you might miss something).

Example

If, in the experiment in the example above, the spring extended a lot when you added a 100 g mass, you may be better using 10 g masses instead.

Tip: Consistently repeating the results is crucial for checking that your results are repeatable.

Trial runs can also help you figure out whether or not your experiment is repeatable. If you repeat it three times and the results are all similar, the experiment is repeatable.

6. Collecting Data

Once you've designed your experiment, you need to get on and do it. Here's a guide to making sure the results you collect are good.

Getting good quality results

When you do an experiment you want your results to be **repeatable**, **reproducible** and as **accurate** and **precise** as possible.

To check repeatability you need to repeat the readings and check that the results are similar — you should repeat each reading at least three times. To make sure your results are reproducible you can cross check them by taking a second set of readings with another instrument (or a different observer).

Your data also needs to be accurate. Really accurate results are those that are really close to the true answer. The accuracy of your results usually depends on your method — you need to make sure you're measuring the right thing and that you don't miss anything that should be included in the measurements. For example, estimating the wavelength of water waves produced by a signal generator by counting the number waves in a set distance isn't very accurate because you might miss some of the waves as they're moving. It's more accurate to use a strobe light to show a 'frozen' shadow pattern of the waves and then count the number of shadows (each shadow represents one wave). See pages 192-193 for more on this experiment.

Your data also needs to be precise. Precise results are ones where the data is all really close to the mean (average) of your repeated results (i.e. not spread out).

> **Tip:** Sometimes, you can work out what result you should get at the end of an experiment (the theoretical result) by doing a bit of maths. If your experiment is accurate there shouldn't be much difference between the theoretical result and the result you actually get.

> **Tip:** For more on means see page 13.

Example

Look at the data in this table. Data set 1 is more precise than data set 2 because all the data in set 1 is really close to the mean, whereas the data in set 2 is more spread out.

Repeat	Data set 1	Data set 2
1	12	11
2	14	17
3	13	14
Mean	13	14

Choosing the right equipment

When doing an experiment, you need to make sure you're using the right equipment for the job. The measuring equipment you use has to be sensitive enough to measure the changes you're looking for.

Example

If you need to measure changes of 1 cm³ you need to use a measuring cylinder that can measure in 1 cm³ steps — it'd be no good trying with one that only measures 10 cm³ steps, it wouldn't be sensitive enough.

The smallest change a measuring instrument can detect is called its **resolution**. For example, some mass balances have a resolution of 1 g, some have a resolution of 0.1 g, and some are even more sensitive.

Figure 1: *Different types of measuring cylinder and glassware — make sure you choose the right one before you start an experiment.*

Also, equipment needs to be **calibrated** by measuring a known value. If there's a difference between the measured and known value, you can use this to correct the inaccuracy of the equipment.

> **Example**
>
> If a known mass is put on a mass balance, but the reading is a different value, you know that the mass balance has not been calibrated properly.

Errors

Random errors

The results of an experiment will always vary a bit due to **random errors** — unpredictable differences caused by things like human errors in measuring.

> **Example**
>
> Errors made when reading from a measuring cylinder are random. You have to estimate or round the level when it's between two marks — so sometimes your figure will be a bit above the real one, and sometimes a bit below.

You can reduce the effect of random errors by taking repeat readings and finding the mean. This will make your results more precise.

Systematic errors

If a measurement is wrong by the same amount every time, it's called a **systematic error**.

> **Example**
>
> If you measured from the very end of your ruler instead of from the 0 cm mark every time, all your measurements would be a bit small.

Just to make things more complicated, if a systematic error is caused by using equipment that isn't zeroed properly it's called a **zero error**. You can compensate for some of these errors if you know about them though.

> **Example**
>
> If a mass balance always reads 1 gram before you put anything on it, all your measurements will be 1 gram too heavy. This is a zero error. You can compensate for this by subtracting 1 gram from all your results.

Anomalous results

Sometimes you get a result that doesn't seem to fit in with the rest at all. These results are called **anomalous results** (or outliers).

> **Example**
>
> Look at the data in this table. The entry that has been circled is an anomalous result because it's much larger than any of the other data values.
>
> | Experiment | A | B | C | D | E | F |
> |---|---|---|---|---|---|---|
> | Acceleration (m/s²) | 1.05 | 1.12 | 1.08 | 8.54 | 1.06 | 1.11 |

You should investigate anomalous results and try to work out what happened. If you can work out what happened (e.g. you measured something totally wrong) you can ignore them when processing your results.

7. Processing Data

Once you've collected some data, you might need to process it.

Organising data

It's really important that your data is organised. Tables are dead useful for organising data. When you draw a table use a ruler, make sure each column has a heading (including the units) and keep it neat and tidy.

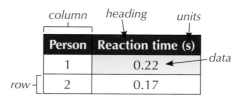

Figure 1: *Table showing the time taken to react to a stimulus for two people.*

Processing your data

When you've collected data from a number of repeats of an experiment, it's useful to summarise it using a few handy-to-use figures.

Mean and range

When you've done repeats of an experiment you should always calculate the **mean** (a type of average). To do this add together all the data values and divide by the total number of values in the sample.

You might also need to calculate the **range** (how spread out the data is). To do this find the largest number and subtract the smallest number from it.

Tip: If you're recording your data as decimals, make sure you give each value to the same number of decimal places.

> **Example**
>
> Look at the data in the table below. The mean and range of each set of data has been calculated.
>
>
>
> | Trolley | Repeat (m/s) | | | Mean (m/s) | Range (m/s) |
> |---------|:---:|:---:|:---:|------------|-------------|
> | | 1 | 2 | 3 | | |
> | A | 3.1 | 3.6 | 3.2 | (3.1 + 3.6 + 3.2) ÷ 3 = 3.3 | 3.6 − 3.1 = 0.5 |
> | B | 4.7 | 5.1 | 5.8 | (4.7 + 5.1 + 5.8) ÷ 3 = 5.2 | 5.8 − 4.7 = 1.1 |

Tip: Annoyingly, it's difficult to see any patterns or relationships in detail just from a table. You need to use some kind of graph or chart for that (see pages 15-16).

Median and mode

There are two more types of average, other than the mean, that you might need to calculate. These are the **median** and the **mode**.

- To calculate the median, put all your data in numerical order — the median is the middle value.

- The number that appears most often in a data set is the mode.

Tip: You should ignore anomalous results when calculating the mean, range, median or mode — see page 12 for more on anomalous results.

> **Example**
>
> **The results of a study investigating the reaction times (in seconds) of students are shown below:**
> **0.10, 0.25, 0.20, 0.15, 0.25, 0.15, 0.25, 0.20, 0.30**
>
> First put the data in numerical order:
> 0.10, 0.15, 0.15, 0.20, 0.20, 0.25, 0.25, 0.25, 0.30
>
> There are nine values, so the median is the 5th number, which is 0.20.
>
> 0.25 comes up three times. No other numbers come up more than twice. So the mode is 0.25.

Tip: If you have an even number of values, the median is the mean of the middle two values.

Uncertainty

Tip: There's more about errors on page 12.

When you repeat a measurement, you often get a slightly different figure each time you do it due to random error. This means that each result has some **uncertainty** to it. The measurements you make will also have some uncertainty in them due to limits in the resolution of the equipment you use. This all means that the mean of a set of results will also have some uncertainty to it. Here's how to calculate the uncertainty of a mean result:

$$\text{uncertainty} = \frac{\text{range}}{2}$$

The larger the range, the less precise your results are and the more uncertainty there will be in your results. Uncertainties are shown using the '±' symbol.

Example

The table below shows the results of an experiment to determine the resistance of a piece of wire in a circuit.

Repeat	1	2	3	mean
Resistance (Ω)	4.20	3.80	3.70	3.90

1. The range is: $4.20 - 3.70 = 0.50 \ \Omega$

2. So the uncertainty of the mean is: range ÷ 2 = $0.50 \div 2 = 0.25 \ \Omega$. You'd write this as $3.90 \pm 0.25 \ \Omega$

Tip: Since uncertainty affects precision, you'll need to think about it when you come to evaluate your results (see page 20).

Measuring a greater amount of something helps to reduce uncertainty. For example, for radioactive decay, measuring the count rate over a longer period compared to a shorter period reduces the percentage uncertainty in your results.

Rounding to significant figures

Exam Tip
If a question asks you to give your answer to a certain number of significant figures, make sure you do this, or you might not get all the marks.

The first **significant figure** (s.f.) of a number is the first digit that isn't a zero. The second, third and fourth significant figures follow on immediately after the first (even if they're zeros). When you're processing your data you may well want to round any really long numbers to a certain number of s.f.

Example

0.6874976 rounds to **0.69 to 2 s.f.** and to **0.687 to 3 s.f.**

Tip: Remember to write down how many significant figures you've rounded to after your answer.

When you're doing calculations using measurements given to a certain number of significant figures, you should give your answer to the lowest number of significant figures that was used in the calculation. If your calculation has multiple steps, only round the final answer, or it won't be as accurate.

Example

For the calculation: $1.2 \div 1.85 = 0.648648648...$

1.2 is given to 2 significant figures. 1.85 is given to 3 significant figures. So the answer should be given to 2 significant figures.

Round the final significant figure (0.6$\underline{4}$8) up to 5: $1.2 \div 1.85 = 0.65$ (2 s.f.)

Tip: When rounding a number, if the next digit after the last significant figure you're using is less than 5 you should round it <u>down</u>, and if it's 5 or more you should round it <u>up</u>.

The lowest number of significant figures in the calculation is used because the fewer digits a measurement has, the less accurate it is. Your answer can only be as accurate as the least accurate measurement in the calculation.

8. Graphs and Charts

It can often be easier to see trends in data by plotting a graph or chart of your results, rather than by looking at numbers in a table.

Plotting your data on a graph or chart

One of the best ways to present your data after you've processed it is to plot your results on a graph or chart. You need to know these rules about drawing graphs and charts:

- Draw it nice and big (covering at least half of the graph paper).

- Label both axes and remember to include the units.

- If you've got more than one set of data include a key.

- Give your graph a title explaining what it is showing.

Whatever type of graph or chart you draw, make sure you follow the rules above. There are lots of different types you can use. The type you should use depends on the type of data you've collected.

Bar charts and histograms

If either the independent or dependent variable is **categoric** or **discrete**, you should use a bar chart to display the data (see Figure 1). If the independent variable is **continuous**, the frequency data should be shown on a histogram. Histograms may look like bar charts, but it's the area of the bars that represents the frequency (rather than height). The height of each bar is called the **frequency density** and is found by dividing the frequency by the class width. (The class width is just the width of the bar on the histogram, see Figure 1.)

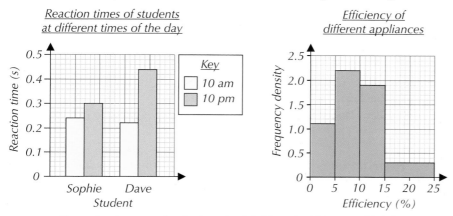

Figure 1: *An example of a bar chart (left) and a histogram (right).*

Plotting points

If the independent and the dependent variable are continuous you should plot points on a graph to display the data. Here are the golden rules specifically for plotting points on graphs:

- Put the independent variable (the thing you change) on the x-axis.

- Put the dependent variable (the thing you measure) on the y-axis.

- To plot the points, use a sharp pencil and make a neat little cross.

Tip: Categoric data is data that comes in distinct categories, e.g. 'state of matter (solid, liquid, gas)' and 'type of material (e.g. wood metal, paper)'. Discrete data can only take certain values, because there are no in-between values, e.g. 'number of people' (because you can't have half a person). Continuous data is numerical data that can have any value within a range, e.g. length, volume, temperature.

Tip: Frequency is just the number of times that something occurs. It's often shown in a frequency table.

Tip: A frequency diagram is a histogram where the width of all the bars are the same and frequency is plotted on the y-axis, rather than frequency density.

Tip: The x-axis is the horizontal axis and the y-axis is the vertical axis.

In general, you shouldn't join the crosses up. Only specific graphs, such as distance-time graphs (page 152) and velocity-time graphs (page 155), will need you to connect every point you plot. Otherwise, you'll need to draw a line of best fit (or a curve of best fit if your points make a curve). When drawing a line (or curve), try to draw the line through or as near to as many points as possible, ignoring anomalous results. When you draw a line of best fit, there should be roughly as many points above the line as underneath it.

Tip: Use the biggest data values you've got to draw a sensible scale on your axes. Here, the highest current is 8.8 A, so it makes sense to label the y-axis up to 10 A.

Tip: If you're not in an exam, you can use a computer to plot your graph and draw your line of best fit for you.

Graph to show current against potential difference

Current (A) / Potential difference (V)

line of best fit

anomalous result

Figure 2: *An example of a graph with points plotted and a line of best fit drawn.*

Correlations

Graphs are used to show the relationship between two variables. Data can show three different types of **correlation** (relationship).

Tip: Just because two variables are correlated doesn't mean that the change in one is causing the change in the other. There might be other factors involved, or it could be due to chance — see pages 19-20 for more.

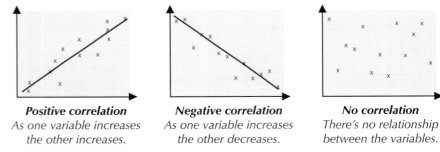

Positive correlation	***Negative correlation***	***No correlation***
As one variable increases the other increases.	*As one variable increases the other decreases.*	*There's no relationship between the variables.*

Figure 3: *Examples of different types of correlations shown on a graph.*

You also need to be able to describe the following types of graphs.

Tip: For variables that are directly proportional, both variables increase (or decrease) in the same ratio.

Tip: You can find out a lot of useful information from the line of best fit you draw. For more on how to get the most out of your graphs, see pages 243-245.

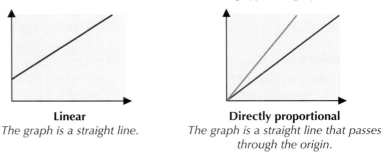

Linear	**Directly proportional**
The graph is a straight line.	*The graph is a straight line that passes through the origin.*

Figure 4: *Examples of linear graphs. The graph on the right shows two linear graphs where the variables are directly proportional to each other.*

9. Units

Using the correct units is important when you're drawing graphs or calculating values with an equation. Otherwise your numbers don't really mean anything.

S.I. units

Lots of different units can be used to describe the same quantity. For example, volume can be given in terms of cubic feet, cubic metres, litres or pints. It would be quite confusing if different scientists used different units to define quantities, as it would be hard to compare people's data. To stop this happening, scientists have come up with a set of standard units, called **S.I. units**, that all scientists use to measure their data. Here are some S.I. units you'll see in physics:

Quantity	S.I. Unit
mass	kilogram, kg
length	metre, m
time	second, s
electric current	ampere, A

Figure 1: Some common S.I. units used in physics.

Tip: S.I. stands for 'Système International', which is French for 'international system'.

Scaling prefixes

Quantities come in a huge range of sizes. For example, the volume of a swimming pool might be around 2 000 000 000 cm³, while the volume of a cup is around 250 cm³. To make the size of numbers more manageable, larger or smaller units are used. Figure 2 shows the prefixes which can be used in front of units (e.g. metres) to make them bigger or smaller:

prefix	tera (T)	giga (G)	mega (M)	kilo (k)	deci (d)	centi (c)	milli (m)	micro (μ)	nano (n)
multiple of unit	10^{12}	10^9	1 000 000 (10^6)	1000	0.1	0.01	0.001	0.000001 (10^{-6})	10^{-9}

Figure 2: Scaling prefixes used with units.

These prefixes are called **scaling prefixes** and they tell you how much bigger or smaller a unit is than the original unit. So one kilometre is one thousand metres.

Converting between units

To swap from one unit to another, all you need to know is what number you have to divide or multiply by to get from the original unit to the new unit — this is called the **conversion factor** and is equal to the number of times the smaller unit goes into the larger unit.

- To go from a bigger unit to a smaller unit, you multiply by the conversion factor.

- To go from a smaller unit to a bigger unit, you divide by the conversion factor.

Exam Tip
If you're going from a smaller unit to a larger unit, your number should get smaller. If you're going from a larger unit to a smaller unit, your number should get larger. This is a handy way to check you've done the conversion correctly.

There are some conversions that'll be particularly useful for physics. Here they are...

Mass can have units of kg and g.

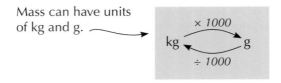

Length can have lots of units, including mm, μm and nm.

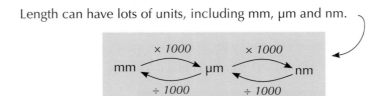

Time can have units of min and s.

Area can have units of m², cm² and mm².

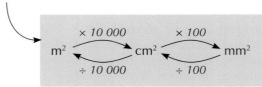

Volume can have units of m³, dm³ and cm³.

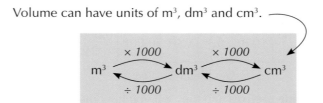

Examples

- To go from dm³ to cm³, you'd multiply by 1000.

  2 dm³ is equal to 2 × 1000 = **2000 cm³**

- To go from grams to kilograms, you'd divide by 1000.

  3400 g is equal to 3400 ÷ 1000 = **3.4 kg**

(MATHS SKILLS)

10. Conclusions and Evaluations

So... you've planned and carried out an amazing experiment, got your data and have processed and presented it in a sensible way. Now it's time to figure out what your data actually tells you, and how much you can trust what it says.

How to draw conclusions

Drawing conclusions might seem pretty straightforward — you just look at your data and say what pattern or relationship you see between the dependent and independent variables.

But you've got to be really careful that your conclusion matches the data you've got and doesn't go any further. You also need to be able to use your results to justify your conclusion (i.e. back up your conclusion with some specific data).

When writing a conclusion you need to refer back to the original hypothesis and say whether the data supports it or not.

Example

This table shows the count rate detected when one of two different materials (A and B) is placed between a radioactive sample and the detector.

Material	Count rate (counts per second)
A	85
B	13
No material	98

The conclusion of this experiment would be that material B blocks more of the radiation from the sample than material A.

The justification for this conclusion is that the count rate was much lower using material B compared with using material A.

You can't conclude that material B blocks more radiation from any other radioactive sample — the results might be completely different.

Correlation and causation

If two things are correlated (i.e. there's a relationship between them) it doesn't necessarily mean that a change in one variable is causing the change in the other — this is really important, don't forget it. There are three possible reasons for a correlation:

Tip: Graphs are useful for seeing whether two variables are correlated (see page 16).

1. Chance

Even though it might seem a bit weird, it's possible that two things show a correlation in a study purely because of chance.

Tip: Causation just means one thing is causing another.

Example

One study might find a correlation between the number of people suffering from insomnia (trouble sleeping) and the distance they live from a wind farm. But other scientists don't get a correlation when they investigate it — the results of the first study are just a fluke.

2. They're linked by a third variable

A lot of the time it may look as if a change in one variable is causing a change in the other, but it isn't — a third variable links the two things.

> **Example**
>
> There's a correlation between water temperature and shark attacks. This isn't because warm water makes sharks crazy. Instead, they're linked by a third variable — the number of people swimming (more people swim when the water's hotter, and with more people in the water shark attacks increase).

3. Causation

Sometimes a change in one variable does cause a change in the other.

> **Example**
>
> There's a correlation between exposure to radiation and cancer. This is because radiation can damage body cells and cause cancer.

You can only conclude that a correlation is due to cause if you've controlled all the variables that could be affecting the result. (For the radiation example, this would include age and exposure to other things that cause cancer.)

Evaluation

An evaluation is a critical analysis of the whole investigation. Here you need to comment on the following points about your experiment and the data you gathered:

- **The method**: Was it valid? Did you control all the other variables to make it a fair test?

- **The quality of your results:** Was there enough evidence to reach a valid conclusion? Were the results repeatable, reproducible, accurate and precise?

- **Anomalous results**: Were any of the results anomalous? If there were none then say so. If there were any, try to explain them — were they caused by errors in measurement? Were there any other variables that could have affected the results? You should comment on the level of uncertainty in your results too.

Once you've thought about these points you can decide how much confidence you have in your conclusion. For example, if your results are repeatable, reproducible and valid and they back up your conclusion then you can have a high degree of confidence in your conclusion.

You can also suggest any changes to the method that would improve the quality of the results, so that you could have more confidence in your conclusion. For example, you might suggest changing the way you controlled a variable, or increasing the number of measurements you took. Taking more measurements at narrower intervals could give you a more accurate result.

You could also make more predictions based on your conclusion, then further experiments could be carried out to test them.

1. Energy Stores and Transfers

Energy is what makes everything happen. It can be transferred between stores, and different things happen depending on which stores it is moving between.

Energy stores

When energy is transferred to an object, the energy is stored in one of the object's **energy stores**. You can think of energy stores as being like buckets that energy can be poured into or taken out of.

Here are the stores you need to know, and some examples of objects with energy in each of these stores:

Energy store	Objects with energy in this store
Kinetic	Anything moving has energy in its kinetic energy store.
Thermal	Any object. The hotter it is, the more energy it has in this store. You may also see thermal energy stores called internal energy stores.
Chemical	Anything that can release energy by a chemical reaction, e.g. food, fuels.
Gravitational Potential	Anything that has mass and is inside a gravitational field.
Elastic Potential	Anything that is stretched (or compressed) e.g. springs.
Electrostatic	Anything with electric charge that is interacting with another electric charge — e.g. two charges that attract or repel each other.
Magnetic	Anything magnetic that is interacting with another magnet — e.g. two magnets that attract or repel each other.
Nuclear	Atomic nuclei have energy in this store that can be released in nuclear reactions.

Energy transfers

A **system** is just a fancy word for a single object (e.g. the air in a piston) or a group of objects (e.g. two colliding vehicles) that you're interested in.

Closed systems are systems where neither matter nor energy can enter or leave. The net change in the total energy of a closed system is always zero.

When a system changes, energy is transferred. It can be transferred into or away from a system, between different objects in the system, or between different types of energy stores.

Learning Objectives:

- Know that an object or group of objects can be considered a system.
- Know that when a system changes, energy is transferred between stores.
- Be able to describe changes in the way energy is stored when energy is transferred in changing systems.
- Know that energy is transferred between stores when work is done by a force or by a current flowing.
- Know the principle of conservation of energy.
- Be able to calculate the amount of energy transferred to stores in a changing system.
- Know and be able to give examples to show that, whenever energy is transferred, some energy will be transferred to non-useful stores (dissipated). This energy is said to be "wasted".
- Be able to describe and give examples of the energy transfers that take place in a closed system, where there is no net change in energy.

Specification References 6.1.1.1, 6.1.2.1

Energy can be transferred between stores in four main ways:

- Mechanically — an object moving due to a force acting on it, e.g. pushing, pulling, stretching or squashing.

- Electrically — a charge (current) moving through a potential difference, e.g. charges moving round a circuit.

- By heating — energy transferred from a hotter object to a colder object, e.g. heating a pan of water on a hob.

- By radiation — energy transferred by e.g. light/sound waves (for example, energy from the Sun reaching Earth by light).

Tip: See Topic 6 for more on energy transfers by radiation.

Tip: Energy is transferred electrically by the moving charges doing work against the electrical resistance of the heating element — see page 88.

Examples

- If you're boiling water in a kettle — you can think of the water as the system. Energy is transferred to the water (from the kettle's heating element) by heating, to the water's thermal energy store (causing the temperature of the water to rise).

  You could also think of the kettle's heating element and the water together as a two-object system. Energy is transferred electrically to the thermal energy store of the kettle's heating element, which transfers energy by heating to the water's thermal energy store.

- The clown in a jack-in-the-box could also be considered as a system. When the lid is opened, energy is transferred mechanically from the elastic potential energy store of the compressed spring to the kinetic energy store and gravitational potential energy store of the clown as the spring extends.

Figure 1: A jack-in-the-box toy. Energy is transferred from the extending spring to the kinetic energy store of the clown.

Exam Tip
You need to be able to calculate the changes in energy involved when work is done by forces (p. 135) or when a charge flows (p. 88-90).

Work done

Work done is just another way of saying energy transferred — they're the same thing. Work can be done by a moving charge (work done against resistance in a circuit, see page 88) or by a force moving an object through a displacement (see page 135).

Here are some examples of energy transfers involving work:

Examples

- The initial force exerted by a person to throw a ball upwards does work. It causes an energy transfer from the chemical energy store of the person's arm to the kinetic energy store of the arm and the ball.

- A ball dropped from a height is accelerated by gravity. The gravitational force does work. It causes energy to be transferred from the ball's gravitational potential energy store to its kinetic energy store (see page 27).

- The friction between a car's brakes and its wheels does work (see page 182). It causes an energy transfer from the wheels' kinetic energy stores to the thermal energy stores of the brakes and the surroundings, causing the car to slow down.

- In a collision between a car and a stationary object, the normal contact force between the car and the object does work. It causes energy to be transferred from the car's kinetic energy store to other energy stores, e.g. the elastic potential and thermal energy stores of the object and the car body. Some energy will also be transferred away by sound waves.

Exam Tip
In the exam, they can ask you to describe the energy transfer in any system. If you understand a few different examples, it'll be much easier to think through whatever they ask you about in the exam.

The conservation of energy principle

Energy always obeys the **conservation of energy principle**:

> Energy can be transferred usefully, stored, or dissipated, but can never be created or destroyed.

You can use the conservation of energy principle to calculate how much energy is transferred to certain stores when a system is changed. You'll see lots of examples of this in physics, and you can only do it because of conservation of energy.

Tip: Dissipated is a fancy way of saying spread out and lost.

Example

A car travelling at a constant speed applies the brakes and comes to a stop.

- The energy in the kinetic energy store of the car is transferred to the thermal energy stores of the brakes (see page 182).

- All the energy in the kinetic energy store is transferred, so by conservation of energy, it must be moved to other stores.

- You can calculate the energy transferred, it's just the energy that the car had in its kinetic energy store before the brakes were applied, given by $\frac{1}{2}mv^2$ — see page 25.

- If you assume all of the energy is transferred to the thermal energy stores of the brakes, then you can calculate the energy in these stores.

- You'll see on page 29 that the energy in an object's thermal energy stores can be found using $mc\Delta\theta$, so you can let $\frac{1}{2}mv^2 = mc\Delta\theta$ in this transfer and work out things like $\Delta\theta$, the temperature change.

Tip: Remember you can calculate energy transferred by heating (page 29) or when work is done by a force (page 135) or by moving charges (pages 88-90) using the formulas given on those pages.

Tip: Another example of using conservation of energy in this way is when an object is falling (without air resistance) — see page 27.

When energy is transferred between stores, not all of the energy is transferred usefully to the store that you want it to go to. Some energy is always dissipated when an energy transfer takes place. Dissipated energy is sometimes called 'wasted energy' because the energy is stored in a way which is not useful (usually energy has been transferred into thermal energy stores). See page 39 for much more on this.

The conservation of energy principle explains why the total energy in a closed system is always the same. No energy can enter or leave a closed system, and since energy cannot be created or destroyed, the total energy is always the same.

> ### Example
>
> Imagine that a hot spoon is put into cold water in a perfectly insulated container (i.e. no energy can be transferred from the water to the surroundings, or vice versa). This system (the spoon and the water) is a closed system.
>
> The spoon will cool down, and the water will warm up, but the total energy of the system will not change. This is because no energy has left or entered the system — it has merely moved between stores within the system.

Practice Questions — Fact Recall

Q1 State the eight different forms of energy store.

Q2 What is meant by a closed system?

Q3 State the conservation of energy principle.

Practice Question — Application

Q1 Describe the main energy transfer between stores that occurs, including the way in which energy is transferred, when each of the following things happen:

a) An arrow is released from a bow.

b) A gas camping stove is used to heat soup.

c) A battery-powered fan is used.

2. Kinetic and Potential Energy Stores

Some of the most common and straightforward energy transfers are between kinetic energy stores and potential energy stores. They have handy formulas so you can easily calculate how much energy is gained or lost.

Kinetic energy stores

Anything that is moving has energy in its **kinetic energy store**. Energy is transferred to this store when an object speeds up and is transferred away from this store when an object slows down.

The energy in the kinetic energy store depends on the object's mass and speed. The greater its mass and the faster it's going, the more energy there will be in its kinetic energy store. It's got a slightly tricky formula, so you'll need to concentrate a bit harder on this one:

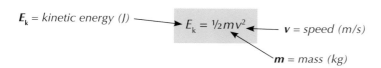

E_k = kinetic energy (J) $E_k = \frac{1}{2}mv^2$ v = speed (m/s)
m = mass (kg)

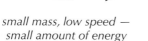 

*small mass, low speed —
small amount of energy
in kinetic energy store*

*large mass, high speed —
large amount of energy
in kinetic energy store*

Figure 1: *A diagram to show how the energy in the kinetic energy store of a moving object depends on its mass (m) and speed (v).*

Learning Objectives:
- Know that all moving objects have energy in their kinetic energy store.
- Know and be able to use $E_k = \frac{1}{2}mv^2$ to calculate the energy in the kinetic energy store of an object.
- Know and be able to use $E_p = mgh$ to calculate the energy transferred to an object's g.p.e. store when it is raised above the ground.
- Be able to make calculations of energy transfers between stores, e.g. between the gravitational potential energy store and kinetic energy store of a falling object.
- Know that a stretched (or compressed) spring has energy in its elastic potential energy store.
- Be able to use $E_e = \frac{1}{2}ke^2$ to calculate the energy in the elastic potential energy store of a stretched (or compressed) spring.

**Specification References
6.1.1.1, 6.1.1.2**

Example

A van of mass 2450 kg is travelling at 40.0 m/s. Calculate the energy in its kinetic energy store.

You just plug the numbers into the formula — but watch the 'v^2'.

$E_k = \frac{1}{2}mv^2 = \frac{1}{2} \times 2450 \times 40.0^2 = 1\ 960\ 000$ J

Example

A moped with 1.17×10^4 J of energy in its kinetic energy store travels at 12.0 m/s. What is the mass of the moped?

$E_k = 1.17 \times 10^4$ J, $v = 12.0$ m/s

Rearranging $E_k = \frac{1}{2}mv^2$,

$m = (2 \times E_k) \div v^2 = (2 \times 1.17 \times 10^4) \div 12.0^2 = 162.5$ kg

Exam Tip
Use this formula triangle (p.242) to rearrange the equation:

E_k
$\frac{1}{2} \times m \times v^2$

Exam Tip
If you need help
with rearranging this
equation, this formula
triangle might help:

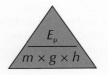

Gravitational potential energy stores

Lifting an object in a gravitational field (page 129) requires work. This causes a transfer of energy to the **gravitational potential energy (g.p.e.) store** of the raised object. The higher an object is lifted, the more energy is transferred to this store.

The amount of energy in an object's g.p.e. store depends on its mass, its height and the strength of the gravitational field the object is in. The amount of energy that is transferred to an object's gravitational potential energy store when it's raised through a certain height can be found by:

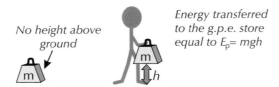

g = gravitational field strength (N/kg)

E_p = gravitational potential energy (J)

$$E_p = mgh$$

h = height (m)

m = mass (kg)

Exam Tip
You'll be given the value
of gravitational field
strength in the exam.

On Earth, the gravitational field strength (g) is approximately 9.8 N/kg.

No height above ground

Energy transferred to the g.p.e. store equal to $E_p = mgh$

Figure 2: A diagram showing how the energy in the gravitational potential energy store of a mass (m) increases when it is lifted to a height (h) in a gravitational field.

Example

A 50 kg mass is slowly raised through a height of 6.0 m. Find the energy transferred to its gravitational potential energy store. The gravitational field strength is 9.8 N/kg.

Just plug the numbers into the formula:
$$E_p = mgh = 50 \times 9.8 \times 6.0 = 2940 \text{ J}$$

Tip: Be careful when
rearranging. Remember
to do the same thing
to each side of the
equation, one step at a
time (see page 241).

Example

A flea of mass 1.0×10^{-3} g jumps vertically from the ground. The gravitational field strength is 9.8 N/kg. At the top of the jump the flea has gained 1.96×10^{-6} J of energy in its g.p.e. store. How high has the flea jumped?

$E_p = 1.96 \times 10^{-6}$ J
$m = 1.0 \times 10^{-3}$ g $= 1.0 \times 10^{-6}$ kg

Rearranging $E_p = mgh$,

$$h = E_p \div (mg) = 1.96 \times 10^{-6} \div (1.0 \times 10^{-6} \times 9.8) = 0.20 \text{ m}$$

Tip: When you're
doing calculations,
give your final answer
to the lowest number
of significant figures
used in any value in the
calculation (see page 14
for more on this).

Energy transfer for falling objects

When something falls, energy from its gravitational potential energy store is transferred to its kinetic energy store. The further is falls, the faster it goes.

For a falling object when there's no air resistance, you can use the principle of conservation of energy to get:

> Energy lost from the g.p.e. store = Energy gained in the kinetic energy store

Tip: Remember, the principle of conservation of energy states that energy can never be created or destroyed — only transferred, stored or dissipated.

energy in g.p.e. store at this height = mgh

energy lost from g.p.e. store = energy gained in kinetic energy store

more energy lost from g.p.e. store = more energy transferred to the kinetic energy store

Figure 3: *A diagram showing that energy is transferred from the g.p.e. store to the kinetic energy store of a falling object. The higher the object is to begin with, the more energy it'll have in its kinetic energy store when it hits the ground.*

You can use this to make calculations of energy transfers when an object falls, using the equations on the previous pages.

Tip: In real life, air resistance (see page 159) acts against all falling objects — it causes some energy to be transferred to other energy stores, e.g. thermal energy stores of the object and surroundings.

Example

The flea from the example on the previous page falls from the top of its jump. Assuming there is no air resistance, calculate the speed of the flea when it hits the ground. Give your answer to 2 significant figures.

All the energy the flea gained in its g.p.e. store by jumping will be transferred back to its kinetic energy store as it falls towards the ground, so E_p at the top of the jump will equal E_k when it hits the ground.

$E_p = 1.96 \times 10^{-6}$ J $= E_k$
$m = 1.0 \times 10^{-6}$ kg

$E_k = \frac{1}{2}mv^2$, so rearrange for v:

$$v = \sqrt{\frac{2E_k}{m}} = \sqrt{\frac{2 \times 1.96 \times 10^{-6}}{1.0 \times 10^{-6}}} = 1.979... = 2.0 \text{ m/s (to 2 s.f.)}$$

Elastic potential energy stores

Stretching or squashing an object can transfer energy to its **elastic potential energy store**. The energy in the elastic potential energy store of a stretched spring (provided it has not been stretched past its limit of proportionality) can be found using the formula from page 141:

E_e = elastic potential energy (J) ⟶ $E_e = \frac{1}{2}ke^2$ ⟵ e = extension (m)

k = spring constant (N/m)

Tip: Remember, although e stands for extension, it can also represent compression (see page 140). Simply use e as the difference between the normal length and the compressed length, and you'll get the energy in the elastic energy store of a compressed elastic object.

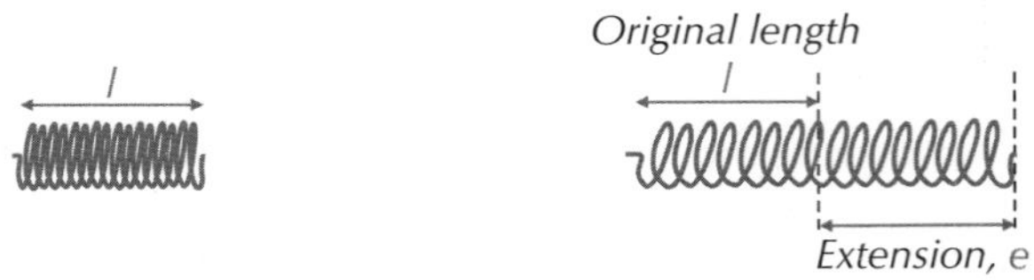

Original length

Unstretched spring has no energy
in its elastic potential energy store.

Stretched spring has energy of ½ke²
in its elastic potential energy store.

Extension, e

Figure 4: *A diagram showing how to find the energy in the*
elastic potential energy store of a stretched spring.

Example

**A spring with spring constant 40 N/m is stretched from its
normal length of 8.0 cm to a stretched length of 23.0 cm.
Calculate the energy transferred to its elastic potential energy store.**

First, find k and e, and place them in the correct units.
$k = 40$ N/m
$e =$ stretched length – normal length $= 23.0 - 8.0 = 15$ cm $= 0.15$ m

Now simply plug the values into the equation:

$$E_e = \tfrac{1}{2}ke^2 = \tfrac{1}{2} \times 40 \times 0.15^2 = 0.45 \text{ J}$$

Practice Questions — Fact Recall

Q1 Which of these has the most energy in its kinetic energy store:
a small dog walking slowly or a large dog running fast? Explain why.

Q2 What is the formula for calculating the energy in an object's kinetic
energy store? What does each term represent and what units should
they be in?

Q3 What is the formula for working out the energy transferred to an
object's gravitational potential energy store? What does each term
represent and what units should they be in?

Q4 What is the formula for working out the energy transferred to
an object's elastic potential energy store? What does each term
represent and what units should they be in?

Tip: Take gravitational
field strength (*g*) to be
9.8 N/kg.

Exam Tip
Watch out for data given
in the 'wrong' units
in the exam. Double-
check the numbers are
in the 'right' units before
you stick them into the
formula.

Practice Questions — Application

Q1 A 25 000 kg plane takes off and climbs to a height of 12 000 m
above its take off point. How much energy has been transferred to
its gravitational potential energy store?

Q2 A spring is stretched by 60 cm, which transfers 18 J of energy to its
elastic potential energy store. What is its spring constant?

Q3 A 12.5 g ball with 40 J of energy in its kinetic energy store is
travelling horizontally through the air. How fast is it moving?

Q4 A 1 kg potato falls to the ground and loses 450 J of energy from its
gravitational potential energy store. Assuming no air resistance, what
is the speed of the potato as it hits the ground?

3. Specific Heat Capacity

Some materials are easier to heat up than others. Specific heat capacity is a measure of how much energy it takes to change the temperature of a material. Let the fun begin...

What is specific heat capacity?

More energy needs to be transferred to the thermal energy store of some materials to increase their temperature than others. For example, you need 4200 J to warm 1 kg of water by 1 °C, but only 139 J to warm 1 kg of mercury by 1 °C.

Materials that need to have a lot of energy transferred to in their thermal energy stores to warm up also transfer a lot of energy when they cool down.

How much energy needs to be transferred to the thermal energy store of a substance before its temperature increases is determined by its **specific heat capacity**.

> Specific heat capacity is the amount of energy needed to raise the temperature of 1 kg of a substance by 1 °C.

The amount of energy transferred to (i.e. stored by) or transferred from (i.e. released by) the thermal energy store of a substance for a given temperature change, $\Delta\theta$, is linked to its specific heat capacity by this equation:

ΔE = change in thermal energy (J) ⟶ $\Delta E = mc\Delta\theta$ ⟵ $\Delta\theta$ = temperature change (°C)

m = mass (kg) c = specific heat capacity (J/kg°C)

Learning Objectives:

- Know that the specific heat capacity of a material is the energy needed to raise the temperature of 1 kg of the material by 1°C.
- Be able to use the equation $\Delta E = mc\Delta\theta$ to calculate the energy transferred to (stored by) or from (released by) the thermal energy store of a substance when its temperature changes.
- Be able to make calculations of energy transfers between energy stores, e.g. between the kinetic energy store of a car and the thermal energy store of its brakes.
- Be able to find the specific heat capacity of various materials, and to link work done with energy transferred to thermal energy stores in the experiment (Required Practical 14).

Specification References
6.1.1.1, 6.1.1.3

Example

Water has a specific heat capacity of 4200 J/kg°C. How much energy is needed to heat 2.00 kg of water from 10.0 °C to 100.0 °C?

First work out the temperature difference, $\Delta\theta$, between the starting and finishing temperatures.

$\Delta\theta = 100.0\ °C - 10.0\ °C = 90.0\ °C$

Then plug the numbers for m, c and $\Delta\theta$ into the formula to find ΔE.

$\Delta E = mc\Delta\theta = 2.00 \times 4200 \times 90.0 = 756\ 000$ J

Tip: Remember, Δ just means 'change in' (see p. 241).

Exam Tip
You'll need to remember everything on this page for Topic 3, where it's needed again.

You can use the formula above with the conservation of energy, just like on page 27, to make calculations for energy transfers in all sorts of situations. See the example on the next page.

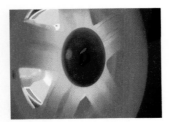

Figure 1: A thermogram showing the temperature differences around a car wheel during braking. White is hottest (where the brakes are) and blue is coolest.

Example

A 3500 kg van travelling at 30.0 m/s applies its brakes and comes to a stop. Estimate the change in temperature of the brakes in this transfer, if their combined mass is 25 kg and their specific heat capacity is 420 J/kg °C.

Assume that all of the energy in the kinetic energy stores of the van is transferred to the thermal energy stores of the brakes. The energy transferred is equal to the energy in the kinetic energy stores, given by $\frac{1}{2}mv^2$ (p. 25).

$E = \frac{1}{2}mv^2 = \frac{1}{2} \times 3500 \times 30.0^2 = 1\ 575\ 000$ J
All this is transferred to the brakes' thermal energy stores,
so $\Delta E = 1\ 575\ 000$ J.

Rearrange $\Delta E = mc\Delta\theta$ to give:
$\Delta\theta = \Delta E \div mc = 1\ 575\ 000 \div (25 \times 420) = 150$ °C

Tip: Remember to carry out a risk assessment before you do any practical. Be careful not to burn yourself when handling the heater.

Tip: If the hole's a lot bigger than the thermometer, you should put a small amount of water in with the thermometer. This lets the thermometer measure the temperature of the block better, as there is no air around it to insulate it from the block.

Investigating specific heat capacity

You can do an experiment to investigate the specific heat capacity of a material. To investigate a solid material (e.g. copper), you'll need a block of the material with two holes in it (for the heater and thermometer to go into, see Figure 2).

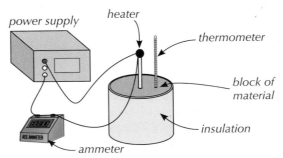

Figure 2: A diagram of the apparatus used to investigate the specific heat capacity of a solid material.

Measure the mass of the block, then wrap it in an insulating layer (e.g. a thick layer of newspaper) to reduce the energy transferred from the block to the surroundings (p. 36). Insert the thermometer and heater as shown in Figure 2.

Measure the initial temperature of the block and set the potential difference, V, of the power supply to be 10 V. Turn on the power supply and start a stop watch. As the block heats up, take readings of the temperature and current, I, every minute for 10 minutes. Keep an eye on the ammeter — the current through the circuit shouldn't change.

When you turn on the power, the current in the circuit (i.e. the moving charges) does work on the heater, transferring energy electrically from the power supply to the heater's thermal energy store. This energy is then transferred to the material's thermal energy store by heating, causing the material's temperature to increase.

Using your measurement of the current and the potential difference of the power supply, you can calculate the power of the heater, using $P = VI$ (p. 90). You can use this to calculate how much energy, E, has been transferred by the heater at the time of each temperature reading using the formula $E = Pt$, where t is the time in seconds since the experiment began.

If you assume all the energy supplied by the heater has been transferred to the block, you can plot a graph of energy transferred to the thermal energy store of the block against temperature. You should get a graph which looks similar to Figure 3.

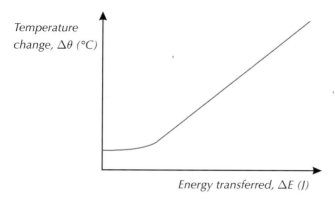

Tip: $\Delta\theta$ is how much the temperature has changed by since the start of the experiment.

Figure 3: *A graph of temperature increase against energy change for a solid block of material heated using the apparatus in Figure 2.*

Since mass (*m*) and specific heat capacity are constant, $\Delta E = mc\Delta\theta$ shows that energy transferred is directly proportional to change in temperature. So the graph should be linear. However, as is shown in Figure 3, your graph may start off curved. You don't need to worry about why this happens, just make sure you ignore the curved part of the graph.

You can find the specific heat capacity of the block using the gradient of the linear part of your graph. The gradient is $\Delta\theta \div \Delta E$, so since $\Delta E = mc\Delta\theta$, the gradient is $1 \div mc$. So the specific heat capacity of the material of the block is: $1 \div$ (gradient × the mass of the block).

You can repeat this experiment with different materials to see how their specific heat capacities compare. You can also investigate the specific heat capacity of liquids with this experiment — just place the heater and thermometer in an insulated beaker filled with the liquid. Remember to measure the mass of the liquid, not the volume.

Tip: If you're just comparing the specific heat capacities, you could use identical masses of each material and identical methods for each material. If *m* and ΔE are constant, then *c* is just related to $\Delta\theta$, so a bigger change in temperature means a smaller specific heat capacity.

Practice Question — Fact Recall

Q1 What is the specific heat capacity of a substance?

Practice Questions — Application

Q1 A kettle heats 0.20 kg of water from a temperature of 20.0 °C to 100.0 °C. Water has a specific heat capacity of 4200 J/kg°C. How much energy is transferred to the thermal energy store of the water?

Q2 A chef heats 400 g of oil to a temperature of 113 °C. The oil is left to cool until it reaches a temperature of 25 °C. The oil transfers 70.4 kJ of energy to its surroundings. Calculate the specific heat capacity of the oil.

- Know that the rate of energy transfer (or work done) is power.
- Know that power is measured in watts, W, and 1 W = 1 J/s.
- Know and be able to use both $P = E \div t$ and $P = W \div t$.
- Be able to describe examples which illustrate the definition of power, e.g. that show that the higher the power, the less time it takes to supply a given amount of energy.

Specification Reference 6.1.1.4

4. Power

Power is a really important concept that pops up all over the place because power is all about how quickly energy is transferred.

What is power?

Power is the rate of energy transfer, or the rate of doing work. Power is measured in watts, W. One watt is equivalent to one joule transferred per second (J/s).

You can calculate power using these equations:

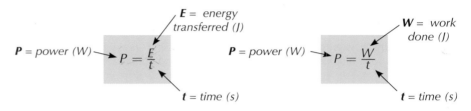

$\boldsymbol{E}$ = energy transferred (J)
$\boldsymbol{P}$ = power (W) — $P = \dfrac{E}{t}$
$\boldsymbol{t}$ = time (s)

$\boldsymbol{W}$ = work done (J)
$\boldsymbol{P}$ = power (W) — $P = \dfrac{W}{t}$
$\boldsymbol{t}$ = time (s)

Tip: These formula triangles might help with rearranging the power equations:

Example

A motor transfers 4.8 kJ of energy in 2 minutes. Find its power.

Energy transferred = 4.8 kJ = 4800 J
Time taken = 2 minutes = 2 × 60 s = 120 s

$$P = \frac{E}{t} = \frac{4800}{120} = 40 \text{ W (or 40 J/s)}$$

Example

How long does it take for a 550 W motor to do 110 J of work?

Rearranging $P = W \div t$,
$\quad t = W \div P$
$\quad\quad = 110 \div 550$
$\quad\quad = 0.2$ s

A powerful machine is not necessarily one which can exert a strong force (although it usually ends up that way). A powerful machine is one which transfers a lot of energy in a short space of time.

Example

Consider two cars that are identical in every way apart from the power of their engines. Both cars race the same distance along a straight race track to a finish line. The car with the more powerful engine will reach the finish line faster than the other car — i.e. it will transfer the same amount of energy, but over less time.

**It takes 8000 J of work to lift a stunt performer to the top of a building.
Motor A can lift the stunt performer to the correct height in 50 s.
Motor B would take 300 s to lift the performer to the same height.
Which motor is most powerful? Calculate the power of this motor.**

Both motors transfer the same amount of energy, but motor A would do it
quicker than motor B. So, motor A is the more powerful motor.

Plug the time taken and work done for motor A into the equation $P = W \div t$
and find the power.
$P = W \div t = 8000 \div 50 = 160 \text{ W}$

Practice Questions — Fact Recall

Q1   What is meant by the term 'power'?

Q2   State the equations for power. What does each term represent and
what units are they measured in?

Practice Questions — Application

Q1   Find the power of the following:

a) A motor that transfers 150 J of energy in 37.5 s.

b) A motor that transfers 79.8 kJ of energy in 42 s.

c) A motor that transfers 6 840 kJ of energy in 9.5 minutes.

Q2   Two lifts, A and B, operate between the ground floor and the second
floor of a building. Lift A's motor has a power of 4800 W, and lift B's
motor has a power of 5200 W. State which of the two lifts will carry
a given load up the two floors in the least time, and explain why.

Q3   How long does each of the following take?

a) A 525 W motor to do 1344 J of work.

b) A 2.86 kW toaster to transfer 1430 J of energy.

Q4   How much energy do the following transfer?

a) A machine with a power of 1240 W running for 35 s.

b) A 1500 W heater switched on for 17 minutes.

Learning Objective:
- Know that the higher a material's thermal conductivity, the faster energy can be transferred through it by conduction.

Specification Reference
6.1.2.1

5. Conduction and Convection

Energy is transferred by heating through solids by conduction, and through liquids and gases by conduction and convection. Both types of energy transfer by heating happen because the particles in a substance move about...

Conduction

> **Conduction** is the process by which vibrating particles transfer energy to neighbouring particles.

Energy transferred to an object by heating is transferred to the thermal energy store of the object. This energy is shared across the kinetic energy stores of the particles in the object.

Tip: You'll see on page 100 that the energy transferred to an object by heating is actually stored in the kinetic energy stores of its particles.

The particles in the part of the object being heated have more energy transferred to their kinetic energy stores, and so vibrate more and collide with each other. These collisions cause energy to be transferred between the particles' kinetic energy stores. This is conduction.

This process continues throughout the object until the energy is spread out evenly across the object. It's then usually transferred to the thermal energy store of the surroundings (or anything else touching the object).

Particles in the hotter part of a solid vibrate more. *Particles collide and pass energy between their kinetic energy stores.*

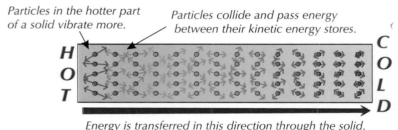

Energy is transferred in this direction through the solid.

Figure 1: *Conduction of energy through a solid.*

Conduction occurs mainly in solids. Particles in liquids and gases are much more free to move around, so their particles collide less frequently, which is why they usually transfer energy by convection instead of conduction.

Tip: There's much more on convection on the next page.

Thermal conductivity is a measure of how quickly energy is transferred through a material in this way. Materials with a high thermal conductivity transfer energy between their particles quickly. The higher a material's thermal conductivity, the faster the energy can be transferred through it by conduction. Materials with a high thermal conductivity are known as thermal conductors, and those with a low thermal conductivity are known as thermal insulators.

> ### Example
>
> Pots and pans are usually made of metal because metals have high thermal conductivity. This means they transfer energy quickly, so the energy is transferred to the food quicker, making cooking quicker. Pan handles are usually made of a thermal insulator. They don't transfer energy by conduction very fast, so the handle stays cool and you don't end up burning your hand when touching it.

Convection

> **Convection** is where energetic particles move away from hotter to cooler regions.

Convection can happen in gases and liquids. Energy is transferred by heating to the thermal energy store of the liquid or gas. Again, this energy is shared across the kinetic energy stores of the gas or liquid's particles.

Unlike in solids, the particles in liquids and gases are able to move around, rather than vibrate in place. When you heat a region of a gas or liquid, the particles move faster and the space between individual particles increases. This causes the density (page 96) of the region being heated to decrease.

Because liquids and gases can flow, the warmer and less dense region will rise above denser, cooler regions. If there is a constant transfer of energy by heating to the substance, a convection current can be created, where the air in the room circulates as regions of it heat up and rise, then cool down and fall.

Figure 2: *You can see convection currents by sticking some potassium permanganate crystals in the bottom of a beaker of cold water. Heat the beaker gently over a Bunsen flame — the potassium permanganate will start to dissolve and make a gorgeous bright purple solution that gets moved around the beaker by the convection currents as the water heats. It's real pretty.*

Example

Heating a room with a radiator relies on creating convection currents in the air of the room.

Energy is transferred from the radiator to the nearby air particles by conduction (the air particles collide with the radiator surface). The air by the radiator becomes warmer and less dense (as the particles move quicker). This warm air rises and is replaced by cooler air. The cooler air is then heated by the radiator.

At the same time, the previously heated air transfers energy to the surroundings (e.g. the walls and contents of the room). It cools, becomes denser and sinks.

This cycle repeats, causing a flow of air to circulate around the room — this is a convection current.

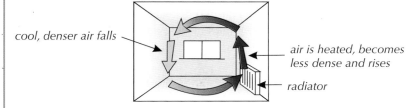

cool, denser air falls

air is heated, becomes less dense and rises

radiator

Figure 3: *A radiator heating a room by convection.*

Tip: The key thing to remember is that convection happens because a heated liquid or gas becomes less dense. This means it moves away, above the cooler (denser) air, taking its energy with it.

Practice Questions — Fact Recall

Q1 What is conduction? Describe how energy is transferred by conduction.

Q2 What is convection?

Q3 In which state of matter does convection not happen?

Tip: See page 97 for more on states of matter.

Learning Objectives:
- Be able to describe how a building's rate of cooling is affected by the thermal conductivity and thickness of its walls.
- Be able to explain a number of methods by which unwanted energy transfers can be reduced.

Specification Reference 6.1.2.1

6. Reducing Unwanted Energy Transfers

Some energy is always transferred to energy stores which are not useful. This is a pain, but there are a number of ways that we can reduce these unwanted transfers and maximise the energy in the useful energy stores.

Thermal insulation

The last thing you want when you've made your house nice and toasty is for that energy to escape outside. The thicker the walls and the lower their thermal conductivity, the slower the rate of energy transfer will be (so the rate of cooling will be slower). You can help reduce the amount of energy lost from a building using **thermal insulators**. Here are some examples...

Tip: Make sure you know how each type of insulation helps reduce the energy lost from a home.

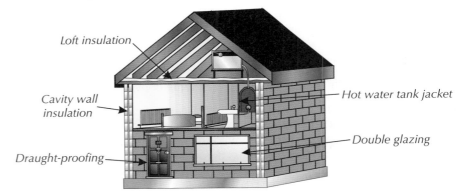

Figure 1: Different methods of insulating a home.

Figure 2: This sleeve on a coffee cup is another example of thermal insulation. It stops your hand getting too hot. They're often made of cardboard with air pockets, as air is a good insulator.

Cavity walls and cavity wall insulation

Some houses have cavity walls, made up of an inner and an outer wall with an air gap in the middle. The air gap reduces the amount of energy transferred by conduction through the walls, because air is an insulator. Using cavity wall insulation (where the cavity wall air gap is filled with a foam) can also reduce energy transfer by convection in the cavity walls.

Loft insulation

Fibreglass is an insulating material made of thin strands of glass that trap pockets of air. A thick layer of fibreglass wool laid out across the whole loft floor reduces conduction to the attic space, as the material (and the trapped air) are insulators. Loft insulation (see Figure 3) reduces the energy transfer by convection, by preventing convection currents from forming.

Double glazing

Double-glazed windows work in the same way as cavity walls — they have an air gap between two sheets of glass to prevent energy transfer by conduction through the windows.

Figure 3: Fibreglass loft insulation.

Draught-proofing

Draught excluders or strips of foam or plastic around doors and windows stop draughts blowing in and out, and reduce energy transfer by convection.

Hot water tank jacket

Putting fibreglass wool around a hot water tank reduces the energy transferred by conduction from the tank's thermal energy store in the same way as loft insulation.

Thick curtains

Big bits of cloth over the window create an air gap between the room and the window, stopping hot air reaching the glass by convection. They also reduce energy transferred by conduction.

Lubrication

Whenever something moves, there's usually at least one frictional force acting against it (page 159). This causes some energy in the system to be dissipated, e.g. air resistance can transfer energy from a falling object's kinetic energy store to its thermal energy store and the thermal energy stores of the surroundings.

For objects that are being rubbed together, **lubricants** can be used to reduce the friction between the objects' surfaces when they move. Lubricants are usually liquids (like oil), so they can flow easily between the objects and coat them (and so reduce the friction across the whole area of contact between the objects). Streamlining can be used to reduce air resistance (see page 159).

Tip: Remember, air resistance causes a frictional force on an object moving through the air (see page 159).

| Examples |

- Lubrication is used on axles in things like cars, fans and turbines. This decreases the amount of energy lost to thermal energy stores due to friction between the axle and its supports when the axle turns.

- Grease can be used to lubricate door hinges and locks if they are stiff, to reduce friction.

Tip: An axle is just a rod that turns. In a car, the wheels are attached to an axle. In a fan or turbine, the blades are attached to an axle.

Practice Questions — Fact Recall

Q1   Explain how installing each of the following types of insulation helps reduce unwanted energy transfers from a home.

   a) Cavity wall insulation

   b) Loft insulation

   c) Double glazing

Q2   Give one example of when lubrication is used to decrease unwanted energy transfers.

- Know and be able to use the equations for efficiency in terms of energy transferred and power.
- Be able to express an efficiency as either a decimal or a percentage.
- **H** Be able to describe ways in which the efficiency of an energy transfer can be improved.

Specification Reference 6.1.2.2

Tip: Input energy is just the energy transferred to the device and useful output energy is the energy transferred to useful energy stores by the device.

Tip: Efficiency is just a number, so it doesn't matter what units your energy values are in. As long as the values for input and output energy transfer are in the same units, you'll get the right answer.

Tip: See page 239 for more on percentages.

Exam Tip
Make sure you think carefully about which value is total input energy transfer, and which is useful output energy transfer. It's easy to get them mixed up.

7. Efficiency

Sometimes it's really handy to know how much energy a device wastes compared to how much it usefully transfers — that's efficiency for you.

What is efficiency?

Useful devices are only useful because they can transfer energy from one energy store to a useful energy store. As you'll probably have gathered by now, some of the input energy is usually wasted by being transferred to a useless energy store — usually a thermal energy store.

The less energy that is 'wasted', the more efficient the device is said to be.

The **efficiency** of an energy transfer can be worked out using this equation:

$$\text{efficiency} = \frac{\text{useful output energy transfer}}{\text{total input energy transfer}}$$

This equation gives you the efficiency as a decimal, but you may be asked to express it as a percentage. To do that, simply multiply your result by 100, and stick the % symbol on the end.

Example 1

An electric fan is supplied with 2000 kJ of energy. 600 kJ of that is transferred to useless thermal energy stores.
What is the efficiency of the fan as a percentage?

Total input energy transfer = 2000 kJ
Useful output energy transfer = total energy in − wasted energy transfer
$\qquad\qquad\qquad = 2000 - 600 = 1400$ kJ

Start by working out the efficiency as a decimal:

$$\text{efficiency} = \frac{\text{useful output energy transfer}}{\text{total input energy transfer}}$$
$$= \frac{1400}{2000}$$
$$= 0.7$$

Then, multiply this by 100 to get the efficiency of the fan as a percentage:

$$\text{efficiency} = 0.7 \times 100 = 70\%$$

Example 2

A lamp with an efficiency of 0.740 is supplied with 350 J of energy.
How much energy is usefully transferred by the lamp?

Rearrange the equation $\text{efficiency} = \dfrac{\text{useful output energy transfer}}{\text{total input energy transfer}}$ to give:

useful output energy transfer = efficiency × total input energy transfer
$$= 0.740 \times 350$$
$$= 259 \text{ J}$$

You might not know the energy inputs and outputs of a device, but you can still calculate its efficiency as long as you know the power input and output:

Tip: Remember, power is the rate of energy transferred, see page 32.

$$\text{efficiency} = \frac{\text{useful power output}}{\text{total power input}}$$

Example

A motor is supplied with 250 W of power and outputs 120 W of useful power. What is the efficiency of the motor? Give your answer as a decimal.

$$\text{efficiency} = \frac{\text{useful power out}}{\text{total power in}}$$
$$= \frac{120}{250}$$
$$= 0.48$$

So the motor has an efficiency of 0.48.

Wasted energy

For any given example you can talk about the input and output energy transfers, but remember this:

> No device is 100% efficient and the wasted energy is usually transferred to useless thermal energy stores.

Tip: See page 23 for more on wasted energy.

Electric heaters are the exception to this. They're usually almost 100% efficient because all the energy is transferred electrically to "useful" thermal energy stores

Ultimately, all energy ends up transferred to thermal energy stores. For example, if you use an electric drill, its transfers energy to lots of different energy stores, but it all quickly ends up in thermal energy stores.

Improving efficiency Higher

You can improve the efficiency of energy transfers by insulating objects, lubricating them or making them more streamlined (see pages 36 and 159).

Example 1 — Higher

An electric fan usefully transfers energy electrically to the kinetic energy store of its blades, to cause the movement of air. It wastes energy in many ways, e.g. through friction between the axle and its supports. The efficiency could be improved by lubricating the axle.

Figure 1: *The internal workings of an electric fan, showing its axle.*

Tip: Improving efficiency is a useful application of science (see page 4), allowing us to maximise the energy transferred to useful energy stores and reduce the overall amount of energy used by appliances.

Example 2 — Higher

A kettle transfers energy by heating to the thermal energy store of the water. A kettle wastes energy by heating the surroundings and by letting steam escape once the water is boiling. It could be made more efficient by insulating the kettle more and by switching off more quickly once the water starts to boil.

Figure 2: *Steam escaping from the spout of a kettle as the water boils.*

Practice Questions — Fact Recall

Q1 State the two equations for efficiency.

Q2 State the one device which is usually almost 100% efficient.

Q3 What eventually happens to all the energy wasted by a device?

Tip: A percentage efficiency must always be less than 100% and a decimal efficiency must always be less than 1.

Practice Questions — Application

Q1 Work out the efficiency of the following devices as a decimal.

a) A device with total power in = 90 W and useful power out = 54 W.

b) A machine supplied with 800 J of energy that wastes 280 J.

Q2 Work out the efficiency of the following devices as a percentage.

a) A device where total power in = 36 W and useful power out = 12.6 W.

b) A lamp that transfers 7.5 kJ of energy, 4.5 kJ of which is transferred usefully away by light, 2.9 kJ of which is transferred by heating to thermal energy stores of the surroundings and 100 J of which is transferred away by sound waves.

Q3 660 kJ of energy is transferred electrically to a TV. It transfers 298 kJ away by light, 197 kJ away by sound and transfers the rest by heating to thermal energy stores.

a) What is the total useful output energy transfer?

b) How much energy is wasted by the TV?

c) What is the efficiency of the TV as a decimal?

Tip: To get from a percentage to a decimal, divide by 100. See p. 239 for more on percentages.

Q4 A machine with an efficiency of 68% transfers 816 J to useful energy stores. What is the total energy transferred to the device?

Q5 A vacuum cleaner works by transferring energy electrically to a motor which turns a fan and causes air to be drawn through the fan. Suggest two ways that a vacuum cleaner could be made more efficient.

Topic 1a Checklist — Make sure you know...

Energy Stores and Transfers

☐ That energy can be stored in: thermal energy stores, kinetic energy stores, gravitational potential energy stores, elastic potential energy stores, chemical energy stores, magnetic energy stores, electrostatic energy stores and nuclear energy stores.

☐ That a system is an object or group of objects.

☐ That energy can be transferred between stores mechanically, electrically, by heating, or by radiation.

☐ How to describe the changes in the way energy is stored when a system changes and energy is transferred.

☐ That energy is transferred when work is done by a force or by a moving charge.

☐ The conservation of energy principle — that energy can be transferred usefully, stored or dissipated, but can never be created or destroyed.

☐ How to calculate the amount of energy transferred into stores in a transfer.

☐ That during most energy transfers, some energy will be 'wasted' or 'dissipated' — i.e. transferred to energy stores which are not useful (usually thermal energy stores), and know some examples of this.

☐ That when energy transfers occur in a closed system, the net energy change of the system is zero, and know some examples of this.

Kinetic and Potential Energy Stores

☐ That any object which is moving has energy in its kinetic energy store.

☐ That the amount of energy in an object's kinetic energy store, E_k, depends on the object's mass, m, and speed, v, and can be found using the equation $E_k = \frac{1}{2}mv^2$.

☐ That an object that is lifted in a gravitational field gains energy in its gravitational potential energy store (and has energy transferred out of it when it is lowered).

☐ That the energy transferred to the gravitational potential energy store of an object, E_p, depends on its mass, m, the gravitational field strength, g, and the change in height of the object, h, and is found using the equation $E_p = mgh$.

☐ How to calculate the changes in how energy is stored for a falling object using the principle of conservation of energy.

☐ That when a spring is stretched (or compressed), energy is transferred to its elastic potential energy store.

☐ That the energy in a spring's elastic potential energy store, E_e, depends on its spring constant, k, and the extension (or compression), e, and be able to use the equation $E_e = \frac{1}{2}ke^2$.

Specific Heat Capacity

☐ That the amount of energy required to increase the temperature of a material depends on the material.

☐ That the amount of energy required to raise the temperature of 1 kg of a material by 1°C is given by the specific heat capacity.

☐ That the energy stored in (or released by) a substance when its temperature changes, ΔE, is determined by the specific heat capacity, and be able to use the equation $\Delta E = mc\Delta\theta$.

cont...

☐ How to calculate energy transfers to and from thermal energy stores using conservation of energy.

☐ How to perform an experiment to investigate the specific heat capacities of various materials.

☐ How, in the experiment above, work done by moving charges transfers energy electrically to thermal energy stores of the heater and the material.

Power

☐ That power is the rate of energy transfer (or work done), and is measured in watts (equivalent to 1 joule per second).

☐ That power, P, depends on the energy transferred (or work done) and the time taken, and is found using the equation $P = E \div t$ or $P = W \div t$.

☐ That for two otherwise identical devices with different powers, the device with the higher power will transfer the same amount of energy in less time.

Conduction and Convection

☐ That conduction is energy transfer by heating where vibrating particles transfer energy to neighbouring particles.

☐ That the higher the thermal conductivity of a material, the faster it will transfer energy by conduction.

☐ That convection is energy transfer by heating where energetic particles move away from hotter to cooler regions.

Reducing Unwanted Energy Transfers

☐ That thick walls with a low thermal conductivity can slow the rate of cooling of a house.

☐ That unwanted energy transfers can be reduced by thermal insulation, e.g. loft insulation in the home.

☐ That unwanted energy transfers can be reduced by reducing friction, through methods such as lubrication (e.g. oil) and streamlining.

Efficiency

☐ That efficiency is the proportion of energy in an energy transfer that is transferred to useful energy stores by a device.

☐ That efficiency can be found by using the equation: $\text{efficiency} = \dfrac{\text{useful output energy transfer}}{\text{total input energy transfer}}$, or $\text{efficiency} = \dfrac{\text{useful power output}}{\text{total power input}}$

☐ How to express efficiency as a decimal and a percentage.

☐ Ⓗ Ways of improving the efficiency of an energy transfer by reducing transfers to useless energy stores.

Exam-style Questions

1   A pot containing water is being heated on a gas hob.

  1.1   Give three energy transfers which are occurring in this scenario.

(3 marks)

  1.2   A second pan is heated at the same power, and contains the same amount of water.
The water in each pan began at the same temperature.
The water in the second pan reaches its boiling point faster.
Suggest a property of material the second pan is made of which could explain this.

(1 mark)

The hot water is poured into a flask, which is then sealed. The flask is made up of a smaller container encased within a larger one. There is a sealed gap between the walls of the two containers which is filled with air, as shown in the diagram below.

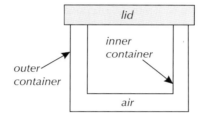

  1.3   Explain how this slows down the rate at which the water cools.

(2 marks)

2   Zaf has a mass of 85.0 kg. He runs up some stairs carrying a 10.0 kg box.
The staircase is 10.0 m high and it takes Zaf 7.0 s to reach the top.

  2.1   How much energy has been transferred to the gravitational potential energy store of Zaf and the box when he reaches the top of the stairs?
The gravitational field strength on Earth is 9.8 N/kg.
Give your answer in joules.

(2 marks)

  2.2   What is Zaf's power output when he runs up the stairs?
Give your answer in watts.

(2 marks)

  2.3   At the top of the stairs Zaf walks along the corridor, still carrying the box.
Calculate Zaf's velocity if the total energy in the kinetic energy store of Zaf and the box is 153.9 J. Give your answer in m/s.

(3 marks)

  2.4   Zaf stops and then drops the box from a height of 1.25 m.
Calculate the speed at which it hits the ground. State any assumptions you make.
Give your answer in m/s and to 2 significant figures.

(4 marks)

3   A remote control car is attached to a spring, and does 4 J of work to stretch the spring by 40 cm over 0.5 s.

3.1   Write down the equation that links power, work done and time.

(1 mark)

3.2   Calculate the useful power output of the car to extend the spring.
Give your answer in W.

(2 marks)

3.3   Calculate the spring constant of the spring.
Use the correct equation from those listed on page 394. Give your answer in N/m.

(3 marks)

3.4   In the energy transfer in **3.1**, the efficiency is 62.5%.
Calculate the total input power of the car. Give your answer in W.

(2 marks)

3.5   Suggest one way that energy is transferred to a thermal energy store (and therefore wasted) by the toy car.

(1 mark)

3.6   Suggest a way to reduce the energy transfer described in **3.4**.

(1 mark)

4   A student wants to investigate the specific heat capacity of water. To do this, they are provided with a beaker, a thermometer, and a heating element connected to a power supply and an ammeter.

4.1* Describe an experiment that the student can perform with this equipment to calculate the specific heat capacity of water.

(6 marks)

4.2   Suggest one safety issue the student should consider when performing a risk assessment for this experiment.

(1 mark)

4.3   The student heats 0.50 kg of water from 10.0 °C to 100.0 °C.
189 kJ of energy was transferred to the water.
Calculate the specific heat capacity of water.
Use the correct equation from those listed on page 284. Give your answer in J/kg°C.

(3 marks)

1. Energy Resources and Their Uses

There are lots of different energy resources that we use today for all sorts of things. But first you need to know your non-renewables from your renewables.

Non-renewable energy resources

Non-renewable energy resources are the three **fossil fuels** and nuclear fuels:

- Coal
- (Natural) gas
- Oil
- Nuclear fuels (uranium and plutonium)

Fossil fuels are natural resources that form underground over millions of years. They are typically burnt to provide energy.

Non-renewable fuels are not being made at the same rate as they are being used and will all run out one day. They all do damage to the environment through emissions or because of issues with their mining, storage and disposal (see pages 54-55 for more), but they do provide most of our energy.

Renewable energy resources

Renewable energy resources are:

- Wind
- Tides
- The Sun (solar)
- Bio-fuel
- Water waves
- Hydroelectricity
- Geothermal

Renewable energy resources can be made at the same rate as they're being used and therefore will never run out. Most of them do damage to the environment, but in less nasty ways than most non-renewables. The trouble is they often don't provide as much energy as non-renewable resources and some of them are unreliable because they depend on the weather.

Use of energy resources

Energy resources, both renewable and non-renewable, are mostly used to generate electricity. There's loads more on how over the next few pages, but two other major uses are transport and heating.

Transport

Transport is one of the most obvious places where fuels are used. Traditionally, non-renewable energy resources have been the main fuel used in transportation:

- Petrol and diesel — fuel created from oil used to power many vehicles (including most cars).
- Coal — used in some old-fashioned steam trains to boil water to produce steam.

Learning Objectives:

- Know the definitions of non-renewable and renewable energy resources and be able to tell which resources are which.
- Know that non-renewable energy resources include fossil fuels (coal, oil and gas) and nuclear fuels (uranium and plutonium).
- Know that renewable energy sources include wind, water waves, tides, hydroelectricity, the Sun (solar), geothermal and bio-fuel.
- Know that energy resources are used for electricity generation, transportation and heating.
- Be able to compare how non-renewable and renewable energy resources are used in transport and heating.

Specification Reference 6.1.3

Figure 1: A bio-fuels filling station in Spain.

Recently, more methods of transportation have started using renewable energy resources, such as bio-fuels. Some vehicles run on pure bio-fuels (see p. 53) or a mix of a bio-fuel and petrol or diesel.

Heating

Energy resources are also used for heating things like your home. Non-renewable resources used for heating include:

- Natural gas — this is the most widely used fuel for heating homes in the UK. The gas is burned to heat water, which is then pumped into radiators throughout the home.

- Oil — some homes are heated by burning oil from a tank instead of gas, especially in remote places where it is difficult to connect to the gas supply.

- Coal — this is commonly burnt in fireplaces.

Renewable energy resources used for heating include:

- Geothermal power — a geothermal (or ground source) heat pump can be used to heat buildings (p. 48-49).

- Solar power — solar water heaters use electromagnetic radiation (see page 200) from the Sun to heat water which is then pumped into radiators in the building.

Electric transport and heating

Both renewable and non-renewable energy resources can also be used to generate electricity used in transport and heating. Electrically powered vehicles (e.g. trains, trams and electric cars) use electricity for transport and electric heaters (e.g. storage heaters) use electricity for heating.

Practice Questions — Fact Recall

Q1 What are the three fossil fuels?

Q2 a) Name four renewable energy sources.

   b) Give one reason why renewable energy resources aren't always used instead of non-renewable energy resources.

Q3 Give one renewable and one non-renewable resource used directly for transport (without the need for generating electricity).

Q4 How can solar power be used to heat buildings without the need for generating electricity?

2. Wind, Solar and Geothermal

Here's the first of many pages looking at using different renewable energy resources to generate electricity. First up: wind, solar and geothermal power...

Learning Objectives:

- Be able to compare the ways that wind power, solar cells and geothermal power are used for electricity generation.
- Describe the environmental issues that come from using different energy resources.
- Understand why certain energy resources are more reliable than others.

Specification Reference 6.1.3

Wind power

Generating electricity from wind involves putting up lots of wind turbines (see Figure 2) where they're exposed to the weather, like on moors or around coasts.

Each wind turbine has its own generator inside it. The electricity is generated directly from the wind turning the blades, which turns the generator.

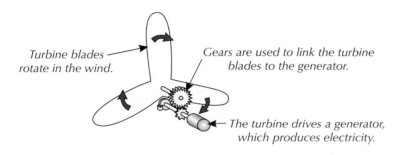

Turbine blades rotate in the wind.

Gears are used to link the turbine blades to the generator.

The turbine drives a generator, which produces electricity.

Figure 1: *The structure of a wind turbine. The blades of the wind turbine rotate in the wind and directly drive a generator, which generates electricity.*

Wind turbines produce no pollution (except for a little bit when they're manufactured), but according to some they do spoil the view (see Figure 2). You need about 1500 wind turbines to replace one coal-fired power station and 1500 of them cover a lot of ground — which would have a big effect on the scenery.

Wind turbines can be very noisy, which can be annoying for people living nearby. There's no permanent damage to the landscape though — if you remove the turbines, you remove the noise and the view returns to normal.

There are also problems with reliability. There's no power when the wind stops and it's impossible to increase supply when there's extra demand. Wind turbines also have to be stopped if the wind is very strong, as they could be damaged. On average, wind turbines produce electricity 70-85% of the time.

The initial costs (to build and set up the wind turbines) are quite high, but there are no fuel costs and minimal running costs.

Figure 2: *A wind farm in the countryside.*

Solar cells

Solar cells generate electric currents directly from the Sun's radiation (see Figure 3). Solar cells cause no pollution, although they do need quite a lot of energy to manufacture in the first place. Initial costs are high but after that the energy is free and running costs almost nil.

Tip: Be careful — solar cells are different to solar water heaters from page 46. Solar cells use some clever electronics to produce electricity from sunlight. Solar water heaters just use sunlight to heat water.

Figure 4: *A solar panel generates electricity during the day, then uses it to power a lamp that lights up the road sign at night.*

Figure 5: *Solar cells and a wind turbine being used to power a house in Hamburg, Germany.*

Exam Tip
You don't need to know exactly how electricity is generated here, but it helps to understand these details, as you'll need to be able to compare the ways different resources are used, their reliability and impact on the environment. If you're taking the Higher exam, you'll need to know how generators work — see page 305.

The solar cell generates electric current directly from the Sun's radiation and so can be plugged straight into electrical components, just like batteries.

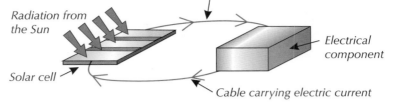

Radiation from the Sun

Solar cell

Electrical component

Cable carrying electric current

Figure 3: *A solar cell generating electric current from the Sun's radiation, connected directly to electrical components.*

Solar cells are often the best source of energy for devices that don't use a lot of energy, or in remote places where it would be difficult to get power from other sources.

> **Examples**
>
> - Calculators, road signs and watches don't use much electricity, so solar cells are ideal for powering them — see Figure 4.
>
> - Space is probably the ultimate remote location — you can't just nip up to a space satellite and top it up with fuel. Instead, satellites use large solar panels to generate the electricity they need.

In sunny countries, solar power is a very reliable source of energy, although it can only generate electricity during the daytime. Solar power can still be cost-effective even in cloudy countries like Britain. Solar cells are usually used to generate electricity on a relatively small scale, e.g. powering individual homes (see Figure 5).

Geothermal power

Geothermal power uses energy in the thermal energy stores of hot underground rocks to generate electricity. The source of much of the energy is the slow decay of various radioactive elements (see page 114), including uranium, deep inside the Earth.

Steam and hot water rise to the surface and are used to drive a turbine. The turbine turns a generator which generates electricity — see Figure 6. This is actually brilliant free energy that's reliable with very little impact on the environment.

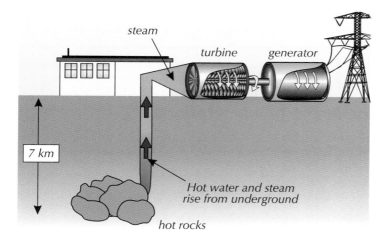

Figure 6: *The structure of a geothermal power station. Hot water and steam from underground drive a turbine, which is connected to a generator.*

In some places, geothermal power is used to heat water or buildings directly, without the need for generating electricity. The main drawback with geothermal power is that there aren't very many suitable locations for power stations. Also, the cost of building a power station is often high compared to the amount of energy we can get out of it.

Figure 7: *The Nesjavellir geothermal power station in Iceland.*

Example

Iceland produces huge amounts of its energy using geothermal power. It is used to heat homes directly and to generate electricity (see Figure 7). Iceland is volcanic, so it has lots of hot rocks lying near to the surface.

Practice Questions — Fact Recall

Q1 How is electricity generated by a wind turbine?

Q2 Give one issue associated with the reliability of using wind power.

Q3 Why are solar cells often used to power devices in remote locations?

Q4 Where does the energy transferred by geothermal power stations come from?

Practice Question — Application

Q1 For each situation below, suggest an appropriate method of generating electricity and explain your answer.

a) Street lights in a remote part of Australia.

b) A road sign on an exposed hillside in the UK.

c) Heating homes in a volcanic part of Iceland.

Figure 2: The Hoover Dam on the Colorado River in the USA — possibly the most well-known hydroelectric power station in the world.

Tip: For more on the national grid, see page 92.

Although hydroelectricity, wave power and tidal power all use water in a similar way, you need to know the details of each, and how they're different.

Hydroelectric power stations

Generating electricity using hydroelectric power usually requires the flooding of a valley by building a big dam. Water is allowed out at a controlled rate through turbines — see Figure 1.

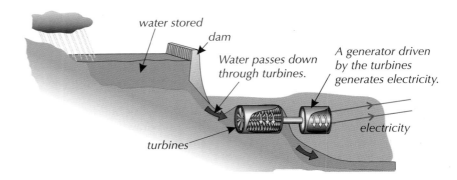

Figure 1: A hydroelectric power station. Water is held back behind a dam. When it's released it passes through turbines, which turn a generator and generates electricity.

There is no pollution, but there is a big impact on the environment. The flooding of the valley leads to rotting vegetation (which releases methane and carbon dioxide) and possible loss of habitat for some species (both animals and humans). Sometimes whole villages are evacuated and flooded to build a dam.

The reservoirs can also look very unsightly when they dry up. Putting hydroelectric power stations in remote valleys tends to reduce their impact on humans.

A big advantage is they can provide an immediate response to an increased demand for electricity. There's no problem with reliability except in times of drought. Initial costs are high, but there's no fuel costs and minimal running costs. It can be a useful way to generate electricity on a small scale in remote areas. However, in these cases it's often not practical or economical to connect it to the national grid.

Example

Almost all of the electricity generated in Norway is hydroelectric. Norway is very mountainous with lots of rivers and valleys, making it ideal for hydroelectric power.

Wave power

To generate electricity using water waves, you need lots of small wave-powered turbines located around the coast. As waves come in to the shore they provide an up and down motion which can be used to drive a generator (see Figure 3).

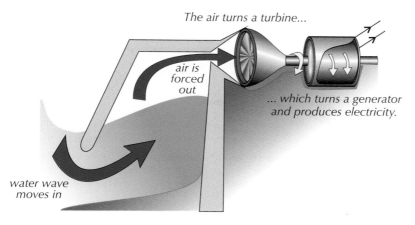

The air turns a turbine...

air is forced out

... which turns a generator and produces electricity.

water wave moves in

Tip: Electricity is also generated when the wave retreats, as air flows back through the turbine.

Figure 3: *A diagram showing how waves can be used to generate electricity. Waves force air through the turbine, which turns a generator and generates electricity.*

There is no pollution produced — the main problems are disturbing the seabed and the habitats of marine animals, spoiling the view and being a hazard to boats. They are fairly unreliable, since waves tend to die out when the wind drops. Initial costs are high, but there are no fuel costs and minimal running costs. Waves are never likely to provide energy on a large scale, but they can be very useful on small islands.

Example

- The Scottish island of Islay lies on the western coast of Scotland and is exposed to the full force of the northern Atlantic Ocean. Because of this and the fact that the island is fairly remote, it's an ideal location for a wave-powered station.

- In 2000 the Islay LIMPET (Land Installed Marine Power Energy Transmitter) was built. This was the first commercial wave power device to be connected to the UK national grid. It provides enough energy to power a few hundred homes.

- As a wave hits the structure, air is forced up through a turbine. When the wave drops, air is sucked back through the turbine. This process repeats every time a wave hits, and electricity is generated.

Figure 4: *The Islay LIMPET wave power station on the coast of Islay, a Scottish Hebridean island.*

Tidal barrages

Tides are produced by the gravitational pull of the Sun and Moon. They are used in lots of ways to generate electricity. The most common method is building a tidal barrage.

Tidal barrages are big dams built across river estuaries, with turbines in them. The turbines, as ever, are connected to electrical generators which turn and generate electricity. As the tide comes in it fills up the estuary to a height of several metres and is held back by the barrage. This water can then be allowed out through the turbines at a controlled speed when there's a height difference of water between the two sides of the barrage.

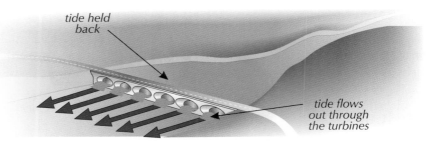

tide held back

tide flows out through the turbines

Figure 5: *The structure of a tidal barrage. Tide water is held back behind the barrage, then allowed to flow through turbines connected to generators, generating electricity.*

Figure 6: *A tidal barrage on the Rance River in France.*

This form of electricity generation causes no pollution — the main problems are preventing free access by boats, spoiling the view and altering the habitat of the wildlife, e.g. wading birds, sea creatures and beasties who live in the sand.

Tides are pretty reliable in the sense that they happen twice a day without fail, and always near to the predicted height. The only drawback is that the height of the tide is variable, so lower (neap) tides will provide significantly less energy than the bigger (spring) tides. They also don't work when the water level is the same either side of the barrage — this happens four times a day because of the tides.

Initial costs are moderately high, but there are no fuel costs and minimal running costs. Even though tidal barrages can only be used in some of the most suitable estuaries, tidal power has the potential for generating a significant amount of energy.

Practice Questions — Fact Recall

Q1 Describe how electricity is generated in a hydroelectric dam.

Q2 Give two environmental problems that can be caused by building hydroelectric dams.

Q3 Explain why hydroelectric dams are often used to generate electricity in remote areas.

Q4 Briefly explain how electricity can be generated from waves.

Q5 The total amount of electricity that can be generated by waves is fairly low. Give one other disadvantage associated with the reliability of generating electricity using waves.

Q6 Briefly explain how a tidal barrage can be used to generate electricity.

4. Bio-fuels and Non-renewables

Bio-fuels, fossil fuels and nuclear fuels are used in much the same way to generate electricity. They're all used to heat water, which turns it into steam that drives a turbine, but they have very different issues affecting them.

Bio-fuels

Bio-fuels are renewable energy resources — they're created from either plant products or animal dung. They can be solid, liquid or gas and can be burnt to produce electricity or run cars in the same way as fossil fuels.

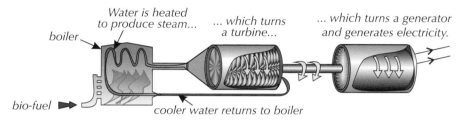

Water is heated to produce steam... ... which turns a turbine... ... which turns a generator and generates electricity.

boiler

bio-fuel ➡ cooler water returns to boiler

Figure 1: *A diagram of how bio-fuels are used to generate electricity. Bio-fuels are burned to heat water, which produces steam. The steam drives a turbine, which drives a generator and generates electricity.*

Learning Objectives:
- Be able to compare the ways that bio-fuels, fossil fuels and nuclear fuels are used for electricity generation.
- Describe the environmental issues that come from using different energy resources.
- Understand why certain energy resources are more reliable than others.

Specification Reference 6.1.3

Bio-fuels are fairly reliable, as crops take a relatively short time to grow and different crops can be grown all year round. However, they cannot respond to immediate energy demands. To combat this, bio-fuels are continuously produced and stored for when they are needed.

The cost to refine bio-fuels is very high and some worry that growing crops specifically for bio-fuels will mean there isn't enough space or water to meet the demands for crops that are grown for food.

Bio-fuels made from plants are theoretically **carbon neutral**:

- The plants that grow to produce the waste absorb CO_2 from the atmosphere as they are growing.

- When the waste is burned, this CO_2 is re-released into the atmosphere. So it has a neutral effect on atmospheric CO_2 levels (although this only really works if you keep growing plants at the same rate you're burning things).

There is still debate regarding the impact of bio-fuels on the environment, once the full production is considered.

Using bio-fuels to generate electricity doesn't just produce carbon dioxide. Bio-fuel production also creates methane emissions — a lot of this comes from the animals.

In some regions, large areas of forest have been cleared to make room to grow bio-fuels (see Figure 2), resulting in lots of species losing their natural habitats. The decay and burning of this vegetation also increases CO_2 and methane emissions.

Bio-fuels have potential, but their use is limited by the amount of available farmland that can be dedicated to their production.

Figure 2: *An oil palm plantation in Indonesia. These crops can be used to make biodiesel.*

Fossil fuels

Most of the electricity we use is generated from fossil fuels (coal, oil, and gas) in big power stations. Figure 3 shows how electricity is generated in a typical fossil fuel power station.

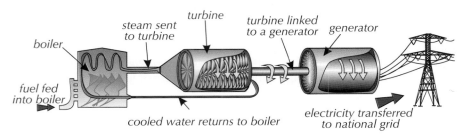

steam sent to turbine — *turbine* — *turbine linked to a generator* — *generator*

boiler

fuel fed into boiler

cooled water returns to boiler

electricity transferred to national grid

Figure 3: *Electricity generation in a fossil fuel power station.*

Exam Tip
You don't need to know exactly how electricity is generated here for the exam, but it helps to know which energy resource is which, as you'll need to compare the ways different resources are used, their reliabilities and any environmental issues they create.

Fossil fuels provide a cost-effective energy resource, that produces large amounts of energy and is readily available. While setup costs of power plants can be higher than other resources, the running costs and fuel extraction costs are fairly low.

They're also reliable — there's enough fuel to meet current demand, and they are extracted from the Earth at a fast enough rate that power plants always have fuel in stock. This means that the power plants can respond quickly to changes in demand (p. 93). However, these fuels are slowly running out. If no new resources are found, some fossil fuel stocks may run out within a hundred years.

All three fossil fuels (coal, oil and gas) release CO_2 into the atmosphere when they're burned. For the same amount of energy produced, coal releases the most CO_2, followed by oil then gas. All this CO_2 adds to the **greenhouse effect** and contributes to global warming. The greenhouse effect is where gases in the Earth's atmosphere (known as greenhouse gases) block radiation from the Sun from leaving the atmosphere. This causes the overall temperature of the atmosphere to rise (i.e. global warming).

Burning coal and oil releases sulfur dioxide, which causes acid rain. Acid rain can be harmful to trees and soils and can have far-reaching effects in ecosystems. Acid rain can be reduced by taking the sulfur out of the fuel before it is burned, or by cleaning up the emissions before they're released into the atmosphere.

Coal mining makes a mess of the landscape, especially "open-cast mining" where huge pits are dug on the surface of the Earth. Oil spillages cause serious environmental problems, affecting animals that live in and around the sea. We try to avoid them, but there's always a chance they'll happen.

Figure 4: *A pelican covered in oil from the Deepwater Horizon oil spill.*

Example

In 2010, an explosion at the oil drilling station Deepwater Horizon in the Gulf of Mexico resulted in the largest accidental oil spill in history. This resulted in thousands of miles of coastline being covered in crude oil, making the area uninhabitable for many local species of animals and plants.

Nuclear fuels

A nuclear power station is mostly the same as the one used for burning fossil fuels (see previous page), but the fuel isn't burnt. Nuclear fission of nuclear fuels such as uranium or plutonium releases the energy to heat water into steam which drives turbines. Nuclear power stations take the longest time of all the power stations to start up.

Nuclear power is 'clean', in that it doesn't cause the release of any harmful gases or other chemicals into the atmosphere. (Transporting nuclear fuel and waste to and from sites does cause a small amount of pollution though, e.g. from transport lorries burning fossil fuels.) It's also reliable — there's enough fuel to meet current demand.

The biggest problem with generating electricity using nuclear fuel is that the nuclear waste produced is very dangerous and difficult to dispose of. This is because it stays highly radioactive (see page 114) for a long time and so needs to be stored safely far away from people's homes.

Nuclear fuel (e.g. uranium and plutonium) is relatively cheap but the overall cost of nuclear power is high due to the cost of the power station and final **decommissioning** — shutting down the power station so it's completely safe and poses no risk to people or the environment.

Nuclear power always carries the risk of an equipment failure leading to major catastrophe, like the Chernobyl disaster in 1986 or the Fukushima disaster in 2011.

Tip: Fission is the process where atoms split and release energy.

Tip: The radiation produced by radioactive materials can be very dangerous to humans.

Figure 5: A nuclear power station at night with steam condensing into water vapour as it leaves the cooling tower.

Practice Questions — Fact Recall

Q1 a) What is meant by a 'carbon neutral' process?

b) Discuss how using bio-fuels to generate electricity could be a carbon neutral process.

Q2 Name two harmful gases that are released into the atmosphere by burning coal.

Q3 a) Which non-renewable resource doesn't directly release harmful gases into the atmosphere when used to generate electricity?

b) Give two problems with using this fuel to generate electricity.

Learning Objectives:
- Understand how the ways we use energy resources have changed over time.
- Understand that although scientists have identified environmental issues with energy resources, other factors can limit our ability to deal with these issues.

Specification Reference
6.1.3

5. Trends in Energy Resource Use

Environmental issues related to energy resources have led us to change the resources we use over time. But it's not always easy to do so...

Reliance on fossil fuels

Over the 20th century, the electricity use of the UK hugely increased as the population got bigger and people began to use electricity for more things.

Since the beginning of the 21st century, electricity use in the UK has been decreasing (slowly), as we get better at making appliances more efficient (p. 38) and try to be more careful with energy use in our homes.

Most of our electricity is produced using fossil fuels (mostly coal and gas) and from nuclear power. Generating electricity isn't the only reason we burn fossil fuels — oil (diesel and petrol) is used to fuel cars, and gas is used to heat homes and cook food.

However, we are trying to increase our use of renewable energy resources (the UK aims to use renewable resources to provide 15% of its total yearly energy by 2020).

Movement towards renewable energy resources

We now know that burning fossil fuels has a lot of negative effects on the environment (p. 54). This makes many people want to use more renewable energy resources that effect the environment less.

(WORKING SCIENTIFICALLY)

People and governments are also becoming increasingly aware that non-renewables will run out one day. Many people think it's better to learn to get by without non-renewables before this happens.

Pressure from other countries and the public has meant that governments have begun to introduce targets for using renewable resources. This in turn puts pressure on energy providers to build new power plants that use renewable resources to make sure they don't lose business and money.

Car companies have also been affected by this change in attitude towards the environment. Electric cars and hybrids (cars powered by two fuels, e.g. petrol and electricity) are already on the market and their popularity is increasing.

Figure 1: *Protest movements have applied pressure to governments to change their energy policies.*

Factors limiting change

(WORKING SCIENTIFICALLY)

Although scientists know about the negative environmental effects of energy resources, they can only give advice and don't have the power to make people, companies or governments change their behaviour. The environmental issues aren't the only ones that matter, either. There are other political, social, ethical and economic issues to consider too (see page 4).

For example, the use of renewables is usually limited by reliability and money. Building new renewable power plants costs money, so some smaller energy providers are reluctant to do this — especially when fossil fuels are such a cost effective way of meeting demand.

Even if new power plants are built, there are a lot of arguments over where they should be. For example, many people don't want to live next to a wind farm, which can lead to them protesting.

Some energy resources like wind power are not as reliable as traditional fossil fuels and cannot increase their power output on demand. This would mean either having to use a combination of different power plants (which would be expensive) or researching ways to improve reliability.

Research into improving the reliability and cost of renewable resources takes time and money. This means that, even with funding, it might be years before improvements are made. In the meantime, dependable power stations using non-renewable resources have to be used.

Making personal changes can also be quite expensive. Hybrid cars are generally more expensive than equivalent petrol cars and things like solar panels for your home are still quite pricey. The cost of these things is slowly going down, but they are still not an option for many people.

Figure 2: *Offshore (at sea) wind turbines are relatively expensive to build and maintain but usually have fewer complaints from locals.*

Practice Questions — Fact Recall

Q1 Why has electricity usage in the UK been decreasing slightly since the start of the of the 21st century?

Q2 Give two limitations on using more renewable energy resources.

Topic 1b Checklist — Make sure you know...

Energy Resources and Their Uses

☐ How renewable and non-renewable energy resources are different.

☐ That coal, gas, oil and nuclear fuels like uranium and plutonium are non-renewable energy resources.

☐ That renewable energy resources include: wind, water waves, tides, hydroelectricity, the Sun (solar), geothermal and bio-fuels.

☐ That energy resources are mostly used for generating electricity, transport and heating.

☐ How certain renewable and non-renewable energy resources are used directly in transport and heating.

Wind, Solar and Geothermal

☐ That wind can be used to generate electricity by driving turbines.

☐ That solar cells generate electricity directly from radiation from the Sun.

cont...

☐ That geothermal power can be used to generate electricity by heating water to form steam which turns a turbine, or to heat buildings directly.

☐ The environmental impacts of using wind power, solar power and geothermal power.

☐ That wind power and solar power have issues with reliability due to the weather.

☐ That geothermal power is reliable once you've found a suitable location for a power station.

Hydroelectricity, Waves and Tides

☐ That in a hydroelectric power station, water flowing through a dam drives turbines directly to generate electricity.

☐ That water waves can be used to generate electricity by forcing air through a turbine.

☐ That the tides can be used to generate power. For example, tidal barrages are dams built across estuaries, where turbines are driven by tide water as it fills and leaves the estuary.

☐ The environmental impacts of using hydroelectric power, wave power and tidal power.

☐ That hydroelectricity is reliable, except in times of drought.

☐ That wave power is unreliable, as it relies on the wind causing waves.

☐ That tidal barrages are reliable as there will always be tides.

Bio-fuels and Non-renewables

☐ That bio-fuels can be burned to heat water into steam that drives a turbine to generate electricity.

☐ That fossil fuels are burned to heat water into steam that drives a turbine to generate electricity.

☐ That, in nuclear power stations, energy released from the fission of uranium or plutonium is used to heat water into steam that drives a turbine to generate electricity.

☐ The environmental impacts of using bio-fuels, fossil fuels and nuclear power to generate electricity.

☐ That fossil fuels, nuclear fuels and bio-fuels are reliable and there are enough to meet current demand, although bio-fuels can't respond to immediate energy demands.

Trends in Energy Resource Use

☐ How our use of different energy resources has changed over time.

☐ That more renewable energy resources are being used due to environmental issues with non-renewables.

☐ That although scientists have shown the environmental issues of certain energy resources, they are still used as other factors affect our ability to deal with these issues.

☐ That the cost and reliability of renewable energy resources are currently their main limitations.

Exam-style Questions

1   The table below shows the percentage of the total electricity produced from each of six energy resources in two different countries.

	Coal	Oil	Gas	Nuclear	Hydroelectric	Wind
Country 1	49.9%	2.4%	20.3%	19.6%	6.0%	1.8%
Country 2	3.9%	4.0%	4.5%	3.1%	84.2%	0.3%

1.1   What percentage of electricity in Country 1 is generated from non-renewable energy sources?

(2 marks)

1.2   Both countries generate the same amount of electricity each year.
Suggest which country will emit more pollution by generating electricity.
Explain your answer.

(2 marks)

1.3   Country 1 is considering reducing the amount of coal it burns and generating some of its electricity from bio-fuels instead. Give **one** environmental impact of using coal to generate electricity.

(1 mark)

1.4   Suggest **one** impact on reliability that switching from coal to generating electricity using bio-fuels may have.

(1 mark)

2   Coal was once the most commonly used resource for generating electricity in the UK.
2.1   Coal is a fossil fuel and a non-renewable energy resource.
Define a non-renewable energy resource.

(1 mark)

2.2   Suggest another use of coal as an energy resource, other than for generating electricity.

(1 mark)

2.3   The use of coal has decreased in recent years so that it is no longer the main fuel for UK power stations.
Suggest **one** environmental reason why the use of coal has decreased.

(1 mark)

2.4   A new coal power station is proposed for an island in Scotland. The island has a number of exposed hills, and regularly experiences windy weather.
Suggest **two** renewable energy resources which would be suitable alternatives to coal to produce electricity on the island, and explain how they are suitable.

(4 marks)

2.5   Give **one** reason why the renewable alternatives may not be able to entirely replace the coal power station as an option for generating the island's power.

(1 mark)

Learning Objectives:

- Know the standard symbols used in circuit diagrams.
- Be able to draw and understand simple circuit diagrams.
- Know that the flow of charge in a circuit is electric current.
- Know that the rate of flow of charge gives the size of the current.
- Know and be able to use the equation $Q = It$.
- Know that at any point in a single closed circuit loop, the current is the same.
- Know that current cannot flow around a circuit without a source of potential difference.

Specification References 6.2.1.1, 6.2.1.2

1. Circuits, Current and Potential Difference

Electricity flows as current around circuits. You may have seen circuit symbols before, but there are quite a few that you need to know. So first things first, let's have a bit of circuit training...

Circuit symbols

You need to know (and be able to draw) each of the following circuit symbols. You'll learn a bit more about some of them later in this section and the next.

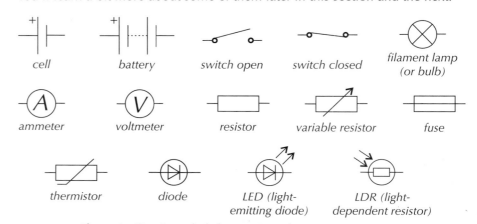

Figure 1: Circuit symbols for a variety of circuit components.

Circuit diagrams

You might be asked to draw a circuit, or to find a problem with one. One thing to make sure of is that your circuit is complete. If a component isn't connected in a circuit properly, it won't work.

A circuit is complete if you can follow a wire from one end of the battery (or other power supply), through any components to the other end of the battery (ignoring any switches) — see Figure 2.

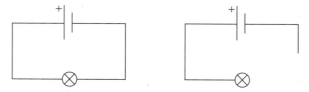

Figure 2: *(Left) A complete circuit. All the wires are joined to something at both ends and the lamp will light. (Right) An incomplete circuit. The lamp won't light.*

Tip: Wires are just represented by straight lines.

Tip: Switches allow you to turn circuits (and so components) on and off. You can ignore them when working out if a circuit is complete, because they can always be closed to complete the circuit.

Voltmeters and ammeters

Voltmeters and ammeters always have to be connected in a circuit in a certain way, as shown in Figure 3, otherwise they won't do what they are meant to.

- A **voltmeter** measures potential difference. It is always connected 'across' a component — this is known as 'in parallel'.

- An **ammeter** measures current. It is always connected 'in line' with a component — this is known as 'in series'.

Tip: Read on to find out about current and potential difference and head to pages 68-76 if you want to learn more about what 'in series' and 'in parallel' mean.

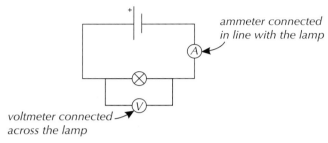

ammeter connected in line with the lamp

voltmeter connected across the lamp

Figure 3: A circuit with a voltmeter and an ammeter connected correctly.

Current

An electric **current** is a flow of electric charge. Cells (and other power supplies) always have a positive terminal (the longer line), and a negative terminal (the shorter line). Current flows from positive to negative around a circuit.

Tip: Electrons carry the charge. They actually flow from negative to positive. But when scientists realised this they didn't want to change the way that current was defined, so we still say it flows from positive to negative.

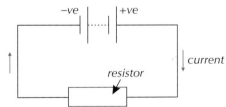

current

resistor

Figure 4: Current flowing from positive to negative in an electric circuit.

The size of the current is the rate of flow of charge. It's measured in amperes, A. When current flows past a point in a circuit for a length of time then the charge that has passed is given by this formula:

Tip: You can use a formula triangle to rearrange the equation for charge. See page 242 for how to use formula triangles.

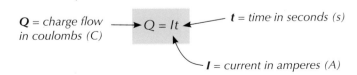

Q = charge flow in coulombs (C) — $Q = It$ — **t** = time in seconds (s)

I = current in amperes (A)

More charge passes around the circuit when a bigger current flows. In a single, closed loop (like the one in Figure 4) the current has the same value everywhere in the circuit (see page 69).

> **Example**
>
> **A battery charger passes a current of 2.5 A through a cell over a period of exactly 4 hours. How much charge does the charger transfer to the cell altogether?**
>
> You've got I = 2.5 A and t = 4 × 60 × 60 s = 14 400 s.
>
> $Q = It = 2.5 × 14\,400 = 36\,000$ C

Tip: You may also see potential difference referred to as voltage, or abbreviated to pd. You'll learn a lot more about pd later on — see pages 89-90.

Potential difference

Electrical charge will only flow around a complete (closed) circuit if there is a **potential difference**, so a current can only flow is there's a source of potential difference. In a simple circuit, this is usually a cell or battery. Potential difference is the driving force that pushes the charge around. Its unit is the volt, V.

Practice Questions — Fact Recall

Q1 Draw the circuit symbol for a:

a) battery   b) resistor   c) fuse   d) lamp   e) diode

Q2 What is an incomplete circuit?

Q3 In what direction does current flow in a circuit?

Q4 What is the formula linking charge, current and time? Write down the units each quantity is measured in.

Q5 What is needed for a current to flow in a circuit?

Practice Questions — Application

Q1 Draw a complete circuit containing a cell, a lamp, and an open switch which can be used to turn the lamp on and off.

Q2 Draw a complete circuit containing a battery, a resistor and a voltmeter measuring the voltage across the resistor.

Q3 Draw a circuit containing a cell, a thermistor and an ammeter.

Q4 In which of these circuits will the lamp be lit up?

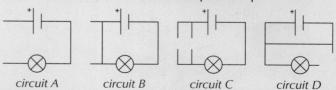

circuit A   circuit B   circuit C   circuit D

Q5 The current through a lamp is 0.2 A. Calculate the time taken for 50 C of charge to pass through the lamp.

Q6 A cell has a charge of 102 C passing through it every minute. Calculate the current flowing through the cell.

2. Resistance and *I-V* Characteristics

Resistance is how much a component in a circuit slows down the flow of current. It's different for each component, and it's related to the size of the current and potential difference.

Resistance

Resistance is anything in the circuit which reduces the flow of current. It is measured in ohms, Ω. The current flowing through a component depends on the potential difference across it, and the resistance of the component. The greater the resistance of a component, the smaller the current that flows (for a given potential difference across the component).

The resistance of a component is linked to potential difference across it and current through it by the following formula:

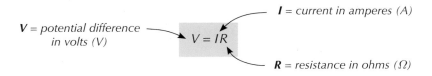

V = potential difference in volts (V) — $V = IR$ — I = current in amperes (A)

R = resistance in ohms (Ω)

Example

Voltmeter *V* reads 6.0 V and resistor *R* has a resistance of 4.0 Ω.
What is the current through ammeter *A*?

Rearrange the formula for $V = IR$.

You need to find I, so the version you need is $I = V \div R$.

$I = V \div R = 6.0 \div 4.0 = 1.5$ A

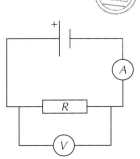

(MATHS SKILLS)

For some components, as the current through them is changed, the resistance of the component changes as well. The resistance of an **ohmic conductor** (e.g. a wire or a resistor), however, doesn't change with the current.

At a constant temperature, the current flowing through an ohmic conductor is directly proportional to the potential difference across it (i.e. R is constant in $V = IR$).

However, a lot of components aren't ohmic — their resistance changes with the current through them. These include certain types of resistor (see pages 80-81), diodes and filament lamps (p. 66).

Learning Objectives:
- Know that the resistance of and potential difference across a component determine the current flowing through it.
- Know and be able to use the equation $V = IR$.
- Know that an ohmic conductor has a constant resistance for any current through it.
- Know, and be able to explain examples of, how the resistance of some components varies with current through them.
- Be able to use a circuit to investigate the effect of wire length on the resistance of a circuit (Required Practical 15).
- Be able to use a circuit to investigate the *I-V* characteristic of a resistor at a constant temperature (ohmic conductor), filament lamp and diode (Required Practical 16).
- Be able to draw, and explain the design and use of, each of the circuits used in these practicals.
- Know the shape of these *I-V* characteristics and link it to the properties and function of the component and whether it is linear or non-linear.

Specification References
6.2.1.3, 6.2.1.4

Investigating factors affecting resistance

The resistance of a circuit can depend on a number of factors, like whether components are in series or parallel, p. 77-79, or the length of wire used in the circuit. You can investigate how the length of a wire affects resistance using the circuit shown in Figure 1.

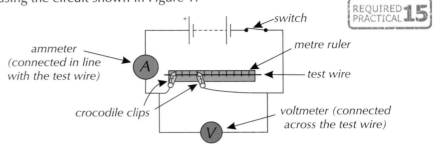

REQUIRED PRACTICAL **15**

Figure 1: A test circuit for investigating how the length of a wire affects circuit resistance.

One crocodile clip is attached to the wire at the 0 cm position on the ruler. It should remain fixed at this point throughout the investigation. The second crocodile clip can be moved left and right along the test wire. The value written on the ruler at the point you attach this clip gives the length of the wire connected in the circuit.

Now you have your test circuit set up, you can begin your investigation. Attach the second crocodile clip to the wire and record the length of the wire between the two crocodile clips. Close the switch and record the current shown on the ammeter and the potential difference shown on the voltmeter.

Move the second crocodile clip, close the switch and record the new length, current and potential difference. Repeat this for a number of different lengths of wire.

Use the data you've recorded to work out the resistance for each length of wire, using $R = V \div I$ (from $V = IR$ on page 63). Plot a graph of resistance against wire length and draw a line of best fit.

The graph you obtain should look like the one shown in Figure 2. It's a straight line through the origin, which means that resistance is directly proportional to length — the longer the wire, the greater the resistance.

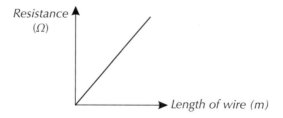

Figure 2: A graph of resistance against wire length for a test wire. It's a straight line which passes through the origin.

Your graph might not actually pass through the origin. It can be hard to attach the first crocodile clip at exactly 0 cm on the meter ruler, so all of your measurements could be slightly shorter or longer than the true values. There is also contact resistance in every circuit, e.g. between the crocodile clips and the components. These would cause systematic errors in your results.

Tip: Make sure you do a risk assessment beforehand — watch out for things like the wire becoming too hot.

Tip: Using a thin wire will give you the best results here. It should also be as straight as possible so your length measurements are accurate.

Tip: The wire may heat up, which will increase its resistance. The larger the current, the more it'll heat up, so using a small pd can help minimise this effect. It's also a good idea to open the switch between readings to let the wire cool down.

Tip: Make sure you take enough measurements to be able to spot a pattern in your graph.

Tip: There are lots of different factors you could test using this setup. Another example would be investigating how the diameter of the wire affects resistance. You'd need a selection of wires of different thicknesses to do this. A micrometer (p.231) would be helpful for measuring their diameters.

Tip: See p.12 for more on systematic errors.

I-V characteristics

REQUIRED PRACTICAL **16**

I-V **characteristics** (current-potential difference graphs) show how the current varies as you change the potential difference across a component. Ohmic conductors (components with constant resistance — p.63) have *I-V* characteristics that are straight lines. They're also known as linear components. Non-linear components, on the other hand, have curved *I-V* characteristics — the resistance changes depending on the current.

Since $V = IR$, you can calculate the resistance at any point of an *I-V* characteristic by reading off the values of V and I and calculating $R = V \div I$. If it's a straight-line graph through the origin, every point will give you the same value of resistance.

You can construct an *I-V* characteristic for a component yourself using the test circuit displayed in Figure 3.

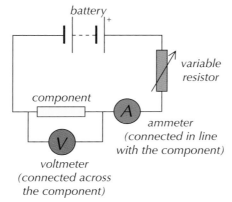

battery

variable resistor

component

ammeter (connected in line with the component)

voltmeter (connected across the component)

Figure 3: *A circuit diagram of a test circuit used to investigate the I-V characteristic of a component.*

To find a component's *I-V* characteristic, begin to vary the resistance of the variable resistor. This alters the current flowing through the circuit and the potential difference across the component.

Each time you use the variable resistor to alter the current, record the potential difference across the component for that value of current. Repeat each reading twice more to get an average pd for each measurement.

Swap over the wires connected to the battery to reverse the direction of the current. Measure negative values of current and potential difference using the same method as described above.

Now you can use your measurements to plot a graph of current against potential difference for the component. This is your *I-V* characteristic. Read on to see some examples of *I-V* characteristics for different components.

Ohmic conductors

The current through an ohmic conductor (at constant temperature) is directly proportional to potential difference, so you get a straight line *I-V* characteristic. A fixed resistor (or a length of wire) is an ohmic conductor, so you could test a few different resistors (or different wires). Different resistances result in straight lines with different slopes — see Figure 6.

Tip: Again, make sure you do a risk assessment for the practical described on this page.

Tip: This type of circuit is a dc (direct current) circuit (see page 86). The component, ammeter and variable resistor are all connected in a line (in series). They can be in any order in the circuit. The voltmeter must be placed across (in parallel with) the component.

Figure 4: *A type of variable resistor. They can be used to control the amount of current flowing in a circuit.*

Tip: Once you've swapped over the wires at the battery, the readings will be negative because the current is flowing through the components in the opposite direction to before.

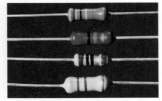

Figure 5: *Different sizes of resistors could be used in this investigation. They typically look like this.*

Tip: Remember, you can calculate the resistance at any point on an *I-V* characteristic using $R = V \div I$.

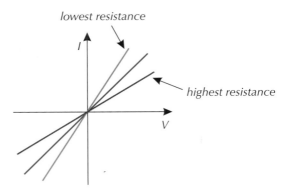

Figure 6: *I-V characteristics for ohmic conductors with different resistances.*

Filament lamps

When an electrical charge flows through a filament lamp, it transfers some energy to the thermal energy store of the filament (page 21), which is designed to heat up and glow. Resistance increases with temperature, so as more current flows through the lamp, the lamp heats up more and the resistance increases. This means less current can flow per unit potential difference, so the graph gets shallower, hence the curve of the *I-V* characteristic is shown in Figure 8.

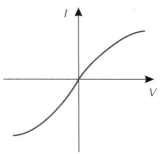

Figure 8: *An I-V characteristic for a filament lamp. It's curved because the resistance is changing.*

Figure 7: *A filament lamp, with filament glowing.*

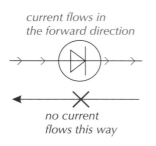

Figure 9: *A diagram illustrating which way current is able to flow in a diode.*

Diodes

A **diode** is a component that only lets current pass through it in one direction. The resistance of a diode depends on the direction of the current — it will happily let current flow through it one way, but will have a very high resistance if the current is reversed.

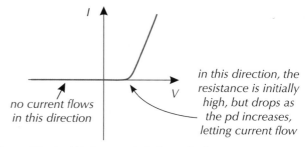

Figure 10: *An I-V characteristic for a diode. Current only flows in one direction.*

If you're investigating the *I-V* characteristic of a diode using the circuit suggested in Figure 3, you'll need to add a protective resistor to the circuit. As diodes have low resistance in one direction, the protective resistor is needed to stop the current getting too high and damaging the diode. Because you're keeping the current quite low, you should also use a milliammeter rather than a regular ammeter.

Tip: A protective resistor is just a fixed resistor connected in series with another component. It increases the overall resistance in the circuit, protecting the other component from too large a current.

Practice Questions — Fact Recall

Q1 What is resistance? What unit is resistance measured in?

Q2 Write down the equation linking resistance, pd and current.

Q3 Draw a circuit diagram of a circuit you could use to investigate how the length of a piece of wire affects the resistance of a circuit.

Q4 What is the relationship between the length of a wire and its resistance?

Q5 Draw a circuit diagram of a circuit you could use to find the *I-V* characteristic of a component.

Q6 How do you find the resistance of a fixed resistor at a constant temperature from its *I-V* characteristic?

Q7 Sketch an *I-V* graph for:

a) an ohmic conductor at a constant temperature   b) a diode

Q8 Describe the resistance of a diode as the current through it flows in:

a) the forwards direction.   b) the backwards direction.

Practice Questions — Application

Q1 A student tests component A using a suitable test circuit and plots a graph of his data, shown on the right. What would you expect component A to be?

Q2 A current of 0.015 A is flowing through a 2.0 Ω resistor. What is the potential difference across the resistor?

Q3 A current of 0.60 A flows through a motor. The potential difference across the motor is 14.4 V. Calculate the resistance of the motor.

Q4 The graph on the right shows the *I-V* characteristic of a resistor at a constant temperature. Calculate its resistance.

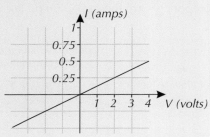

Learning Objectives:

- Know that series circuits are one way of connecting electrical components.
- Be able to construct series circuits from circuit diagrams.
- Understand how series circuits can be used to measure quantities and test components.
- Know that the total potential difference from the power supply is shared between all components connected in series.
- Know that the current through each component connected in series is the same.
- Know that the total resistance of components in series is the sum of the resistances of each component.
- Understand why adding resistors in series increases the total resistance.
- Know how to calculate pd, resistance and current in series circuits.

Specification Reference 6.2.2

So you've got the basics of circuit components covered... but how are you going to connect them? Components can either be connected in series or parallel. First up, series circuits — they're basically just big loops.

Components in series

In **series circuits**, the different components are connected in a line, end to end, between the positive and negative ends of the power supply (except for voltmeters, which are always connected across a component — see page 61).

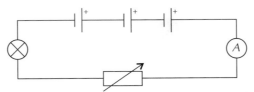

Figure 1: *A circuit in which each component is connected in series — you can draw a single line that travels along the wires and passes through every component once before returning to your starting point.*

If you remove or disconnect one component, the circuit is broken and they all stop. This is generally not very handy, and in practice very few things are connected in series. But you can design series circuits to simply measure quantities and test components (e.g. the test circuit on page 65, and the sensor circuit coming up on page 81).

Potential difference in series circuits

There is a bigger potential difference (pd) when more cells are connected in series, provided the cells are all connected the same way. For example, when two cells with a potential difference of 1.5 V are connected in series, they supply 3 V between them (see Figure 2 on the next page). You just add up all the individual cell pds to find the total power source pd.

In series circuits the total potential difference of the supply is shared between the various components. So the potential differences round a series circuit always add up to equal the source potential difference. If two or more components are the same, the pd across them will also be the same.

Tip: Ammeters are always connected in series with the components that they are measuring the current through — even if the circuit is not a series circuit (p.61).

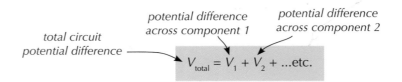

total circuit potential difference

potential difference across component 1

potential difference across component 2

$$V_{total} = V_1 + V_2 + ...etc.$$

Example

In the diagram, two cells and two lamps are connected in series. The total potential difference across the circuit is the sum of the pds of the two batteries, so:

$$V = 1.5\,V + 1.5\,V = 3.0\,V$$

The potential differences, V_1 and V_2, of the two lamps add up to 3.0 V:

$$V = V_1 + V_2 = 3.0\,V$$

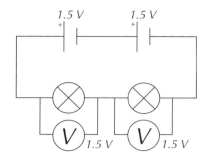

Figure 2: A circuit diagram containing two cells and two identical lamps connected in series. The potential difference from the cells is split evenly across the lamps.

Tip: Remember, voltmeters are always connected across the component they are measuring.

Figure 3: Christmas tree lights are often connected in series. The bulbs can be very small because the mains voltage is shared out between them.

Current in series circuits

In series circuits the same current flows through all parts of the circuit:

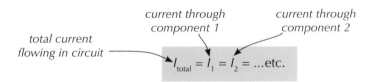

current through component 1

current through component 2

total current flowing in circuit

$$I_{total} = I_1 = I_2 = ...etc.$$

The size of the current is determined by the total potential difference of the cells and the total resistance of the circuit, using the equation $V = IR$ (from page 63).

Tip: This is why ammeters must be connected in series — so that the same current flows through the ammeter and the component that you want to measure the current through.

Example

In the diagram, two lamps are connected in series. The current through each lamp (and in fact the whole circuit) is exactly the same.

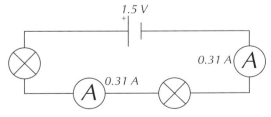

Figure 4: A series circuit containing two lamps and two ammeters, showing that the current is the same throughout the circuit.

Resistance in series circuits

In series circuits the total resistance is just the sum of all the resistances:

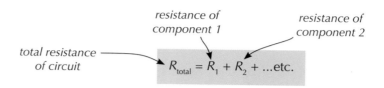

This is because by adding a resistor in series, the two resistors have to share the total pd. The potential difference across each resistor is lower, so the current through each resistor is also lower. In a series circuit, the current is the same everywhere so the total current in the circuit is reduced when a resistor is added. This means that the total resistance of the circuit increases.

The bigger the resistance of a component, the bigger its share of the total potential difference.

Example

Find the total resistance of this circuit.

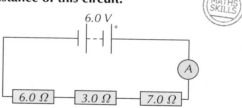

The total resistance of a series circuit is the sum of the resistances of each component:

$$R = 6.0\ \Omega + 3.0\ \Omega + 7.0\ \Omega = 16\ \Omega$$

Find the current through the circuit.

- The total potential difference in the circuit is equal to the battery potential difference: $V = 6.0$ V.

- Rearrange the equation $V = IR$ and plug in the values of V and R to find the total current:

$$I = V \div R = 6.0 \div 16 = 0.375\ \text{A}$$

Find the potential difference across the 6.0 Ω resistor.

- The current is the same everywhere in the circuit, so the current through the 6.0 Ω resistor is $I = 0.375$ A.

- The resistance of the resistor is clearly (I hope...) $R = 6.0\ \Omega$.

- Use the equation $V = IR$:

$$V = IR = 0.375 \times 6.0 = 2.25\ \text{V}$$

Tip: The resistance of the ammeter and wires is so small that you don't need to worry about it.

Summary of series circuits

There are four simple rules to remember for series circuits:

- The pd of the cells adds up to the source pd.

- The source pd is split across the components.

- The current is the same through all the components.

- The total resistance of the circuit is the sum of all the resistances of the separate components.

You'll need to be able to use these rules in all sorts of circuit examples in the exam, so make sure you know them.

Practice Questions — Fact Recall

Q1 What does 'connected in series' mean?

Q2 What type of circuit component must always be connected in series?

Q3 How should you connect extra cells in a circuit in order to increase the total potential difference across the circuit?

Q4 True or false? Every component connected in series has the same potential difference across it.

Q5 What can you say about the current through each component connected in series?

Q6 Explain why adding a resistor in series increases the total resistance.

Practice Questions — Application

Q1 The circuit shown has a 7 Ω resistor and a filament lamp in series. Ammeter A reads a constant value of 1.5 A.

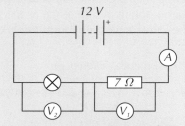

a) What is the current through the filament lamp?

b) What potential difference will voltmeter V_1 measure?

c) What potential difference will voltmeter V_2 measure?

d) What is the resistance of the filament lamp?

Tip: Remember the total V across the circuit will be equal to $V_1 + V_2$.

Learning Objectives:
- Know that parallel circuits are one way of connecting electrical components.
- Know the difference between series and parallel circuits.
- Be able to construct parallel circuits from circuit diagrams.
- Know that the pd across each component in parallel is the same.
- Know that the total current of a parallel circuit is the sum of the currents through each branch.
- Know that the total resistance of a parallel circuit is less than the resistance of the branch with the smallest resistance.
- Understand why adding resistors in parallel decreases the total resistance.
- Know that circuits can contain a combination of components wired in parallel and components wired in series.

Specification Reference
6.2.2

4. Parallel Circuits

In parallel circuits, components or groups of components are on their own separate loop or branch. They're much more useful than series circuits because you can turn off each loop separately, without turning off the rest.

Components in parallel

Unlike components in series, components connected in **parallel** each have their own branch in a circuit connected to the positive and negative terminals of the supply (except ammeters which are always connected in series). If you remove or disconnect one of them, it will hardly affect the others at all. This is because current can still flow in a complete loop (page 60) from one end of the power supply to the other through the branches that are still connected.

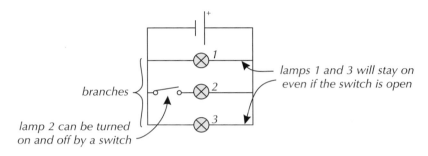

branches

lamps 1 and 3 will stay on even if the switch is open

lamp 2 can be turned on and off by a switch

Figure 1: *A circuit diagram with three lamps connected in parallel, one of which can be switched on and off by a switch.*

This is obviously how most things must be connected, for example in cars and in household electrics. You have to be able to switch everything on and off separately. Everyday circuits often include a mixture of series and parallel parts (see page 75).

Potential difference in parallel circuits

In parallel circuits, all components get the full source pd. Each branch in a parallel circuit has the same potential difference as the power supply, so the potential difference is the same across all components connected in parallel:

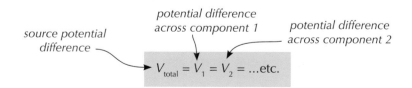

source potential difference

potential difference across component 1

potential difference across component 2

$$V_{total} = V_1 = V_2 = ...etc.$$

Tip: Voltmeters must be connected in parallel with the component that they're measuring because that's the only way they'll have the same pd across them as the component.

This means that identical lamps connected in parallel will all be at the same brightness.

Everything electrical in a car is connected in parallel. Parallel connection is essential in a car to give these two features:

- Everything can be turned on and off separately.

- Everything always has the full pd of the battery across it. This is useful because it means that you can listen to the radio on full blast without it having much effect on the brightness of your lights.

The only slight effect is that when you turn lots of things on the lights may briefly go a bit dim because the battery can't provide full potential difference under heavy load. This is normally a very slight effect. You can spot the same thing at home when you turn a kettle on, if you watch very carefully.

Figure 2: A car dashboard. Everything that you can turn on and off from your dashboard will be on its own parallel circuit branch connected to the car battery.

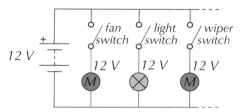

Figure 3: A circuit diagram to give an idea of how the electronic components in a car are connected in a parallel circuit.

Tip: M is the symbol for a motor.

Current in parallel circuits

In parallel circuits the total current flowing around the circuit is equal to the total of all the currents through the separate branches.

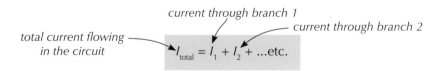

$$I_{total} = I_1 + I_2 + ...\text{etc.}$$

This means that unlike voltage, the current going through each branch is less than the total current in the circuit. Whenever the circuit splits into one or more branches, a certain amount of the current flows through each branch.

The current through each component inside a branch is the same — it's like a mini series circuit. The same amount of current that entered the branch must then leave the branch when it rejoins the rest of the circuit.

If two identical components are connected in parallel then the same current will flow through each component.

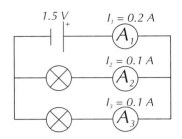

Example

Two lamps connected in parallel will share the total current in the circuit. In Figure 4:

$$I_1 = I_2 + I_3$$

Figure 4: *A circuit diagram showing identical lamps connected in parallel.*

Resistance in parallel circuits

If you have two resistors in parallel, their total resistance is less than the resistance of the smallest of the two resistors. So adding a resistor in parallel reduces the total resistance.

This can be tough to get your head around, but think about it like this:

In parallel, both resistors have the same potential difference across them as the source. This means the 'pushing force' making the current flow is the same as the source pd for each resistor you add.

But by adding another additional loop, the current has more than one direction to go in. This increases the total current that can flow around the circuit. Using $V = IR$, an increase in current means a decrease in the total resistance of the circuit.

Tip: This last bit is important — adding another loop to the circuit increases the current in the circuit (because there are more paths where charge is flowing).

Tip: You might see the answer in this example written as $R_{total} < 4\ \Omega$. This just means that the total resistance is less than 4 Ω.

Example

In the circuit shown in Figure 5, there are three resistors connected in parallel.

In a parallel circuit, the total resistance is smaller than the smallest resistance on an individual branch. Therefore, the total resistance of the circuit in Figure 5 is less than 4 Ω.

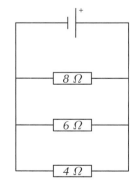

Figure 5: *A circuit diagram showing three resistors connected in parallel.*

Summary of parallel circuits

There are three rules for parallel circuits. Know them well:

- The pd across each branch is the same as the source pd.

- The current is split across the branches, and the total current is the sum of the current of each branch.

- The total resistance of a parallel circuit is less than the smallest resistance of an individual circuit branch.

Tip: Remember for parallel circuits:
$I_{total} = I_1 + I_2 + ...$etc. and
$V_{total} = V_1 = V_2 = ...$etc.

Example

Find the potential difference across, and the current through, resistor Y in the circuit shown.

The resistors are all connected in parallel, so the pd across each resistor in the circuit is the same as the supply pd. So the pd across resistor Y is 6 V.

The total current through the circuit is the same as the sum of the currents in the branches:

$$5.5 \text{ A} = 1.5 \text{ A} + I_2 + 1.0 \text{ A}$$

Rearranging to find I_2:

$$I_2 = 5.5 \text{ A} - 1.5 \text{ A} - 1.0 \text{ A} = 3.0 \text{ A}$$

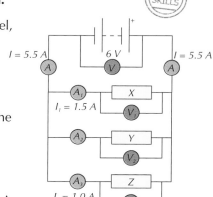

Mixed series and parallel circuits

You can have a circuit that contains components connected in series and components connected in parallel — see Figure 6. Just make sure you apply the right rules to the right bits.

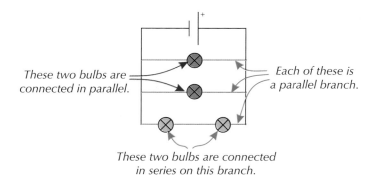

These two bulbs are connected in parallel.

Each of these is a parallel branch.

These two bulbs are connected in series on this branch.

Figure 6: *A circuit with components connected in series and parallel with each other.*

Exam Tip
You might have to deal with simple circuits that are a mixture of parallel and series like this in the exam, so make sure you understand what's going on at each component.

In the circuit shown in Figure 7, the potential difference across each branch would be 1.5 V.

On the branch with two lamps connected in series, the pd is then split between the two lamps (page 68).

$$1.5 \text{ V} = V_1 + V_2 = V_3$$

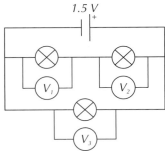

Figure 7: *A circuit diagram showing lamps connected in parallel and in series.*

Practice Questions — Fact Recall

Q1 What does 'connected in parallel' mean?

Q2 Why are parallel circuits more useful than series circuits in household electrics?

Q3 What can you say about the potential difference across all the components connected in parallel with a power supply? Assume each component is on a branch with no other components.

Q4 If you know the current in every branch of a parallel circuit, how can you work out the total current in the circuit?

Practice Questions — Application

Q1 A parallel circuit is shown. When the switch is closed, ammeter A reads 0.75 A.

a) Calculate the pd shown by voltmeter V.

b) The total current in the circuit is 2.0 A. Calculate the resistance of the lamp.

c) Is the total resistance of the circuit more than, equal to, or less than your answer to b)?

Tip: Look back at page 71 for series circuit rules.

Q2 Look at the circuit shown below.

a) If switch S is open, ammeter A reads 0.70 A. Find the potential difference across the battery.

b) If switch S is closed, ammeter A reads 0.50 A.

i) Find the potential difference across lamp B.

ii) Find the potential difference across resistor R_2.

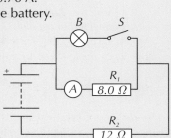

5. Investigating Resistance

As you've seen over the past few pages, the way a component is connected in a circuit determines how it contributes to the total resistance of the circuit. You can investigate this yourself by adding identical resistors in series and parallel and measuring the effect on resistance.

Resistance in series and parallel circuits

Investigating resistance for resistors in series

Before you get started, you'll need to make sure you have at least four identical resistors.

Start by constructing the circuit shown in Figure 1 using one of the resistors. Make a note of the potential difference of the battery (V).

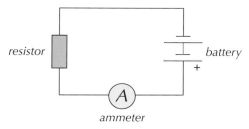

Figure 1: *A circuit diagram of the initial circuit for investigating resistance of resistors in series, with a single resistor connected in series.*

To carry out the investigation, follow these steps:

1. Measure the current through the circuit using the ammeter. Use this and the pd of the battery to calculate the resistance of the circuit using $R = V \div I$ (from $V = IR$, see page 63).

2. Add another resistor, in series with the first (as shown in Figure 2).

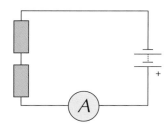

Figure 2: *A circuit diagram of the circuit in Figure 1, with a second resistor added in series with the first.*

3. Again, measure the current through the circuit and use this and the pd of the battery to calculate the overall resistance of the circuit.

4. Repeat steps 2 and 3 until you've added all of your resistors.

Now you've got your results, plot a graph of the number of identical resistors against the total resistance of the circuit. Your graph should look similar to the one shown in Figure 3.

Learning Objective:
- Be able to use a circuit to investigate the effect of connecting resistors in series and in parallel on the resistance of a circuit (Required Practical 15).

Specification Reference
6.2.1.3

Tip: As always, remember to carry out a risk assessment for this practical before you start your investigation.

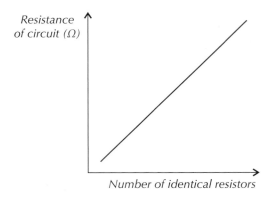

Resistance of circuit (Ω)

Number of identical resistors

Figure 3: *A graph of total resistance of a circuit against number of identical resistors connected in series.*

Tip: To refresh your memory on how current, potential difference and resistance behave in series circuits, check out pages 68-71.

You should find that adding resistors in series increases the total resistance of the circuit — i.e. adding a resistor decreases the total current through the circuit. The more resistors you add, the larger the resistance of the whole circuit. These results agree with the rules for resistance in series on page 70.

Investigating resistance for resistors in parallel

Using the same equipment as before (so the experiment is a fair test), build the same initial circuit shown in Figure 1, and carry out the following steps:

1. Measure the total current through the circuit and calculate the resistance of the circuit using $R = V \div I$ (again, V is the potential difference of the battery).

2. Next, add another resistor, in parallel with the first, as shown in Figure 4.

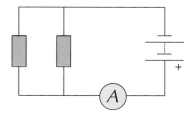

Figure 4: *A circuit diagram of the circuit in Figure 1, with a second resistor added in parallel with the first.*

Tip: Remember, ohmic conductors (like fixed resistors) only have a constant resistance at a constant temperature. Disconnecting the battery between readings will stop your circuit getting too hot, which could affect your results.

3. Measure the total current through the circuit and use this and the potential difference of the battery to calculate the overall resistance of the circuit.

4. Repeat steps 2 and 3 until you've added all of your resistors.

Just like before, use your results to plot a graph of the number of identical resistors in the circuit against the total resistance. You should get a graph which looks like the one shown in Figure 5.

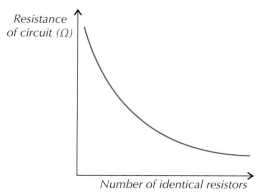

Resistance of circuit (Ω)

Number of identical resistors

Figure 5: *A graph of total resistance of a circuit against number of identical resistors connected in parallel.*

Tip: You need to be able to explain why the resistance decreases when a component is added in parallel (see page 74).

When you add resistors in parallel, the total current through the circuit increases — so the total resistance of the circuit has decreased. The more resistors you add, the smaller the overall resistance becomes — as shown by the graph in Figure 4. These results agree with the rules for adding resistors in parallel from page 74.

Practice Question — Application

Q1 A student wants to investigate how the resistance of a circuit changes as they connect more resistors in parallel. They have six identical 1 Ω resistors, a battery and an ammeter.

a) Draw a circuit diagram of the circuit they should construct to find the total resistance of the circuit when three resistors are connected in parallel.

b) The student's results are displayed in the table below.

Number of 1 Ω resistors	Total resistance (Ω)
1	1.00
2	0.50
3	0.33
4	0.25
5	0.20
6	0.17

Plot a graph of their results, and draw a line of best fit.

c) Explain the trend shown by the results.

- Know that the resistance of an LDR decreases with increasing light intensity.
- Know some applications of LDRs.
- Know that the resistance of a thermistor decreases with increasing temperature.
- Know some applications of thermistors.
- Understand how LDRs and thermistors can be used in circuits, e.g. simple sensor circuits.

Specification Reference
6.2.1.4

6. LDRs and Thermistors

You've just got two more circuit devices to learn about in this section — LDRs and thermistors...

Light-dependent resistors (LDRs)

An **LDR** is a resistor that is dependent on the intensity of light. Simple really.

- In bright light, the resistance falls (see Figure 1).

- In darkness, the resistance is highest.

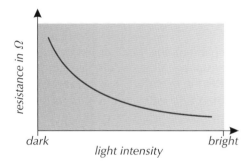

Figure 1: *A graph of resistance against light intensity for a light-dependent resistor (LDR).*

LDRs can be used where a function depends on light levels, e.g. when you want a component to only work in the dark.

Figure 2: *An LDR (top) and its circuit symbol (bottom).*

Examples

- Automatic night lights and outdoor lighting such as street lights use LDRs. When the light level falls, the resistance of the LDR increases to a level that triggers the light to turn on.

- Some burglar detectors use LDRs too. A light beam is shone at an LDR. If someone walks in front of it and breaks the light beam, the resistance of the LDR shoots up and an alarm is triggered.

Figure 3: *Automatic street lighting on a motorway.*

There's more on how these applications work on the next page.

Thermistors

Thermistors are another type of resistor — their resistance depends on their temperature. A thermistor's resistance decreases as the temperature increases.

- In hot conditions, the resistance drops (see Figure 4).

- In cool conditions, the resistance goes up.

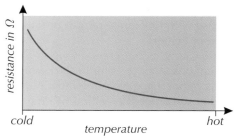

Figure 4: *A graph of resistance against temperature for a thermistor.*

Figure 5: *An example of one type of thermistor (top), and its circuit symbol (bottom).*

Thermistors are useful in temperature detectors called thermostats. They are connected in a circuit where their resistance can be measured. As resistance varies with temperature, knowing the resistance means you can detect the temperature of the thermistor (and its surroundings). Thermostats can be used in car engine temperature sensors to make sure the engine isn't overheating.

Application in sensor circuits

Most applications of LDRs and thermistors involve a sensor circuit. Figure 6 shows a typical sensor circuit.

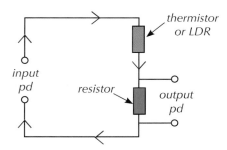

Figure 6: *A circuit diagram of a typical sensor circuit using a thermistor or LDR.*

If you have two circuit components in series, they share out the potential difference of the power supply relative to their resistances — the bigger the component's resistance relative to another's, the more pd it takes.

In the circuit shown, if the resistance of the thermistor or LDR increases, it takes a bigger share of the input pd from the power supply, so the pd across the resistor (the output pd) falls.

> **Tip:** For a reminder on pd and resistance in series circuits, see pages 71.

If the resistance of the thermistor or LDR decreases (i.e. the thermistor gets hotter or more light shines on the LDR) it takes a smaller share of the input pd, so the output pd rises.

You can use this effect in circuits that use the output pd across the resistor to power another component.

Example

An air conditioning circuit can be connected to the output pd of a thermistor circuit — as the temperature rises, the resistance of the thermistor decreases and the pd across the resistor increases. This increases the pd supplied to the air conditioning circuit, helping to cool the room down.

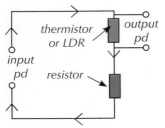

Figure 7: *An alternative sensor circuit for increasing pd with decreasing temperature/light.*

You could have the output pd across the thermistor/LDR instead, if you wanted the pd to increase with low temperatures or dark conditions (e.g. for an automatic night light or heater).

In most everyday applications, a more complicated switching circuit is often used to make something happen at a certain temperature or light level (e.g. a thermostat can be used to switch on the central heating when a room gets to a certain temperature).

Practice Questions — Fact Recall

Q1   How can you lower the resistance of an LDR?

Q2   Sketch a graph of resistance against temperature for a thermistor.

Q3   Give one application of:

   a) LDRs   b) thermistors

Practice Question — Application

Q1   The circuit shown forms part of a burglar alarm. The ohmmeter measures the resistance of the component it is connected to. The circuit is connected to another circuit containing an alarm — if the resistance rises above a certain level, the alarm is sounded.

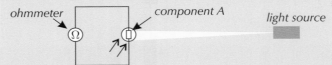

   a) What is component A?

   b) A cat passes through the beam of light.
      Explain why this causes the alarm to sound.

Topic 2a Checklist — Make sure you know...

Circuits, Current and Potential Difference

☐ The circuit symbols for: a cell, a battery, a switch (open and closed), a filament lamp, an ammeter, a voltmeter, a resistor, a variable resistor, a fuse, a thermistor, a diode, an LED and an LDR.

☐ How to construct a basic circuit diagram.

☐ That voltmeters must be connected across (i.e. in parallel with) a component and ammeters must be connected in line (i.e. in series) with a component.

☐ That current is the flow of electric charge.

☐ That the size of the current (I) is the rate of flow of charge, and that the charge (Q) that flows in a given time (t) is defined by the equation $Q = It$.

☐ That at any point in a single closed loop, the current has the same value.

☐ That potential difference is the driving force that pushes current around a circuit.

cont...

Resistance and *I-V* Characteristics

☐ That resistance reduces the flow of current.

☐ That the current (*I*) through, potential difference (*V*) across, and resistance (*R*) of a component are related by the equation $V = IR$.

☐ That ohmic conductors have a resistance which does not change with a changing current.

☐ How to construct and use a circuit to investigate the effect of wire length on circuit resistance.

☐ How to investigate the *I-V* characteristics of an ohmic conductor, a filament lamp and a diode.

☐ The *I-V* characteristics for these three components and how to explain their shape with respect to how resistance changes with current, including whether they are linear or non-linear.

Series Circuits

☐ That series circuits have all components (besides voltmeters) connected in-line on a single loop.

☐ That multiple sources of potential difference connected in series add together to give the total pd.

☐ That the pd provided by a power supply is shared between all the components in the circuit.

☐ That the current through each component in a series circuit is the same.

☐ That the total resistance of a series circuit is the sum of the resistances of all components in the circuit.

☐ How to explain why adding resistors in series increases the total resistance of the circuit.

☐ How to calculate current, potential difference and resistance in a series circuit.

Parallel Circuits

☐ That parallel circuits have components which are each connected on their own branch of the circuit.

☐ That the potential difference across each parallel branch is the same.

☐ That current is split between parallel branches.

☐ That the total resistance of resistors in parallel is less than the resistance of the smallest resistor.

☐ How to explain why adding resistors in parallel decreases the total resistance of the circuit.

Investigating Resistance

☐ How to perform experiments to investigate how adding resistors in series and in parallel affects the total resistance of a circuit.

LDRs and Thermistors

☐ That the resistance of an LDR (light dependent resistor) decreases with increasing light intensity.

☐ That the resistance of a thermistor decreases with increasing temperature.

☐ Applications of LDRs (e.g. street lighting and burglar alarms) and thermistors (e.g. thermostats).

☐ How an LDR or thermistor can be used to construct simple sensor circuits.

Exam-style Questions

1   A physics student is carrying out a series of experiments to investigate the properties of a filament lamp.

1.1   The student wants to measure the current passing through the lamp using an ammeter. State how the student should connect the ammeter in the circuit, and explain why this is the case.

(2 marks)

1.2   Sketch the *I-V* characteristic of a filament lamp.

(1 mark)

1.3   Is a filament lamp an ohmic conductor? Explain your answer.

(1 mark)

The student now uses the filament lamp in a simple sensor circuit, so that the lamp gets brighter as the temperature decreases. The circuit consists of a filament lamp, a thermistor, a resistor, and a cell.

1.4   Draw a circuit diagram of a possible arrangement for this sensor circuit.

(3 marks)

1.5   Across which component should the lamp be connected if the student instead wishes to make the lamp increase in brightness as the temperature increases?

(1 mark)

2   An electric motor and filament lamp are connected in parallel to a battery, as shown.

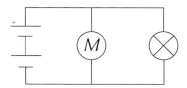

The total size of the electric current in the circuit is 1.2 A. It takes 30 seconds to move 15 C of charge through the motor. The potential difference across the motor is 14 V.

2.1   What is the size of the electric current in a circuit a measure of?

(1 mark)

2.2   What is the potential difference across the battery?

(1 mark)

2.3   Calculate the current passing through the filament lamp.
Give your answer in amperes.

(5 marks)

2.4   Calculate the resistance of the filament lamp.
Give your answer in ohms.

(4 marks)

3 The circuit shown was used to record values of the current through and the potential difference across component X at a constant temperature.

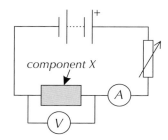

3.1 Explain how the variable resistor is used to change the current in a circuit.

(1 mark)

The data collected for component X using this circuit is displayed on the graph.

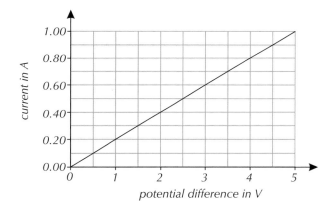

3.2 What is component X?

(1 mark)

3.3 Calculate the resistance of component X.

(3 marks)

3.4 Component Y is the same type of component as component X but has a higher resistance at the same temperature. Which of the three graphs below shows the *I-V* graphs of component X and component Y? Explain your answer.

(2 marks)

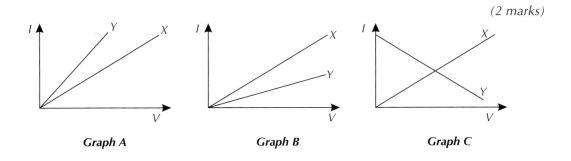

Graph A   *Graph B*   *Graph C*

1. Electricity in the Home

We use electricity all the time without thinking about it but there's actually a lot to think about. There are two-types of electricity, ac and dc, and there's a lot of clever wiring in all our appliances that keep us safe.

Ac and dc supplies

There are two types of electricity supplies — **alternating current (ac)** and **direct current (dc)**. In ac supplies the current is constantly changing direction. Alternating currents are produced by alternating voltages in which the positive and negative ends keep alternating.

The UK domestic mains supply (the electricity in your home) is an ac supply at around 230 V. The frequency of the ac mains supply (how often the current changes direction) is 50 cycles per second or 50 Hz (hertz).

By contrast, cells and batteries supply direct current (dc). Direct current is a current that is always flowing in the same direction. It's created by a direct voltage — where the positive and negative ends of the source are fixed.

Three-core cables

Most electrical appliances are connected to the mains supply by **three-core cables**. This means that they have three wires inside them, each with a core of copper and a coloured plastic coating. The colour of the insulation on each cable shows its purpose — the colours are always the same for every appliance. This is so that it is easy to tell the different wires apart.

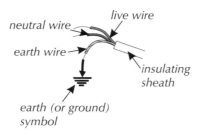

Figure 1: *A three-core electrical cable showing the live, neutral and earth wires.*

- The brown **live wire** is what provides the alternating potential difference (at about 230 V) from the mains supply.

- The blue **neutral wire** completes the circuit and carries away current. It is around 0 V.

- The green and yellow **earth wire** is also at 0 V. It is for protecting the wiring and for safety — it stops the appliance casing from becoming live. It doesn't usually carry a current — only when there's a fault.

The live wire

Your body (just like the earth) is at 0 V. This means that if you touch the live wire, a large potential difference (pd) is produced across your body and a current flows through you. This causes a large electric shock which could injure or even kill you.

Even if a plug socket or a light switch is turned off (i.e. the switch is open) there is still a danger of an electric shock. A current isn't flowing, but there is still a pd in the live wire. If you made contact with the live wire, your body would provide a link between the supply and the earth, so a current would flow through you.

Any connection between live and the earth can be dangerous. If the link creates a low resistance path to the earth, a huge current will flow, which could result in a fire.

Figure 2: *A three-core electrical cable with a live wire, a neutral wire and an earth wire.*

Tip: A low resistance path is a path with low electrical resistance. Since $V = IR$ (page 63), a large current will flow through a low resistance path.

Practice Questions — Fact Recall

Q1 What is direct current (dc)?

Q2 What does ac stand for? How is it different from dc?

Q3 What is the colour coding of the wires in a three-core cable?

Q4 a) Describe the potential difference in the live and neutral wires in a three-core electrical cable.

b) What is the role of the earth wire in a three-core cable?

Learning Objectives:

- Know that a moving charge transfers energy, and so work is done when it flows in a circuit.
- Know that electrical appliances transfer energy electrically.
- Understand how various different appliances transfer energy from a power source to useful energy stores.
- Know that the energy transferred is determined by the power of an appliance and amount of time it's used for.
- Understand that a higher power means more energy is transferred per second.
- Know the amount of energy transferred is found by $E = Pt$.
- Know that power is measured in watts, W.
- Understand the connection between the power rating of a device and the energy transferred between stores when they are used.
- Know the amount of energy transferred by electrical work can be found by $E = QV$.
- Know that the power of a device is related to the pd across it and current through it by $P = VI$.
- Know that the power of a device is related to the current through it and its resistance by $P = I^2R$.

Specification References
  6.2.4.1, 6.2.4.2

2. Power and Energy Transfer

All the useful things electricity can do are due to the transfer of energy. Energy is transferred between stores electrically (like you saw on page 22) by electrical appliances. Power tells us how quickly an appliance transfers energy.

Energy transfers in electrical appliances

You know from page 61 that electric current is the flow of electric charge. When a charge moves, it transfers energy. This is because the charge does work against the resistance of the circuit, and work done is the same as energy transferred. Electrical appliances are designed to transfer energy to components in a circuit when a current flows.

> **Example**
>
> - Kettles transfer energy electrically from the mains ac supply to the thermal energy store of the heating element inside the kettle.
>
> - Energy is transferred electrically from the battery of a handheld fan to the kinetic energy store of the fan's motor.

Of course, no appliance transfers all energy completely usefully. Whenever a current flows through anything with electrical resistance (which is pretty much everything) then energy is transferred to the thermal energy stores of the components (and then the surroundings). The higher the current, the more energy is transferred to these thermal energy stores. You can calculate the efficiency of any electrical appliance (i.e. work out how much energy is transferred usefully). See page 38 for more on how to do this.

> **Example**
>
> Filament bulbs work by passing a current through a very thin wire, heating it up so much that it glows. Rather obviously, they waste a lot of energy through transfer to the thermal energy stores of the wire and surroundings compared to the amount of energy usefully transferred to generate light.

Power and energy transfer

The total energy transferred by an appliance depends on how long the appliance is on for and the power at which it's operating.

The **power** of an appliance is the energy that it transfers per second. So the more energy it transfers in a given time, the higher the power.

The amount of energy transferred by electrical work is given by:

$$E = Pt$$

E = energy transferred (J) t = time (s) P = power (W)

> **Example**
>
> **If a 2.5 kW kettle is on for 5 minutes, how much energy is transferred by the kettle?**
>
> First make sure the numbers are in the right units:
>
> > power = 2.5 kW = 2500 W
> > time = 5 minutes = 300 s
>
> Then substitute into the formula:
>
> > $E = Pt = 2500 \times 300 = 750\ 000$ J

Tip: Remember: 1 kW = 1000 W.

Appliances are often given a power rating — they're labelled with the maximum safe power that they can operate at. You can usually take this to be their maximum operating power. The power rating tells you the maximum amount of energy transferred between stores per second when the appliance is in use. This helps customers choose between models — the lower the power rating, the less electricity an appliance uses in a given time, so the cheaper it is to run.

But a higher power doesn't necessarily mean that it transfers more energy usefully. An appliance may be more powerful than another, but less efficient, meaning that it might still only transfer the same amount of energy (or even less) to useful stores (see page 38).

Figure 1: *A label showing the voltage and power rating of an electrical appliance.*

Potential difference and energy transfer

When an electrical charge (Q) goes through a change in potential difference (V), then energy (E) is transferred. Energy is supplied to the charge at the power source to 'raise' it through a potential. The charge gives up this energy when it 'falls' through any potential drop in components elsewhere in the circuit, as shown in Figure 2.

Tip: Remember that energy is transferred when a moving charge does work against resistance in a circuit.

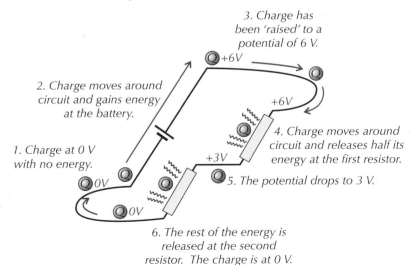

3. Charge has been 'raised' to a potential of 6 V.

2. Charge moves around circuit and gains energy at the battery.

1. Charge at 0 V with no energy.

4. Charge moves around circuit and releases half its energy at the first resistor.

5. The potential drops to 3 V.

6. The rest of the energy is released at the second resistor. The charge is at 0 V.

Figure 2: *An electrical charge passing round a circuit and transferring energy through circuit components. As it does this, its potential changes.*

The potential difference between two points is the energy transferred per unit charge passing between the two points and you can calculate it using this formula:

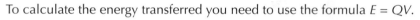

$\boldsymbol{E}$ = energy transferred (J) ⟶ $E = QV$ ⟵ $\boldsymbol{V}$ = potential difference (V)

$\boldsymbol{Q}$ = charge (C)

So a bigger change in pd means more energy is transferred for a given charge passing through the circuit.

Tip: A battery with a bigger pd will supply more energy because the charge is raised up "higher" at the start (see Figure 2).

Example

The motor in an electric toothbrush is attached to a 3.0 V battery. The total charge that passes a point in the motor circuit during use is 140 C. Calculate the energy transferred by the motor. Explain why the energy transferred to the kinetic energy stores of the motor will be less than the energy you calculated.

To calculate the energy transferred you need to use the formula $E = QV$.

charge = 140 C, potential difference = 3.0 V

$E = QV = 140 \times 3.0 = 420$ J

The energy transferred to the kinetic energy stores of the motor will be less than 420 J because the motor won't be 100% efficient. Not all the of the energy will be transferred to the motor's kinetic energy stores — some of it will be transferred into the thermal energy store of the motor and surroundings.

Tip: There's more about efficiency on page 38.

Power, potential difference and current

If you know the potential difference across an appliance and the current flowing through it, you can work out its power using this formula:

$\boldsymbol{P}$ = power (W) ⟶ $P = VI$ ⟵ $\boldsymbol{I}$ = current (A)

$\boldsymbol{V}$ = potential difference (V)

Tip: So a higher power means a greater current flows for a given pd.

You can also find the power if you don't know the potential difference. To do this, stick $V = IR$ from page 63 into $P = VI$, giving:

$\boldsymbol{P}$ = power (W) ⟶ $P = I^2R$ ⟵ $\boldsymbol{R}$ = resistance (Ω)

$\boldsymbol{I}$ = current (A)

Example 1

What's the power input of a light bulb that draws 0.20 A of current from a 230 V supply?

Just put the numbers into the equation:

$$P = VI = 230 \times 0.20$$
$$= 46 \text{ W}$$

Example 2

The motor in a toy car has a resistance of 25 Ω and an operating power of 64 W. Find the current it draws from the battery.

You don't know the potential difference, so you'll have to use $P = I^2R$. Rearrange the equation for power to make current the subject:

$$P = I^2R \text{ , so } I = \sqrt{\frac{P}{R}}$$

(MATHS SKILLS)

Then put the numbers in:

$$I = \sqrt{\frac{P}{R}} = \sqrt{\frac{64}{25}} = 1.6 \text{ A}$$

Practice Questions — Fact Recall

Q1 a) Give two examples of appliances that transfer energy electrically.

   b) For each appliance given in part a), give one energy store that energy is transferred to electrically.

Q2 How is energy wasted when electric charge flows through a circuit component with electrical resistance?

Q3 What is the formula for working out the power of an appliance in terms of the energy it transfers? What does each term represent and what are their units?

Q4 What is the formula that relates power, current and potential difference? What units are each of them measured in?

Practice Questions — Application

Q1 A homeowner is choosing a cooker. Cooker A is rated at 9800 W and cooker B is rated at 10 200 W. Which cooker will use the most energy in 20 minutes?

Q2 An appliance draws 3.0 A of current from the mains supply (230 V). What's the power of the appliance?

Q3 A 2.0 kW heater is on for 30 minutes. How much energy does it transfer?

Q4 Calculate the potential difference a 4.0 C charge passes through when it transfers 22 J of energy.

Q5 A 0.2 A current flows through a 40 W filament lamp. Calculate the resistance of the filament lamp.

Q6 Microwave A is rated at 900 W and takes 4 minutes to cook a ready meal. Microwave B is rated at 650 W and takes 6 minutes to cook a ready meal. Assuming both microwaves are working at maximum power, which transfers the most energy in cooking the meal?

Learning Objectives:
- Know that the national grid is a network of cables and transformers.
- Know that it is used to transfer electrical power from power stations to the consumer.
- Understand why the national grid is an efficient way of distributing electrical energy.
- Know that step-up transformers are used to increase the pd before transmission, and step-down transformers are used to decrease the pd to safe levels for consumers.

Specification Reference
6.2.4.3

3. The National Grid

Now you know how electricity powers our appliances, you might be wondering how it gets to us in the first place. That's where the national grid comes in. Whoever you pay for your electricity, it's the national grid that gets it to you.

Distributing electricity

The **national grid** is the network of cables and transformers that covers the UK and connects power stations to consumers (anyone who's using electricity). The national grid transfers electrical power from power stations anywhere on the grid (the supply) to anywhere else on the grid where it's needed (the demand) — e.g. homes and industry.

To transmit the huge amount of power needed, you either need a high potential difference, or a high current (as $P = VI$, page 90). The problem with high current is that you lose loads of energy as the wires heat up and energy is transferred to the thermal energy stores of the surroundings.

It's much cheaper to boost the pd up really high (to 400 000 V) and keep the current relatively low. For a given power, increasing the pd decreases the current, which decreases the energy lost by heating the wires and the surroundings. This makes the national grid an efficient way of transferring energy.

Transformers

A **transformer** is a device used in the national grid to change the potential difference of an electrical supply. Getting the potential difference to 400 000 V for transmission requires transformers as well as big pylons and huge insulators. It's still cheaper than transmitting it through smaller wires at a high current with lots of energy loss though.

The transformers have to step the potential difference up at one end, for efficient transmission, and then bring it back down to safe, usable levels at the other end. The potential difference is increased ('stepped up') using a step-up transformer. It's then reduced again ('stepped down') for domestic use using a step-down transformer, as shown in Figure 1.

Tip: Remember that power is the energy transferred in a given time, so a higher power means more energy transferred.

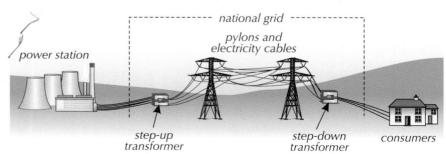

Figure 1: *A diagram of the national grid distributing electricity from a power station to consumers.*

Meeting demand

Throughout the day, electricity usage (the demand) changes. Power stations have to produce enough electricity for everyone to have it when they need it.

In order to do this, demand for electricity needs to be predicted. Demand increases when people get up in the morning, come home from school or work and when it starts to get dark or cold outside and people put the lights and heating on. Popular events like a sporting final being shown on TV could also cause a peak in demand.

Power stations often run at well below their maximum power output, so there's spare capacity to cope with a high demand, even if there's an unexpected shut-down of another station. Lots of smaller power stations that can start up quickly are also kept on standby just in case.

Tip: See pages 45-57 for more on electricity generation and trends in energy usage.

Practice Questions — Fact Recall

Q1 a) What does a transformer do?

b) Why are transformers used in the national grid?

Q2 What does each label A-E represent in this diagram?

Q3 a) State two times of the day when demand for electricity increases.

b) Suggest two ways in which electricity providers can prepare for unexpected increases in demand.

Topic 2b Checklist — Make sure you know...

Electricity in the Home

☐ That there are two types of electricity — alternating current and direct current.

☐ That alternating current (ac) is constantly changing its direction of flow.

☐ That alternating current is produced by an alternating voltage, where the positive and negative ends are always alternating.

☐ That mains electricity is a source of ac with a potential difference of 230 V and frequency of 50 Hz.

☐ That direct current (dc) flows in a fixed direction.

☐ That direct current is produced by a direct voltage.

☐ That most electrical appliances are connected to the mains by three-core cables.

☐ That three-core cables consist of a brown-coated live wire, a blue-coated neutral wire and a green-and-yellow-coated earth wire.

cont...

- [ ] That the live wire carries current to the device, and provides the alternating pd of 230 V.
- [ ] That the neutral wire carries current away from the device, and is at around 0 V.
- [ ] That the earth wire is a safety feature which does not carry current unless there is a fault, and is at 0 V.
- [ ] That your body is at 0 V.
- [ ] That touching a live wire causes an electric shock due to the potential difference between the wire and your body, which causes a current to flow through you.
- [ ] That connections between the live wire and the earth are dangerous due to the large currents that flow through them.

Power and Energy Transfer

- [ ] That work is done when charge flows in a circuit.
- [ ] That electrical appliances are designed to transfer energy electrically to a useful energy store.
- [ ] Some examples of appliances and how they transfer energy electrically to a useful energy store.
- [ ] That the energy transferred by an appliance depends on its power and the time it is switched on for.
- [ ] That the higher the power of a device, the more energy it transfers in a given time.
- [ ] That the amount of energy transferred by an appliance is given by the formula $E = Pt$.
- [ ] That power is measured in watts, W.
- [ ] How the power rating of a device informs the consumer of how much energy it will need to operate.
- [ ] That the energy transferred to or from an electrical charge across a potential difference is given by the formula $E = QV$.
- [ ] That the power of a device or component can be found using the formulas $P = VI$ and $P = I^2R$.

The National Grid

- [ ] That the national grid is a network of cables and transformers which transfers electrical power from power stations to consumers.
- [ ] That for a given power, increasing the potential difference will decrease the current.
- [ ] That low-current transmission is more efficient, as less energy is transferred to thermal energy stores which are not useful.
- [ ] That potential difference can be increased (stepped up) and decreased (stepped down) by transformers.
- [ ] That pd is increased by step-up transformers for distribution, and decreased by step-down transformers to safe levels for consumers at the other end.
- [ ] How the national grid forms an efficient system for distributing electrical power to consumers.
- [ ] How demand can change throughout the day and what actions are taken to ensure enough power can be supplied to meet unexpected high demand.

Exam-style Questions

1   A kettle with a metal casing is linked to the mains electricity using a three-core cable.
The three-core cable has a live wire, an earth wire and a neutral wire inside it.

1.1   Complete the sentence by selecting the correct answer from the options given.

The live wire has a (brown   /   blue   /   green and yellow   ) coating.

(1 mark)

1.2   Write down the equation that links power, potential difference and current.

(1 mark)

1.3   The kettle operates at 230 V and 575 W.
Calculate the current flowing through the kettle. Give your answer in amperes.

(3 marks)

1.4   The kettle's cable is frayed, and the live wire is exposed.
Explain how this could cause a fire.

(3 marks)

2   A kitchen contains a 2.55 kW oven and a 1.15 kW dishwasher.
Both appliances are connected to the UK mains supply.

2.1   State the potential difference and frequency of the UK mains supply.

(2 marks)

The national grid is used to transmit electrical power from power
stations to consumers. The electrical power is transmitted at a
higher potential difference than is safe for use in homes.

2.2   Explain why the electrical power is transmitted at a high potential difference.

(3 marks)

The oven transfers 7 038 000 J of energy in the time it takes to cook a particular meal.

2.3   Write down the equation that links energy transferred, power and time.

(1 mark)

2.4   Calculate how long it takes to cook the meal. Give your answer in seconds.

(3 marks)

2.5   Write down the equation that links energy transferred, charge and potential difference.

(1 mark)

2.6   Calculate the total amount of charge that passes through the oven in the
time it takes to cook the meal. Give your answer in coulombs.

(3 marks)

2.7   Calculate the operating current of the dishwasher. Give your answer in amperes.

(3 marks)

1. Density and States of Matter

The particle model of matter can be used to help describe the densities of substances and the different states of matter. It says that everything is made up of lots of tiny particles.

Learning Objectives:
- Know and be able to use the equation for the density of a substance.
- Know what the three states of matter are, and be able to describe their properties using the particle model.
- Understand how the particle model can explain why substances have different densities.
- Be able to represent the particle model of the three states of matter with simple diagrams.
- Be able to measure the density of a liquid or any shape of solid using appropriate apparatus (Required Practical 17).

Specification Reference 6.3.1.1

Density

Density is a measure of the 'compactness' of a substance. It relates the mass of a substance to how much space it takes up (i.e. it's a substance's mass per unit volume).

There's a formula for finding the density of a substance:

$$\rho = density\ (kg/m^3) \longrightarrow \rho = \frac{m}{V} \longleftarrow m = mass\ (kg)$$
$$V = volume\ (m^3)$$

Density can also be measured in g/cm^3 (1 g/cm^3 = 1000 kg/m^3).

> **Example**
>
> **A copper cube has sides of length 5.0 cm. The density of copper is 8.96 g/cm^3. Find the mass of the cube.**
>
>
>
> First find the cube's volume:
>
> $V = 5.0 \times 5.0 \times 5.0 = 125\ cm^3$
>
> Now substitute into the rearranged formula:
>
> $m = \rho V = 8.96 \times 125 = 1120\ g$

The density of an object depends on what it's made of. It can be explained using the particle model of matter.

A dense material has its particles packed tightly together. The particles in a less dense material are more spread out — if you compressed the material, its particles would move closer together, and it would become more dense. (You wouldn't be changing its mass, but you would be decreasing its volume.)

Tip: The symbol for density is the Greek letter rho (ρ) — it looks like a *p* but it isn't. The formula triangle for the density equation looks like this:

States of matter

Three **states of matter** are solid (e.g. ice), liquid (e.g. water) and gas (e.g. water vapour). The particles of a substance in each state are the same — only the arrangement and energy of the particles are different.

Solids

In solids, strong forces of attraction hold the particles close together in a fixed, regular arrangement. The particles don't have much energy so they can only vibrate about their fixed positions.

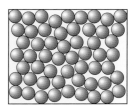

A particle

Figure 1: The particles in a solid.

Liquids

There are weaker forces of attraction between the particles in liquids. The particles are close together, but can move past each other, and form irregular arrangements. They have more energy than the particles in a solid — they move in random directions at low speeds.

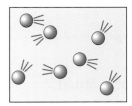

Figure 3: The particles in a liquid.

Gases

There are almost no forces of attraction between the particles in a gas. The particles have more energy than those in liquids and solids — they are free to move, and travel in random directions at high speeds.

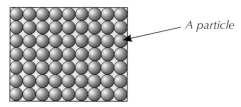

Figure 4: The particle arrangement in a gas.

Figure 2: The three states of water — ice, water and water vapour.

Exam Tip
You might be asked to use a picture or model in the exam to describe a state of matter — so make sure you know this page inside out.

Properties of solids, liquids and gases

The particle model helps to explain the properties of different states of matter.

- The density of a substance is generally highest when it is in solid form as the particles are closest together. Liquids tend to be less dense than solids. Gases are the least dense — their particles are spaced far apart.

- Gases and liquids can flow because their particles can move past each other. The particles in a solid can't move anywhere — they can only vibrate in their fixed positions, so solids can't flow.

- Gases are compressible. The particles in a gas are very spread out, which means you can squash a gas into a smaller volume — you're just reducing the distance between particles. The particles in liquids and solids can't really get much closer together, which is why only gases are easily compressible.

Measuring density

REQUIRED PRACTICAL 17

You need to be able to measure the density of a substance. The method you should use depends on the type of substance.

Measuring the density of a solid object

First, use a balance to measure the object's mass (see p. 231). You then need to find its volume. If it's a regular solid, like a cuboid, you might be able to measure its dimensions with a ruler and calculate its volume. For an irregular solid, you can find its volume by submerging it in a eureka can of water.

A eureka can (or displacement can) is essentially a beaker with a spout — you can see this in Figure 5. To use one, fill it with water so the water level is above the spout. Let the water drain from the spout, leaving the water level just below the start of the spout. (This way, when you put your solid object in, all the water displaced will pass through the spout, giving you the correct volume.)

Place an empty measuring cylinder below the end of the spout. When you put your solid object in the eureka can, it causes the water level to rise and water to flow out of the spout.

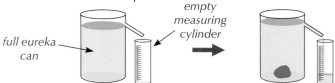

Figure 6: A eureka can and measuring cylinder being used to measure a solid's volume.

Once the spout has stopped dripping, you can measure the volume of the water in the measuring cylinder (see p. 233 for more on this). This is the volume of your solid object.

Now you can substitute the object's mass and volume into the density formula from page 96 to find its density.

Measuring the density of a liquid

Place a measuring cylinder on a balance and zero the balance (see p. 231). Pour 10 ml of the liquid into the measuring cylinder and record its mass.

Pour another 10 ml into the measuring cylinder and record the total volume and mass. Repeat this process until the cylinder is full.

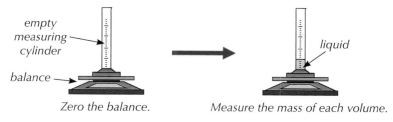

Figure 7: Using a balance to find the mass of liquid in a measuring cylinder.

For each set of measurements, use the formula from page 96 to find the density. Finally, take an average of your calculated densities. This will give you a more precise (p. 11) value for the density of the liquid.

Tip: As with all practicals, make sure you do a risk assessment for this practical.

Tip: The volume of a cube or cuboid is length × width × height.

Figure 5: An experiment to measure the density of a solid block. A string is used so the block can easily be removed.

Tip: You can't use this method if the object floats — the object will only displace a volume of water equal to the part of the object that's below the water line.

Tip: The measuring cylinder will give you the volume in ml. To convert to cm³, use 1 ml = 1 cm³.

Tip: To find the average, add up all the densities, then divide by the number of values. See page 13 for more.

Practice Questions — Fact Recall

Q1 What is the formula for density?

Q2 What are the three states of matter?

Q3 Explain the arrangement, movement and energy of the particles in a solid.

Q4 Describe how the arrangement, movement and energy of particles in a liquid is different to that in a solid.

Q5 In which state of matter do particles have the most energy?

Q6 What pieces of apparatus would you need to measure the density of an irregular solid object?

Practice Questions — Application

Q1 A block of material is in the shape of a cuboid. It has sides of length 3.0 cm, 4.5 cm and 6.0 cm, and a total mass of 0.324 kg. Find the density of the block.

Q2 The diagram below shows a box filled with small light polystyrene balls. A small fan is fitted at the bottom of the box. This apparatus can be used to model the particles in different states of matter.

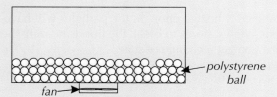

a) What state of matter is modelled by the balls at the bottom of the box when the fan is turned off? Explain your answer.

The fan is turned on, causing the small balls to fly around the inside of the box at high speeds.

b) What state of matter do the balls now model?

c) Use this model to explain the different densities of the two states of matter in parts a) and b).

Learning Objectives:

- Know how energy is stored in a system by its particles.
- Know what is meant by the term 'internal energy'.
- Know that heating a system increases the energy of its particles.
- Understand that this heating will either cause an increase in temperature or a change of state.
- Know that if there is a temperature increase, its size depends on the material, the mass of the material and the energy supplied.
- Know all the different ways a substance can change state.
- Know what is meant by a physical change and how it differs from a chemical change.
- Be able to explain how a change of state is a physical change that conserves mass.
- Understand that when a substance changes state, the energy transferred changes the internal energy — but not the substance's temperature.
- Recognise and understand heating and cooling graphs for a substance undergoing changes of state.

Specification References
6.3.1.2, 6.3.2.1, 6.3.2.2, 6.3.2.3

Tip: Sublimating is the change of state from a solid directly to a gas.

2. Internal Energy and Changes of State

The state that a substance is in has a lot to do with temperature. You need to make sure you know all about specific heat capacity as part of this topic, so go back to pages 29-31 and make sure it's all fresh in your mind.

Internal energy

The particles in a system vibrate or move around — they have energy in their kinetic energy stores. They also have energy in their potential energy stores due to their positions — but you don't need to worry about this.

The energy stored in a system is stored by its particles (atoms and molecules). The **internal energy** of a system is the total energy that its particles have in their kinetic and potential energy stores.

Heating the system transfers energy to its particles (they gain energy in their kinetic energy stores and move faster), increasing the internal energy. This leads to a change in temperature (or a change in state, see below). The size of the temperature change depends on the mass of the substance, what it's made of (its specific heat capacity) and the energy input. Make sure you remember all of the stuff on specific heat capacity from p. 29 — particularly how to use the formula.

If the substance is heated enough, the particles will have enough energy in their kinetic energy stores to break the bonds holding them together. This means you get a change of state.

What is a change of state?

When you heat a liquid, it boils (or evaporates) and becomes a gas. When you heat a solid, it melts and becomes a liquid (or sublimates to become a gas). These are both changes of state.

The state can also change due to cooling. Energy is transferred from the kinetic energy stores of the particles, so they move slower and start to form bonds. They don't have enough energy to overcome the bonds.

All the changes of state are shown in Figure 1 below:

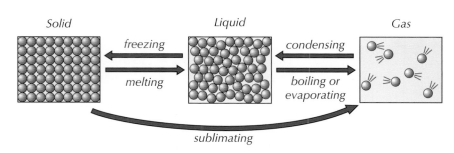

Figure 1: The different changes of state.

A change of state is a **physical change** (rather than a chemical change). This means you don't end up with a new substance — it's the same substance as you started with, just in a different form.

If you reverse a change of state (e.g. freeze a substance that has been melted), the substance will return to its original form and get back its original properties.

The number of particles doesn't change — they're just arranged differently. This means mass is conserved — none of it is lost when the substance changes state.

Tip: Remember, a substance has the same particles whether it's a solid, liquid or gas — only the arrangement and energy of the particles change.

Figure 2: Energy transferred by heating from this person's hand is enough to melt gallium metal.

> **Example**
>
> As the ice in Figure 3 melts, the reading on the balance will stay the same. The mass of the beaker's contents will be conserved through the change of state.
>
>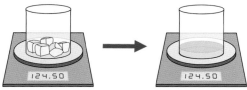
>
> **Figure 3:** A beaker of ice melting on a balance.

Breaking bonds

When a substance is melting or boiling, you're still putting in energy and so increasing the internal energy, but the energy's used for breaking intermolecular bonds rather than raising the temperature.

There are flat spots on the heating graph in Figure 5, where energy is being transferred by heating but not being used to change the temperature.

Figure 4: When the water reaches its boiling point, the energy transferred is used to break intermolecular bonds, not to increase temperature.

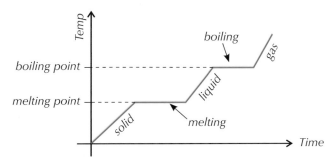

Figure 5: Heating graph, showing temperature against time for a substance which is being heated.

When a substance is condensing or freezing, bonds are forming between particles, which releases energy. This means the internal energy decreases, but the temperature doesn't go down until all the substance has turned to liquid (condensing) or a solid (freezing).

The flat parts of the graph in Figure 6 show this energy transfer.

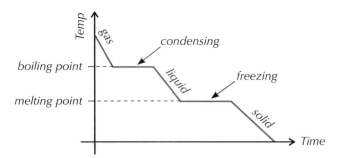

Figure 6: *Cooling graph, showing temperature against time for a substance which is being cooled.*

Practice Questions — Fact Recall

Q1   What is the definition of internal energy?

Q2   Give one way in which you can transfer energy to the particles in a system.

Q3   Name five different changes of state.

Q4   A change of state is a physical change.
     Explain what is meant by the term 'physical change'.

Q5   Does a change of state conserve mass? Explain your answer.

Q6   Sketch a graph of temperature against time for a solid being heated so that it undergoes two changes of state. Label the points at which the substance changes state.

Practice Questions — Application

Q1   A kettle is filled with water and switched on. Explain, in terms of energy stores, what happens to the particles in the water as it is heated to boiling point by the kettle.

Q2   Steam from a shower forms condensation on a bathroom window. Explain why this happens in terms of the steam particles.

3. Specific Latent Heat

So energy is transferred to break (or form) intermolecular bonds and change state. It's all to do with specific latent heat...

What is specific latent heat?

Specific latent heat (SLH) is the amount of energy needed to change 1 kg of a substance from one state to another without changing its temperature. For cooling, specific latent heat is the energy released by a change in state. Specific latent heat is different for different materials, and for changing between different states.

The specific latent heat for changing between a solid and a liquid (melting or freezing) is called the **specific latent heat of fusion**. The specific latent heat for changing between a liquid and a gas (evaporating, boiling or condensing) is called the **specific latent heat of vaporisation**.

You can work out the energy needed (or released) in joules when a substance of mass m changes state using this formula:

E = energy for a change in state (J) $\longrightarrow$ $E = mL$ $\longleftarrow$ L = specific latent heat (J/kg)

m = mass (kg)

Don't get confused with specific heat capacity (p. 29), which relates to a temperature rise of 1°C. Specific latent heat is about changes of state where there's no temperature change.

Practice Questions — Fact Recall

Q1 State the two different types of specific latent heat for a substance, and describe the difference between them.

Q2 What are the units of specific latent heat?

Practice Questions — Application

Q1 The specific latent heat of fusion for water is 334 000 J/kg. An ice cube of mass 25.0 g is at 0 °C. How much energy is needed to melt the ice cube?

Q2 The specific latent heat of vaporisation for a liquid is 1 550 000 J/kg. What mass of the liquid (already at its boiling point) would be completely boiled by 4 960 000 J of energy?

Learning Objectives:

- Know what is meant by the term 'latent heat' and 'specific latent heat'.
- Be able to use the equation for specific latent heat.
- Know the difference between specific latent heat of fusion and specific latent heat of vaporisation.
- Know how specific heat capacity and specific latent heat differ.

Specification Reference 6.3.2.3

Tip: If you're finding mass or SLH, you'll need to rearrange. Here's the formula triangle:

Learning Objectives:

- Know that gas particles are in constant random motion and understand how temperature links to the average energy in the kinetic stores of these particles.

- Understand how the motion of gas particles is linked to its temperature and pressure.

- Understand how a change in temperature of a gas at constant volume leads to a change in gas pressure.

Specification Reference
6.3.3.1

4. Particle Motion in Gases

The temperature of a gas determines the energy in the kinetic stores of its particles. It can also affect the pressure and the volume of the gas.

Temperature of gases

The particles in a gas are constantly moving with random directions and speeds. If you increase the temperature of a gas, you transfer energy into the kinetic energy stores of its particles (you saw this on p. 100).

The temperature of a gas is related to the average energy in the kinetic energy stores of the particles in the gas. The higher the temperature, the higher the average energy.

So as you increase the temperature of a gas, the average speed of its particles increases. This is because the energy in the particles' kinetic energy stores is $\frac{1}{2}mv^2$ (see p. 25).

Gas pressure

As gas particles move about at high speeds, they bang into each other and whatever else happens to get in the way. When they collide with a surface, they exert a force on it.

Pressure is force per unit area, so this means they exert a pressure too. In a sealed container, the outward gas pressure is the total force exerted by all of the particles in the gas on a unit area of the container walls.

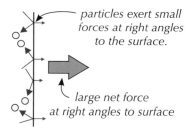

particles exert small forces at right angles to the surface.

large net force at right angles to surface

Figure 1: *Gas pressure on a surface.*

Faster particles and more collisions with the walls of the container both lead to an increase in net force, and so gas pressure. Increasing temperature will increase the speed and the number of collisions, and so the pressure (if volume is kept constant).

Practice Questions — Fact Recall

Q1   Describe the motion of the particles in a gas.

Q2   A gas is stored inside a sealed container. How does the gas exert an outwards pressure on the walls of the container?

Q3   Explain why increasing the temperature of a fixed volume of gas will increase the pressure of the gas.

Topic 3 Checklist — Make sure you know...

Density and States of Matter

☐ How to calculate the density of a material.

☐ That a dense material has its particles packed closely together and a less dense material has its particles more spread out.

☐ That the three states of matter are solid, liquid and gas and how the particles are arranged in these states, including how to draw diagrams to show this.

☐ How the arrangement of particles in a material affects the properties of the material, including density.

☐ How to measure the density of a solid or liquid.

Internal Energy and Changes of State

☐ That energy is stored in a system by its particles and that the internal energy of a system is the total energy that its particles have in their kinetic and potential energy stores.

☐ That heating a system transfers energy to its particles, increasing the internal energy and causing either a change in temperature or a change of state.

☐ That the change in a material's temperature due to heating depends on the mass of the substance, what it's made from (its specific heat capacity) and the energy input.

☐ That heating or cooling a substance can lead to a change of state and that the different changes of state are freezing, melting, boiling/evaporating, condensing and sublimating.

☐ That a change of state is a physical change (not a chemical change) that conserves mass and that reversing a change of state will return a substance to its original form.

☐ That energy transferred to (or from) a substance which is changing state is used to break (or form) bonds, rather than to change the substance's temperature.

☐ That graphs of temperature against time for substances being heated or cooled have flat spots which show changes of state, where energy transferred does not cause a change in temperature, and how to sketch these graphs.

Specific Latent Heat

☐ What the terms latent heat and specific latent heat mean and the difference between specific latent heat of vaporisation and specific latent heat of fusion.

☐ How to use the equation for specific latent heat.

☐ How specific heat capacity and specific latent heat differ.

Particle Motion in Gases

☐ That the particles in a gas are constantly moving with random directions and speeds.

☐ That an increase in temperature causes an increase in the average speed of gas particles.

☐ That particles colliding with the walls of a container exert a force, and so a pressure, on the container.

☐ That an increase in temperature for a gas at constant volume leads to an increase in pressure.

Exam-style Questions

1   A physicist is carrying out an experiment with a substance which is in solid form. She needs 450 g of the substance for the experiment. The density of the substance when it is a solid is 9 g/cm³.

1.1   Write down the equation that links density, mass and volume.

(1 mark)

1.2   Calculate the volume of the solid substance that the physicist needs for the experiment. Give your answer in cm³.

(3 marks)

The physicist heats the substance for 300 seconds. The graph in **Figure 1** shows how the substance's temperature changes over this time period.

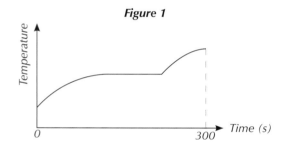

Figure 1

1.3   In what state of matter is the substance at the end of the time period shown? Explain your answer.

(2 marks)

1.4   What is the mass of the substance at the end of the time period shown? Explain your answer.

(2 marks)

2   A sample of gas is stored in a sealed container. The volume of the container is 0.08 m³ and the density of the gas inside the container is 0.025 kg/m³.

2.1   Calculate the mass of the gas sample. Give your answer in kg.

(3 marks)

2.2   The gas is condensed, so that it is all turned into a liquid. 5 kJ of energy is released during the change of state. Find the specific latent heat of vaporisation of the gas. Give the correct units. Use the correct equation from the equations listed on page 284.

(4 marks)

2.3   Will the density of the sample now be equal to, less than, or greater than 0.025 kg/m³? Explain your answer.

(2 marks)

3   A student has an unknown liquid. He wants to know the density of the liquid.

3.1   Describe a method that the student could use to find the liquid's density.

(4 marks)

The student heats a sample of the liquid. He records the liquid's temperature every 5 seconds. The temperature of the heater is 200 °C. The student notices that the temperature of the liquid never increases past 85 °C.

3.2   Explain why this is the case.

(3 marks)

4   A substance in solid form is at its melting temperature. 67 500 J of energy is transferred to the solid, causing it to melt. The specific latent heat of fusion for the substance is 450 000 J/kg.

4.1   Define the specific latent heat of fusion.

(2 marks)

4.2   Find the mass of the substance. Give your answer in kg.
Use the correct equation from the equations listed on page 284.

(3 marks)

4.3   Explain why it is important that the solid was already at its melting temperature for your calculation in **4.1**.

(2 marks)

5   The diagram in **Figure 2** shows the arrangement of particles in a block of ice.

Figure 2

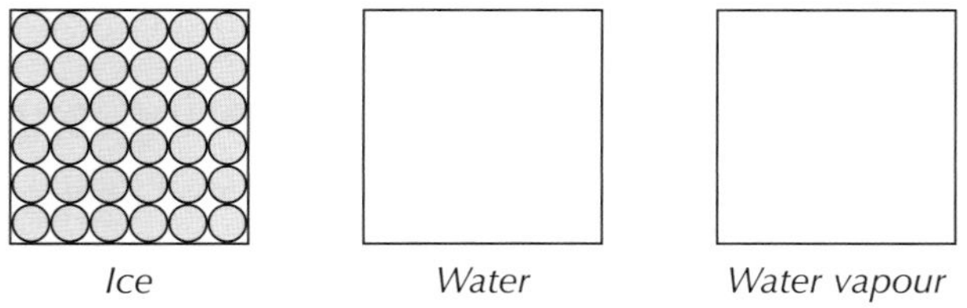

Ice   Water   Water vapour

5.1   Copy and complete the other two boxes to show the particle arrangement of water and water vapour.

(2 marks)

5.2   Water and water vapour are able to flow, but ice is not. Explain why this is the case.

(2 marks)

5.3   Explain whether each of ice, water and water vapour are easily compressible.

(4 marks)

Learning Objectives:

- Know that atoms were originally thought to be tiny balls of matter that could not be split into smaller pieces.

- Know that the discovery of the electron led to the creation of the plum pudding model.

- Know that the plum pudding model describes atoms as a sphere of positive charge with negative electrons inside them.

- Know how the results of the alpha particle scattering experiment suggested mass and positive charge was concentrated at the centre of the atom — leading to the atomic model changing.

- Know that the results of the alpha particle scattering experiment led to the creation of the nuclear model.

- Understand how new experimental evidence leads to old scientific models being changed, or new ones being created.

Specification Reference
6.4.1.3

1. The History of the Atom

You'll be learning about the 'nuclear model' of the atom shortly. But first it's time for a trip back in time to see how scientists came up with it. And it's got a bit to do with plum puddings.

The plum pudding model

The Greeks were the first to think about **atoms**. A man called Democritus in the 5th century BC thought that all matter was made up of identical lumps called "atomos". But that's about as far as the theory got until the 1800s...

In 1804 John Dalton agreed with Democritus that matter was made up of tiny spheres ("atoms") that couldn't be broken up, but he reckoned that each element was made up of a different type of "atom".

Nearly 100 years later, J J Thomson discovered particles called **electrons** that could be removed from atoms. So Dalton's theory wasn't quite right (atoms could be broken up). Thomson suggested that atoms were spheres of positive charge with tiny negative electrons stuck in them like fruit in a plum pudding — the plum pudding model.

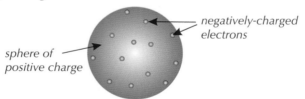

negatively-charged electrons

sphere of positive charge

Figure 1: *The plum pudding model of the atom.*

That "plum pudding" theory didn't last very long though...

The alpha particle scattering experiment

In 1909 scientist's in Rutherford's lab tried firing a beam of **alpha particles** (see p. 114) at thin gold foil — they used a set-up similar to Figure 2. A circular detector screen surrounds the gold foil and the alpha source, and is used to detect alpha particles deflected by any angle. This was the alpha particle scattering experiment.

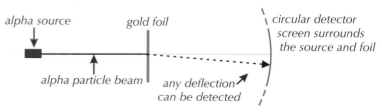

alpha source   *gold foil*   *circular detector screen surrounds the source and foil*

alpha particle beam   *any deflection can be detected*

Figure 2: *The experimental set-up for detecting whether alpha particles have been scattered by gold foil.*

They expected that the positively-charged alpha particles would go straight through or be slightly deflected by the electrons if the plum pudding model was true.

In fact, most of the alpha particles did go straight through the foil, but some were deflected more than they had expected and the odd one came straight back at them. This was frankly a bit of a shocker. The results of the alpha particle scattering experiment showed that atoms must have small, positively-charged **nuclei** at the centre (see Figure 3).

Tip: 'Nuclei' is the plural of 'nucleus'.

Here's why:

- Most of the atom must be empty space because most of the alpha particles passed straight through the foil.

- The nucleus must have a large positive charge as some positively-charged alpha particles were repelled and deflected by a big angle.

- The nucleus must be small as very few alpha particles were deflected back.

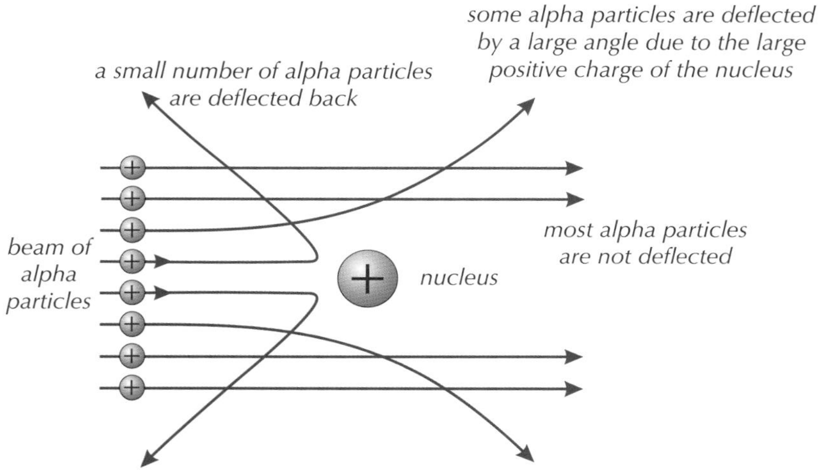

Tip: Positively-charged alpha particles are repelled by positive (like) charges and attracted by negative (opposite) charges.

some alpha particles are deflected by a large angle due to the large positive charge of the nucleus

a small number of alpha particles are deflected back

beam of alpha particles

nucleus

most alpha particles are not deflected

Figure 3: A diagram showing some positively-charged alpha particles passing straight through a gold atom and some being deflected by the atom's nucleus.

Tip: These results provided new evidence, causing the accepted model of the atom to be changed — see pages 1-2 for more on how new theories are accepted with new evidence.

WORKING SCIENTIFICALLY

This led to the first **nuclear model** of the atom that we still use an adapted version of today (see page 110).

Figure 4: The New Zealand physicist Ernest Rutherford.

Practice Questions — Fact Recall

Q1 Describe the plum pudding model of the atom.

Q2 What results were expected from the alpha particle scattering experiment?

Q3 What results were seen in the alpha particle scattering experiment? How did they show that the atom has a small, positively-charged nucleus and is mostly empty space?

- Know how the nuclear model has been adapted over time.

- Understand the differences between the nuclear model and the plum pudding model.

- Know that atoms consist of a nucleus, made up of protons and neutrons, orbited by electrons.

- Know the radius of an atom is about 1×10^{-10} m.

- Know that the nucleus contains most of the mass of an atom and is 10 000 times smaller than the atom.

- Know that protons and electrons have equal and opposite charges.

- Know that atoms are not charged and contain an equal number of protons and electrons.

- Know that electrons are arranged in energy levels in an atom and move between them when they absorb and emit EM radiation.

- Know all atoms of an element have the same number of protons.

- Know what the mass number and atomic number of an element tell you.

- Be able to use the notation $_Z^A X$.

- Know that an ion is an atom with too few or too many electrons.

- Know that isotopes of an element have atoms with different numbers of neutrons.

Specification References
6.4.1.1, 6.4.1.2, 6.4.1.3

2. The Structure of the Atom

So now you know how it came to replace the plum pudding model, it's time to learn what the current nuclear model of the atom actually says.

Development of the nuclear model

The alpha particle scattering experiment led to the creation of the nuclear model, but it still needed fine-tuning. Niels Bohr adapted the initial model — he concluded that electrons orbiting the nucleus can only do so at certain distances. These distances are called energy levels.

Evidence from further experiments changed the model to think of the positively charged nucleus as a group of particles (protons) which all had the same positive charge that added up to the overall charge of the nucleus. In 1932, about 20 years after the idea of the nucleus was accepted, James Chadwick proved the existence of the neutron, which explained the imbalance between atomic and mass numbers (see page 111).

All these discoveries played a part in the development of the nuclear model of the atom that we have today.

The current nuclear model

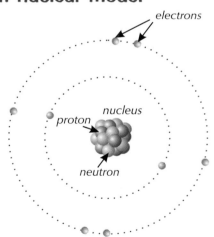

Figure 1: *The atom (not to scale).*

According to the nuclear model, the atom contains three types of particles:

- **electrons** (which are negatively charged),

- **protons** (which are positively charged) and

- **neutrons** (which are neutral — they have no charge).

The nucleus is at the centre of the atom. It is tiny but it makes up most of the mass of the atom. It contains protons and neutrons — which gives it an overall positive charge. The radius of the nucleus is about 10 000 times smaller than the radius of the atom.

The rest of the atom is mostly empty space. Negative electrons whizz round the outside of the nucleus really fast. They give the atom its overall size — the radius of an atom is about 1×10^{-10} m.

Each particle has a relative mass and a relative charge. Relative just means in relation to the other particles — it's so you can compare their masses and charges. It's useful to learn the relative charge and mass of each particle:

particle	mass	charge
proton	1	+1
neutron	1	0
electron	$\frac{1}{2000}$	−1

Figure 2: *The relative masses and charges of the particles in the atom.*

Atoms have no charge overall. The charge on an electron is the same size as the charge on a proton — but opposite (see Figure 2). This means the number of protons always equals the number of electrons in a neutral atom.

Electrons can move within (or sometimes leave) the energy levels of an atom. If they gain energy by absorbing EM radiation (page 201) they move to a higher energy level, further from the nucleus. If they release EM radiation, they move to a lower energy level that is closer to the nucleus.

Atomic number and mass number

You need to know how to describe the number of protons and neutrons in a nucleus:

▪ The number of protons in the nucleus of an atom is called the **atomic number**.

▪ The number of protons plus the number of neutrons in the nucleus of an atom is called the **mass number**.

An element can be described using the mass number and atomic number of its atoms. The notation looks like this:

mass number $\longrightarrow A$ X $\longleftarrow$ symbol of the element
atomic number $\longrightarrow Z$

Atoms of an element always have the same atomic number (i.e. the same number of protons and so the same charge on the nucleus), but they can have different mass numbers (these are called isotopes — see the next page).

Examples

▪ An atom of carbon with 6 protons and 6 neutrons would be $^{12}_{6}C$.

▪ An atom of oxygen with 8 protons and 9 neutrons would be $^{17}_{8}O$.

Ions

Tip: Atoms and ions of the same element have the same number of protons in their nuclei. An element is defined by the number of protons in the nuclei of its ions or atoms, e.g. an ion or atom with eight protons in its nucleus is the element oxygen.

Atoms are neutral, but if some electrons are added or removed, the atom becomes a charged particle called an **ion**. The ions still have the same number of protons and neutrons as usual, but a different number of electrons.

If an atom has had electrons added or removed and has become an ion, it is said to have been ionised. This process is called ionisation.

Tip: Most of the ionisation you'll be asked about will involve electrons being knocked off atoms, creating positive ions. This is how ionising radiation (page 114) works — it never adds electrons to an atom.

Example

an oxygen atom with 8 protons, 8 neutrons and 8 electrons

an oxygen ion with 8 protons, 8 neutrons and 6 electrons

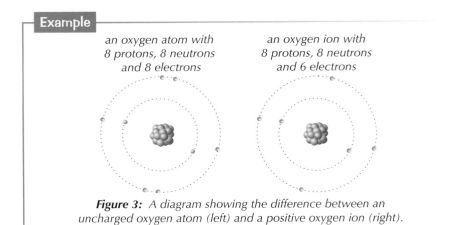

Figure 3: A diagram showing the difference between an uncharged oxygen atom (left) and a positive oxygen ion (right).

Isotopes

Tip: Don't get confused between the charge of a nucleus and the charge of an atom. Nuclei are positively charged, but atoms are neutral (unless they've been ionised).

Isotopes are different forms of the same element. Isotopes have atoms with the same number of protons but a different number of neutrons.

This means they have the same atomic number (and so the same charge on the nucleus), but different mass numbers.

Example

Carbon-12 and carbon-14 are good examples of isotopes:

carbon-12, $^{12}_{6}C$

carbon-14, $^{14}_{6}C$

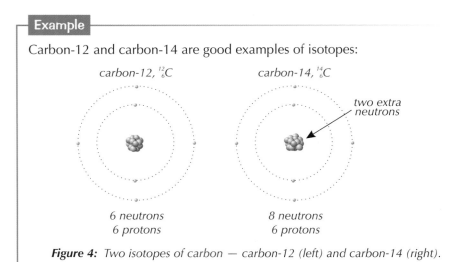

two extra neutrons

6 neutrons
6 protons

8 neutrons
6 protons

Figure 4: Two isotopes of carbon — carbon-12 (left) and carbon-14 (right).

All elements have different isotopes, but there are usually only one or two stable ones. The unstable isotopes are radioactive, which means they decay into other elements and give out radiation (see page 114).

Practice Questions — Fact Recall

Q1 What three types of particle make up an atom?

Q2 Which subatomic particle in an atom is not found in the nucleus?

Q3 What is the relative mass and charge of a neutron?

Q4 What can you say about the number of protons and electrons in a neutral atom? Why?

Q5 What is meant by atomic number and mass number?

Q6 What can you say about the atomic number of two atoms of the same element?

Q7 What is an isotope of an element?

Practice Question — Application

Q1 Particle A has 17 protons, 18 neutrons and 16 electrons.
Particle B has 17 protons, 20 neutrons and 17 electrons.

a) What is the overall charge of particle A?

b) Explain how you know that particle A is an ion.

c) Explain how you know that particles A and B are isotopes of the same element.

Tip: You can work out the overall charge on a particle by adding up the relative charges of all its subatomic particles.

- Know that radioactive decay is where unstable nuclei emit radiation to try and become more stable.
- Know that radioactive substances may emit neutrons, alpha particles, beta particles or gamma rays from their nuclei.
- Know that an alpha particle consists of two protons and two neutrons.
- Know that a beta particle is a high-speed electron.
- Know that beta particles are emitted when a neutron changes into a proton.
- Know that a gamma ray is a high frequency electromagnetic wave.
- Know the penetration, range in air and ionising power of alpha, beta and gamma radiation.
- Understand some of the uses of alpha, beta and gamma radiation and be able to evaluate the best source for a particular use.
- Know that alpha decay changes the mass and charge of a nucleus, beta decay changes only the charge and gamma radiation changes neither.
- Know the nuclear equation symbols for alpha and beta particles.
- Be able to construct and balance nuclear equations of alpha and beta decay.

Specification References
6.4.2.1, 6.4.2.2

3. Radioactivity

Radioactivity is all to do with things randomly giving out radiation. Some radiation is ionising, which means it can knock electrons off atoms to create ions. You need to know about three types of ionising radiation.

Radioactive decay

Unstable isotopes tend to decay into other elements and give out radiation as they try to become more stable. This process is called **radioactive decay**.

This process is entirely random. This means that if you have a load of unstable nuclei, you can't say when any one of them is going to decay, and neither can you do anything at all to make a decay happen. It's completely unaffected by physical conditions like temperature, or by any sort of chemical bonding, etc.

Radioactive substances emit ionising radiation. Ionising radiation is radiation that knocks electrons off atoms, creating positive ions. The ionising power of a radiation source tells you how easily it can do this.

Radioactive substances spit out one or more types of ionising radiation from their nucleus as they decay. The types you need to know about are **alpha**, **beta** and **gamma**. They can also release neutrons (n) as they decay, as they try to rebalance their atomic and mass numbers.

Alpha decay

Alpha radiation is when an **alpha particle**, α, is emitted from the nucleus. An alpha particle is two neutrons and two protons — the same as a helium nucleus. When an atom decays by emitting an alpha particle, two protons and two neutrons are lost from the nucleus.

As protons have a relative charge of +1, alpha emission decreases the charge on the nucleus (and the atomic number) by 2. The mass number decreases by 4, as protons and neutrons each have a relative mass of 1. See page 116 for an example.

| unstable nucleus | An alpha particle (two neutrons and two protons) is lost from the nucleus. |

Figure 1: *An unstable nucleus decaying by emitting an alpha particle.*

Alpha particles are relatively big, heavy and slow-moving. This means they don't penetrate very far into materials and are stopped quickly. They only travel a few centimetres in air and are absorbed by a sheet of paper.

Because of their size they are strongly ionising — they bash into a lot of atoms and knock electrons off them before they slow down, which creates lots of ions.

> **Example**
>
> Alpha radiation is used in smoke detectors. It ionises air particles, causing a current to flow. If there is smoke in the air, the smoke binds to the ions, reducing the number available to carry a current. The current falls and the alarm sounds.

Beta decay

A **beta particle**, β, is just a fast-moving electron released by a nucleus. So it has virtually no mass and a relative charge of –1 (see page 111).

When a nucleus decays by beta decay, a neutron turns into a proton in the nucleus, releasing a β-particle. This increases the charge on the nucleus (and the atomic number) by 1 but leaves the mass number unchanged. See page 117 for an example.

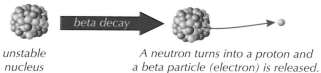

unstable
nucleus

A neutron turns into a proton and a beta particle (electron) is released.

Figure 2: An unstable nucleus decaying by emitting a beta particle.

Beta particles move quite fast and they are quite small. They are moderately ionising and penetrate moderately far into materials before colliding. They have a range in air of a few metres and can be absorbed by a sheet of aluminium (around 5 mm thick).

> **Example**
>
> Beta emitters are used to test the thickness of thin sheets of metal, as the particles are not immediately absorbed by the material like alpha radiation would be, and do not penetrate as far as gamma rays.

Gamma decay

Gamma rays, γ, are very short wavelength electromagnetic (EM) waves (see page 200) released by the nucleus. Gamma rays have no mass and no charge.

They penetrate far into materials without being stopped and pass straight through air. This means they are weakly ionising because they tend to pass through rather than collide with atoms. Eventually they hit something and do damage. They can be absorbed by thick sheets of lead or metres of concrete.

> **Example**
>
> Gamma radiation is used in situations where a source needs to be detected through a thick material — e.g. for detecting cracks or blockages in underground pipes, or flaws in thick sheets of metal.

Nuclear equations

You can write alpha and beta decays as nuclear equations. They are just equations that show what atoms you start with, what radiation is emitted and what atoms you're left with. The mass and atomic numbers have to balance on both sides of the equation (before and after decay).

You don't write nuclear equations for gamma decays because they do not change the atomic mass or atomic number of the atom. Gamma emission is just a way of getting rid of excess energy, and can happen after an alpha or beta decay.

Tip: You don't need to know why a neutron turning into a proton releases a beta particle, but make sure you know that it comes from the nucleus. It's not just one of the electrons that are whizzing around outside the nucleus jumping off.

Tip: In both alpha and beta decay, a new element will be formed, as the number of protons in the nucleus (the atomic number) changes.

Exam Tip
You may be asked to talk about how the properties of different types of radiation make them suitable for different uses.

Tip: Gamma radiation is slightly different to alpha and beta radiation because it's an EM wave instead of a particle.

You'll need to be familiar with the notation on page 111, and how alpha and beta particles can be written in this notation:

- Alpha particles are helium nuclei (symbol: He or α) with 2 protons and 2 neutrons, so they are written $^4_2$He.

- Beta particles are electrons (symbol: e or β) so they have no protons or neutrons, and the mass number is 0. The number of protons is 0, but we write –1 where the atomic number goes because a beta particle has a charge of –1. This helps us balance the charges on each side. So a beta particle is written $^0_{-1}$e.

Example 1 — alpha decay

Uranium-238 can decay into thorium-234 by emitting an alpha particle. Uranium has 92 protons and thorium has 90 protons.

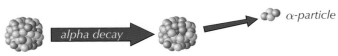

uranium-238   *thorium-234*

The nuclear equation for this decay looks like this:

$$^{238}_{92}\text{U} \longrightarrow ^{234}_{90}\text{Th} + ^4_2\text{He}$$

On the left-hand side:

- The mass number is 238.

- The atomic number is 92.

On the right-hand side:

- The total of the mass numbers is: 234 + 4 = 238.

- The total of the atomic numbers is: 90 + 2 = 92.

So both sides of the equation balance.

Example 2 — alpha decay

Balance the following equation: $^{238}_{94}$Pu $\longrightarrow$ $^{234}_{....}$U + $^{....}_2$He

Make these equations balance: 238 $\longrightarrow$ 234 + ...

94 $\longrightarrow$ ..... + 2

Balancing mass numbers, 238 = 234 + **4**, so the mass number of He is 4.

Balancing atomic numbers, 94 = **92** + 2, so the atomic number of U is 92.

The full equation is:

$$^{238}_{94}\text{Pu} \longrightarrow ^{234}_{92}\text{U} + ^4_2\text{He}$$

Example 3 — beta decay

Carbon-14 can decay into nitrogen-14 by emitting a beta particle (when a neutron turns into a proton).

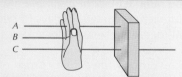

carbon-14   nitrogen-14   β-particle

The equation is: $^{14}_{6}C \rightarrow {}^{14}_{7}N + {}^{0}_{-1}e$

and the mass and atomic numbers balance on each side. Brill.

Practice Questions — Fact Recall

Q1   What does it mean if a substance is radioactive?

Q2   How can you change the rate of radioactive decay?

Q3   Put alpha, beta and gamma radiation in order of their ionising strength.

Q4   Describe what each type of radiation named in Q3 is made of.

Q5   What 2 numbers must be equal on both sides of a nuclear equation?

Practice Questions — Application

Q1   This diagram shows the paths of three types of radiation, A, B and C, being directed towards a human hand and a thick metal sheet.

   a) Which radiation (A or B) is more penetrating? How can you tell?

   b) Which radiation (A or B) is likely to be alpha radiation? Why?

   c) Explain what radiation C is likely to be and how you know.

Q2   Americium-241 decays into neptunium-237. The nuclear equation for this decay is:

$$^{241}_{95}Am \longrightarrow {}^{237}_{93}Np + {}^{4}_{2}He$$

   What type of decay is this — alpha or beta?

Q3   Radium-228 decays into actinium-228 by emitting an electron.

   a) What is the name of this decay?

   b) Complete the following nuclear equation for this decay:

$$^{.....}_{88}Ra \longrightarrow {}^{228}_{.....}Ac + {}^{0}_{-1}e$$

Q4   Radioactivity can be used to measure the thickness of paper during manufacture. A beta source is placed on one side of the paper, and a detector detects how much beta radiation gets through it. Explain why this process couldn't use:

   a) an alpha source.   b) a gamma source.

- Know that radioactive decay is a random process.
- Know that count rate is the number of radiation counts measured per second by a detector (e.g. a Geiger-Müller tube).
- Know that you cannot predict when an individual nucleus will decay, but with a large enough sample you can estimate how long it will take for the number of radioactive nuclei to halve.
- Know that the rate at which unstable nuclei decay is the activity, and that it is measured in Bq (becquerels).
- Know that the half-life of a radioactive isotope is the time for the activity of (or the number of unstable nuclei in) a sample to halve.
- Be able to find the half-life of a given isotope from information provided.
- **H** Be able to calculate the reduction in activity, count rate or number of nuclei as a ratio of the initial value after a given number of half-lives.

Specification References
6.4.2.1, 6.4.2.3

4. Activity and Half-life

Radioactive samples give out less and less radiation over time, but they never stop giving out radiation altogether.

Activity

Radioactive substances will give out radiation from the nuclei of their atoms — no matter what. This radiation can be measured with a **Geiger-Muller tube** and counter, which records the count-rate — the number of radiation counts reaching it per second.

Radioactive decay is entirely random. So you can't predict exactly which nucleus in a sample will decay next, or when any one of them will decay. But you can find out the time it takes for the amount of radiation emitted by a source to halve, this is known as the **half-life**. It can be used to make predictions about radioactive sources, even though their decays are random.

Half-life can be used to find the rate at which a source decays — its **activity**. Activity is measured in becquerels, Bq (where 1 Bq is 1 decay per second).

Half-life

The radioactivity of a sample always decreases over time. Each time a radioactive nucleus decays to become a stable nucleus, the activity as a whole will decrease — so older sources emit less radiation.

How quickly the activity drops off varies a lot. For some isotopes, it takes just a few hours before nearly all of the unstable nuclei have decayed, whilst others last for millions of years.

The problem with trying to measure this is that the activity never reaches zero, which is why we have to use the idea of **half-life** to measure how quickly the activity drops off.

Learn the definition of half-life:

> Half-life is the time it takes for the number of nuclei of a radioactive isotope in a sample to halve.

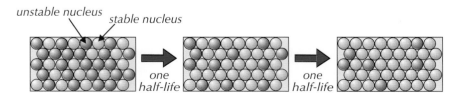

Figure 1: A diagram showing how the number of unstable nuclei of a radioactive isotope in a sample decreases over two half-lives.

In other words, it is the time it takes for the count rate (the number of radioactive emissions detected per unit of time) or activity from a sample containing the isotope to fall to half its initial level.

Calculating half-life

You can work out the half-life of a radioactive isotope if you're given a little information. Or if you know the half-life, you can work out how long it will take for the activity to drop a certain amount.

Half-life is maybe a little confusing, but exam calculations on it are straightforward as long as you do them slowly, step by step. Like this:

Example

The activity of a radioisotope is 640 cpm (counts per minute).
Two hours later it has fallen to 80 cpm.
Find the half-life of the sample.

You must go through it in short simple steps like this:

		after one half-life		after two half-lives		after three half-lives
initial count		↓		↓		↓
↓						
640	(÷2)	320	(÷2)	160	(÷2)	80

It takes three half-lives for the activity to fall from 640 to 80. Hence two hours represents three half-lives, so the half-life is 120 mins ÷ 3 = 40 minutes.

Tip: A radioisotope is just a radioactive isotope.

Example — **Higher**

The initial activity of a sample is 640 Bq. Calculate the percentage reduction in activity after two half-lives.

Find the activity after each half-life.

      1 half-life: $640 \div 2 = 320$ Bq
      2 half-lives: $320 \div 2 = 160$ Bq

So the reduction in activity is: $640 - 160 = 480$ Bq

Then write this as a percentage: $\frac{480}{640} \times 100 = \textbf{75\%}$

Exam Tip **H**
You may be asked to give a ratio showing the decline of activity, count rate or number of nuclei after a certain number of half-lives as a percentage of the initial activity like this.

Using graphs

You can plot or use a graph of radioactive activity against time to work out the half-life of a radioactive isotope.

The data for the graph will usually be several readings of activity which may have been taken with a Geiger-Müller tube with a counter.

The graph will always be shaped like the one shown in Figure 3.

The half-life is found from the graph by finding the time interval on the bottom axis corresponding to a halving of the activity on the vertical axis.

Figure 2: *You can do an experiment to simulate half-life using cubes with one black face. The cubes represent unstable nuclei and if they land black-side up, they have 'decayed'. Take note of how many cubes you start with and throw them all, removing any that 'decay'. Count the number remaining, then throw those remaining cubes again. Plotting your results on a graph will allow you to calculate the 'half-life' in 'number of throws'.*

Tip: Remember — activity never drops to zero, so the graph will never touch the horizontal axis.

Example

Figure 3 shows how the activity of a radioactive sample decreases with time. The half-life can be found form the graph as follows:

- The initial activity is 80, so after one half-life it will be 40 (and after two it will be 20 and after three it will be 10).

- To find the half-life of the sample, draw a line from 40 on the activity axis across to the curve and down to the time axis (green dotted line). This tells you that the half-life is 4 hours.

- You can check you were right by doing the same for an activity of 20 and checking that you get a time of 8, and so on...

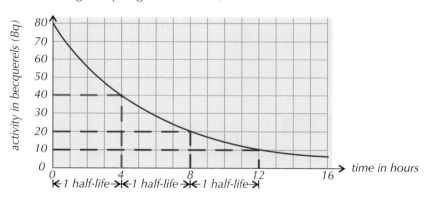

Figure 3: *A graph of activity against time for a radioisotope.*

Practice Questions — Fact Recall

Q1 Why can we not measure the time it takes for a radioactive sample to decay completely?

Q2 Write down two definitions of half-life.

Practice Questions — Application

Q1 A radioactive source with a half-life of 15 minutes has an initial count rate of 240 cpm. What will the count rate be after 1 hour?

Q2 A radioactive source has an initial count rate of 16 cpm and after 2 hours it has decreased to 4 cpm. What is the half-life of this source?

Q3 The activity of a source is 32 Bq. After how many half-lives will the activity have dropped to 4 Bq?

Q4 Find the half-life of the radioisotope from this graph of the activity of the radioisotope against time.

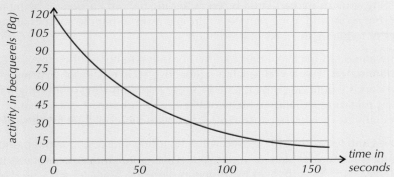

Tip: Make sure you read the axes carefully — you don't want to be saying the half-life is 'so many' hours when it's actually 'so many' seconds.

Q5 The initial activity of a radioactive source is 9600 Bq. Calculate the activity after 3 half-lives as a percentage of the initial activity.

Learning Objectives:
- Know that exposure to radiation from a radioactive source is known as irradiation.
- Know that the unwanted presence of radioactive atoms on or in another material is known as contamination.
- Know some precautions which can be taken to minimise the risk of irradiation and contamination.
- Understand how the hazards of irradiation and contamination vary depending on the type of radiation.
- Be able to compare the dangers associated with contamination and irradiation.
- Understand the importance of publishing research into the effects of radiation on human health.

Specification Reference 6.4.2.4

5. Irradiation and Contamination

Radiation can cause harm to your body. How dangerous a radiation source is depends on which type of radiation it emits and how you're using it.

What are irradiation and contamination?

Objects near a radioactive source are **irradiated** by it. This simply means they're exposed to the radiation. Irradiating something does not make it radioactive, but exposure to radiation can be harmful to living things.

Keeping sources in lead-lined boxes, standing behind barriers or being in a different room and using remote-controlled arms to handle sources are all ways of reducing the risks of irradiation.

If unwanted radioactive atoms get onto or into a material, then it is said to be **contaminated**. E.g. if you touch a radioactive source without wearing gloves, your hands would be contaminated. These contaminating atoms might then decay, releasing radiation which could cause you harm. Contamination is especially dangerous because radioactive particles could get inside your body.

Gloves and tongs should be used when handling sources, to avoid particles getting stuck to your skin or under your nails. Some industrial workers wear protective suits to stop them breathing in particles.

Contamination or irradiation can cause different amounts of harm based on the radiation type:

- Outside the body, beta and gamma sources are the most dangerous. This is because beta and gamma can penetrate the body and get to the delicate organs. Alpha is less dangerous because it can't penetrate the skin and is easily blocked by a small air gap. High levels of irradiation from all sources are dangerous, but especially from ones that emit beta and gamma.

- Inside the body, alpha sources are the most dangerous. They do all their damage in a very localised area. Beta and gamma sources are less dangerous inside the body because they mostly pass straight out without doing much damage (they have a lower ionising power). So contamination, rather than irradiation, is the major concern when working with alpha sources.

The more we understand how different types of radiation affect our bodies, the better we can protect ourselves when using them. This is one of the reasons why it's so important that research about this is published. The data is peer-reviewed and can quickly become accepted, leading to many improvements in our use of radioactive sources.

WORKING SCIENTIFICALLY

Practice Questions — Fact Recall

Q1 State what is meant by the terms irradiation and contamination.

Q2 Which type(s) of ionising radiation is most dangerous outside the body? Why?

Q3 Which type(s) of ionising radiation is most dangerous inside the body? Why?

Topic 4 Checklist — Make sure you know...

The History of the Atom

☐ How the concept of the atom has developed over time.

☐ That the plum pudding model describes an atom as a sphere of positive charge studded with negatively charged electrons.

☐ How the results of the alpha particle scattering experiment showed that the atom must contain a small, positively charged nucleus at the centre and how this led to the nuclear model of the atom.

The Structure of the Atom

☐ How the nuclear model was adapted and altered to give its current form.

☐ That the nuclear model of the atom describes the atom as a small, central nucleus containing protons and neutrons, with electrons moving around outside of the nucleus.

☐ The radius of an atom is approximately 1×10^{-10} m and the nucleus is more than 10 000 times smaller.

☐ The relative charges and masses of electrons, protons and neutrons.

☐ That an atom has no overall charge because the number of protons and electrons is equal and they have equal and opposite charges.

☐ That the atomic number of an atom is the number of protons in its nucleus and the mass number of an atom is the number of protons and neutrons in its nucleus.

☐ That every atom of an element has the same number of protons (atomic number).

☐ That an ion is an atom with fewer or more electrons than protons, giving it an overall charge.

☐ That isotopes are forms of an element that have atoms with the same atomic number but different mass numbers.

Radioactivity

☐ That a radioactive substance will undergo radioactive decay, where it gives out radiation from the nuclei of its atoms, and know that this is a random process.

☐ That when a substance undergoes radioactive decay it may emit alpha particles, beta particles, gamma rays or neutrons from its nucleus.

☐ That alpha decay is the process of a nucleus giving out an alpha particle, which is made up of two protons and two neutrons. It is strongly ionising and weakly penetrating.

☐ That beta decay is the process of a nucleus giving out a beta particle, which is an electron. It is moderately ionising and moderately penetrating.

☐ That gamma decay is where a nucleus gives out gamma rays, which are short-wavelength EM waves. Gamma rays are weakly ionising and strongly penetrating, passing straight through air.

☐ How alpha, beta and gamma decay affect the mass and atomic number of the nucleus.

☐ Examples of applications of radioactive sources in everyday life, e.g. alpha sources in smoke detectors.

☐ How to balance nuclear equations for alpha and beta decay.

cont...

Activity and Half-life

☐ The definitions of activity and count rate.

☐ That although radioactive decay random, the time taken for the activity to half can be predicted.

☐ That radioactive half-life is the average time it takes for the number of nuclei in a radioactive isotope sample to halve, or the time it takes for the count rate (or activity) to reach half of its initial level.

☐ How to find the half-life of a radioactive substance, including from activity-time graphs.

Irradiation and Contamination

☐ That exposure to radiation is known as irradiation.

☐ That the unwanted presence of radioactive material on (or in) an object is known as contamination.

☐ The relative hazards of contamination and irradiation for different sources.

☐ The precautions that should be taken when handling radioactive substances.

Exam-style Questions

1   The diagram shows two atoms.

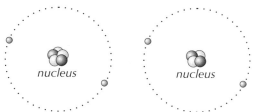

1.1   Put these three words into the following sentences.
You may only use each word once.

| protons | neutrons | electrons |

The nucleus contains _____ and _____.

The numbers of protons and _____ in a neutral atom are equal.

(2 marks)

1.2   The two atoms shown are isotopes of each other. Describe the similarities and
differences in the nuclei of two different isotopes of the same element.

(1 mark)

2   This incomplete table gives some information about three types of ionising radiation.

Radiation type:	Made up of:	Stopped by:
Alpha particles		Thin paper
	Electrons	Thin aluminium
Gamma rays	Short-wavelength EM waves	Thick lead

2.1   Complete the table.

(2 marks)

2.2   Explain what is meant by the term 'ionising'.

(1 mark)

2.3   Alpha sources are the most dangerous radioactive sources when inside the body.
Explain why.

(1 mark)

2.4   With respect to the atomic number and mass number, describe how the nucleus
changes when it emits an alpha particle.

(2 marks)

2.5   State what happens in the nucleus when it emits a beta particle.

(1 mark)

3   In March 2011, the Fukushima nuclear power plant in Japan was damaged by a tsunami and leaked some nuclear radiation into the air. One of the radioactive isotopes that was leaked in this incident was caesium-137, which has a half-life of 30 years.

3.1   Explain what it means for caesium-137 to have a half-life of 30 years.

(1 mark)

3.2   A sample containing caesium-137 is found to have an activity of 24 Bq.
Calculate what the activity of the sample will be in 90 years' time.

(3 marks)

Shortly after the disaster, the Japanese government decided to evacuate all people from their homes within a 12 mile radius of the power plant, because there were high levels of radiation in the air compared to normal, due to the disaster.

3.3   No one was allowed to move back into any of these homes until at least one year later. Suggest why it takes such a long time for evacuated areas to be considered safe after a nuclear disaster.

(1 mark)

Caesium-137 decays into barium-137.
The following incomplete equation shows this decay:

$$^{137}_{55}\text{Cs} \longrightarrow \ ^{137}_{.....}\text{Ba} + \ ^{0}_{-1}\text{e}$$

3.4   What type of radiation is being given out in this decay?

(1 mark)

3.5   Complete the nuclear equation for this decay.

(1 mark)

4*   An underground pipe is thought to be cracked, so that the substance carried by the pipe is leaking out. An engineer intends to use a radioactive isotope to locate the cracks. The isotope is put into the substance carried by the pipe. A radiation detector on the ground is moved along above the pipe, as shown.

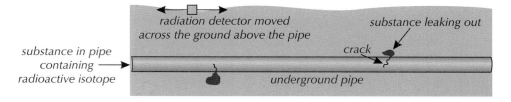

Describe how the engineer would be able to tell where there was a crack in the pipe. Explain what type of radiation the isotope in the pipe should emit and what the half-life of the source should be.

(6 marks)

1. Contact and Non-Contact Forces

Before you learn about forces, you need to understand the difference between vector and scalar quantities.

Vectors and scalars

Force is a **vector** quantity — vector quantities have a magnitude (size) and a direction. Lots of physical quantities are vector quantities — some examples are force, velocity, displacement, acceleration and momentum.

Some physical quantities have magnitude but no direction. These are called **scalar** quantities, and some examples are speed, distance, mass, temperature and time.

Vectors are usually represented by an arrow — the length of the arrow shows the magnitude, and the direction of the arrow shows the direction of the quantity.

> ### Example
>
> Velocity is a vector, but speed is a scalar quantity. The bikes in Figure 1 are travelling at the same speed, *v* (the length of each arrow is the same). They have different velocities because they are travelling in different directions.
>
>
>
> *Figure 1: Two motorcycles travelling in opposite directions have the same speed but a different velocity.*

Contact and non-contact forces

A **force** is a push or a pull on an object that is caused by it interacting with something. All forces are either contact or non-contact forces.

When two objects have to be touching for a force to act, that force is called a contact force. For example, friction, air resistance, tension in ropes and the normal contact force (page 128) are all contact forces. If the objects do not need to be touching for the force to act, the force is a non-contact force. Magnetic forces, gravitational forces and electrostatic forces are all non-contact forces.

When two objects interact, there is a force produced on both objects. An interaction pair is a pair of forces that are equal and opposite and act on two interacting objects. (This is basically Newton's Third Law — see p. 169.)

(page 128), (see p. 169.)

Learning Objectives:

- Know that vector quantities have both magnitude and direction.
- Know that scalar quantities only have a magnitude.
- Know that force is a vector.
- Know how arrows can be used to represent a vector quantity.
- Be able to define a force as the push or pull acting on an object due to an interaction with another object.
- Know the difference between contact forces and non-contact forces, including examples of both.
- Be able to describe the forces between two objects interacting with each other.
- Be able to represent the forces between two interacting objects as vectors.

Specification References 6.5.1.1, 6.5.1.2

Figure 2: A sledge being pulled. The tension in the rope is an example of a contact force.

Examples

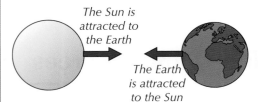

The Sun is attracted to the Earth

The Earth is attracted to the Sun

The Sun and the Earth are attracted to each other by a gravitational force. This is a non-contact force. An equal but opposite force of attraction is felt by both the Sun and the Earth.

A chair exerts a force on the ground, whilst the ground pushes back at the chair with the same force (the normal contact force). Equal but opposite forces are felt by both the chair and the ground.

Ground pushes on chair

Chair pushes on ground

Practice Questions — Fact Recall

Q1 What is the difference between a vector quantity and a scalar quantity?

Q2 State whether the following are vector quantities or scalar quantities:

a) force

b) acceleration

c) speed

d) velocity

e) temperature

Q3 What is meant by a contact force?

Q4 What is meant by a non-contact force?

Q5 What is an interaction pair?

Practice Question — Application

Q1 The diagram shows a boat travelling at a constant velocity. Draw another diagram of the boat, this time with an arrow showing what the velocity of the boat would be if it was travelling at a higher speed in the opposite direction.

2. Weight, Mass and Gravity

Gravity is pretty important. It not only gives everything a weight, it also keeps us glued to Earth.

Gravitational force

Gravity attracts all masses, but you only notice it when one or more of the masses are really big, e.g. a planet. Anything near a planet or star is attracted to it very strongly.

This has two important effects:

1. On the surface of a planet, it makes all things accelerate (see page 150) towards the ground.

2. It gives everything a weight (see below).

Weight and mass

Weight and mass are not the same — mass is just the amount of 'stuff' in an object. For any given object this will have the same value anywhere in the universe.

Weight is the force acting on an object due to gravity (the pull of the gravitational force on the object). This force is caused by gravitational fields, and the size of the force depends on the gravitational field strength. Close to Earth, this force is caused by the gravitational field around the Earth.

Gravitational field strength varies with location. It's stronger the closer you are to the mass causing the field, and stronger for larger masses. The weight of an object depends on the strength of the gravitational field at the location of the object. This means that the weight of an object changes with its location.

An object has the same mass whether it's on Earth or on the Moon — but its weight will be different. A 1 kg mass will weigh less on the Moon than it does on Earth (about 1.6 N on the Moon compared to about 9.8 N on Earth). This is because the gravitational field strength on the surface of the Moon is less.

Measuring weight

Weight is a force measured in newtons. You can think of the force as acting from a single point on the object, called its centre of mass (a point at which you assume the whole mass is concentrated). For a uniform object (one that's the same density throughout, p. 96, and a regular shape), this will be at the centre of the object.

centre of mass

weight

Figure 2: *Any object with a mass will have a point at which its weight appears to act, known as the centre of mass.*

Weight is measured using a calibrated spring balance (newtonmeter — see Figure 1). Mass isn't a force. It's measured in kilograms with a mass balance.

Learning Objectives:
- Be able to define weight as the force acting on an object due to gravity.
- Know that the gravitational force acting on an object close to Earth is due to the Earth's gravitational field.
- Know that the weight of an object is dependent on the gravitational field strength at the object's location.
- Know that weight is measured using a calibrated spring balance.
- Understand what is meant by the centre of mass of an object.
- Know the equation that relates weight, mass and gravitational field strength.
- Understand that weight is directly proportional to mass.

Specification Reference 6.5.1.3

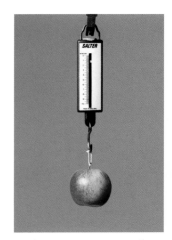

Figure 1: *Measuring the weight of an apple using a newtonmeter.*

Calculating weight

Tip: When you see two letters written next to each other in an equation, it means they're multiplied together. So *mg* just means *m* × *g*.

You can calculate the weight of an object if you know its mass (*m*) and the strength of the gravitational field at that point (*g*):

W = weight in N ⟶ $W = mg$ ⟵ *m* = mass in kg

g = gravitational field strength in N/kg

Tip: The ≈ sign means 'approximately equal to'.

For Earth, *g* ≈ 9.8 N/kg and for the Moon it's around 1.6 N/kg. Increasing the mass of an object increases its weight. If you double the mass, the weight doubles too, so you can say that weight and mass are directly proportional.

Exam Tip
You'll always be given a value of *g* to use in the exam.

You can write this, using the direct proportionality symbol, as $W \propto m$.

Example 1

What is the weight, in newtons, of a 5 kg mass, both on Earth (*g* = 9.8 N/kg) and on the Moon (*g* = 1.6 N/kg)?

Just use the formula $W = mg$ in each case:

On Earth:	On the Moon:
$W = mg = 5 \times 9.8$	$W = mg = 5 \times 1.6$
$= 49$ N	$= 8$ N

Tip: The value of *g* is greater for Earth than the Moon because Earth has a stronger gravitational field.

Example 2

The value of *g* on Mars is 3.71 N/kg. What is the mass of a buggy if its weight on Mars is 4452 N?

Just rearrange the formula to make mass the subject, then plug in the correct numbers:

$$W = mg, \text{ so } m = W \div g = 4452 \div 3.71 = 1200 \text{ kg}$$

Tip: Remember — the mass of an object is always the same, no matter where it is.

Tip: You can use a formula triangle to help rearrange this equation:

There's more on formula triangles on page 242.

Practice Questions — Fact Recall

Q1   Define weight.

Q2   What is meant by the centre of mass of an object?

Q3   What apparatus is used to measure the weight of an object on Earth?

Practice Question — Application

Q1   A rock on Earth has a mass of 15 kg. *g* on Earth = 9.8 N/kg.

   a) Calculate the weight of the rock on Earth.

   b) What would happen to the mass of the rock if it was moved to the surface of the Moon?

3. Resultant Forces

Resultant forces can help make it easier to work out what's going on in a complicated situation with lots of forces involved.

What is a resultant force?

The notion of a **resultant force** is a really important one for you to get your head round. In most real situations there are at least two forces acting on an object, but thinking about the resultant force can simplify all that.

If you have a number of forces acting at a single point, you can replace them with a single force which has the same effect as all the original forces acting all together. This single, overall force you get is called the resultant force.

Determining the resultant force

If the forces on an object all act along the same line (in the same or opposite directions), the resultant force is found by finding the sum of all the forces.

To do this, set a direction as being positive. Then add all the forces acting in that direction and subtract all the forces acting in the opposite direction.

Example

A vintage sports car is driving along with a driving force of 1000 N. Air resistance of 600 N is acting in the opposite direction. What is the resultant horizontal force on the car?

Do a sketch to visualise the problem. The driving force and the air resistance can be drawn as shown on the right. Weight and the normal contact force are also acting vertically on the car, but we can ignore them as we're only interested in horizontal forces.

air resistance 600 N   driving force 1000 N

Set the forwards direction as the positive, then add any forces in this direction and subtract any forces in the opposite direction.

So the resultant force = 1000 − 600 = 400 N (forwards).

You can use another diagram to show the resultant force acting on the car:

resultant force 400 N

Free body diagrams `Higher`

You need to be able to describe all the forces acting on an isolated object or a system (p. 21) — i.e. every force acting on the object or system but none of the forces the object or system exerts on the rest of the world.

This can be shown on a **free body diagram**. Each force is represented by an arrow — the lengths of the arrows show the relative magnitudes of the forces and the directions of the arrows show the directions of the forces. You can use a free body diagram to help you figure out the resultant force on an object.

Learning Objectives:

- Know that the resultant force acting on an object has the same effect as all the individual forces acting on that object.

- Be able to calculate the resultant of two forces acting on an object along the same line.

- **H** Be able to give examples of the forces acting on a single object.

- **H** Be able to use free body diagrams to show the forces acting on an object and the resultant force.

- **H** Be able to use scale drawings to find the resultant force acting on an object and to determine whether an object is in equilibrium.

- **H** Be able to resolve a force into two components that have the same combined effect as the force.

Specification Reference 6.5.1.4

Figure 1: *A tug of war is an example of two forces acting in opposite directions. If the two forces have the same magnitude, the rope will not move.*

Example — Higher

This free body diagram shows the forces acting on a person who's running.

Air resistance acts in the opposite direction to the forwards thrust.

The person's weight acts downwards and the normal contact force acts upwards.

The weight and normal contact arrows are the same length, so these two forces balance and the resultant vertical force is zero.

The thrust arrow is longer than the air resistance arrow, so there is a resultant force in the direction of motion (forwards).

normal contact force from ground

thrust

air resistance

weight

Tip: If the air resistance arrow was the same length as the thrust arrow, then they would balance too. There would be no resultant force and the person would be in equilibrium (see the next page for more on this).

Scale drawings Higher

You can also use scale drawings to find the resultant force acting on an object. First draw all the forces acting on an object 'tip-to-tail', making sure they're to scale and in the correct directions.

Then draw a straight line from the start of the first force to the end of the last force — this is the resultant force. Measure the length of the resultant force on the diagram to find the magnitude and measure the angle to find the direction of the force.

Tip: H Scale drawings are particularly useful when working with forces that are acting at different angles.

Example — Higher

A man is on an electric bicycle that has a driving force of 4 N north. However, the wind produces a force of 3 N east. Find the magnitude and direction of the resultant force.

Start by doing a scale drawing of the forces acting, tip-to-tail. Make sure you choose a sensible scale (e.g. 1 cm = 1 N).

Draw the resultant from the tail of the first arrow to the tip of the last arrow. Measure the length of the resultant with a ruler and use the scale to find the force in N. Then use a protractor to measure the direction as a bearing.

Tip: H Drawing forces 'to scale' means each unit of length represents the same quantity. So in this example, each cm drawn represents 1 N of force.

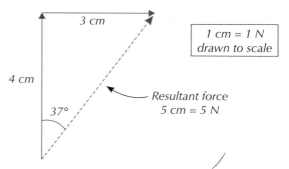

3 cm

4 cm

37°

*Resultant force
5 cm = 5 N*

*1 cm = 1 N
drawn to scale*

Tip: H A bearing is an angle measured clockwise from north, given as a 3 digit number, e.g. 10° = 010°.

The resultant force is 5 N on a bearing of 037°.

Balanced forces

If all of the forces acting on an object combine to give a resultant force of zero, the forces are balanced and the object is in **equilibrium**. On a scale diagram, this means that the tip of the last force you draw should end where the tail of the first force you drew begins. E.g. for three forces, the scale diagram will form a triangle.

> **Tip:** **H** For an object in equilibrium, it can be useful to think of the forces 'cancelling each other out'.

Example — **Higher**

The free body diagram for an object is shown on the right.

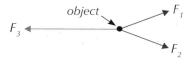

If all the forces acting on the object are drawn tip-to-tail, a complete loop is formed. This shows that the object is in equilibrium.

> **Tip:** **H** If the object wasn't in equilibrium, the forces wouldn't join up at the end to form a complete loop.

You might be given the forces acting on an object and told to find a missing force, given that the object is in equilibrium. To do this, draw out the forces you do know (to scale and tip-to-tail), then join the end of the last force to the start of the first force. This line is the missing force, so you can measure its size and direction.

> **Tip:** **H** When trying to find a missing force for an object in equilibrium, make sure you draw it in the correct direction. All the arrows should point in the same direction around the loop — unlike when you're trying to find the resultant.

Resolving forces

Not all forces act horizontally or vertically — some act at awkward angles. To make these easier to deal with, they can be split into two "components" at right angles to each other (usually horizontal and vertical). Acting together, these components have the same effect as the single force.

You can resolve a force (split it into components) by drawing it on a square grid. Draw the force to scale, and then add the horizontal and vertical components using the grid lines. Then you can just measure them.

Figure 2: A force, F, split into horizontal and vertical components, drawn on a square grid.

> **Tip:** **H** Resolving forces is a bit like the reverse of finding the resultant. They sound similar, so make sure you don't get them mixed up.

Example — **Higher**

The scale diagram shows a toy car being pulled along horizontally by a string. The tension in the string has a magnitude of 2.5 N. Resolve the tension to find the magnitude of this force acting in the direction of the car's motion.

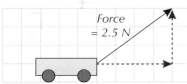

Measure the length of the black arrow — it's 2.5 cm.
The resultant force = 2.5 N, so the scale is 1 cm = 1 N.

The dotted arrows show the force resolved into two components. The car is moving horizontally, and the length of the horizontal component = 2 cm.
So the magnitude of the force acting in the direction of the car's motion = 2 N.

> **Tip:** **H** You need to find the scale of the diagram to work out the magnitude of the horizontal component.

Practice Questions — Fact Recall

Q1 What is meant by the resultant force acting on an object?

Q2 What is a free body diagram?

Q3 Describe how a scale diagram of all the forces acting on an object can be used to determine whether the object is in equilibrium.

Q4 What is meant by 'resolving a force'?

Practice Questions — Application

Q1 A bike is being pushed. The magnitude of the force pushing the bike forwards is equal to 87 N. A resistive force with a magnitude of 24 N is acting in the opposite direction. Find the magnitude and direction of the resultant of these forces.

Q2 A boat is being pulled by three tugboats. The boat also experiences a frictional force from the water. These forces are shown to scale on the diagram below. Using a scale diagram, work out whether the boat is in equilibrium.

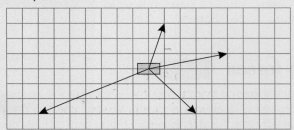

Q3 A box is being dragged along a table. The direction of the force that is pulling the box is parallel to the surface of the table. Draw a free body diagram to show all the forces acting on the box. (You can assume there is no friction between the box and the table.)

Tip: **H** Don't forget to include the weight and normal contact force in your free body diagram.

Q4 A train is being pulled along a track (shown in blue) with a force of 20 N. A frictional force and a reaction force from the side of the track act on the train. A scale diagram of the train, as viewed from above, is shown below. By resolving forces, find the resultant force acting on the train in its direction of motion.

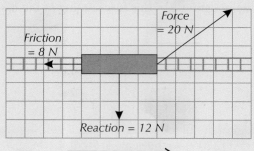

Tip: **H** When finding the resultant force in the direction of motion, you don't need to take into account any components that are at right angles to the direction of motion.

4. Work Done

If a force moves an object from one position to another, energy must be transferred from one energy store to another.

What is work done?

In physics '**work done**' has a specific meaning, and you need to know what that is.

> Work done is the energy transferred when a force moves an object through a distance.

Luckily, it's not as complicated as that statement makes it sound.

Try this:

1. Whenever something moves, something else might be providing some sort of 'effort' to move it (see Figure 2 on the next page).

2. The thing putting the effort in needs a source of energy (like fuel or food etc.).

3. It then does 'work' by moving the object — energy is transferred from one store to another.

4. Whether this energy is transferred 'usefully' (e.g. by lifting a load) or is 'wasted' (e.g. transferred to the thermal energy stores of the surroundings), you can still say that 'work is done'.

So work done is simply the energy transferred when a force acts on an object. You can work out how much work is done using the following formula:

$$W = \text{work done (J)} \longrightarrow W = Fs \longleftarrow \begin{array}{l} F = \text{force (N)} \\ s = \text{distance (m)} \end{array}$$

One joule of work is done when a force of one newton causes an object to move a distance of one metre. So one joule is equal to one newton metre: $1\text{ J} = 1\text{ Nm}$. You need to be able to convert between J and Nm.

Example

Some kids drag a tractor tyre 5 m over the ground. They pull with a resultant force of 340 N in the direction of motion. Find the work done to move the tyre.

Force = 340 N   Distance = 5 m

Then put the numbers into the formula for work done:

$$W = Fs = 340 \times 5 = 1700\text{ J}$$

Learning Objectives:

- Know that if a force is applied to an object and displaces it, the force does work on the object.
- Know the equation that relates work done, force and distance moved.
- Understand that 1 J of work is done when a force of 1 N moves an object 1 m and be able to convert between J and Nm.
- Be able to describe the energy transfers that are involved when work is done on an object.
- Understand that work done against friction can cause a rise in the temperature of an object and its surroundings.

Specification Reference 6.5.2

Tip: There's more about energy being transferred and work done on pages 21-23.

Tip: The distance, s, in the equation is the distance moved in the direction of the force, F.

Tip: The formula triangle for this equation is:

Energy transfers

Remember, 'work done' and 'energy transferred' are one and the same. (And they're both given in joules.)

Energy is transferred from the chemical energy store of the person to their kinetic energy store.

Energy is transferred to thermal energy stores and to the kinetic energy store of the broom, causing it to move through a distance, so work is done.

Figure 2: A diagram showing how work is done when a person supplies energy to a broom and sweeps.

Figure 1: A wheelchair user pushing the wheels of her chair. She does work against friction by transferring energy from her chemical energy store to the kinetic energy store of the chair.

When you push something along a rough surface (like a carpet) you are doing work against frictional forces. Energy is transferred to the kinetic energy store of the object because it starts moving, but some is also transferred to the thermal energy stores of the object, the surface and the surroundings due to friction (p. 159). This causes the overall temperature of the object and surface to increase (like rubbing your hands together to warm them up).

Example

A brick is pushed along rough ground with a total force of 45 N. The brick moves a distance of 1.4 m. Find the total energy transferred.

Force = 45 N   Distance = 1.4 m

Energy transferred is the same as work done, so just use the equation:

$$W = Fs = 45 \times 1.4 = 63 \text{ J}$$

So the energy transferred is 63 J

> **Tip:** Here, you're finding the total energy transferred. Some of this is transferred usefully to the brick's kinetic energy stores. The rest is transferred to thermal energy stores due to work done against friction.

Practice Questions — Fact Recall

Q1 Define work done.

Q2 What is 1 joule in newton metres?

Q3 Explain why doing work against friction can cause a rise in temperature.

Practice Questions — Application

Q1 A child pulls a sledge across snow for 14 m. The resultant force applied over this distance is 24 N. Calculate the work done to move the sledge.

Q2 a) A bike is pushed 20 m using a steady force of 250 N in the direction of motion. How much energy is transferred?

   b) If the bike continues to be pushed with the same force, calculate how far the bike will move if 750 J of work is done.

> **Tip:** Remember — work done and energy transferred are the same thing.

Topic 5a Checklist — Make sure you know...

Contact and Non-Contact Forces

☐ That scalar quantities only have magnitude but vector quantities have magnitude and direction.

☐ That when an arrow is used to represent a vector, the size of the arrow indicates the magnitude of the vector and the direction of the arrow shows the direction of the vector.

☐ That a force on an object is defined as the push or pull acting on the object and is a vector.

☐ That a contact force between two interacting objects is a result of them touching and a non-contact force between two interacting objects can occur when they are not touching.

Weight, Mass and Gravity

☐ That gravity is responsible for giving objects weight.

☐ That the force due to gravity at the Earth's surface is a result of the Earth's gravitational field.

☐ That gravitational field strength at a point is responsible for an object's weight at that point.

☐ That a calibrated spring balance is used for measuring weight.

☐ That the centre of mass of an object is the point at which the object's weight appears to act.

☐ The equation weight = mass × gravitational field strength.

Resultant Forces

☐ That the resultant force acting on an object is the single force that has the same effect as the original forces all acting together.

☐ How to calculate the resultant of two forces acting on an object along the same line.

☐ H How to describe all of the forces acting on a single object.

☐ H That a free body diagram of an object shows all the forces acting on the object.

☐ H How scale drawings can be used to find the resultant force acting on an object.

☐ H How free body diagrams and scale drawings can be used to show that all the forces acting on an object are balanced and so the object is in equilibrium.

☐ H How to resolve a force into two components that are at right angles to each other.

Work Done

☐ That work is done on an object when a force displaces it and that it can be calculated using work done = force × distance (moved along the line of action of the force), where work done is measured in joules or newton metres.

☐ That if a force of 1 N is applied to an object over a distance of 1 m, then 1 J of work is done.

☐ How to convert between J (joules) and Nm (newton metres).

☐ How to describe the energy transfers for a situation in which work is done on an object.

☐ That if work is done against friction then energy can be transferred to thermal energy stores, causing an increase in temperature of the object and surroundings.

Exam-style Questions

1   A 1.8 kg book is resting on a table. The gravitational field strength = 9.8 N/kg.

   1.1   Calculate the weight of the book. Give your answer to 2 significant figures.

(2 marks)

   1.2   A 5 N force is applied to the book so that the book slides across the table.
A 1.4 N frictional force acts on the book in the opposite direction.
These two forces are shown in the diagram below. The diagram is not to scale.

Calculate the magnitude of the resultant force acting on the book.

(1 mark)

   1.3   The work done by the resultant force to move the book across the table is 19.8 J.
Calculate the distance travelled by the book.

(3 marks)

2   A canal boat is towed along by two horses on the bank. Each horse is pulling the
canal boat with a different force. The diagram shown is to scale.

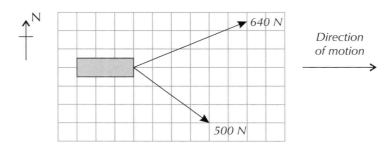

   2.1   Are the horses pulling the canal boat with a contact force or a non-contact force?

(1 mark)

   2.2   Calculate the total force provided by the horses in the direction of the canal boat's
motion.

(4 marks)

   2.3   There is a drag force on the boat acting in the opposite direction to its motion.
If the resultant force acting on the boat in the direction of its motion is 800 N,
calculate the magnitude of the drag force.

(1 mark)

1. Elastic Objects

Learning Objectives:

- Know that in order to stretch, bend or compress an object, at least two forces must be applied to it.
- Know what is meant by elastically deformed and inelastically deformed.
- Know that the force applied to an elastic object is directly proportional to the extension of the object, up to the limit of proportionality.
- Know and be able to use the equation $F = ke$, where k is the spring constant and e is the extension or compression of the object.
- Understand that work is done on a spring when it is stretched or compressed.
- Understand that for elastic deformations, all work done on a spring to stretch or compress it is transferred to its elastic potential energy store.
- Be able to calculate the work done in stretching (or compressing) a spring using the equation for the energy in its elastic potential energy store.

Specification Reference
6.5.3

Applying forces to some objects can cause them to stretch. Stretching an object can either be a permanent change or a temporary change.

Elastic and inelastic deformation

When you apply a force to an object you may cause it to stretch, compress or bend. To change the shape of an object in this way, you need more than one force acting on the object, in different directions (otherwise the object would simply move in the direction of the applied force, instead of changing shape).

An object has been **elastically deformed** if it can go back to its original shape and length after the force has been removed. An object has been **inelastically deformed** if it doesn't return to its original shape and length after the force has been removed (i.e. it's been permanently deformed). Objects which can be elastically deformed are called **elastic objects** (e.g. a spring).

Examples

If a spring is supported at the top and a weight is attached to the bottom, it stretches.

A spring can also be compressed or bent by applying forces at different points.

Figure 1: *A spring can be stretched, compressed or bent when more than one force is acting on it. The extension, e, of a stretched spring is the difference between its stretched length and its original length (i.e. with no force applied).*

Force and extension

The extension of a stretched spring (or other elastic object) is directly proportional to the load or force applied — so $F \propto e$ (see p. 241). This is true as long as you don't stretch it too far — more on this shortly.

Figure 2: *A bungee jumper leaping from a bridge. The bungee cord is an elastic object which stretches due to the person's weight. Look back at page 129 for a reminder on weight.*

This is the equation:

k = spring constant (N/m)

F = force (N) ⟶ $F = ke$

e = extension (m)

The spring constant depends on the material that you are stretching — a stiffer spring has a greater spring constant.

The equation also works for compression (where e is just the difference between the natural and compressed lengths — the compression).

Example 1

When no force is applied, a spring has a length of 23.2 cm. When a lead ball is suspended from it, the spring extends to a length of 25.1 cm. If the spring constant k = 60 N/m, calculate the weight of the lead ball.

Start by finding the extension of the spring after the lead ball is attached:

$$e = 25.1 - 23.2 = 1.9 \text{ cm}$$

Be careful with units here — the formula uses extension in metres, so make sure you convert any numbers first:

$$1.9 \text{ cm} = 1.9 \div 100 \text{ m} = 0.019 \text{ m}$$

Then put the numbers into the equation for force:

$$F = ke = 60 \times 0.019 = 1.14 \text{ N}$$

Tip: There's more on converting between units on pages 17-18.

Tip: You might find rearranging equations easier if you use a formula triangle:

Example 2

A 12 N force is used to compress a spring with a spring constant of 96 N/kg. Calculate the compression of the spring.

Rearrange the formula to make e the subject:

$$F = ke, \text{ so } e = F \div k$$

Then put the right numbers in:

$$e = 12 \div 96 = 0.125 \text{ m}$$

The limit of proportionality

There's a limit to the amount of force you can apply to an object for the extension to keep on increasing proportionally. This limit is known as the **limit of proportionality**. Figure 3 shows a graph of force against extension for an object. The limit of proportionality is the point at which the graph starts to curve. It's marked as point P on the graph in Figure 3.

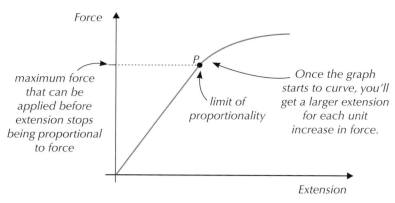

maximum force that can be applied before extension stops being proportional to force

limit of proportionality

Once the graph starts to curve, you'll get a larger extension for each unit increase in force.

Figure 3: *A graph showing the force applied to an object against its extension. The force is proportional to extension up to the limit of proportionality.*

Tip: The graph below point P shows a linear relationship, and the graph above point P shows a non-linear relationship. See pages 243-245 for more on linear and non-linear graphs.

Tip: You may also see extension-force graphs (similar, but with the axes swapped around). The graph will curve upwards instead:

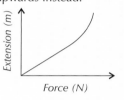

Elastic potential energy store

Work is done when a force stretches or compresses an object and causes energy to be transferred. If the object is elastically deformed, ALL this energy is transferred to the object's elastic potential energy store.

As long as a spring is not stretched past its limit of proportionality, the work done in stretching or compressing the spring can be found using:

E_e = elastic potential energy (J)

$$E_e = \frac{1}{2} ke^2$$

k = spring constant (N/m)

e = extension (m)

Tip: Take a look at page 21 for more on energy stores.

For elastic deformation, this formula can be used to calculate the energy stored in a spring's elastic potential energy store. It's also the energy transferred to the spring as it's deformed (or transferred by the spring as it returns to its original shape).

The work done, or energy stored in the elastic potential energy store, for a particular force (or extension) can also be found by calculating the area under the linear force-extension graph up to that force (or extension).

Tip: If a stretched spring is released, the energy stored in its elastic potential energy store will be transferred to its kinetic energy store as it springs back to its original size and shape.

Tip: See page 245 for more on the area under a graph.

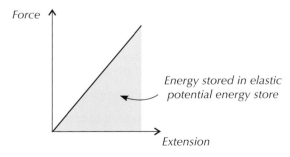

Energy stored in elastic potential energy store

Figure 4: *The area under the force-extension graph of an elastic object is equal to the energy stored in the elastic potential energy store of the object.*

Tip: If an object is deformed inelastically, some of the work done will transfer energy into other energy stores (e.g. the thermal energy store of the object), not just the elastic potential energy store.

Example

A spring has a spring constant of 1.2 N/m. Assuming the spring deforms elastically, calculate the total energy transferred to its elastic potential energy store when it is extended by 0.20 m.

Substitute the numbers into the equation:

$$E_e = \tfrac{1}{2}ke^2 = \tfrac{1}{2} \times 1.2 \times 0.20^2 = 0.024 \text{ J}$$

Tip: Don't forget to square the extension when calculating the energy transferred to the elastic potential energy store.

Practice Questions — Fact Recall

Q1 Explain why more than one force needs to be applied to a spring in order to stretch it.

Q2 What is an elastic object?

Q3 Give the equation that relates the force applied to a spring, the spring constant of the spring and the extension of the spring. Give the units of each term.

Q4 What is the limit of proportionality?

Q5 A spring is elastically deformed. How much of the energy transferred to the spring is released when the spring is released? Explain your answer.

Practice Questions — Application

Q1 A rubber band has a spring constant of 34 N/m. Calculate the force required to stretch the rubber band from 0.50 m to 0.75 m.

Q2 The graph shows a force-extension graph for a spring. Which point marks the spring's limit of proportionality?

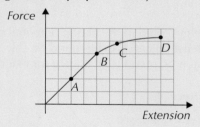

Q3 a) Spring A is compressed from 16 cm to 12 cm when a force of 0.80 N is applied to it. Calculate the spring constant of spring A.

b) Calculate the work done on spring A as it is compressed.

c) The same force is then applied to spring B. It compresses spring B by a smaller amount than it compressed spring A. Is the spring constant of spring B higher than, lower than or equal to the spring constant of spring A?

Exam Tip
Remember to make sure all your values are in the right units before you substitute them into an equation. For example, extension, e, should be in metres for Q3.

2. Investigating Springs

You can investigate the behaviour of a spring using a simple experiment. From the experiment, you can find the limit of proportionality of the spring and its spring constant.

REQUIRED
PRACTICAL **18**

Apparatus and setup

Set up the apparatus as shown in Figure 1.

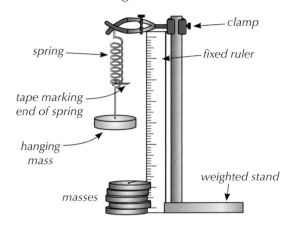

Figure 1: Experimental setup used to investigate a spring.

You could do a quick pilot experiment first to check your masses are a suitable size. Using the spring you'll be testing (or an identical one), load it with masses one at a time, up to a total of five masses. Using the ruler, check that the spring extends by the same amount each time. If adding one of these masses causes the spring to stretch by more than the previous ones, you have gone beyond the spring's limit of proportionality. If this happens, you'll need to use smaller masses. Otherwise, you won't end up with enough values to plot your graph later on.

If the spring does go past its limit of proportionality during the pilot experiment, it could start to deform inelastically and so you'll have to replace it with another (identical) spring in the real thing.

Carrying out the experiment

Make sure you have plenty of masses and calculate their weights (the force that will be applied to the spring) using $W = mg$ (p. 130).

Using the ruler, measure the natural length of the spring (the length when no hanging mass is attached). Make sure you take the reading at eye level and use a marker (e.g. a thin strip of tape, as shown in Figure 1) to make the reading more accurate.

Add a mass to the spring and allow the spring to come to rest. Measure the spring's new length. Record the weight added and work out the extension (the change in length). Repeat this process, recording the total weight attached and calculating the total extension (total length minus natural length) each time, until you have enough measurements (no fewer than 6).

Learning Objectives:
- Be able to investigate the relationship between the force applied to a spring and its extension (Required Practical 18).
- Be able to find the spring constant from a force-extension graph for a linear force-extension relationship.
- Know the difference between linear and non-linear force-extension relationships.

Specification Reference 6.5.3

Tip: You must make sure the ruler and spring are vertical to make sure your measurements are as accurate as possible.

Tip: It's okay to go past the limit of proportionality when you're doing the real thing, but you need to make sure you've recorded enough measurements to plot the linear part of the graph beforehand.

Tip: You should wear safety goggles when carrying out this experiment to protect your eyes in case the spring snaps. Make sure you do a risk assessment to identify any other hazards before you start.

Tip: You first saw force-extension graphs on page 141.

Tip: You could also plot the force on the x-axis and the extension on the y-axis. You would still get an initial straight line graph, but then it would start to curve upwards:

You can still find the spring constant from the linear part of this graph — it's equal to $\dfrac{1}{gradient}$.

Tip: Once you've got your graph, you could use it to find the weight of an object. Hang the object from the spring, measure the extension, then use your graph to find the corresponding weight (force). This will only work if you didn't deform the spring inelastically during the experiment and the object's weight is within the range you plotted.

Tip: To check whether the deformation is elastic or inelastic, you can remove each mass temporarily and check whether the spring goes back to the previous extension.

Analysing the results

Plot a force-extension graph of your results and draw a line of best fit. For each measurement, the force you should plot is the total weight of the masses attached to the spring. The extension is the difference between the spring's length with that total weight attached and its natural length. Take a look at pages 15-16 for more information on how to plot graphs.

The graph will only start to curve if you exceed the limit of proportionality when you're adding the masses. Don't worry if yours doesn't start to curve — as long as you've got the straight line bit, you'll be able to find the spring constant. But you will need the start of the curve if you want to find the limit of proportionality. Figure 2 shows how your results might look.

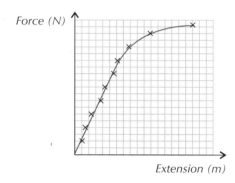

Figure 2: *Graph of force against extension for a spring.*

When the line of best fit is a straight line, it means there is a linear relationship between force and extension (they're directly proportional, see page 243).

You know that $F = ke$, and the gradient of the straight line is:

$$\frac{\text{change in } y}{\text{change in } x} = \frac{F}{e} = k$$

So to find the spring constant, you just need to work out the gradient of the straight line.

When the line begins to bend, the relationship between force and extension is non-linear — the spring stretches more for each unit increase in force. So the point where the line starts to curve is the spring's limit of proportionality.

Practice Questions — Fact Recall

Q1 When carrying out an experiment to find the spring constant of a spring, explain why it is a good idea to carry out a pilot experiment first on an identical spring.

Q2 Give a safety procedure that should be carried out when doing an experiment to find the spring constant of a spring.

Q3 How is the spring constant of a spring found from a force-extension graph?

Topic 5b Checklist — Make sure you know...

Elastic Objects

☐ That at least two forces must be applied to an object in order to stretch, compress or bend it.

☐ That the force applied to an elastic object is directly proportional to the extension or compression of the object up to the limit of proportionality.

☐ The equation $F = ke$ (force (N) = spring constant (N/m) × extension (m)) and how to use it.

☐ That the limit of proportionality is the point beyond which the extension of an elastic object no longer increases proportionally with the force applied to the object.

☐ Know that an object undergoing elastic deformation will return to its original size and shape once all forces have been removed from it.

☐ Know that an object undergoing inelastic deformation will not return to its original size and shape once all forces have been removed from it.

☐ That work must be done on a spring to stretch or compress it.

☐ That for elastic deformation, the work done to stretch or compress a spring is all transferred to the spring's elastic potential energy store.

☐ That the equation $E_e = \frac{1}{2}ke^2$ (elastic potential energy = 0.5 × spring constant × extension²) is used to calculate the energy transferred to the elastic potential energy store when an elastic object is stretched up to the limit of proportionality.

Investigating Springs

☐ The experiment that can be used to investigate the relationship between the force applied to a spring and the extension of the spring, including the setup and how to record and analyse the results.

☐ That the spring constant of a spring can be found by calculating the gradient of the linear part of the spring's force-extension graph.

Exam-style Questions

1   A student carries out an experiment to investigate how the extension of a spring changes as an increasing force is applied to it. She plots her results on a force-extension graph and draws a line of best fit. Her results are shown below. When drawing the line of best fit, the student assumes the data point recorded when a force of 0.70 N is applied to the spring is anomalous.

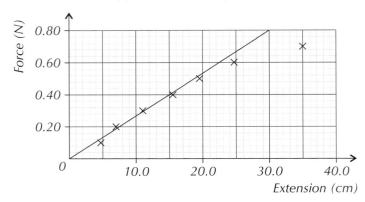

1.1   Explain why the student is wrong to assume the data point is anomalous. Suggest how the student could find out whether it is anomalous or not.

(2 marks)

1.2   The student decides to repeat the experiment. Suggest why a second identical spring should be used rather than the same spring.

(2 marks)

1.3   Using the graph, calculate the spring constant of the spring.

(3 marks)

2   A mass is put on a spring as shown in the diagram. The mass compresses the spring, which remains vertical during the compression. The spring has a spring constant of 160 N/m, and the length of the spring changes from 165 mm to 140 mm when the mass is put on top of it.

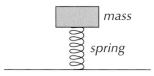

2.1   Calculate the weight of the mass. Give your answer in N.

(3 marks)

2.2   Calculate the energy stored in the elastic potential energy store of the spring. Use the correct equation from those listed on page 284. Give your answer in J.

(2 marks)

1. Distance, Displacement, Speed and Velocity

Some of your bread and butter physics here — it's all about things that are moving. Make sure you really understand it, otherwise things could get tricksy.

Distance and displacement

You met vectors and scalars on page 127. A scalar quantity has magnitude but no direction, whereas a vector quantity has magnitude and direction.

Distance is a scalar quantity — it's just how far an object has moved. **Displacement** is a vector quantity. It measures the distance and direction in a straight line from an object's starting point to its finishing point. The direction could be relative to a point, e.g. towards the school, or a bearing (which is a three-digit angle from north, e.g. 035°).

> **Example**
>
> **A person walks 5 m north and then 5 m south.**
> **Calculate the distance they travel and their displacement.**
>
> Distance travelled = 5 + 5 = 10 m
> Displacement = 0 m as they have ended up back at their starting position.

Speed and velocity

Speed and **velocity** both measure how fast you're going, but speed is a scalar and velocity is a vector:

1. Speed is just how fast you're going with no regard to the direction, for example 30 mph or 20 m/s.

2. Velocity is how fast you're going and in which direction, for example 30 mph north or 20 m/s on a bearing of 060°.

> **Example**
>
> The cars below are all travelling at the same speed of 0.5 m/s, but they're all moving in different directions, so all have a different velocity.
>
>

Learning Objectives:
- Know what distance and displacement are.
- Know that distance is a scalar quantity and displacement is a vector quantity.
- Be able to give the magnitude and direction of an object's displacement.
- Know that speed is a scalar quantity and velocity (speed in a given direction) is a vector quantity.
- **H** Understand that an object can have a constant speed but a changing velocity, e.g. circular motion.
- Know that things rarely move at constant speeds in real life (e.g. moving objects, sound and wind).
- Be able to give typical values for walking, running and cycling speeds, vehicle speeds and the speed of sound.
- Know some factors that affect the speed of walking, running and cycling.
- Know and be able to use the equation $s = vt$ to calculate speed using measurements of distance and time.
- Be able to calculate the speed of uniform motion and the average speed of non-uniform motion.

Specification References
6.5.4.1.1, 6.5.4.1.2, 6.5.4.1.3

Figure 1: People on a Ferris wheel will have a constant speed but a changing velocity as the wheel turns.

Moving in a circle Higher

You can have objects travelling at a constant speed with a changing velocity. This happens when the object is changing direction whilst staying at the same speed.

An object moving in a circle at a constant speed has a constantly changing velocity, as the direction is always changing, for example a car going around a roundabout.

Everyday speeds

Objects rarely travel at a constant speed. E.g. when you walk, run or travel in a car, your speed is always changing. Whilst every person, train, bus etc. is different, there is usually a typical speed that each object travels at. Remember these typical speeds for everyday objects:

> A person walking — 1.5 m/s   A car — 25 m/s
> A person running — 3 m/s   A train — 55 m/s
> A person cycling — 6 m/s   A plane — 250 m/s

Tip: It might help to remember that running is about half the speed of cycling, and walking is about half the speed of running.

Lots of different things can affect the speed something travels at. For example, the speed at which a person can walk, run or cycle depends on their fitness, their age, the distance travelled and the terrain (what kind of land they're moving over, e.g. roads, fields), as well as many other factors.

It's not only the speed of objects that varies. The speed of sound is 330 m/s in air and changes depending on what the sound waves are travelling through. Similarly, wind speed can be affected by things like changes in temperature and atmospheric pressure as well as whether there are any large buildings or structures nearby (for example, forests can reduce the speed of the air travelling through them).

Calculating speed

If an object is travelling at a constant speed, then its distance, speed and time are related by the formula:

Tip: This equation can be written in a formula triangle:

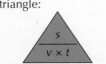

s = distance travelled (m) $s = vt$ v = speed (m/s)
                                            t = time (s)

Example

A cat is walking at a speed of 0.4 m/s. Calculate how far the cat walks in 50 s and how long it takes to walk 32 m.

To find how far the cat walks in 50 s:
$$s = vt = 0.4 \times 50 = 20 \text{ m/s}$$

To find the time it takes the cat to walk 32 m, rearrange the equation:
$$t = s \div v = 32 \div 0.4 = 80 \text{ s}$$

If you want to measure the speed of an object that's moving with a constant speed, you should time how long it takes the object to travel a certain distance, e.g. using a ruler and a stopwatch, and use the equation to find the speed.

For an object that isn't travelling at a constant speed, you can use the equation to calculate the average speed. Just use the total distance travelled by the object and the total time taken to travel that distance.

Example

A lorry moves at a steady speed and travels 24 m in 30 s. The lorry then slows down and travels a further 45 m in 70 s before stopping. Calculate the average speed of the lorry for the whole time that it's moving.

Total distance travelled = 24 + 45 = 69 m
Total time taken to travel 69 m = 30 + 70 = 100 s

Rearrange the equation and substitute in the values for distance and time to find the average speed:
$s = vt$, so $v = s \div t = 69 \div 100 = 0.69$ m/s

Practice Questions — Fact Recall

Q1 State whether the following quantities are scalars or vectors.

a) displacement   b) speed   c) velocity   d) distance

Q2 How can an object have a constant speed and a changing velocity?

Q3 Give a typical speed for when someone is:

a) cycling,   b) running,   c) walking.

Q4 Give the equation that relates speed, distance and time, for an object travelling at a constant speed. Give the units of each term.

Practice Questions — Application

Q1 A car drives 16 m east, then 25 m south, then 16 m west.

a) Calculate the distance travelled by the car.

b) Calculate the displacement of the car.

Q2 A person walks for 18 s. Estimate the distance that they will have walked during this time.

Q3 A train travels from station A to station B at a constant speed of 45 m/s. It takes the train 120 s to reach station B. The train then travels at a constant speed of 60 m/s to station C. Stations B and C are 16.8 km apart.

a) Calculate how far apart stations A and B are.

b) Calculate how long it takes for the train to travel from station B to station C.

c) Find the average speed of the train between stations A and C.

Tip: For Q2, think about the typical speed that a person will walk at.

- Know what acceleration is.
- Know and be able to use the equation for calculating the average acceleration of an object.
- Know that an object that is slowing down is decelerating.
- Be able to estimate everyday accelerations.
- Be able to use the equation $v^2 - u^2 = 2as$.
- Know that the acceleration of a falling object near the Earth's surface is about 9.8 m/s².

Specification Reference 6.5.4.1.5

2. Acceleration

How quickly an object changes its speed is all to do with its acceleration.

What is acceleration?

Acceleration is definitely not the same as velocity or speed:

- Acceleration is how quickly the velocity is changing.
- This change in velocity can be a change in speed, or a change in direction, or both.

You can calculate the acceleration of an object using the formula below. If acceleration isn't constant, this will give you the average acceleration over that period.

$$a = \frac{\Delta v}{t}$$

a = acceleration (m/s²)
Δv = change in velocity (m/s)
t = time taken (s)

Δv, the change in velocity , is just 'final velocity – initial velocity' (see page 241 for more on the Δ symbol). So if an object is slowing down, the change in velocity will be negative, giving a negative acceleration. A negative acceleration is just a deceleration.

Any calculations you do will involve objects travelling in a straight line, so you won't need to worry about a change in direction. The units of acceleration are m/s² — don't get them confused with the units for speed and velocity, m/s.

Example

Find the average acceleration of a dog whose velocity goes from 2 m/s to 6 m/s in 5 s.

Calculate Δv first: Δv = final velocity – initial velocity = 6 – 2 = 4 m/s

Then substitute the numbers into the acceleration formula:

$a = \frac{\Delta v}{t} = 4 \div 5 = 0.8$ m/s²

Figure 1: *When cheetahs start running, they can get to a high velocity very quickly, which means they have a very high acceleration.*

Everyday accelerations

You might have to estimate the acceleration (or deceleration) of an object. To do this, you'll need to use the typical speeds from page 148.

Example

A car is travelling along a road, when it collides with a tree and comes to a stop. Estimate the deceleration of the car.

- First, give a sensible speed for the car to be travelling at and estimate how long it would take the car to stop. The ~ symbol just means it's an approximate value (or answer).

A typical speed for a car is ~25 m/s. The car comes to a stop in ~1 s.

- Put these numbers into the acceleration equation.

$a = \Delta v \div t = (-25) \div 1 = -25$ m/s² — so the deceleration is ~25 m/s²

Tip: Δv is negative as the car is slowing down. You can ignore the minus sign in the answer, because you've been asked for a deceleration.

Uniform acceleration

Constant acceleration is sometimes called uniform acceleration. You can use this equation for uniform acceleration:

v = final velocity (m/s) ⟶ $\qquad$ a = acceleration (m/s²)

$$v^2 - u^2 = 2as$$

u = initial velocity (m/s) ⟶ $\qquad$ s = distance (m)

Acceleration due to gravity (g) is uniform for objects falling freely under gravity. It's roughly equal to 9.8 m/s² near the Earth's surface and has the same value as gravitational field strength (p. 130).

Tip: If you struggle to remember which velocity is which, think of it this way — u comes before v in the alphabet, so u is initial velocity and v is final velocity.

Example

A ball has been dropped from the top of a building. The velocity of the ball when it is 2.25 m from the ground is 6.0 m/s. Calculate the velocity of the ball when it reaches the ground. You can assume there is no air resistance.

- First, rearrange the equation so v^2 is on one side, and then put the numbers in.

$$v^2 = 2as + u^2 = (2 \times 9.8 \times 2.25) + 6.0^2 = 80.1$$

- Finally, square root the whole thing.

$$v = \sqrt{80.1} = 8.94... = 8.9 \text{ m/s (to 2 s.f.)}$$

Tip: You'll come across air resistance, and how it affects motion, a bit later (see page 159).

Tip: See page 14 for more on significant figures.

Practice Questions — Fact Recall

Q1 What is acceleration?

Q2 What are the units of acceleration?

Practice Questions — Application

Q1 A car is travelling forwards at 25 m/s and the driver applies the brakes. The car's velocity drops steadily for 5 seconds until it becomes 10 m/s. Find its acceleration during this time.

Q2 A cheetah begins from rest and accelerates at an average acceleration of 4 m/s² over a period of 5 s. Calculate the speed of the cheetah after this time.

Tip: If an object starts from rest, its initial velocity is 0 m/s.

Q3 A runner is running at a steady velocity of 5.6 m/s. When she is 38.1 m away from the finish line, she accelerates at a constant rate. If her velocity at the finish line is 7.1 m/s, what was her acceleration as she approached the finish line?

Q4 An apple falls from a tree and hits the ground at a speed of 6.0 m/s. Calculate the height the apple fell from. You can assume there is no air resistance.

Tip: Remember acceleration due to gravity is about 9.8 m/s².

3. Distance-Time Graphs

Learning Objectives:

- Know that an object moving in a straight line can be shown on a distance-time graph.
- Be able to draw and interpret distance-time graphs.
- Know that the gradient of a distance-time graph for a moving object is equal to the speed of the object.
- **H** Know that the speed of an accelerating object at a certain time can be found from the object's distance-time graph, by calculating the gradient of the tangent to the graph at that time.

Specification Reference
6.5.4.1.4

Distance-time graphs show how far an object is from a point at a given time. They're useful in physics because they help keep track of an object's motion.

What are distance-time graphs?

Distance-time graphs are a good way of describing the motion of something travelling in a straight line. They have time on the horizontal axis and distance on the vertical axis.

Speed = distance ÷ time (see page 148), so the gradient (slope) of a distance-time graph tells you how fast your object is travelling. This is because the gradient is the change in the distance (vertical axis) divided by the change in time (horizontal axis).

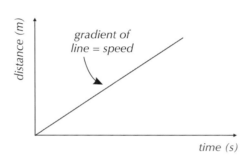

Figure 1: *A basic distance-time graph.*

Tip: Take a look at page 243 for how to calculate the gradient of a straight-line graph.

Drawing and interpreting distance-time graphs

You need to be able to draw and interpret distance-time graphs in the exam. Here are some important points to remember for an object's distance-time graph:

1. Gradient = speed.

2. Straight uphill sections mean it is travelling at a steady speed.

3. The steeper the graph, the faster it's going.

4. Flat sections are where it's stationary — it's stopped.

5. Curves represent acceleration (speeding up) or deceleration (slowing down) (page 150).

6. A steepening curve means it's accelerating/speeding up — the gradient is increasing.

7. A levelling off curve means it's decelerating/slowing down — the gradient is decreasing.

Example

This distance-time graph shows an object that moves off from its starting point at a steady speed for 20 s, then stops for 20 s. It then accelerates for 25 s and decelerates for 25 s before resuming a steady speed for 30 s.

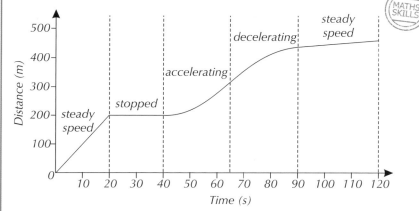

The object's speed during the first 20 s can be found from the gradient:

$$\text{gradient} = \frac{\text{change in the vertical}}{\text{change in the horizontal}} = \frac{200 - 0}{20 - 0} = 10 \text{ m/s}$$

Tip: The speed of the object is faster in the first 20 s compared to the speed of the object in the last 30 s. You can tell because the gradient is steeper in the first 20 s.

Tip: Be careful with the units on the axes of these graphs. Here you have distance in m and time in s, so you get speed in m/s. But you may have to deal with graphs with axes in other units of distance (e.g. kilometres) and time (e.g. hours).

Calculating speed for accelerating objects Higher

If an object is changing speed (accelerating), you can find its speed at a point by finding the gradient of the tangent to the curve at that point.

Tip: Take a look at page 245 for more on drawing tangents.

Example — Higher

The graph below is the distance-time graph for a bike accelerating for 30 s and then travelling at a steady speed for 5 s.

The speed of the bike at 25 s can be found by drawing a tangent to the curve (shown by the red line) at 25 s and then finding the gradient of the tangent:

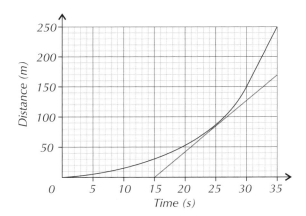

$$\text{gradient} = \frac{\text{change in the vertical}}{\text{change in the horizontal}} = \frac{170 - 0}{35 - 15} = 8.5 \text{ m/s}$$

Tip: When drawing a tangent, always make it as long as possible, so it's easier to work out the gradient.

Practice Questions — Fact Recall

Q1 What does the gradient of a distance-time graph represent?

Q2 What does a flat section on a distance-time graph tell you?

Q3 What does a curved section on a distance-time graph represent?

Q4 How would you calculate the speed of an accelerating object at a given time from its distance-time graph?

Practice Questions — Application

Q1 For this distance-time graph, say what's happening to the speed of the object in each of the sections labelled *A*, *B*, *C* and *D*.

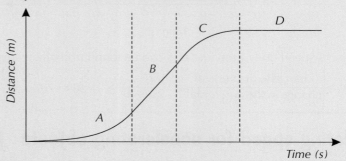

Q2 An object moving in a straight line accelerates for 10 seconds and then moves at a steady speed for 5 seconds. Describe the distance-time graph for the object during this time.

Q3 Look at this table showing the distance travelled (in a straight line) by a toy car over a period of time. The car initially moves with a constant speed, then stops, accelerates for 6 seconds, then stops.

Time (s)	0	2	4	6	8	10	12	14	16
Distance (m)	0.0	2.0	4.0	4.0	4.0	7.0	7.8	8.0	8.0

a) Plot these values and join the points on a distance-time graph to represent the car's motion.

b) Calculate the speed of the car between 0 and 4 seconds.

c) Estimate the speed of the car at 10 seconds.

4. Velocity-Time Graphs

Velocity can be plotted against time to help find out about an object's motion.

Velocity-time graphs

You can plot a **velocity-time graph** to show an object's motion. Time goes on the horizontal axis and velocity goes on the vertical axis.

Acceleration is the change in an object's velocity over time (see page 150). So the gradient of a velocity-time graph tells you the acceleration of your object. This is because the gradient is the change in the velocity (vertical axis) divided by the change in time (horizontal axis).

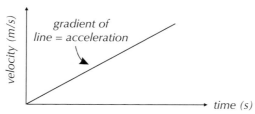

Figure 1: *A basic velocity-time graph.*

Here are some important things about velocity-time graphs:

1. The gradient of a velocity-time graph gives the object's acceleration.
2. Flat sections represent steady speed.
3. The steeper the graph, the greater the acceleration or deceleration.
4. Uphill sections are acceleration.
5. Downhill sections are deceleration.
6. A curve means changing acceleration.

Example

This velocity-time graph shows an object that accelerates from rest to 20 m/s in 20 seconds then travels at a steady velocity for 20 seconds. It then accelerates at an increasing rate for 30 seconds, travels at a steady 40 m/s for a further 30 seconds and finally decelerates back to rest in 20 seconds.

(MATHS SKILLS)

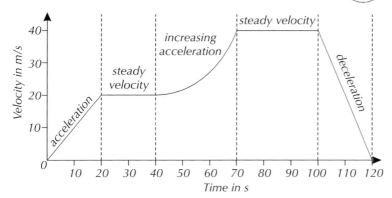

Learning Objectives:

- Be able to draw and interpret velocity-time graphs for moving objects.
- Be able to find an object's acceleration by calculating the gradient of its velocity-time graph.
- **H** Know that the area under a velocity-time graph is equal to distance travelled (or displacement), and be able to calculate this.
- **H** Be able to find the area under a velocity-time graph by counting the squares under the graph.

Specification Reference 6.5.4.1.5

Tip: Make sure you don't get confused between velocity-time graphs and distance-time graphs (which you met on page 152).

Tip: If an object wasn't moving, its velocity-time graph would just be a straight line along the x-axis, i.e. velocity = 0 m/s.

Acceleration on a velocity-time graph

The acceleration of an object can be found by calculating the gradient of its velocity-time graph.

Tip: This is the same method as finding the speed from a distance-time graph (see page 153).

Tip: If the graph is curved, the acceleration is changing and you can find the acceleration at a point using a tangent, in the same way as on page 153.

Example

This is a velocity-time graph for a race car accelerating from 0 to 50 m/s. Calculate the acceleration of the car between 3 and 6 seconds.

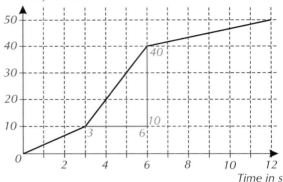

$$\text{acceleration} = \text{gradient}$$
$$= \frac{\text{change in vertical}}{\text{change in horizontal}} = \frac{(40 - 10)}{(6 - 3)} = 10 \, \text{m/s}^2$$

Distance travelled on a velocity-time graph `Higher`

The area beneath a velocity-time graph gives the distance travelled (or displacement). The distance travelled in any time interval is equal to the area under the velocity-time graph in that interval.

Example 1 `Higher`

Tip: **H** If you know the direction of the velocity, you can find the displacement using the area.

For the same car as in the previous example, calculate the distance travelled between 3 and 6 seconds.

- The distance travelled is equal to the area under the graph, so look at the graph between 3 and 6 seconds. It might seem difficult to work out the area of this part of the graph, but you can make it easier by splitting the area into a triangle (**A**) and a rectangle (**B**).

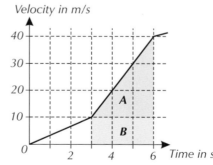

Tip: **H** You could also use the 'counting the squares method' (see the next page) to find the area under the graph.

- You can then calculate the area of each shape individually:

$$\text{Area}_A = \frac{1}{2} \times \text{base} \times \text{height} \qquad \text{Area}_B = \text{base} \times \text{height}$$
$$= \frac{1}{2} \times 3 \times 30 = 45 \qquad\qquad\qquad = 3 \times 10 = 30$$

- Then just find the total area by adding Area_A and Area_B together:

   distance travelled = total area under graph = 45 + 30 = 75 m

You can also find the area under a graph using the 'counting the squares method'. First you need to find out the distance each square of the grid represents. To do this, multiply the width of one square (in seconds) by the height of one square (in metres per second).

Then you just multiply this by the number of squares under the graph. If there are multiple squares that are partly under the graph, you can add them together to make whole squares (see the example below).

This is the best method to use when working with an irregularly-shaped area under a graph.

Example 2 | Higher

The graph below is a velocity-time graph. You can estimate the distance travelled in the first 10 s by counting the number of squares under the graph (shown by the shaded area).

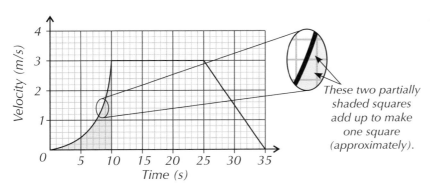

These two partially shaded squares add up to make one square (approximately).

Total number of shaded squares ≈ 32

Distance represented by one square = width of square × height of square
= 1 s × 0.2 m/s = 0.2 m

So total distance travelled in 10 s = 32 × 0.2 = 6.4 m

Tip: **H** Using this method with a curved graph gives you an estimate of the distance travelled by an object.

Tip: **H** As you go through and count the squares, it helps to put a dot in the square once it's been counted. That way you don't lose track of what's been counted and what hasn't.

Practice Questions — Fact Recall

Q1   What does the gradient of a velocity-time graph represent?

Q2   What does the area under a velocity-time graph represent?

Tip: Make sure you talk about what's happening to the <u>acceleration</u> in Q1, not the velocity.

Q1 For this velocity-time graph, say what's happening to the acceleration of the object in each of the sections labelled *A*, *B*, *C* and *D*.

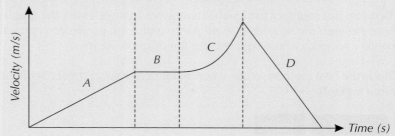

Q2 Below is a velocity-time graph for a cyclist during a race.

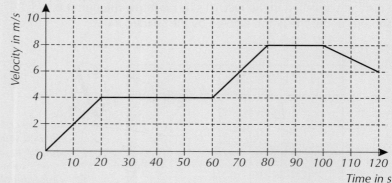

Tip: Remember, acceleration can have a negative value (in which case it can be called deceleration).

a) What's the cyclist's velocity at 40 seconds?

b) During which part(s) of the race is the cyclist decelerating?

c) What's the cyclist's acceleration between 60 and 80 seconds?

d) How far does the cyclist travel in the first 60 seconds of the race?

Q3 A car travels forwards at 25 m/s for 3 s before the driver applies the brakes. The car decelerates steadily for 5 seconds until its velocity becomes 10 m/s. Plot a velocity-time graph to show this and, using the graph, find its acceleration whilst it's slowing down.

Q4 The velocity-time graph for a helicopter travelling in a straight line is shown below. Estimate the distance travelled by the helicopter in the first 20 s of its motion.

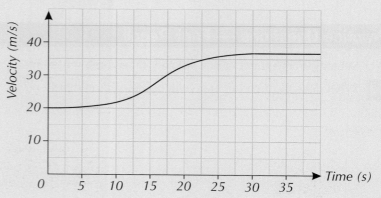

5. Terminal Velocity

In an ideal world, things would just move freely without needing any external driving force, but realistically friction is there to stop that. It's not all bad though — without friction we'd never be able to stop and take a break.

Learning Objectives:
- Know that the frictional forces that oppose the motion of an object moving through a fluid increase with the object's speed.
- Know that an object falling through a fluid accelerates due to gravity until the frictional forces equal the object's weight and it reaches its terminal velocity — the resultant force acting on it is zero.

Specification Reference 6.5.4.1.5

Friction

If an object has no force propelling it along it will always slow down and stop because of **friction** (unless you're in space, where there's nothing to rub against).

Friction always acts in the opposite direction to movement. To travel at a steady speed, the driving force needs to balance the frictional forces (this will be covered in more detail on page 162).

(this will be covered in more detail on page 162).

Example

If a car is travelling at a steady speed, the force provided by the engine is exactly the same as the resistive forces acting on the car.

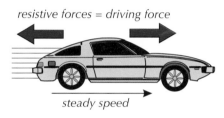

resistive forces = driving force

steady speed

You get friction between two surfaces in contact or when an object passes through a **fluid** — in which case it's usually called drag. A fluid is just a gas or a liquid — e.g. air, water, oil, etc.

Drag

Most of the resistive forces are caused by **air resistance** or "**drag**". The most important factor by far in reducing drag in fluids is keeping the shape of the object streamlined. A streamlined object is one that allows fluids to flow over it easily, so they don't slow down the object much as it passes through them.

The opposite extreme is a parachute which is about as high a drag as you can get — which is, of course, the whole idea.

Figure 1: *Fish have streamlined bodies that reduce drag from the water (a fluid).*

Example

A sports car is designed to allow fluids to flow over it easily, reducing drag and letting it move through air without much effort. Vans aren't designed to go particularly fast and so their design is much less streamlined. This means they have to use a greater driving force to move at the same speed as a sports car.

Frictional forces from fluids always increase with speed. A car has much more friction to work against when travelling at 70 mph compared to 30 mph. So at 70 mph the engine has to work much harder just to maintain a steady speed.

Figure 2: *A car moving at 30 mph and 70 mph. As the speed of a car increases, the frictional forces acting on it increase, so the engine works harder to maintain a steady speed.*

Ways of increasing the top speed of a vehicle

There are two main ways of changing a vehicle to increase its top speed:

1. Reducing drag.
    This can be done by altering the shape of the vehicle to make it more streamlined.

2. Increasing the power of the vehicle's engine.
    This way, the driving force becomes larger and so the drag force on the vehicle will equal the driving force at a higher speed.

Figure 3: *Racing cars have incredibly powerful engines as well as a low, streamlined body. This is what helps them shoot round the track at breakneck speeds.*

Terminal velocity

Generally when an object falls through a very large distance, it won't just keep accelerating at the same rate until it hits the ground. Its acceleration will decrease until it reaches a steady velocity, called its **terminal velocity**.

When a falling object first sets off, the force of gravity is much greater than the frictional force slowing it down, so it accelerates. As the object moves faster, the frictional forces that act on it become greater.

This gradually reduces the acceleration until eventually the frictional force is equal to the accelerating force — the resultant force will be zero. If there is zero resultant force, then the object will no longer accelerate (see page 162). It will have reached its maximum speed — or terminal velocity — and will fall at a steady speed.

Factors affecting terminal velocity

The terminal velocity of a falling object depends on its shape and area. The accelerating force acting on all falling objects is gravity and it would make them all fall at the same rate, if it wasn't for resistance.

Figure 4: *Apollo 15 astronaut David Scott demonstrating that a hammer and a feather fall to the ground at the same speed on the Moon.*

This means that on the Moon, where there's no air, rocks and feathers dropped simultaneously from the same height will hit the ground together. However, on Earth, air resistance causes things to fall at different speeds, and the terminal velocity of any object is determined by its drag in comparison to its weight. The frictional force depends on its shape and area.

Example 1

If you dropped a marble and a beach ball off a tall building, the marble's terminal velocity would be higher than the terminal velocity of the beach ball. This is because there is more air resistance acting on the beach ball at any given speed, as the beach ball has a larger surface area than the marble.

So the beach ball spends less time accelerating (and so doesn't speed up as much) before the air resistance is large enough to equal the accelerating force. So its terminal velocity must be lower than that of the marble.

Example 2

The most important example is the human skydiver. Without their parachute open they have quite a small area and a force of "$W = mg$" pulling them down. They reach a terminal velocity of about 120 mph.

But with the parachute open, there's much more air resistance (at any given speed) and still only the same force "$W = mg$" pulling them down. This means their terminal velocity comes right down to about 15 mph, which is a safe speed to hit the ground at.

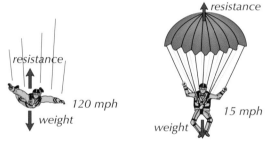

Figure 5: A skydiver at terminal velocity with and without a parachute. Resistance has become equal to weight in both cases — the difference is the speed at which this has happened.

Figure 6: A BASE jumper using a parachute to slow down his free fall so that he can land safely.

Practice Questions — Fact Recall

Q1 What must the resistive forces acting on a car be equal to if the car is travelling at a steady speed over flat ground?

Q2 What's drag?

Q3 What's the relationship between an object's speed and the drag it experiences?

Q4 Describe how a free-falling object reaches terminal velocity.

Practice Questions — Application

Q1 Why does a feather fall slower than a rock on Earth but not on the Moon?

Q2 Explain, in terms of forces, why using a parachute reduces a skydiver's terminal velocity.

Tip: When a skydiver is at terminal velocity, the resultant force acting on them is zero (see p. 162 for more on resultant forces and motion).

6. Newton's First Law

Resultant forces are often described as being 'non-zero' (i.e. there is one) or 'zero' (i.e. there isn't one) — and you need to know their effects.

Resultant forces

The size and direction of a resultant force (see page 131) acting on an object will dictate what happens to its motion. **Newton's First Law** says that a resultant force is needed to make something start moving, speed up, slow down or change direction. So an object will remain stationary or moving at a constant velocity unless a resultant force acts upon it.

Zero resultant force

Objects don't just start moving on their own — if there's no resultant force acting on a stationary object, there's no acceleration and it will just stay put.

> If the resultant force on a stationary object is zero, the object will remain stationary.

Example 1

A ball is being held stationary by two taut strings. The force to the left (F_1) is the same size as the force to the right (F_2). So, even though forces are acting on it in both directions, the resultant force on it is zero. Consequently, it remains stationary.

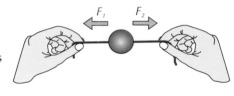

If there's no resultant force acting on an object, it won't change velocity. That means if it's already moving, it will just keep moving at the same velocity.

> If the resultant force on a moving object is zero, it'll just carry on moving at the same velocity.

If any object (be it a train, a car, a horse, or anything else really) is moving at a constant velocity then the forces on it must all be balanced. Never let yourself stray down the path of thinking that things need a constant resultant force to keep them moving — this is a common misconception.

To keep going at a steady velocity, there must be zero resultant force. This doesn't mean there must be no driving force — it means the driving force is balanced by other forces, like friction and air resistance.

Example 2

A van travelling at a steady velocity has zero resultant force acting on it. This is because the driving force from the engine is balanced by friction forces.

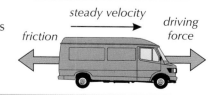

steady velocity

driving force

friction

Non-zero resultant force

In most situations, there will be a resultant force acting on an object.

> If there is a non-zero resultant force on an object, its velocity will change (it will accelerate in the direction of the force).

Tip: Remember — when an object accelerates, its velocity changes, and a change in velocity means a change in speed or direction of motion (or both) (see page 150).

This applies to both stationary objects and ones that are already moving. When a resultant force acts on an object, the change in velocity it experiences can take five different forms:

- starting
- stopping
- changing direction
- speeding up
- slowing down

Tip: **H** On a free body diagram (see page 131), if there's a resultant force, then the total size of the arrows in one direction will be different to the total size of the arrows in the opposite direction.

Example 1 — continued

One of the hands lets go of the string that's keeping the ball stationary. Now the ball experiences a resultant force of F_2 to the right, and accelerates in that direction.

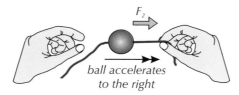

ball accelerates to the right

Practice Question — Fact Recall

Q1 Say what will happen to the object in each of the following cases:

a) No resultant force acting on a stationary object.

b) A resultant force acting on a stationary object.

c) No resultant force acting on a moving object.

d) A resultant force acting on a moving object in the same direction as its motion.

e) A resultant force acting on a moving object in the opposite direction to its motion.

Practice Question — Application

Q1 If a rocket is moving through space at a steady velocity, what can you say about the resultant force acting on the rocket?

Figure 1: *When a rocket is launched, there needs to be a force acting upwards that is larger than the weight of the rocket, so that it accelerates away from Earth.*

- Know that Newton's Second Law says that an object's acceleration is directly proportional to the resultant force acting on it and inversely proportional to its mass.

- Know and be able to use the equation *F = ma*, where *F* is the resultant force acting on an object.

- Be able to estimate the resultant forces acting in everyday accelerations and be able to use the '~' symbol.

- **H** Know that the inertia of an object is the tendency for its motion to remain unchanged.

- **H** Know that an object's inertial mass is given as the ratio of force over acceleration, and that it measures how difficult it is to change the object's velocity.

Specification References
6.5.4.2.1, 6.5.4.2.2

7. Newton's Second Law and Inertia

So you've seen from Newton's First Law that an object will accelerate if there's a non-zero resultant force acting on it. You can find the size of the acceleration using Newton's Second Law.

What is Newton's Second Law?

Newton's Second Law has two points that you need to know:

- The larger the resultant force acting on an object, the more the object accelerates — the force and the acceleration are directly proportional. You can write this as $F \propto a$.

- Acceleration is also inversely proportional to the mass of the object — so an object with a larger mass will accelerate less than one with a smaller mass (for a fixed resultant force).

There's an incredibly useful formula that describes Newton's Second Law:

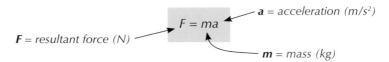

$$F = ma$$

a = acceleration (m/s²)

F = resultant force (N)

m = mass (kg)

This formula can be used to calculate the acceleration produced by a resultant force, or the size of the resultant force producing an acceleration.

Example 1

A car with a mass of 1250 kg has an engine that provides a driving force of 5200 N. At 70 mph the drag force acting on the car is 5100 N. Find its acceleration at 70 mph.

- First calculate the resultant force acting on the car:

  Resultant force = 5200 − 5100 = 100 N

- Then work out the acceleration of the car:

  $a = F \div m = 100 \div 1250 = 0.080$ m/s²

Example 2

A car with a mass of 900 kg accelerates from rest with an initial acceleration of 2.5 m/s². Calculate the resultant force required to produce this acceleration.

At the point that the car's just about to start moving, the driving force of the engine provides an acceleration of 2.5 m/s². As the car is still stationary (just), there's no drag, and so the resultant force is just the driving force. So:

$F = ma = 900 \times 2.5 = 2250$ N

Tip: If you need to, you can use this formula triangle for *F = ma*:

Tip: Once the car has started moving, it will experience a drag force, so the resultant force will be the driving force minus the drag force.

Estimating forces

You can use Newton's Second Law to get an idea of the forces involved in everyday transport. Large forces are needed to produce large accelerations:

Tip: For more on estimating typical speeds, check out page 148. For more on estimating typical accelerations, head to page 150.

Example

Estimate the resultant force on a car as it accelerates from rest to a typical speed in 10 s.

- First you need to estimate the acceleration of the car. To do this, you should use typical speeds from page 148.

    A typical speed of a car is ~25 m/s.
    It takes 10 s to reach this.

    So $a = \frac{\Delta v}{t} = 25 \div 10 = 2.5$ m/s^2

- Then estimate the mass of the car.

    Mass of a car is ~1000 kg.

- Finally, put these numbers into Newton's Second Law.

    $F = ma = 1000 \times 2.5 = 2500$ N
    So the resultant force is ~2500 N.

Exam Tip
Knowing some typical vehicle masses could come in very handy in the exam:
A car ~ 1000 kg
A single-decker bus ~ 10 000 kg
A loaded lorry ~ 30 000 kg.

The '~' sign used in the example above means 'approximately'. Make sure you use it when asked to estimate the value of something.

Inertia `Higher`

You saw on page 162 that until acted upon by a resultant force, objects at rest stay at rest and objects moving at a steady speed will stay moving at that speed. This is Newton's First Law. This tendency to continue in the same state of motion is called **inertia** (or in other words, it's the tendency to continue moving at the same velocity).

An object's **inertial mass** measures how difficult it is to change the velocity of the object. Imagine that a bowling ball and a golf ball roll towards you with the same velocity. It would require a larger force to stop the bowling ball than the golf ball in the same time. This is because the bowling ball has a larger inertial mass.

Inertial mass can be found using Newton's Second Law, $F = ma$. Rearranging this gives:

F = resultant force (N)

$$m = \frac{F}{a}$$

m = inertial mass (kg)

a = acceleration (m/s^2)

So inertial mass is just the ratio of force over acceleration.

Figure 1: *A full trolley will accelerate less for a given pushing force then an empty one would, as it has a larger mass.*

Practice Questions — Fact Recall

Q1 What is Newton's Second Law?

Q2 Write down the formula used for calculating the resultant force
acting on an object from its mass and its acceleration. Say what
each term represents and the units it's measured in.

Q3 What is inertia?

Q4 What is inertial mass?

Practice Questions — Application

Q1 Two identical remote-control cars take part in a straight race across
flat ground. One of the cars is loaded with a large rock. Which of
the two will win the race? Explain your answer.

Q2 When a catapult is released, it applies 303 N of force to a rock with
a mass of 1.5 kg. Find the acceleration of the rock at this point.

Q3 Two cars are starting from rest at full power, as shown below.
Which engine is providing a larger driving force?
Assume there are no resistive forces acting on the cars.

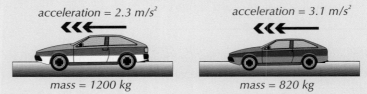

acceleration = 2.3 m/s²   acceleration = 3.1 m/s²

mass = 1200 kg   mass = 820 kg

Q4 A car accelerates from a speed of 5 m/s to its typical speed in 20 s.
Estimate the resultant force on the car.

8. Investigating Motion

Here's an experiment you can do to investigate Newton's Second Law.
You just need to get your hands on a trolley, a light gate and some masses.

REQUIRED
PRACTICAL **19**

Setting up the experiment

This experiment makes use of a light gate. A light gate is an arch-shaped piece of equipment which sends a beam of light from one side of the arch (or 'gate') to the other. When something passes through the gate, it interrupts this beam of light. When used with a computer or data logger, the light gate can detect an interruption and measure how long the interruption lasted.

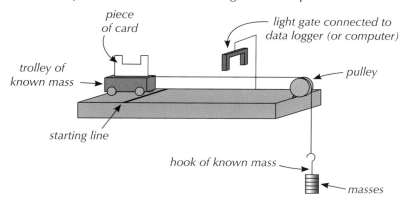

piece of card

light gate connected to data logger (or computer)

trolley of known mass

pulley

starting line

hook of known mass

masses

Figure 1: *The experimental setup for investigating Newton's Second Law.*

Set up the apparatus as shown in Figure 1. The trolley should hold a piece of card with a gap in the middle that will interrupt the signal on the light gate twice. If you measure the length of each bit of card that will pass through the light gate and input this into the software, the light gate can measure the velocity for each bit of card. It does this using $v = s \div t$ (page 148), where s is the length of each bit of card and t is the duration of the interruption.

The software can also work out the acceleration of the trolley, using $a = \Delta v \div t$ (page 150). Here, Δv is the difference between the two velocities it has measured, and t is the amount of time that has passed between the first and second interruptions of the light gate signal.

Connect the trolley to a piece of string that goes over a pulley and is connected on the other side to a hook (that you know the mass of and can add more masses to). Mark a starting line on the table the trolley is on, and place the trolley so that its front end is lined up with it. This way, when the trolley moves it will always have travelled the same distance when it reaches the light gate. You should make sure the string and table are the right length so that your trolley passes through the light gate before the masses hit the floor or the trolley hits the pulley, otherwise the accelerating force will be removed before the acceleration has been recorded.

The weight of the hook and any masses attached to it will provide the accelerating force that causes the trolley to move when released. This force is equal to the total mass of the hook and masses (m) × acceleration due to gravity (g) — which is just $W = mg$ (see page 130).

Learning Objectives:

- Be able to investigate how the force on, and the mass of, an object affect its acceleration. (Required Practical 19)

Specification Reference 6.5.4.2.2

Figure 2: *The beam in a light gate being interrupted by a piece of card attached to a trolley.*

Tip: You could also do this experiment with two light gates and a card without a gap.

Tip: The friction between the trolley and the bench might affect your acceleration measurements. You could use an air track to reduce this friction (a track which hovers a trolley on jets of air), or use a slightly sloped surface to use gravity to compensate for friction.

Carrying out the experiment

Hold the trolley so the string between the trolley and pulley is horizontal and taut (not loose and touching the table). Next, release the trolley and record the acceleration measured by the light gate as the trolley passes through it. This is the acceleration of the whole system (trolley, hook and masses). Repeat this twice more and calculate the average acceleration (see page 13).

You can use this setup to investigate the effect that varying the force and mass has on the trolley's acceleration.

Varying the mass

To investigate the effect of varying the mass, add masses to the trolley one at a time. This will increase the mass of the system. Don't add masses to the hook, or you'll change the force. Record the average acceleration each time you add a mass.

Varying the force

To investigate the effect of varying the force, you need to keep the total mass of the system the same, but change the weight on the hook. To do this, start with all the masses loaded onto the trolley, and transfer the masses to the hook one at a time, recording the new acceleration each time you transfer one of the masses. This will increase the accelerating force while keeping the mass of the system the same, as you're only transferring the masses from one part of the system (the trolley) to another (the hook).

The results

You can use Newton's Second Law, $F = ma$, to explain the results. In this case, F = weight of the hanging masses and hook, m = mass of the whole system (trolley, hook and any added masses) and a = acceleration of the system.

By adding masses to the trolley, you increase the mass of the whole system, but keep the force applied to the system the same. This should lead to a decrease in the acceleration of the trolley, as acceleration is inversely proportional to mass ($a = F \div m$).

By transferring masses from the trolley to the hook, you are increasing the accelerating force without changing the mass of the system. Increasing the force should lead to an increase in the acceleration of the trolley, because a is directly proportional to F. If you were to plot a graph of acceleration against force, the graph should be a straight line through the origin.

Tip: Remember — always carry out a risk assessment before doing a practical. In this experiment, watch out for the string snapping or the masses landing on people's toes.

Tip: Remember, the force acting on the system (the trolley, hook and masses) is equal to the weight of the hook and the masses attached to it. So adding masses to the hook changes the weight, which changes the force.

Tip: $F = ma$ was introduced on page 164.

Practice Question — Fact Recall

Q1 A trolley has a constant force acting on it which causes it to travel in a straight line.

a) What would happen to the acceleration of the trolley if a mass was added to it?

b) What would happen to the acceleration of the trolley if the force acting on it decreased?

9. Newton's Third Law

Newton's Third Law is just as important as the other two. If it wasn't true, then we'd never be able to sit anywhere without falling to the centre of the Earth.

What is Newton's Third Law?

When two objects interact, they apply forces to each other. These forces always act in the opposite direction to each other. You've probably heard the law in physics that "every action has an equal and opposite reaction" — this is **Newton's Third Law**, which is defined as:

> When two objects interact, the forces they exert on each other are equal and opposite.

If you push something, say a shopping trolley, the trolley will push back against you, just as hard. And as soon as you stop pushing, so does the trolley.

So far so good. The slightly tricky thing to get your head round is this — if the forces are always equal, how does anything ever go anywhere? The important thing to remember is that the two forces are acting on different objects.

Example

Think about a pair of ice skaters.

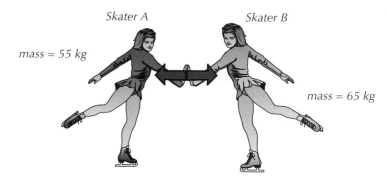

Skater A   Skater B

mass = 55 kg

mass = 65 kg

When skater A pushes on skater B (with a force), she feels an equal and opposite force from skater B's hand (the 'normal contact' force). Both skaters feel the same sized force, in opposite directions, and so accelerate away from each other.

Skater A will be accelerated more than skater B, though, because she has a smaller mass — $a = F \div m$ (see page 164). It's the same sort of thing when you go swimming. You push back against the water with your arms and legs, and the water pushes you forwards with an equal-sized force in the opposite direction.

Learning Objectives:

- Know that Newton's Third Law states that two interacting objects will exert equal and opposite forces on each other.

- Be able to use Newton's Third Law to explain different situations in which objects are in equilibrium.

Specification Reference 6.5.4.2.3

Figure 1: *British physicist Sir Isaac Newton, who is famous for his three laws.*

Tip: In this example, the two objects interacting are the two skaters.

Equilibrium

It's easy to get confused with Newton's Third Law and an object in equilibrium.
You need to be careful about which forces you say are equal and opposite.

Example 1

An example of Newton's Third Law in an equilibrium situation is a man pushing against a wall. As the man pushes the wall, there is a normal contact force acting back on him. These two forces are the same size. As the man applies a force and pushes the wall, the wall 'pushes back' on him with an equal force.

Example 2

A book resting on a table is in equilibrium. The weight of the book is equal to the normal contact force. But this is NOT Newton's Third Law because the two forces are different types, and both acting on the book.

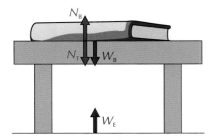

In this situation, Newton's Third Law is:

- The normal contact force acting on the book (from the table), N_B, is equal to the normal contact force acting on the table (from the book), N_T.

- The weight of the book being pulled down by Earth, W_B, is equal to the weight of the Earth being pulled up by the book, W_E.

Practice Question — Fact Recall

Q1   What is Newton's Third Law?

Practice Question — Application

Q1   A ball hanging on the end of a piece of string is in equilibrium. It only has two forces acting on it — its weight acting downwards and tension in the string acting upwards. State whether this is an example of Newton's Third Law or not. Explain your answer.

Topic 5c Checklist — Make sure you know...

Distance, Displacement, Speed and Velocity

- [ ] That distance and speed are scalar quantities.
- [ ] That displacement is a vector quantity and is the distance and direction in a straight line from an object's starting point to its finishing point.
- [ ] How to give the displacement of an object in terms of its magnitude and direction.
- [ ] That velocity is a vector quantity and is the speed of an object and its direction.
- [ ] **H** Examples of when an object has a constant speed and a changing velocity, e.g. an object moving in a circle.
- [ ] That things don't often travel at a constant speed.
- [ ] That a typical speed of someone walking is 1.5 m/s, of someone running is 3 m/s and of someone cycling is 6 m/s, and the factors that these values depend on.
- [ ] The typical speeds of everyday vehicles.
- [ ] That the speed of sound and the speed of wind vary.
- [ ] The equation distance (m) = velocity (m/s) × time (s) ($s = vt$) and how to use it for uniform and non-uniform motion.

Acceleration

- [ ] That acceleration is a measure of how quickly velocity is changing.
- [ ] The equation acceleration (m/s^2) = change in velocity (m/s) ÷ time (s) ($a = \Delta v \div t$) and how to use it.
- [ ] That an object that is slowing down is decelerating (and will have negative acceleration).
- [ ] How to make calculations to estimate everyday accelerations.
- [ ] How to use the equation $v^2 - u^2 = 2as$, including what all the letters represent.
- [ ] That when an object is free falling on Earth, it has an acceleration of about 9.8 m/s^2.

Distance-Time Graphs

- [ ] How to sketch a distance-time graph for an object from a description of its motion.
- [ ] How to interpret a distance-time graph.
- [ ] That the speed of an object can be found by calculating the gradient of its distance-time graph.
- [ ] **H** That finding the gradient of a tangent to a curve on a distance-time graph will give the speed of an accelerating object at that point.

Velocity-Time Graphs

- [ ] How to sketch a velocity-time graph for an object from a description of its motion.
- [ ] How to interpret a velocity-time graph.

cont...

☐ That the acceleration of an object can be found by calculating the gradient of its velocity-time graph.

☐ H That the distance travelled by an object can be found by calculating the area under its velocity-time graph, and how to find the area under a graph by counting squares.

Terminal Velocity

☐ That the faster an object moves through a fluid, the larger the frictional force acting on the object.

☐ That the force of gravity is what normally causes a falling object to initially accelerate.

☐ That terminal velocity is the velocity at which the resultant force acting on a falling object is equal to zero.

☐ How certain factors affect the terminal velocity of an object.

Newton's First Law

☐ That an object will remain stationary or at a constant velocity if the resultant force on it is zero.

☐ That a vehicle will move at a steady speed if the driving forces and resistive forces are equal.

☐ That an object will change its velocity (speed and/or direction) if there is a non-zero resultant force acting on it.

☐ How to explain the motion of an object using Newton's First Law.

Newton's Second Law and Inertia

☐ That Newton's Second Law says that acceleration is directly proportional to the resultant force and inversely proportional to mass.

☐ The equation force (N) = mass (kg) × acceleration (m/s²) ($F = ma$) and how to use it.

☐ How to estimate the resultant forces acting in everyday accelerations.

☐ H That the tendency of an object to stay at a constant velocity is known as inertia.

☐ H That the inertial mass of an object is a measure of how difficult it is to change its velocity, and that it is given as the ratio of force over acceleration.

Investigating Motion

☐ How to carry out an experiment that investigates the effect of changing the resultant force on, and the mass of, an object on its acceleration.

Newton's Third Law

☐ That Newton's Third Law says that when two objects interact, they will exert equal and opposite forces on each other.

☐ How to explain objects in equilibrium in terms of Newton's Third Law.

Exam-style Questions

1   This is a velocity-time graph for a car during a journey to the local shops.

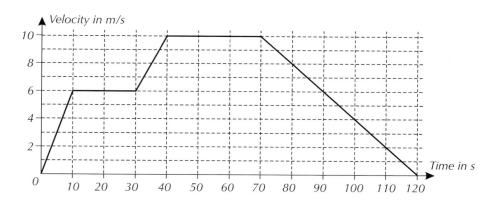

1.1   During which time period(s) does the graph show a negative acceleration?

(1 mark)

1.2   Calculate the acceleration of the car between 30 and 40 seconds.
Show clearly how you work out your answer. Give your answer in m/s².

(3 marks)

1.3   If the car has a mass of 980 kg, calculate the resultant force acting on the car between 30 and 40 seconds. Give your answer in N.

(2 marks)

1.4   Use the graph to calculate how far the car travels between 30 and 40 seconds.
Show clearly how you work out your answer. Give your answer in m.

(3 marks)

1.5   The graph below shows how the distance the car has travelled from its starting point changes for the same journey.
Explain three things about the shape of the graph that are incorrect.

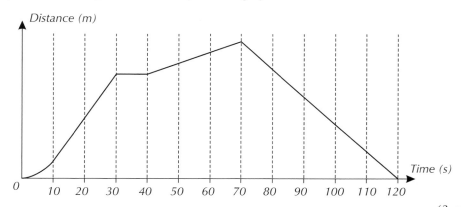

(3 marks)

2   A student sets up the experiment shown below in order to investigate the effect of
varying the force acting on a trolley.

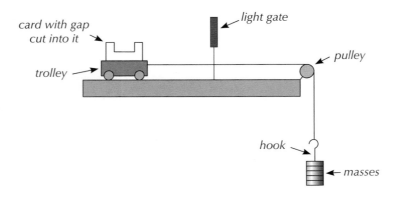

2.1   State what provides the force that causes the trolley to accelerate.

(1 mark)

2.2   Explain how the force can be decreased whilst keeping the mass of the system
constant.

(1 mark)

2.3   Explain why there is a gap cut into the piece of card.

(2 marks)

2.4   The force acting on the trolley is doubled. Explain what will happen to the
acceleration of the trolley.

(2 marks)

3   A 25 000 kg truck is travelling along a straight, flat road at its top speed of 28 m/s.

3.1   What is the resultant force acting on the truck?

(1 mark)

3.2   Calculate how long it takes the truck to travel 448 m.
Write down any equations you use. Give your answer in s.

(3 marks)

3.3   Explain why changing the body of the truck to make it
more streamlined will increase its top speed.

(2 marks)

The truck stops applying a driving force when it is travelling at 28 m/s.
The total frictional force acting on the truck is 35 000 N.

3.4   Calculate how far the truck travels before coming to a stop, assuming the frictional
force is constant. Use the correct equation from the equations listed on page 284.

(4 marks)

4   A skydiver jumps from a plane and reaches terminal velocity after 15 seconds.

4.1   Choose the correct answer to complete the sentence.

Before reaching terminal velocity, the force due to gravity is
(greater than / smaller than / the same as) the resistive force due to air resistance.

(1 mark)

4.2   Choose the correct answer to complete the sentence.

After reaching terminal velocity, the force due to gravity is
(greater than / smaller than / the same as) the resistive force due to air resistance.

(1 mark)

After 40 seconds the skydiver opens a parachute.

4.3   State the effect opening the parachute will have on the skydiver's terminal velocity.

(1 mark)

4.4   State the effect opening the parachute will have on the resistive
forces acting on the skydiver at a given speed.

(1 mark)

5   An astronaut is on a spacewalk where gravitational forces and air resistance acting on
the astronaut are assumed to be 0. He pushes against a rock with a force *F*, as shown.

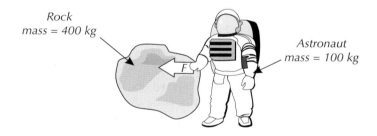

Rock
mass = 400 kg

Astronaut
mass = 100 kg

F

5.1   The rock applies a force on the astronaut.
State the size and direction, relative to *F*, of this force.

(1 mark)

The astronaut pushes against the rock for 1.2 seconds and he accelerates during this
time. After this point the astronaut moves away from the rock at a velocity of 3 m/s.

5.2   Calculate the acceleration of the astronaut while he's in contact with the rock.
Give your answer in m/s².

(2 marks)

5.3   Calculate the size of force *F*. Give your answer in N.

(2 marks)

1. Stopping Distances

Stopping distances are important — awareness of them can make the difference between crashing and not. It's easy to get stopping, braking and thinking distances confused, so make sure you learn what each one means.

Stopping distance

In an emergency (e.g. a hazard ahead in the road), a driver may perform an emergency stop. This is where maximum force is applied by the brakes in order to stop the car in the shortest possible distance. The longer it takes to perform an emergency stop, the higher the risk of crashing into whatever's in front.

The total **stopping distance** of a vehicle is the distance covered in the time between the driver first spotting a hazard and the vehicle coming to a complete stop. The total stopping distance is the sum of the thinking distance and the braking distance.

> **stopping distance = thinking distance + braking distance**

- The **thinking distance** is the distance the vehicle travels during the driver's reaction time (the time between seeing a hazard and applying the brakes).

- The **braking distance** is the distance the vehicle travels after the brakes are applied until it comes to a complete stop, as a result of the braking force.

> **Example**
>
> **A driver sees a hazard on the road and brakes. His thinking distance is 11 m and his braking distance is 32 m. Find his stopping distance.**
>
> Stopping distance = thinking distance + braking distance
> = 11 + 32 = 43 m

Many factors affect your total stopping distance — and you can break it down into thinking distance and braking distance to look at the factors that affect each of these.

Thinking distance

Thinking distance is affected by two main factors:

1. How fast you're going — whatever your reaction time, the faster you're going, the further you'll go in that time.

2. How quick to respond you are, i.e. your **reaction time** — this can be affected by tiredness, drugs, alcohol and a lack of concentration. A typical reaction time is between 0.2 and 0.9 s.

Braking distance

Braking distance is affected by four main factors:

1. How fast you're going — the faster you're going, the further it takes to stop. (See the next page for more on this.)

2. How good your brakes are — all brakes must be checked and maintained regularly. Worn or faulty brakes won't be able to apply as much force as well-maintained brakes and could let you down catastrophically just when you need them the most, i.e. in an emergency.

3. How good the tyres are — tyres should have a minimum tread depth of 1.6 mm. In wet conditions, the tread pattern helps to stop water getting trapped between the tyres and the road — they provide a channel through which the water can 'escape'. With too little tread, the tyres may lose contact with the ground, causing the vehicle to slide.

4. How good the grip is — as well as the condition of the tyres, this depends on the weather conditions and the road surface. Water, ice, leaves, diesel spills, muck on the road etc. can greatly increase the braking distance. They can result in reduced friction between the tyres and the road — so you travel further before stopping and may skid. Often you only discover this when you try to brake hard.

You need to be able to describe the factors affecting stopping distance and how this affects safety — especially in an emergency stop. For example, icy conditions increase the chance of skidding (and so increase the stopping distance) so the driver needs to leave more space between their vehicle and the vehicle in front of them. The longer your stopping distance, the more space you need to leave in front in order to stop safely.

Figure 1: *A good tyre tread depth helps reduce braking distance.*

Figure 2: *Petrol spills on roads can reduce grip and cause tyres to skid, increasing the braking distance.*

Typical stopping distances

Looking at things simply — for any given braking force, the faster you're going, the greater your stopping distance. Figure 3 shows typical stopping distances at different speeds taken from the Highway Code.

The actual stopping distance will depend on the vehicle and the driver, but if the hazard is closer than the distances shown then it's likely there will be a collision.

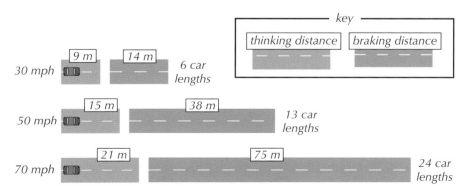

Figure 3: *Typical stopping distances taken from the Highway Code.*

Tip: Don't forget — things like bad weather and road conditions will make stopping distances even longer.

Tip: The speed limits for lorries in the UK are lower than for cars — their increased weight means they take longer to stop.

To avoid an accident, drivers need to leave enough space between their car and the one in front so that if they had to stop suddenly they would have time to do so safely. 'Enough space' means the stopping distance for whatever speed they're going at.

Speed limits are really important because speed affects the stopping distance so much.

Speed and stopping distance

Speed affects braking distance more than thinking distance. As a car speeds up, the thinking distance increases at the same rate as the speed — so they're directly proportional. For example, if speed doubles (increases by a scale factor of 2), thinking distance also doubles (increases by a factor of 2).

This is because the thinking time (how long it takes the driver to apply the brakes) stays pretty constant — but the higher the speed, the more distance you cover in that same time.

Braking distance, however, increases faster the more you speed up. If speed doubles, braking distance increases 4-fold (2^2). And if speed trebles, braking distance increases 9-fold (3^2). So the braking distance increases with the square of the scale factor of the speed increase.

Braking distance increases in this way because when a vehicle brakes, work must be done to transfer energy away from the vehicle's kinetic energy store. The energy in a vehicle's kinetic energy store is $\frac{1}{2}mv^2$ (see page 25). So if speed doubles, kinetic energy increases 4-fold. Therefore, the work that must be done to stop the vehicle increases 4-fold too.

Tip: For more on how work is done to stop a car, see page 182.

Work done is equal to force × distance ($W = Fs$, page 135) and the braking force is constant (at its maximum). So this means that the braking distance also increases 4-fold.

> ### Example
>
> **When travelling at 20 mph, a driver's thinking distance is 6.0 m and their braking distance is 6.0 m. Estimate their total stopping distance at 80 mph.**
>
>
>
> First work out the scale factor of the speed increase: $80 \div 20 = 4$
>
> Look at each of the thinking and braking distances separately. Start with the thinking distance — it's directly proportional to speed, so simply multiply the thinking distance at 20 mph by the scale factor:
>
> $$6.0 \times 4 = 24 \text{ m}$$
>
> Now look at the braking distance — it increases by the square of the scale factor of the speed increase, so multiply the original braking distance by the scale factor squared:
>
> $$6.0 \times 4^2 = 96 \text{ m}$$
>
> Finally, stopping distance is the sum of thinking and braking distance, so:
>
> $$\text{Stopping distance at 80 mph} = 24 + 96 = 120 \text{ m}$$

Tip: So, when travelling four times faster, your thinking distance will be four times longer and your braking distance will be sixteen (4^2) times longer.

Practice Questions — Fact Recall

Q1   Define stopping distance, thinking distance and braking distance.

Q2   Other than speed, name three factors that affect braking distance.

Q3   Say whether each of the following would affect the thinking distance
     or the braking distance of a vehicle:

   a) Ice on the road   b) Alcohol intake of the driver

   c) Tiredness of the driver   d) Petrol spills

Practice Questions — Application

Q1   A driver in a car has a thinking distance of 15 m and a braking
     distance of 38 m. What's the stopping distance of the car?

Q2   Sasha is driving her colleagues home from work on a winter evening.
     Explain three factors which could affect the distance she travels
     before stopping after a hazard appears in the road.

Q3   A driver, travelling at 30 mph, makes an emergency stop.
     Their thinking distance is 9.0 m and their braking distance is 14.0 m.
     The driver then accelerates to a new speed of 60 mph. Estimate:

   a) the thinking distance at 60 mph.

   b) the braking distance at 60 mph.

   c) the stopping distance at 60 mph.

Tip: With this type of
question, the first thing
to do is find the scale
factor of the speed
increase.

2. Reaction Times

Your reaction time is an important factor in determining your thinking distance. You can measure reaction times in the classroom really easily.

Testing reaction times

Everyone's reaction times are different, and many different factors affect it (see page 176). You can do a simple experiment to investigate your reaction time.

As reaction times are so short, you haven't got a chance of measuring one with a stopwatch. One way of measuring reaction times is to use a computer-based test (e.g. clicking a mouse when the screen changes colour). Another is the ruler-drop test.

The ruler-drop test

Sit with your arm resting on the edge of a table (this should stop you moving your arm up or down during the test). Get someone else to hold a ruler so it hangs between your thumb and forefinger, lined up with zero. You may need a third person to be at eye level with the ruler to check it's lined up.

Without giving any warning, the person holding the ruler should drop it. At this point, close your thumb and finger to try and catch the ruler as quickly as possible.

The measurement on the ruler at the point where it's caught is how far the ruler dropped in the time it took you to react. The longer the distance, the longer the reaction time.

Figure 1: *The minimum reaction time for a human is thought to be 0.1 seconds. In high-level races, any athlete starting within 0.1 s of the starting gun is considered to have false-started. This is measured by computerised sensors built into the starting blocks.*

Tip: A 30 cm ruler should work for measuring most people's reaction times. However, you could use a metre ruler if necessary.

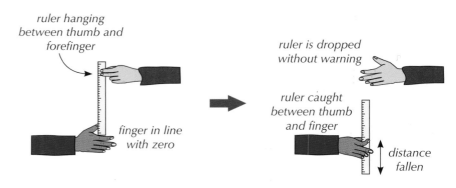

Figure 2: *A diagram of the two main stages of the ruler-drop test.*

You can calculate how long the ruler falls for (the reaction time) because acceleration due to gravity is constant (roughly 9.8 m/s²). See the next page for an example calculation.

Tip: For a refresher on calculations with acceleration due to gravity, see page 151.

Tip: Remember — the distance must be in metres to use this equation. To convert from cm to m, you divide by 100.

Remember, a typical human reaction time is between 0.2 s and 0.9 s, so you should get results in this range.

It's pretty hard to do this experiment accurately, so you should do a lot of repeats. The results will be better if the ruler falls straight down — you might want to add a blob of modelling clay to the bottom to stop it from waving about. Make sure it's a fair test — use the same ruler for each repeat and have the same person dropping it.

Tip: See page 176 for other factors that can affect reaction times and increase the thinking distance of someone driving a vehicle.

You could try to investigate some factors affecting reaction time, e.g. you could introduce distractions by having some music playing or by having someone talk to you while the test takes place. Remember to still do lots of repeats and calculate the mean reaction time with distractions, which you can compare to the mean reaction time without distractions.

Practice Question — Fact Recall

Q1 Describe the main steps involved in measuring your reaction time using the ruler-drop test.

Practice Question — Application

Q1 A student's reaction time is tested using the ruler drop test. She repeats the test three times, grabbing the ruler at 3.0 cm, 5.0 cm and 7.0 cm.

a) Calculate the average distance, in centimetres, at which the student grabbed the ruler.

b) Using your answer to part a), calculate their reaction time. Use $g = 9.8$ m/s^2.

c) The student later repeated the test at the end of the school day. The average reaction time was longer than that from earlier in the day. Suggest a reason for this.

3. Braking and Energy Transfer

Braking works by transferring energy away from the kinetic energy stores of the wheels. This is because work is done against friction.

Learning Objectives:

- Understand the energy transfers which occur when a vehicle brakes.
- Understand why braking increases the temperature of a vehicle's brakes.
- Know that a greater speed means a larger braking force is needed to stop a vehicle in a given distance.
- Know that a greater braking force means a larger deceleration.
- Understand why large decelerations can be dangerous.
- **H** Be able to estimate the force required to produce a deceleration of a vehicle in a typical road situation.

Specification Reference 6.5.4.3.4

Braking and friction

Braking relies on friction between the brakes and the wheels. When the brake pedal is pushed, this causes the brake pads to be pressed onto the wheels. This contact causes friction, which causes work to be done.

The work done between the brakes and the wheels transfers energy from the kinetic energy stores of the wheels to the thermal energy stores of the brakes. This means that the temperature of the brakes increases.

The faster a vehicle is going, the more energy it has in its kinetic energy stores, so the more work needs to be done to stop it. This means that a greater braking force is needed to make it stop within a certain distance. A larger braking force means a larger deceleration.

Very large decelerations mean lots of work is done, so lots of energy is transferred to thermal energy stores and the brakes become really hot. If they overheat, they can stop working and can cause the driver to lose control of the vehicle.

Estimating the braking force   Higher

You can estimate the force involved in accelerations of vehicles using the typical values from page 148.

Example — Higher

A car travelling at a typical speed makes an emergency stop to avoid hitting a hazard 50 m ahead. Estimate the braking force needed to produce this deceleration.

The typical speed of a car is $v = {\sim}25$ m/s
and its typical mass is $m = {\sim}1000$ kg

Assume the deceleration is uniform and rearrange $v^2 - u^2 = 2as$ to find the deceleration.
$$a = (v^2 - u^2) \div 2s = (0^2 - 25^2) \div (2 \times 50) = -6.25 \text{ m/s}^2$$

Then use $F = ma$ to estimate the force using the typical mass.
$$F = 1000 \times 6.25 = 6250 \text{ N}$$

So F is ${\sim}6250$ N   (The ~ symbol just means it's an approximate value.)

Tip: For more on constant acceleration calculations, see page 151.

Tip: You don't need to keep the minus sign on the acceleration during the force calculation — you just want to know the size of the force, not the direction.

Practice Questions — Application

Q1 A driver makes an emergency stop from a high speed, causing the brakes to overheat. Explain why the brakes overheat.

Q2 A car is travelling at 30 m/s and brakes to avoid hitting a hazard 45 m away. Estimate the braking force needed to produce this deceleration.

4. Momentum `Higher`

If something is moving along, it'll have some momentum. How much depends on its mass and velocity. If it collides with something, it'll 'share' its momentum with it...

Momentum `Higher`

Momentum is a property of moving objects. The greater the mass of an object and the greater its velocity (see p. 147) the more momentum the object has.

Momentum is a **vector** quantity (see page 127) — it has size and direction (like velocity, but not speed). You can work out the momentum of an object using:

$$\mathbf{p} = momentum\ (kg\ m/s) \longrightarrow \boxed{p = mv} \longleftarrow v = velocity\ (m/s)$$
$$\mathbf{m} = mass\ (kg)$$

Learning Objectives:
- **H** Understand what momentum is.
- **H** Remember and be able to use the formula $p = mv$.
- **H** Know that conservation of momentum says that, in a closed system, the total momentum before and after an event are equal.
- **H** Be able to describe and explain an event (e.g. a collision) in terms of momentum.

Specification References 6.5.5.1, 6.5.5.2

Example 1 — `Higher`

A 1800 kg rhino is running north at 9.50 m/s. How much momentum does it have?

$p = mv = 1800 \times 9.50 = 17\ 100$ kg m/s to the north

Example 2 — `Higher`

A 40.0 kg rock that is falling off a cliff has 484 kg m/s momentum. What is the rock's velocity?

Rearranging $p = mv$, $v = p \div m = 484 \div 40.0 = 12.1$ m/s downwards

---

Tip: **H** Use this formula triangle to help you rearrange the formula:

Conservation of momentum `Higher`

In a closed system, the total momentum before an event (e.g. a collision or an explosion) is the same as after the event. This is called **conservation of momentum**.

In some collisions, the objects bump into one another and stay stuck (for example, if you throw a lump of clay at a wall). In other collisions, the objects bounce off each other (e.g. when snooker balls hit each other). In both types of collision, the momentum is always conserved (if it's a closed system).

If the momentum before an event is zero, then the momentum after will also be zero. Before an explosion, the momentum is zero. After the explosion, the pieces fly off in different directions, so that the individual momentums of each piece cancel each other out and the total momentum is zero.

Tip: **H** A closed system is just a fancy way of saying that no external forces act.

Figure 1: Ice skaters rely on momentum to keep themselves moving across the ice.

Tip: **H** You can think of the momentum of the white ball being 'shared out' between the two balls after the collision. That's why the white ball's velocity decreases.

In snooker, balls of the same size and mass collide with each other. Each collision is an event where the momentum of each ball changes, but the overall momentum stays the same (momentum is conserved).

Before:  *After:*

In the diagram, the red ball is initially stationary, so it has zero momentum. The white ball is moving with a velocity v, so has a momentum of $p = mv$.

The white ball then hits the red ball, causing it to move. The red ball now has momentum. The white ball continues moving, but at a much smaller velocity (and so a much smaller momentum).

The combined momentum of the red and white ball is equal to the original momentum of the white ball, mv.

Practice Questions — Fact Recall

Q1 What does the momentum of an object depend on?

Q2 What is the formula for calculating the momentum of an object? Say what each term represents and what its units are.

Q3 How is the momentum before and after a collision linked?

Practice Questions — Application

Q1 Work out the momentum of the following:

a) A 100 g magnet moving north at 0.6 m/s.

b) A 0.80 g bug travelling to the left at 12 m/s.

c) A 5.2 kg rock falling vertically downwards 8.0 m/s.

Q2 A stationary gas canister explodes. What is the momentum of the system before and after the explosion? Explain how you know.

Q3 What is the velocity of the following?

a) A 0.95 kg turtle swimming south with 3.04 kg m/s momentum.

b) A 2000 kg car travelling east with 45 000 kg m/s of momentum.

Q4 What is the mass of the following?

a) A child skiing at 0.75 m/s with 31.5 kg m/s momentum.

b) A dog running at 7.5 m/s with 210 kg m/s of momentum.

Topic 5d Checklist — Make sure you know...

Stopping Distances

- ☐ That the stopping distance is a measure of the distance it takes a vehicle to stop in an emergency.
- ☐ That the stopping distance of a vehicle is the sum of the thinking distance and braking distance.
- ☐ That the thinking distance is the distance travelled between the driver noticing a hazard and applying the brakes.
- ☐ That the braking distance is the distance a vehicle travels between the brakes being applied and the vehicle coming to a stop.
- ☐ That both the thinking and braking distance depend on the speed at which the vehicle is travelling.
- ☐ That a typical human reaction time is between 0.2 s and 0.9 s.
- ☐ Factors that can affect braking distance and thinking distance, and the implications on safety in an emergency.
- ☐ Some typical stopping distances at typical speeds, and be able to estimate how speed affects the distance required to stop in an emergency.

Reaction Times

- ☐ How to carry out a simple experiment to measure (and calculate) reaction times.
- ☐ Typical results expected when measuring human reaction times.

Braking and Energy Transfer

- ☐ That when brakes are applied, friction acts against the movement of the wheels, transferring energy from the kinetic energy stores of the wheels to the thermal energy stores of the brakes.
- ☐ That the faster a vehicle is travelling, the greater the braking force required to stop in a given distance.
- ☐ Why large decelerations can be dangerous.
- ☐ H How to estimate the force required to produce a deceleration.

Momentum

- ☐ H That momentum is a property of every moving object.
- ☐ H That momentum (p) has both magnitude and direction, and is a product of the mass (m) and velocity (v) of an object, $p = mv$.
- ☐ H That momentum is conserved — in a closed system, the total momentum before a collision is equal to the total momentum after.
- ☐ H How to describe and explain events (e.g. collisions) in terms of momentum.
- ☐ H How to calculate the momentum, mass or velocity of objects in a collision using conservation of momentum.

Exam-style Questions

1   A truck is travelling along a straight, flat road at its top speed of 30 m/s.
On a clear, dry day, the truck's stopping distance with this driver is 84 m.
The stopping distance is the sum of the thinking distance and the braking distance.

1.1   Explain why the truck's stopping distance when travelling at the same speed in the same conditions may be different for a different driver.

(1 mark)

1.2   The braking distance of the truck is 60 m. The mass of the truck is 2000 kg.
Calculate the force required for it to decelerate to rest in the braking distance given.
Use the correct equation from those listed on page 284. Give your answer in newtons.

(4 marks)

1.3   To stop the truck, the driver applies the brakes. Explain, in terms of energy transfer, how the brakes cause the car to slow down and come to a stop.

(2 marks)

1.4   When descending a steep hill, the truck picks up speed and the driver has to brake harshly. Explain how this could stop the brakes from working. You should refer to energy transfer in your answer.

(3 marks)

1.5   Earlier that week, the truck was driving along the same route in heavy rain.
State and explain **two** ways in which this could make the truck more likely to hit an obstacle in the road.

(2 marks)

2   A white snooker ball collides with a stationary blue snooker ball. Both balls have a mass of 0.16 kg. Before the collision, the white ball moves to the right at 0.5 m/s.

Before collision

white ball   *stationary blue ball*

0.5 m/s

0.16 kg   *0.16 kg*

2.1   What is meant by the conservation of momentum?

(1 mark)

2.2   Calculate the total momentum of the system before the collision.
Give your answer in kg m/s.

(3 marks)

2.3   After the collision, both balls are moving to the right. Compare the velocity and momentum of each ball after the collision with that of the white ball before the collision. You should refer to conservation of momentum in your answer.

(4 marks)

1. Wave Basics

Waves move through substances carrying energy from one place to another — and once they've gone, it's as if they were never there.

What is a wave?

A **wave** is an oscillation (vibration) that transfers energy without transferring any matter, by making the particles of the substance (or fields) that it is travelling through oscillate.

Waves can be either transverse or longitudinal. These words sound complicated but they describe something simple — the direction of the wave oscillations.

Transverse waves

Waves transfer energy in the same direction that they travel. **Transverse waves** oscillate at right angles to the direction that they travel in.

> In transverse waves the oscillations are perpendicular (at 90°) to the direction of energy transfer of the wave.

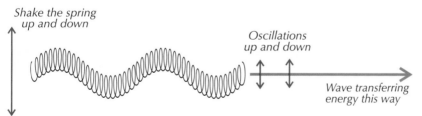

Shake the spring up and down

Oscillations up and down

Wave transferring energy this way

Figure 1: *A transverse wave on a spring.*

Examples of transverse waves include: light and all other electromagnetic waves (p. 200), ripples on water and waves on strings or springs when wiggled up and down (see Figure 1).

Longitudinal waves

Longitudinal waves have oscillations along the same line as they travel. They have areas of compression, in which the particles are bunched together, and areas of rarefaction, in which the particles are spread out — see Figure 2.

> In longitudinal waves the oscillations are parallel to the direction of energy transfer of the wave.

Examples of longitudinal waves include sound waves and a spring when you push the end (see Figure 2).

Learning Objectives:
- Know that waves can be transverse or longitudinal.
- Understand that the oscillations in a transverse wave are perpendicular to the direction in which the wave transfers energy, whereas in a longitudinal wave they are parallel.
- Know that longitudinal waves have compressions and rarefactions.
- Know some examples of transverse and longitudinal waves, e.g. that ripples on water are transverse waves and sound waves are longitudinal.
- Understand and be able to give examples to show that travelling waves transfer energy but do not transfer matter.

Specification Reference 6.6.1.1

Exam Tip
In the exam, it's really important that you say the direction <u>of energy transfer</u> of the wave. You might not get full marks for just saying the direction of the wave.

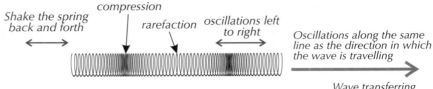

compression

rarefaction oscillations left to right

Shake the spring back and forth

Oscillations along the same line as the direction in which the wave is travelling

Wave transferring energy this way

Figure 2: *A longitudinal wave on a spring.*

Figure 3: *The energy transferred by earthquake waves can be seen in the damage they cause.*

Tip: Waves that need a medium to travel in are classed as mechanical waves. They include water waves, waves in springs and strings, seismic waves and sound waves. Electromagnetic waves are an example of non-mechanical waves (see page 200).

Waves and matter

All waves transfer energy in the direction in which they are travelling, but they don't transfer matter. When waves travel through a medium (a material), such as air or water, the particles of the medium oscillate and transfer energy between each other, but overall the particles stay in the same place — only energy is transferred. You need to be able to describe some observations that provide evidence for this idea, so make sure you know these examples.

Examples

- Ripples on a water surface cause floating objects, e.g. twigs or birds, to just bob up and down. They don't move the object across the water to the edge. This is evidence that the wave travels but not the water.

- If you strum a guitar string and create sound waves, the sound waves don't carry the air away from the guitar to create a vacuum (completely empty space).

Practice Questions — Fact Recall

Q1 Waves can be transverse or longitudinal.

a) What is meant by a transverse wave?

b) Give an example of a transverse wave.

c) What is meant by a longitudinal wave?

Q2 What is meant by areas of compression and rarefaction in a longitudinal wave?

Q3 Which of the following waves is longitudinal?

　　A light　　**B** sound　　**C** water ripples

Q4 Do water waves cause water molecules to travel across the water's surface? Describe an observation which supports this.

2. Features of Waves

Describing a wave as 'really big and fast' might work for surfers, but physicists need a more accurate way — and that's where amplitude, wavelength, frequency and period come in.

Representing waves

A wave can be represented on a set of axes — a line is drawn to show the displacement of the particles from their undisturbed positions at a moment in time. It is as if a transverse wave had been set up in a piece of string and a 'snapshot' taken of it. Crests and troughs are just points of maximum positive and maximum negative displacement from the particle's rest position — see Figure 1.

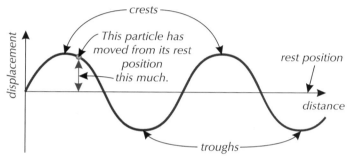

Figure 1: A diagram showing the displacements of particles along a wave.

Wave measurements

There are a few measurements that you can use to describe waves...

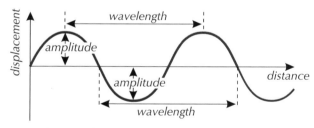

Figure 2: A diagram showing the amplitude and wavelength of a wave.

- The **amplitude** of a wave is the maximum displacement of a point on the wave from its undisturbed (or rest) position. In other words it's the distance from the undisturbed position to a crest or a trough.

- The **wavelength** is the distance between the same point on two adjacent waves. So on a transverse wave it may be the distance between the crest of one wave and the crest of the next wave.

- **Frequency** is the number of complete waves passing a certain point per second. Frequency is measured in hertz (Hz). 1 Hz is 1 wave per second.

Learning Objectives:

- Know what the amplitude, wavelength, frequency and period of a wave are and be able to describe a wave's motion in terms of these principles.

- Be able to show the amplitude and wavelength on a diagram of a wave.

- Be able to calculate the period of a wave given its frequency.

Specification Reference 6.6.1.2

Tip: You might see a wave represented with the horizontal axis showing time instead of distance.

This shows the displacement of a single particle as time passes. Oscilloscope traces are often like this (page 236).

Tip: Amplitude is <u>not</u> the distance from a trough to a crest — it's an easy mistake to make, so watch out...

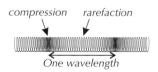

Figure 3: On a longitudinal wave, the distance between the centres of two adjacent compressions is the wavelength.

The period of a wave

The **period** of a wave is the amount of time it takes for a full cycle of the wave to be completed. In other words, it's the length of time between one crest passing a point and the next crest passing the same point.

You can find the period of a wave from the frequency using this equation:

$$\text{Period} = \frac{1}{\text{frequency}}$$

or:

$$T = \frac{1}{f}$$

T = period (s)

f = frequency (Hz)

Tip: You can use a formula triangle to rearrange the equation.

$$\frac{1}{T \times f}$$

Example

A buoy measures the frequency of an ocean wave as 0.2 Hz. Calculate the period of this wave.

The frequency is in the correct unit (Hz), so 0.2 Hz can be substituted directly into the formula $T = \frac{1}{f}$:

$$T = \frac{1}{f} = \frac{1}{0.2} = 5 \text{ seconds}$$

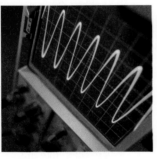

Figure 4: An oscilloscope screen showing a waveform. The amplitude, wavelength and frequency can be found from it.

Practice Question — Fact Recall

Q1 What is:

a) the amplitude of a wave?

b) the wavelength of a wave?

c) the frequency of a wave?

d) the period of a wave?

Practice Questions — Application

Q1 The diagram below shows a man shaking a spring up and down to produce a wave. What is the wavelength of the wave?

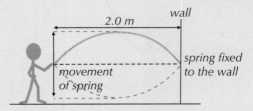

Q2 An oscilloscope is used to display the wave below.

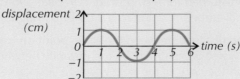

a) What is the amplitude and the period of the wave shown?

b) Calculate the frequency of the wave.

3. Wave Speed

Learning Objectives:
- Know what the term 'wave speed' means.
- Be able to remember and use the wave equation, $v = f\lambda$, and know that it applies to all waves.
- Be able to describe how the speed of sound waves in air can be measured.
- Be able to measure the speed of ripples in water, and of waves in a solid using suitable apparatus to take appropriate measurements. (Required Practical 20)

Specification Reference 6.6.1.2

A wave's speed is how fast it moves. Finding it is a bit trickier than finding the speed of, say, a car, so that's what the next few pages are all about. Luckily, there's a formula for it though.

The wave equation

The wave speed is the speed at which energy is being transferred (or the speed the wave is moving at). You use this equation, called the wave equation, to work it out:

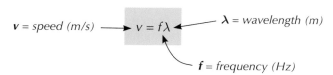

v = speed (m/s) ⟶ $v = f\lambda$ ⟵ λ = wavelength (m)

f = frequency (Hz)

The wave equation applies to all waves, so it's really useful.

Example 1

A paddle vibrating up and down in a pool is used to produce waves on the water. The wavelength of each wave is 1.2 m and exactly 2 complete waves are produced per second. Calculate the speed of the wave.

The number of waves produced per second is the frequency.

So $f = 2$ Hz and $\lambda = 1.2$ m.

Substitute these into the wave equation:

$v = f\lambda = 2 \times 1.2 = 2.4$ m/s

Tip: The symbol for wavelength is the Greek letter λ, which is called 'lambda'.

Example 2

A wave has a frequency of 4.0×10^7 Hz and a speed
of 3.0×10^8 m/s. Find its wavelength.

You're trying to find λ using f and v, so you've got to rearrange the equation.

So $\lambda = v \div f = (3.0 \times 10^8) \div (4.0 \times 10^7) = 7.5$ m

---

Tip: Make sure you can rearrange the formula to calculate either frequency or wavelength. Here's the formula triangle.

Measuring the speed of sound in air

To measure the speed of sound, you need to find the frequency and the wavelength of a sound wave — you can then use the wave equation $v = f\lambda$.

You can generate a sound wave with a specific frequency by attaching a signal generator to a speaker. This sound wave can then be detected by microphones, which convert it to a trace on an oscilloscope.

Tip: When you state the speed of sound, you should say what it's travelling through. Sound moves at different speeds through different materials.

Method

Set up your equipment as shown below, with both microphones next to the speaker. The detected wave at each microphone can be seen as a separate wave on the oscilloscope.

Figure 1: *The initial set-up of apparatus when measuring the speed of sound in air.*

Slowly move one microphone away from the speaker. Its wave will shift sideways on the oscilloscope. Keep moving it until the two waves on the oscilloscope are aligned once more. At this point the microphones will be exactly one wavelength apart, so measure the distance between them.

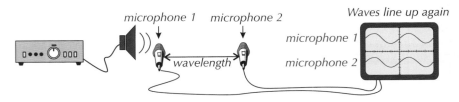

Figure 2: *Arrangement of apparatus when the microphones are one wavelength apart.*

You can then use the formula $v = f\lambda$ to find the speed (v) of the sound wave passing through the air — the frequency (f) of the wave will be equal to the frequency set by the signal generator.

The speed of sound in air is around 330 m/s, so check that your results roughly agree with this.

Measuring the speed of water ripples

You can see water ripples, but they tend to move a bit too quickly for their measurements to be taken. This method is basically a way to get a still image of them. Again, you use a signal generator to produce waves of a known frequency, but this time you attach it to the dipper of a ripple tank.

A ripple tank is a shallow glass tank used to show the properties of waves. The glass bottom of a ripple tank means a light can be shone on the tank from above to project the wave pattern onto a screen below. This makes it much easier to measure the waves without disturbing them (see Figure 3).

Method

Set up your equipment as shown in Figure 3. Fill your ripple tank with water to a depth of around 5 mm. Connect your dipper to the signal generator and set it off at a known frequency. Dim the lights and turn on the strobe light — you'll see a wave pattern made by the shadows of the wave crests on the screen below the tank.

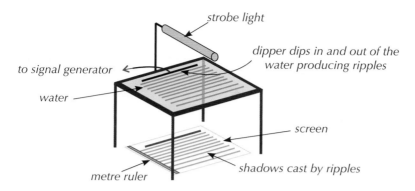

Figure 3: Apparatus for measuring the speed of ripples using a strobe light.

Tip: Measure the wavelength by looking at the screen from underneath the ripple tank — don't look at it through the water. Your view will be distorted by refraction (see page 195).

Increase the frequency of the strobe light until the wave pattern on the screen appears to 'freeze' and stop moving. This happens when the frequency of the waves and the strobe light are equal — the waves appear not to move because they are being lit at the same point in their cycle each time.

Tip: The strobe is a good piece of equipment to use because it allows you to measure a still pattern instead of a constantly moving one.

The distance between each shadow line is equal to one wavelength. Measure the distance between shadow lines that are 10 wavelengths apart using a metre ruler, then divide this distance by 10 to find the average wavelength. This is a suitable method for measuring small wavelengths (see page 231).

You can then use the formula $v = f\lambda$ to find the speed (v) of the ripples, where f is the frequency of the signal generator and strobe light.

Tip: The shadow lines may be very close together, so you'll get a more accurate measurement for wavelength if you measure ten spaces and divide, rather than try to measure one space.

WORKING SCIENTIFICALLY

Observing a wave on a string

REQUIRED PRACTICAL **20**

You can also measure waves on a string. To do this, you need a taut string and a piece of kit called a vibration transducer. A vibration transducer will convert an electrical signal from a signal generator into vibrations. When it's attached to a taut string, waves are formed on the string.

You can ensure your string is taut by connecting one end to the vibration transducer and passing it over a pulley with masses hanging from the other end. This will keep it pulled nice and tight.

Tip: Remember to carry out a risk assessment for each investigation. Be careful of the string snapping and the masses falling.

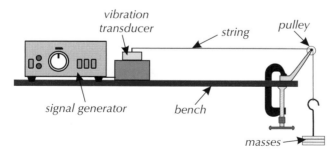

Figure 4: The experimental set-up for measuring the speed of waves along a string.

Set up the equipment as shown, then turn on the signal generator and vibration transducer. The string will start to vibrate.

Adjust the frequency of the signal generator until there's a clear wave on the string (see Figure 5). The frequency you need will depend on the length of string between the pulley and the transducer, and the masses you've used.

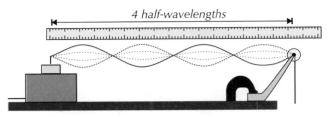

4 half-wavelengths

Figure 5: A diagram showing how to measure the wavelength of a clear wave shape on your apparatus.

Tip: This set-up is suitable for investigating waves on a string because it's easy to see and measure the wavelength (and frequency).

You need to measure the wavelength of these waves. The best way to do this accurately is to measure the length of four or five half-wavelengths (or as many as you can) in one go, then divide to get the average half-wavelength. You can then double this average to get a full wavelength.

The frequency of the wave is whatever the signal generator is set to (you could also measure it with a strobe, as in the water ripple experiment). You can then find the speed of the wave using $v = f\lambda$.

Practice Questions — Fact Recall

Q1 Write down the wave equation. Say what each symbol stands for and the units that it is measured in.

Q2 Describe a way of measuring the speed of sound in air.

Q3 What is the approximate speed of sound in air?

Q4 A wave is generated on a taut string using a vibration transducer. Describe how the speed of the waves on the string can be measured.

Practice Questions — Application

Q1 Calculate the speed of a wave with a wavelength of 0.45 m and a frequency of 15 Hz.

Q2 The speed of sound in a seawater sample is known to be 1500 m/s. A sound wave with a frequency of 3 kHz is produced under water. Calculate the wavelength of this sound wave.

Q3 A light wave has a wavelength of 7.5×10^{-7} m and travels at 3.0×10^{8} m/s. What is its frequency?

Q4 A signal generator connected to the paddle in a ripple tank is set to 100 Hz. The frequency of a strobe light positioned above the ripple tank is adjusted until the shadows cast by the ripples on the screen below are stationary. The diagram below shows part of the shadow pattern.

1 cm (not to scale)

Calculate the speed of the ripples.

4. Refraction of Waves

Learning Objectives:
- Be able to draw ray diagrams to show the refraction of waves as they move from one material to another.
- **H** Know that refraction is caused by the differences in wave speeds in different substances.
- **H** Be able to draw wavefront diagrams to explain refraction.

Specification References
6.6.2.2

When a wave hits the boundary between the substance it's moving through and a new substance, it sometimes carries on moving through the new substance — but its direction may change.

Waves at a boundary

Waves travel through different materials, e.g. air, water, glass. When they arrive at a boundary between two different materials, three things can happen:

Absorption — The waves may be absorbed by the material the wave is trying to cross into. This transfers energy to the material's energy stores (see p. 21).

Reflection — The waves may bounce back.

Transmission — The waves may be transmitted. This means that they carry on travelling through the new material. However, they often undergo **refraction** — there's more on this to follow.

In reality, a combination of all three of these will usually occur at a boundary.

Refraction basics and ray diagrams

When a wave reaches the boundary between two different materials, it can be transmitted through the new material. If it hits the boundary at an angle, it changes direction — it's refracted.

A **ray** is a straight line showing the path a wave, such as light, travels along. You can show the path taken by a light ray on a ray diagram.

1. Draw the boundary between the two materials and then add in the **normal** (a straight line that is at 90° to the boundary). The normal is usually shown as a dotted line.
2. Draw an incoming (incident) ray that meets the normal at the boundary. The angle between the ray and the normal is the **angle of incidence**. (If you're given this angle, make sure to draw it carefully with a protractor.)
3. Now draw the refracted ray on the other side of the boundary. The angle that the refracted ray makes with the normal is called the **angle of refraction**.
4. The angle of refraction could be smaller than the angle of incidence (e.g. when light moves from air into a glass block — see Figure 2) or bigger than the angle of incidence (e.g. when light moves from glass into air — see Figure 3).

Figure 1: Refraction of light waves causes objects to look distorted when they are underwater. The light is bent when it passes through boundaries between media.

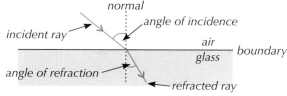

Figure 2: Refraction of a light ray moving from air into glass. When the light is refracted, it bends towards the normal.

Tip: Ray diagrams are mainly used to show the refraction of light, but all types of waves can be refracted. Different types of waves will just be refracted differently.

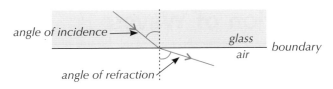

Figure 3: *Refraction of a light ray moving from glass into air. When the light refracts, it bends away from the normal.*

Tip: A ray that hits the boundary at 90° won't change direction.

incident ray

boundary

If a ray travels along the normal and hits the boundary at 90°, it'll pass through without changing direction. The angles of incidence and refraction will both be 0°.

More on refraction   Higher

Refraction occurs because waves travel faster in some materials than others, so the speed of a wave can change as it crosses a boundary. When a wave refracts, its speed changes, but its frequency remains the same.

Since the speed, wavelength and frequency of a wave are all related by the wave equation ($v = f\lambda$ — see page 191), if the speed changes but the frequency is constant, the wavelength must change. If the speed of the wave increases, its wavelength increases. If the speed decreases, so does the wavelength.

The optical density of a material is a measure of how quickly light travels through it — the higher the optical density, the slower light travels.

Tip: **H** You might also hear the term 'refractive index'. This is just a measure of a material's optical density. The bigger the refractive index, the more optically dense it is.

Wavefronts

Wavefronts are imaginary lines drawn through certain points on waves, e.g. through each crest. They're perpendicular (at right angles) to the direction in which the wave is moving (and so perpendicular to the line you'd draw in a ray diagram).

Figure 4 is a wavefront diagram showing light waves travelling along a normal to a boundary. The wavefronts are closer together in the more optically dense material, showing the decrease in wavelength.

Tip: **H** The wave travelling along the normal isn't refracted, but its speed and wavelength still change.

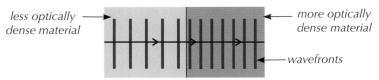

Figure 4: *A wavefront diagram showing light travelling along a normal to a boundary.*

Wavefront diagrams are useful for explaining why refraction happens. When a wave crosses a boundary into a new substance at an angle to the normal, one end of it enters the new material before the rest of the wave. This means that end changes speed before the rest of the wave, causing the wave to change direction.

Which way the wave bends depends on whether it moves faster or slower in the new medium.

▪ If a wave slows down at a boundary, it bends towards the normal.

▪ If a wave speeds up at a boundary, it bends away from the normal.

Figure 5 shows a light wave entering a more optically dense material. The wave moves more slowly in the new material, so it bends towards the normal. The angle of refraction is smaller than the angle of incidence.

more optically dense material

normal

less optically dense material

Figure 5: *A light wave entering a more optically dense material at an angle to the normal.*

Figure 6 shows a light wave entering a less optically dense material. It moves faster in the new substance, so it bends away from the normal. The angle of refraction is greater than the angle of incidence.

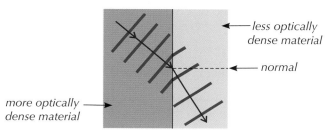

less optically dense material

normal

more optically dense material

Figure 6: *A light wave entering a less optically dense material at an angle to the normal.*

> **Tip:** **H** Imagine driving a go-kart in the direction of the wave, and that the denser medium is a pool of mud. One side of the go-kart will reach the mud first and slow down. The other side of the go-kart isn't yet in the mud so it carries on moving quickly, causing the go-kart to swing round, changing direction.

Practice Questions — Fact Recall

Q1   What is refraction?

Q2   Draw a ray diagram to show the refraction of a light wave crossing from air into a glass block at an angle to the normal.

Q3   What happens to the path of a wave if it crosses the boundary between two media travelling along the normal?

Q4   What happens to the speed, wavelength and frequency of a light wave as it crosses into a medium with a lower optical density?

Q5   How is decreased wavelength shown on a wavefront diagram?

Q6   Describe the refraction of a wave that crosses a boundary at an angle to the normal and speeds up.

> **Tip:** You don't need to know how to work out the amount that waves change direction, just that they do.

Practice Questions — Application

Q1   Draw a ray diagram to show a light wave hitting a boundary between two substances with an angle of incidence of 40° and an angle of refraction of 60°.

Q2   Choose the correct word to make this statement true.
The wave in Q1 **slows down / speeds up** as it enters the new substance.

Topic 6a Checklist — Make sure you know...

Wave Basics

- [ ] That waves are vibrations that transfer energy by causing particles (or fields) to vibrate.
- [ ] That there are two types of wave — transverse (e.g. water ripples) and longitudinal (e.g. sound waves).
- [ ] That the vibrations in transverse waves are perpendicular to the direction of energy transfer.
- [ ] That longitudinal waves have regions of compression and rarefaction, and that their vibrations are parallel to the direction of energy transfer.
- [ ] Examples showing that waves transfer energy as they travel through matter, but do not transfer the matter itself.

Features of Waves

- [ ] What the amplitude, wavelength, frequency and period of a wave are, and how to describe a wave using them.
- [ ] How to represent amplitude and wavelength on a diagram of a wave.
- [ ] How to calculate the period of a wave from the frequency, and vice versa.

Wave Speed

- [ ] That the wave equation, $v = f\lambda$, applies to all waves and how to use it.
- [ ] How to measure the speed of sound in air and the speed of water ripples and waves on strings using suitable apparatus to make measurements.

Refraction of Waves

- [ ] That waves can be reflected, absorbed or transmitted when they meet the boundary between two different materials.
- [ ] How to draw ray diagrams to show the refraction of waves as they move between types of matter.
- [ ] **H** That the difference in the speed of waves in different substances causes refraction.
- [ ] **H** How to use wavefront diagrams to explain refraction.

Exam-style Questions

1   The diagram below shows a transverse wave on a rope.

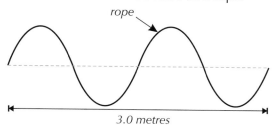

rope

3.0 metres

1.1   What is the wavelength of the wave on the rope?

(1 mark)

1.2   Complete the sentence below by selecting the correct answer from the options given.

Increasing the (frequency / wavelength / amplitude) of the wave on the rope will increase the number of complete waves passing a point on the rope each second.

(1 mark)

The frequency of the wave is 2 Hz.

1.3   Calculate the period of the wave. Give your answer in seconds.
Use the correct equation from the equations listed on page 284.

(2 marks)

1.4   Write down the equation linking wave speed, wavelength and frequency.

(1 mark)

1.5   Calculate the speed of the waves. Give your answer in m/s.

(2 marks)

2   A student shines a ray of light from a ray box at a transparent glass block and measures the angle of incidence and the angle of refraction.

2.1   The student measures the angle of incidence as 47° and the angle of refraction as 32°. Construct a ray diagram to show the refraction of the light ray.

(2 marks)

The wavefront diagram below shows the wave during this investigation.

2.2*   Explain what this diagram shows happening to the wave in terms of wavelength, speed and direction.

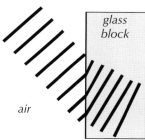

glass block

air

(6 marks)

1. What are Electromagnetic Waves?

Electromagnetic waves are a group of waves that all travel at the same speed in a vacuum. All the different wavelengths of EM waves form a spectrum.

The electromagnetic (EM) spectrum

Electromagnetic waves are a group of transverse waves (see page 187). They are sometimes called electromagnetic radiation. They consist of vibrating electric and magnetic fields, which is why they can travel through a vacuum — they don't rely on vibrating matter.

EM waves form a spectrum of waves with different wavelengths. The spectrum is continuous — meaning there's no gaps in it.

> The **electromagnetic (EM) spectrum** is a continuous spectrum of all the possible wavelengths of electromagnetic waves.

As electromagnetic waves with longer wavelengths have lower frequencies, you can also say that it's a spectrum of all the possible frequencies of electromagnetic waves.

EM waves are grouped into seven basic types according to their wavelength (or frequency), but remember the spectrum is continuous — so the different regions actually merge into each other, see Figure 1.

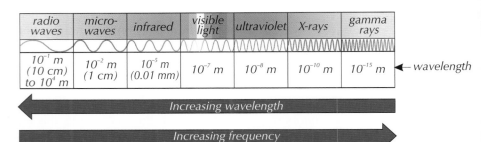

Figure 1: The electromagnetic spectrum, with decreasing wavelength and increasing frequency from left to right.

All the different types of EM wave travel at the same speed (about 3×10^8 m/s) in a vacuum (e.g. space). They travel slightly slower in air, but still all at the same speed as each other.

Electromagnetic waves with different wavelengths (or frequencies) have different properties. The properties of the different types of electromagnetic waves are covered later on in the topic. Our eyes can only detect electromagnetic waves that fall into the visible light part of the spectrum.

Electromagnetic waves and energy

All electromagnetic waves transfer energy from a source to an absorber.

Example 1

A hot object (the source) transfers energy by emitting infrared radiation, which is absorbed by the surroundings.

Example 2 — **Higher**

Oscillating electrons (the source) in a radio transmitter produce radio waves. These transfer energy to a receiver where it causes the electrons in the receiver to oscillate — see page 203.

Exam Tip
Make sure you can give some examples of EM energy transfer. Another example is microwaves transferring energy to cook food (see p. 205 for more on this).

Atomic changes and electromagnetic waves

Electromagnetic waves can be produced by changes inside atoms. These could be changes to the arrangement of electrons or changes within the nucleus.

Electron changes

If an atom absorbs energy, some of its electrons move to higher energy levels within the atom. When each electron falls back down to its original level, an electromagnetic wave is produced.

Tip: There are several ways of transferring energy into the energy stores of atoms and their electrons. E.g. energy can be transferred electrically or by heating.

Tip: See page 110 for more on atomic structure and energy levels.

The electron absorbs energy and is excited to a higher energy level.   *The electron falls back down and the excess energy is released as an electromagnetic wave.*

Figure 2: *Electromagnetic waves are produced when excited electrons fall back down.*

Different atoms have different energy levels, so there are lots of possible changes that can happen within atoms and molecules. This is why electromagnetic waves produced in this way have such a large range of frequencies. The higher the frequency of an electromagnetic wave, the more energy it transfers. So an atomic change that releases a lot of energy will produce a high-frequency electromagnetic wave.

The huge number of possible changes within atoms also allows a wide range of frequencies of electromagnetic radiation to be absorbed by electrons.

Nuclear changes

Gamma rays are high-energy electromagnetic waves which come from changes in the nuclei of atoms. Basically, unstable nuclei of radioactive atoms decay, giving out particles — there's more on the types of particles on pages 114-115. After spitting out a particle, the nucleus might need to get rid of some extra energy. It does this by giving out a gamma ray.

Figure 3: *Neon signs work by passing electricity through neon gas. This excites electrons in the neon atoms. When the electrons fall back down, waves from the visible light part of the EM spectrum are produced.*

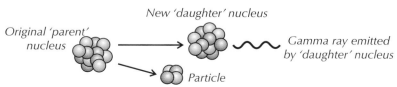

New 'daughter' nucleus

Original 'parent' nucleus

Gamma ray emitted by 'daughter' nucleus

Particle

Figure 4: *Radioactive decay resulting in gamma ray emission.*

Electromagnetic waves and matter

When any wave meets a boundary between two different materials, it can be reflected, absorbed or transmitted (see page 195). Electromagnetic waves of different wavelengths are reflected, absorbed or transmitted differently when they meet a boundary. This is one of the reasons why different types of electromagnetic waves have different uses (see pages 203-208).

Also, EM waves with different wavelengths are refracted (see page 195) by different amounts — see below for an example of this.

Example

White light is made up of all the wavelengths of electromagnetic radiation in the visible part of the spectrum. Each narrow band of wavelengths corresponds to a different colour, from red to violet. The different wavelengths all bend (refract) by different amounts when they enter and leave a prism, so the colours are separated out.

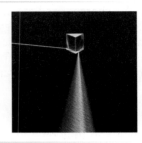

Practice Questions — Fact Recall

Q1 Are electromagnetic waves transverse or longitudinal?

Q2 What is the electromagnetic spectrum?

Q3 Write down the seven types of electromagnetic radiation in order of increasing wavelength.

Q4 Which type of electromagnetic wave has the highest frequency?

Q5 What can you say about the speed of different types of electromagnetic wave travelling in a vacuum?

Q6 Give an example of a situation in which electromagnetic waves transfer energy from a source to an absorber.

Q7 Describe two types of atomic change that produce electromagnetic waves.

Q8 What can happen to an electromagnetic wave when it meets the boundary between two substances? Will the exact same thing always happen to any type of electromagnetic wave when it meets the same boundary?

Practice Question — Application

Q1 An electromagnetic wave source produces microwaves.

a) The wave source is adjusted so that it produces EM waves with a lower frequency. What effect does this have on the wavelength of the waves produced?

b) The wave source is now giving out a different type of electromagnetic radiation. What type of electromagnetic radiation is it now giving out?

Tip: Remember, you might hear electromagnetic waves called electromagnetic radiation — they're the same thing.

2. Radio Waves

Radio waves are the electromagnetic waves with the longest wavelengths (between about 10 cm and 10 000 m — see page 200). This huge range is split up further into short-, medium- and long-wave radio signals.

How are radio waves produced?

You can produce **radio waves** using an alternating current (ac) in an electrical circuit. Alternating currents are made up of oscillating charges (electrons). As the charges oscillate, they produce oscillating electric and magnetic fields, i.e. electromagnetic waves, which is what radio waves are (see page 200). The frequency of the radio waves produced will be equal to the frequency of the alternating current. The object in which charges oscillate to create the radio waves is called a transmitter.

How are radio waves received?

When transmitted radio waves reach a receiver, the radio waves are absorbed. The energy carried by the waves is transferred to the kinetic energy stores of the electrons in the material of the receiver. This causes the electrons to oscillate and, if the receiver is part of a complete electrical circuit, it generates an alternating current. This current has the same frequency as the radio wave that generated it.

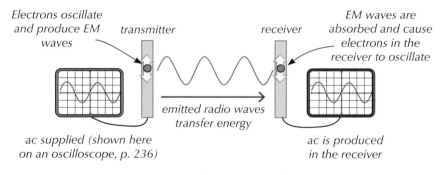

Figure 1: *A diagram showing how radio waves are produced, transmitted and received.*

Using radio waves for communication

Radio waves are used mainly for radio and TV signals. They are sent out by transmitters and received by TV or radio aerials (receivers). Different wavelengths of radio wave are used in different ways.

If you're doing Higher tier exams, you'll need to be able to recall the properties that make radio waves suited to each of their uses. But even if you're not doing Higher tier, you could still be asked to apply anything you already know about EM waves to their use in a practical context. So make sure you understand the stuff on the next page.

Learning Objectives:

- **H** Know that oscillations in electric currents can produce radio waves.
- **H** Know that a radio wave causes oscillations in a receiver, which can produce an alternating current of the same frequency as the radio wave.
- Know some practical applications of radio waves.
- **H** Know why radio waves are suited to these uses.

Specification References 6.6.2.3, 6.6.2.4

Tip: Oscillating means moving back and forth, i.e. vibrating.

Tip: See page 86 for more on alternating current.

Long-wave radio

Long-wave radio (wavelengths of 1 – 10 km) can be transmitted and received halfway round the world because long wavelengths diffract (bend) around the curved surface of the Earth (see Figure 3). Long-wave radio wavelengths can also diffract around hills, into tunnels and all sorts. This diffraction effect makes it possible for radio signals to be received even if the receiver isn't in the line of sight of the transmitter.

Short-wave radio

Short-wave radio signals (wavelengths of about 10 m – 100 m) don't diffract around the Earth's curve, but they can still be received at large distances from the transmitter. They are reflected between the Earth and the ionosphere — an electrically charged layer in the Earth's upper **atmosphere** (see Figure 3).

Bluetooth® uses short-wave radio waves to send data over short distances between devices without wires (e.g. wireless headsets so you can use your phone while driving a car).

Medium-wave radio

Medium-wave signals (well, the shorter ones) can also reflect from the ionosphere, depending on atmospheric conditions and the time of day.

TV signals and FM radio

The radio waves used for TV and FM radio transmissions have very short wavelengths (10 cm – 10 m). To get reception, you must be in direct sight of the transmitter — the signal doesn't bend around hills or travel far through buildings.

Tip: The receiver being in the line of sight of the transmitter just means there are no obstacles directly in between them.

Figure 2: A television aerial raised high above a house to increase the signal quality. The aerial needs to be in direct sight of the transmitter as the radio waves used for TV signals do not diffract around large obstacles.

Tip: The type of TV that's transmitted by radio waves is known as terrestrial TV. It's different from satellite TV, which uses microwaves relayed by satellites in space (see page 205), and cable TV, where the signal travels through wires.

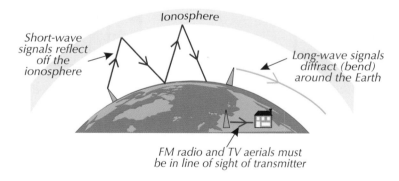

Figure 3: A diagram showing how different wavelength radio waves travel.

Practice Questions — Fact Recall

Q1 What type of current is used to produce radio waves?

Q2 Give two uses of radio waves.

Q3 Short-wave and medium-wave radio signals can reflect off layers in the Earth's atmosphere. Suggest why this lets them be used to broadcast radio over long distances.

3. More EM Waves and their Uses

Because of their different properties, different electromagnetic waves are used for a range of different purposes, from communications to treating cancer.

Useful properties of EM waves

Just as with radio waves, if you're doing Higher tier exams, you'll need to be able to recall the properties that make each of the following EM waves suited to each of their uses. But even if you're not doing Higher tier, you could still be asked to apply anything you already know about EM waves to their use in a practical context. So make sure you understand everything over the next few pages.

Microwaves

The **microwave** region of the EM spectrum covers a range of different wavelengths. The short wavelength microwaves have different properties from the long wavelength microwaves, which means they have different uses.

Satellite communications

Communication to and from satellites usually uses microwaves. This is because certain wavelengths of microwave can pass easily through the Earth's atmosphere without really being reflected, refracted, diffracted or absorbed, which means they can reach satellites. Satellite communications have a range of applications, e.g. satellite TV, satellite phones and internet, and military communications.

For all types of satellite communications, the signal from a transmitter is transmitted into space, where it's picked up by the satellite's receiver orbiting high above the Earth. The satellite transmits the signal back to Earth in a different direction, where it's received by a satellite receiver on the ground. There is a slight time delay between the signal being sent and received because of the long distance the signal has to travel.

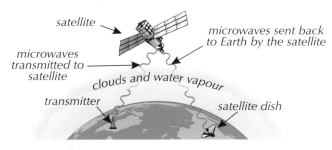

Figure 1: A diagram showing how microwaves are used for satellite communication.

Cooking

The wavelengths of microwaves used in satellite communications pass through the Earth's watery atmosphere. However, the microwaves used in microwave ovens have wavelengths which allow them to be absorbed by water molecules in food.

Learning Objectives:

- Know that microwaves are used for satellite communication and for cooking.
- Know that infrared radiation is used in cooking and that it allows infrared cameras and electric heaters to work.
- Know that visible light is used for communications via fibre optic cables.
- Know that ultraviolet light allows energy efficient lamps and sun tanning lamps to work.
- Know some of the medical applications of X-rays and gamma rays.
- **H** Know why each type of EM wave is suited to its uses.

Specification Reference 6.6.2.4

Tip: Satellite TV uses microwaves but terrestrial TV (normal TV) uses radio waves (see previous page).

Figure 2: The TV satellite dishes on these flats point in specific directions in order to receive the microwave signal from a space satellite.

These microwaves penetrate up to a few centimetres into the food before being absorbed and transferring the energy they are carrying to the thermal energy stores of the water molecules in the food, causing the water to heat up. The water molecules then transfer this energy to the rest of the molecules in the food, which quickly cooks it.

Infrared radiation

Going along the EM spectrum in order of decreasing wavelength, **infrared (IR) radiation** comes next. Its uses are related to temperature.

Infrared cameras

Infrared (IR) radiation is given out by all objects — and the hotter the object, the more IR radiation it gives out. Infrared cameras can be used to detect infrared radiation and monitor temperature. The camera detects the IR radiation and turns it into an electrical signal, which is displayed on a screen as a picture.

Figure 3: An infrared camera being used to monitor the skin temperature of people arriving at an airport. Raised skin temperature can be a sign of illnesses such as bird flu.

Examples

- The heat loss through different parts of a house can be detected using an infrared camera. Colour coding is used to show different amounts of infrared.

hot
cold

- Infrared cameras can also be used as night-vision equipment by the military and by the police to spot criminals. Often the image isn't colour-coded — the hotter an object is compared to its surroundings, the brighter it appears. It works best at night when the surroundings are colder.

person cannot be seen in the dark

night-vision camera senses heat difference between person and surroundings

---

Cooking

Absorbing IR radiation causes objects to get hotter. This means that food can be cooked using IR radiation — the temperature of the food increases when it absorbs IR radiation, e.g. from a toaster's heating element, see Figure 4.

Electric heaters

Electric heaters heat a room in the same way. They contain a long piece of wire that heats up when a current flows through it. This wire then emits lots of infrared radiation (and a little visible light — the wire glows). The emitted IR radiation is absorbed by objects and the air in the room — energy is transferred by the IR waves to the thermal energy stores of the objects, causing their temperature to increase.

Figure 4: The element of a toaster heats up and emits infrared radiation. This is absorbed by the bread, causing it to 'toast'.

Visible light

You could argue that the most important use of **visible light** is allowing us to see. However, make sure you know about the following use too.

Fibre optic cables

Optical fibres are thin glass or plastic fibres that can carry data (e.g. from telephones or computers) over long distances. Pulses of visible light are used, because when the light hits the walls of the fibres, it's reflected back into the fibre. This means the light is bounced back and forth until it reaches the end of the fibre.

Visible light is also suited to this use as it will travel down the fibre without being absorbed or scattered much, so the signal hardly weakens at all.

Figure 5: A fibre optic cable which contains a bundle of optical fibres.

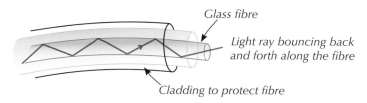

Glass fibre

Light ray bouncing back and forth along the fibre

Cladding to protect fibre

Figure 6: An optical fibre transmitting a pulse of visible light.

Ultraviolet radiation

Ultraviolet (UV) radiation is produced by the Sun, and exposure to it is what gives people a suntan.

Sun tanning lamps

When it's not sunny, some people go to tanning salons where UV lamps are used to give them an artificial suntan. However, overexposure to UV radiation can be dangerous (see page 211 for more details).

Security ink

Fluorescence is a property of certain chemicals. When UV radiation hits them, it's absorbed and visible light is emitted. That's why fluorescent colours look so bright — they actually emit light. Security pens can be used to mark valuable items, such as laptops, with fluorescent ink. Under UV light the ink will glow (fluoresce), but it's invisible otherwise. This can help the police identify your property if it's stolen. Fluorescent ink is also used as a security feature in banknotes — see Figure 7.

Figure 7: Banknotes contain a fluorescent ink pattern, making them harder to forge. It only shows up under UV light of the correct frequency.

Energy efficient lamps

Fluorescent lamps and bulbs use fluorescence too. They have glass tubes which are coated on the inside with a fluorescent material and then filled with a mixture of mercury and noble gases such as neon and argon. When the electrical current is switched on, electrons in the mercury atoms are excited to higher energy levels. When they fall back down, the energy is released as UV radiation (see page 201). The UV radiation hits the fluorescent coating and is converted into visible light. A lamp of this type is far more energy efficient than an older-style incandescent lamp containing a wire filament.

Figure 8: This compact fluorescent lamp has a glass tube which is coiled so that it fits in the same space as an incandescent bulb.

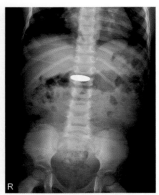

Figure 9: An X-ray showing a swallowed coin. No X-rays have passed through the coin, so that part of the plate has remained bright white.

Tip: X-rays can also be used to sterilise medical equipment. X-rays don't damage the equipment or its packaging, they leave no residue, and the source of the X-rays can be switched on and off easily.

X-rays and gamma rays

X-rays and **gamma rays** are really useful in medicine.

Medical imaging

Radiographers in hospitals take X-ray 'photographs' of people to see if they have any broken bones. X-rays pass easily through flesh but not so easily through denser material like bone or metal. So it's the amount of radiation that's absorbed (or not absorbed) that gives you an X-ray image.

X-rays are directed through a patient towards a detector plate. The plate starts off white, and the bits that are exposed to the fewest X-rays (i.e. the areas where X-rays have been absorbed by bone on the way through the patient) remain white. The bits where the X-rays have passed through soft tissue without being absorbed turn black. So an X-ray image is really a negative image.

Gamma rays can also be used as a **medical tracer**. A gamma-emitting isotope is injected or swallowed by the patient. The gamma radiation emitted by the isotope can be detected outside the patient's body because gamma rays can easily pass through the body. The isotope is traced as it travels through the body, which can help doctors to investigate whether the patient's internal organs are functioning as they should be.

Medical treatment

Radiographers use X-rays (and also gamma rays) to treat people with cancer — this is **radiotherapy**. High doses of these rays kill living cells, so they are directed towards cancer cells. However, great care has to be taken to avoid killing too many normal, healthy cells.

Practice Questions — Fact Recall

Q1 What two types of EM radiation are commonly used in cooking?

Q2 How does an electric heater heat a room?

Q3 How is visible light sent through optical fibres?

Q4 Give two ways in which ultraviolet radiation is used.

Q5 Why are X-rays useful in medical imaging?

Practice Question — Application

Q1 A wildlife documentary team used night-vision equipment to detect a rhino hiding in the bushes. They took two images, A and B, as shown. The temperature scale of the images is also shown.

image A

image B

cold

hot

One image was taken during the night and one was taken during the day, but they forgot to label them. Which image was taken during the night, image A or image B? Explain how you know.

4. Investigating Infrared Radiation

You saw on p. 206 that all objects emit infrared radiation, but now it's time to see how the surface of the object affects how much it emits.

Learning Objective:
- Be able to investigate how surface colours and textures affect the amount of radiation a material emits or absorbs. (Required Practical 21)

Specification Reference 6.6.2.2

Investigating IR emissions

REQUIRED PRACTICAL **21**

The amount of infrared radiation emitted from an object is not just dependent on its temperature (p. 206). It's also dependent on the material of its surface.

A Leslie cube is a hollow, watertight, metal cube made of e.g. aluminium, whose four vertical faces have different surfaces (for example, matt black paint, matt white paint, shiny metal and dull metal). You can use them to investigate IR emission by different surfaces (see below).

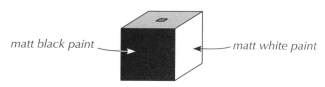

matt black paint ——→   ←—— matt white paint

Figure 1: *An example of a Leslie cube showing two vertical faces.*

Figure 2: *Runners often wrap themselves in space blankets after a race. They're light coloured and shiny to reduce heat loss by radiation.*

Method

Place an empty Leslie cube on a heatproof mat and fill it with boiling water from a kettle. Wait a while for the cube to warm up, then hold a thermometer against each of the four vertical faces of the cube. You should find that all four faces are the same temperature.

Next hold an infrared detector a set distance (e.g. 10 cm) away from one of the cube's vertical faces, and record the amount of IR radiation it detects. Repeat this measurement for each of the cube's vertical faces. Make sure you position the detector at the same distance from the cube each time.

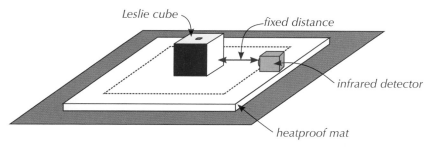

Leslie cube   fixed distance

infrared detector

heatproof mat

Figure 3: *The setup of an investigation into the infrared radiation emitted by different surfaces.*

Tip: It's important to be careful when you're doing this experiment. Don't try to move the cube when it's full of boiling water — you might burn your hands. Also, take care when carrying the kettle of boiling water and when pouring the water into the cube. And, as with all practical investigations, make sure you do a risk assessment before you start.

Results

You should find that you detect more infrared radiation from darker surfaces on the Leslie cube than from lighter ones, and more from matt surfaces than from shiny ones. As always, you should do the experiment more than once, to make sure your results are repeatable (p. 8).

Tip: A bar chart (p. 15) is a good way to display your results from this experiment.

Investigating IR absorptions

REQUIRED PRACTICAL 21

The amount of infrared radiation absorbed by different materials also depends on the material. You can do an experiment to show this, using a bunsen burner and some candle wax.

- Set up the equipment as shown in Figure 4. Two ball bearings are each stuck to one side of a metal plate with solid pieces of candle wax. The other sides of these plates are then faced towards the flame.

- The sides of the plates that are facing towards the flame each have a different surface colour — one is matt black and the other is silver.

- The ball bearing on the black plate will fall first as the black surface absorbs more infrared radiation — transferring more energy to the thermal energy store of the wax. This means the wax on the black plate melts before the wax on the silver plate.

Tip: Be very careful with the bunsen burner — make sure not to put anything which could catch fire near the flame. Take care with the metal plates too. Make sure you leave them to cool before you touch them once you've finished the experiment.

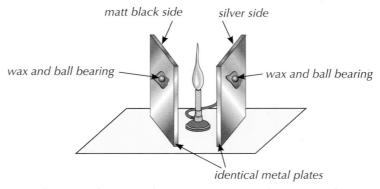

matt black side   *silver side*

wax and ball bearing   *wax and ball bearing*

identical metal plates

Figure 4: *The setup of an investigation into the amount of infrared radiation absorbed by different surfaces.*

Practice Questions — Fact Recall

Q1   What is a Leslie cube? Describe an investigation in which it is used.

Q2   For the experimental setup shown in Figure 4, explain the purpose of the wax and ball bearings on each plate.

5. Dangers of EM Radiation

As you've seen on pages 203-208, electromagnetic radiation is really useful. However, it can be pretty harmful too.

Which types of EM radiation are most damaging?

When EM radiation enters living tissue — like you — it's often harmless, but sometimes it creates havoc. The effects of each type of radiation are based on how much energy the wave transfers. Low frequency waves, like radio waves, don't transfer much energy and mostly pass through soft tissue without being absorbed. High frequency waves like UV, X-rays and gamma rays all transfer lots of energy and so can cause lots of damage.

What harm does radiation cause?

UV radiation damages surface cells, which can lead to sunburn and cause skin to age prematurely. More serious effects include damage to the eyes, which can lead to blindness, and an increased risk of skin cancer.

X-rays and gamma rays are types of **ionising radiation**. This means that they carry enough energy to knock electrons off of atoms. This can kill cells or cause gene mutations which can lead to cancer.

Measuring the risk of harm from radiation

Exposure to ultraviolet radiation, X-rays and gamma rays can be harmful to the human body, but these types of radiation are very useful in medical imaging and treatment. Before any of these types of EM radiation are used, people look at whether the benefits outweigh the health risks.

For example, the risk of a person involved in a car accident developing cancer from having an X-ray photograph taken is much smaller than the potential health risk of not finding and treating their injuries.

Radiation dose

The **radiation dose**, measured in sieverts, is a measure of the risk of harm from the body being exposed to radiation (it's not just a measure of the quantity of radiation that hits someone). Radiation dose takes into account:

- The total amount of radiation absorbed.

- How harmful the type of radiation is.

- The type of body tissue absorbing the radiation. Some types of body tissue are more easily damaged by radiation than others.

Learning Objectives:

- Know the types of harm that UV waves, X-rays and gamma rays can cause to the human body.

- Know that radiation dose (in Sv or mSv) is a measure of the risk that exposure to radiation will cause harm to the body.

- Know that the effect of radiation on the body depends on the type of EM radiation and how big the dose is.

- Be able to use data related to radiation dose to understand the risk under different circumstances.

Specification Reference 6.6.2.3

Figure 1: *UV radiation has been shown to be a cause of cataracts, a leading cause of blindness across the world. A cataract is a clouding of the lens in the eye.*

Figure 2: *UV radiation is used to treat skin conditions such as psoriasis. Special goggles must be worn to prevent damage to the eyes.*

A CT scan uses X-rays and a computer to build up a picture of the inside of a patient's body. The table below shows the radiation dose received by two different parts of a patient's body when those body parts are scanned.

	Radiation dose (mSv)
Head	2.0
Chest	8.0

If a patient has a CT scan on their chest, it is four times more likely to cause harm than if they had a head scan.

Tip: A sievert is pretty big, so you'll often see doses in millisieverts (mSv), where 1000 mSv = 1 Sv.

Practice Questions — Fact Recall

Q1 Describe two ways in which UV radiation can damage the body.

Q2 What is meant by ionising radiation?

Q3 Name two types of ionising radiation.

Q4 What effect can gamma rays have on the body?

Q5 What does the radiation dose tell you?

Q6 What does the radiation dose depend on?

Practice Question — Application

Figure 3: In a CT scan, lots of X-rays are taken from different angles to build up a detailed image of inside the body.

Q1 A patient's pelvis is being examined. It can either be examined with a single X-ray photograph or with a CT scan.
An X-ray of the pelvis gives a radiation dose of 0.7 mSv.
A CT scan of the pelvis gives a radiation dose of 7 mSv.

a) How much larger is the added risk of harm if the patient has a CT scan?

b) A single dental X-ray photograph gives a radiation dose of 0.004 mSv. Suggest why this dose is different from the dose from an X-ray of the pelvis.

Topic 6b Checklist — Make sure you know...

What are Electromagnetic Waves?

☐ That electromagnetic waves are a group of transverse waves that all transfer energy from a source to an absorber and all travel at the same speed in a vacuum or in air.

☐ That the EM spectrum is a continuous spectrum of all the possible wavelengths (or frequencies) of EM waves, split into seven types: radio waves, microwaves, infrared, visible light, ultraviolet, X-rays and gamma rays (in order of decreasing wavelength/increasing frequency).

☐ That our eyes can only detect waves from the visible light part of the EM spectrum.

cont...

- [ ] That changes in atoms can generate EM waves and that gamma rays can be produced by changes in the nucleus.
- [ ] That different EM waves interact differently with different substances.

Radio Waves

- [ ] **H** That radio waves are produced by oscillating charges in an alternating electric current.
- [ ] **H** That when radio waves are absorbed by a receiver, they cause oscillations, which can lead to alternating currents of the same frequencies as the radio waves.
- [ ] How radio waves are used to transmit TV and radio.
- [ ] **H** Why radio waves are suitable for use in TV and radio communications.

More EM Waves and their Uses

- [ ] That microwaves are used for satellite communications and cooking food.
- [ ] How infrared radiation can be used in cooking, and how it allows electric heaters and infrared cameras to work.
- [ ] How fibre optic communications use visible light.
- [ ] How ultraviolet light allows energy efficient lamps and sun tanning lamps to work.
- [ ] How X-rays are used in medical imaging and treatments, e.g. to kill cancer cells.
- [ ] How gamma rays are used as medical tracers.
- [ ] **H** Why certain EM waves are suited to their uses.

Investigating Infrared Radiation

- [ ] How to investigate which surfaces emit or absorb infrared radiation better than others.

Dangers of EM Radiation

- [ ] That UV waves can harm the body (e.g. through premature skin ageing and an increased risk of skin cancer).
- [ ] X-rays and gamma rays are forms of ionising radiation which can cause gene mutations and cancer.
- [ ] That radiation dose (measured in sieverts) is a measure of the risk of harm due to exposure to radiation, and that 1000 mSv = 1 Sv.
- [ ] That radiation dose depends on the radiation type, the amount absorbed and the area of the body exposed.
- [ ] Be able to understand the risks of exposure to radiation in given situations.

Exam-style Questions

1   The diagram below shows the electromagnetic spectrum.

radio waves	microwaves	infrared	visible light	A	X-rays	gamma rays

   →

   1.1   Name a property of electromagnetic waves that decreases across the electromagnetic spectrum in the direction of the arrow shown.

(1 mark)

   1.2   Which type of radiation is represented by the letter **A** in the diagram?

(1 mark)

   1.3   Which two types of electromagnetic wave are used for transmitting TV signals?

(2 marks)

2   The table below shows the radiation dose of some X-ray scans.

	Abdomen	Spine	Teeth (Dental)
Radiation dose (mSv)	0.7	1.5	0.004

   2.1   How many times greater is the risk of harm from having a single abdominal X-ray scan than from having a single dental X-ray?

(2 marks)

   2.2   Explain why exposure to X-rays can be harmful to humans.

(2 marks)

   2.3   Many dentists recommend regular dental X-rays to check for hidden problems. Suggest why it is not recommended that people have regular X-rays of the spine to screen for problems.

(2 marks)

3   A number of electromagnetic waves are used for communications purposes.

   3.1   Describe how radio waves are transmitted and received, with reference to alternating current.

(4 marks)

          X-ray telescopes detect X-ray emissions from astronomical objects.

   3.2   There are no X-ray telescopes on the Earth's surface. They are all mounted on satellites in space. Suggest a reason for this.

(2 marks)

          Microwaves are used to communicate the observations of X-ray telescopes through the Earth's watery atmosphere. Some wavelengths of microwaves are transmitted by water, but some are absorbed.

   3.3   Explain why the wavelengths of microwaves used in a microwave oven could not be used to communicate with satellites.

(2 marks)

4 The setup below shows the apparatus for an investigation into the amount of radiation emitted by different surfaces. Half of a shiny aluminium can is painted matt black and the can is filled with boiling water. An infrared sensor, connected to a data logger, points towards the matt black side of the can and records the amount of infrared radiation it detects. The can is then turned around so that the detector points towards the shiny silver side of the can and another reading is taken.

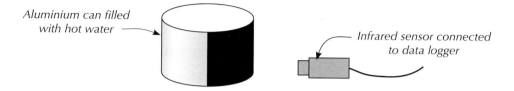

Aluminium can filled with hot water

Infrared sensor connected to data logger

The results of the investigation are shown in the graph below.

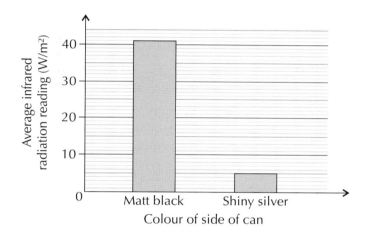

4.1 Give the average infrared radiation reading for the matt black surface in W/m².

(1 mark)

A thermometer is held so that it is touching the outside of the can. The temperature shown by the thermometer is the same when it is held against the shiny surface as when it is held against the black surface.

4.2 Explain why the results from the infrared sensor are different for each surface, while the thermometer readings are the same for each surface.

(2 marks)

The water was left in the can and the IR reading was taken again 15 minutes later.

4.3 Describe how you would expect this reading to differ from the earlier one, giving a reason for your answer.

(2 marks)

Another can, identical to the original, is painted matt silver and filled with boiling water. The IR radiation emitted is then measured in the same way as described above.

4.4 Suggest whether the IR radiation reading will be higher or lower than each of the readings above. Explain your answer.

(3 marks)

1. Magnetic Fields

Magnetic fields are responsible for the non-contact force experienced by magnetic materials. All magnets have one.

What is a magnetic field?

A magnet has a **magnetic field** around it. It's the magnetic field that causes magnetic objects to be attracted or repelled by a magnet, and they don't just exist around magnets.

> A magnetic field is a region where magnets, magnetic materials (like iron and steel), and also wires carrying currents, experience a force acting on them.

This magnetic force is a non-contact force — it can act between objects that are not physically touching each other.

A magnetic field can be represented by a field diagram (see Figure 1). A field diagram is just a series of lines that show where a magnetic field exists and its direction. All magnets have two poles, where the field is strongest — a north (or north seeking) pole and south (or south seeking) pole. Magnetic field lines have arrows on them that always point from north to south. The direction of the field lines show the direction of the force a north pole would feel if it was placed in that location. The stronger the magnetic field at any point, the closer together the field lines are. The further away from a magnet you get, the weaker the field.

Example

This is the magnetic field around a bar magnet. It's strongest at the north and south poles, where the field lines are closest together.

A north pole placed here will feel a force to the right

Figure 1: *A field diagram showing the magnetic field around a bar magnet.*

The force between a magnet and a **magnetic material** is always attractive, no matter the pole (see next page).

The force between two magnets placed close to each other can be attractive or repulsive.

- Two poles that are the same (these are called 'like poles') will repel each other (see Figure 2).

- Two different poles ('unlike poles') will attract each other (see Figure 3).

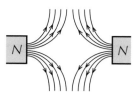

Figure 2: *The magnetic field between two like poles repelling each other.*

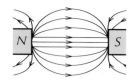

Figure 3: *The magnetic field between two unlike poles attracting each other.*

Tip: Remember, the direction of the field lines is the direction of the force a north pole would feel in that location.

Compasses

Inside a compass is a tiny bar magnet. The north pole of this magnet is attracted to the south pole of any other magnet it is near. So the compass points in the direction of the magnetic field it is in. You can move a compass around a magnet and trace its position on some paper to build up a picture of what the magnetic field looks like.

When they're not near a magnet, compasses always point north. This is because the Earth generates its own magnetic field, which shows that the inside (core) of the Earth must be magnetic.

Figure 4: *A series of compasses pointing along the magnetic field lines of a bar magnet, which are also shown by iron filings.*

Permanent and induced magnets

There are two types of magnet — **permanent magnets** and **induced magnets**. Permanent magnets produce their own magnetic fields. Induced magnets are magnetic materials that turn into magnets when they're in a magnetic field.

The force between permanent and induced magnets is always attractive (as with all magnetic materials). When you take away the magnetic field, induced magnets quickly lose their magnetism (or most of it) and stop producing a magnetic field.

Tip: As well as iron and steel, other magnetic materials include nickel and cobalt.

> **Example**
>
> The magnetic material becomes magnetised when it is brought near the bar magnet. It has its own poles and magnetic field.
>
>
>
>   permanent magnet   induced magnet
>
> Figure 5: *A diagram of magnetic poles induced in a magnetic material when it is brought near to a bar magnet.*

Practice Questions — Fact Recall

Q1   What is a magnetic field?

Q2   Draw the magnetic field lines around a bar magnet.

Q3   How do we know that the Earth's core is magnetic?

Q4   Describe what is meant by an 'induced magnet'.

Learning Objectives:
- Know that a current-carrying wire has a magnetic field.
- Know how to demonstrate the magnetic properties of a current-carrying wire, e.g. by using a compass.
- Be able to draw the magnetic field around a straight current-carrying wire.
- Know how the strength of this magnetic field varies with distance from the wire and size of current in the wire.
- Understand why coiling a current-carrying wire into a solenoid increases the magnetic field strength.
- Be able to draw the magnetic field of a solenoid.
- Know that the magnetic field inside a solenoid is strong and uniform, and the field outside a solenoid is similar to a bar magnet.
- Know that adding an iron core to a solenoid increases the strength of the magnetic field.
- Know that a solenoid with an iron core is known as an electromagnet.

Specification Reference
6.7.2.1

2. Electromagnetism

Magnets aren't the only things with magnetic fields — anything that's carrying an electric current also has one. This can have some clever applications.

The magnetic field around a current-carrying wire

When a current (see p. 61) flows through a wire, a magnetic field is created around the wire. The field is made up of concentric circles (circles which share the same centre) perpendicular to the wire, with the wire in the centre (see Figure 1).

You can see this by placing a compass near a wire which is carrying a current. As you move the compass, it will trace the direction of the magnetic field.

Changing the direction of the current changes the direction of the magnetic field — use the **right-hand thumb rule** to work out which way it goes:

The right-hand thumb rule

Using your right hand, point your thumb in the direction of the current, and curl your fingers. The direction of your fingers is the direction of the field.

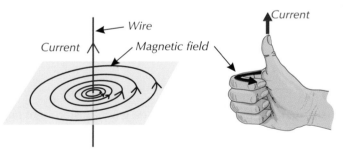

Figure 1: *A diagram showing how a magnetic field is created around a current-carrying wire, alongside a demonstration of the right-hand thumb rule.*

The strength of the magnetic field produced changes with the current and the distance from the wire. The larger the current through the wire, or the closer to the wire you are, the stronger the field is.

Solenoids

You can increase the strength of the magnetic field that a wire produces by wrapping the wire into a coil called a **solenoid**.

This happens because the field lines around each loop of wire line up with each other and form the magnetic field shown in Figure 2.

The result is lots of field lines pointing in the same direction that are very close to each other. As you saw on page 216, the closer together the field lines are, the stronger the field is.

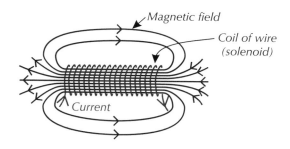

Figure 2: *A field diagram showing the magnetic field created around a current-carrying solenoid.*

The magnetic field inside a solenoid is strong and uniform (it has the same strength and direction at every point in that region). Outside the coil, the magnetic field is just like the one round a bar magnet.

Figure 3: *Iron filings showing the magnetic field lines around a current-carrying solenoid.*

You can increase the strength of the magnetic field of a solenoid even more by putting a block of iron in the centre of the coil. The iron core becomes an induced magnet whenever current is flowing. The magnetic field of the core and the coil combine, making a stronger magnet overall.

If you stop the current, the magnetic field disappears. A solenoid with an iron core (a magnet whose magnetic field can be turned on and off by an electric current) is called an **electromagnet**.

Uses of electromagnets

Magnets you can switch on and off (electromagnets) are really useful. They're usually used because they're so quick to turn on and off or because they can create a varying force.

Figure 4: *An electromagnet used in the Large Hadron Collider at CERN. Solenoids can be used to make incredibly large and powerful magnets.*

Example 1

Magnets can be used to attract and pick up things made from magnetic materials like iron and steel. Electromagnets are used in some cranes, e.g. in scrap yards and steel works.

If an ordinary magnet was used, the crane would be able to pick up the scrap metal etc., but then wouldn't let it go, which isn't very helpful.

Using an electromagnet means the magnet can be switched on when you want to pick stuff up, then switched off when you want to drop it, which is far more useful.

Figure 5: *A scrap yard crane that uses an electromagnet. The electromagnet is switched off when the crane needs to drop the metal.*

Q1 In the right-hand thumb rule, what does your thumb represent?
    What do your fingers represent?

Q2 Draw the magnetic field of a solenoid.

Q3 State how you can increase the strength of the magnetic field
    produced by a solenoid.

Q4 Describe what an electromagnet is and explain how it works.

Q5 Give one use of an electromagnet.

Practice Questions — Application

Q1 A current-carrying wire (shown by the red dot) produces the
    following magnetic field pattern when viewed from above.

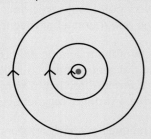

a) What direction is the current flowing in?

b) In what direction would the field lines point if the current began
   flowing in the opposite direction?

Tip: You'll need to use
the right-hand thumb
rule to find the direction
of the current.

3. The Motor Effect Higher

Learning Objectives:

- **H** Know that a current-carrying conductor and a magnet exert a force on one another while the conductor is inside the magnet's magnetic field. This is the motor effect.
- **H** Know that the size of the force due to the motor effect depends on the current, the length of conductor inside the field and the magnetic flux density.
- **H** Know how to use the equation $F = BIl$.
- **H** Know and be able to use Fleming's left-hand rule.

Specification Reference
6.7.2.2

If the magnetic field produced by a current-carrying wire is within a magnetic field in the first place, the interacting fields can make things start to move...

What is the motor effect?

As you know from page 218, passing an electric current through a wire (or other **conductor**) produces a magnetic field around the wire. If you put that wire into another magnetic field, you end up with two magnetic fields combining. The result is that the wire and the magnet exert a force on each other.

When a current-carrying wire in a magnetic field experiences a force it is known as the **motor effect**.

Figure 1: A diagram of the magnetic field interactions which lead to the motor effect. The red dot represents a wire carrying current out of the page (towards you).

Increasing the strength of the magnetic field, or the size of the current flowing through the wire, will increase the size of the force.

To experience the full force, the wire has to be at 90° to the magnetic field (see Figure 2). If the wire runs along parallel to the magnetic field it won't experience any force at all. At angles in between it'll feel some force.

Example **Higher**

A straight current-carrying wire will experience a force if it is placed at right angles to a magnetic field. The force will be at 90° to both the wire and the magnetic field.

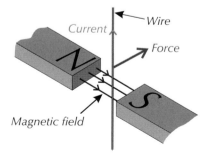

Figure 2: A diagram showing the force on a current-carrying wire placed at 90° to a magnetic field.

Tip: H You'll see how to work out the size and direction of the force on the next few pages.

As the motor effect results in a force, it's a handy way of producing movement.

Example **Higher**

A horseshoe magnet is used to provide a magnetic field. A conducting bar is placed on two conducting rails fixed at 90° to the magnetic field (see Figure 4).

If a current is applied to the rails, the current will flow through the bar (at 90° to the field) and the motor effect will cause the bar to experience a force.

The bar is free to move, so it will roll in the direction of the force. As in the previous example, the force on the conductor is at 90° to both the conductor and the magnetic field.

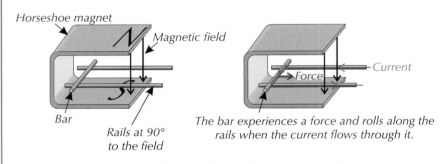

The bar experiences a force and rolls along the rails when the current flows through it.

Figure 4: *A diagram showing how the motor effect can be used to produce movement.*

Calculating the size of the force

The force acting on a conductor in a magnetic field depends on three things:

- The **magnetic flux density** — how many field (flux) lines there are in a region. This shows the strength of the magnetic field. It is represented by the symbol B and is measured in tesla (T).

- The size of the current through the conductor, I.

- The length of the conductor that's in the magnetic field, l.

When the current is at 90° to the magnetic field it is in, then you can calculate the size of the force using the equation:

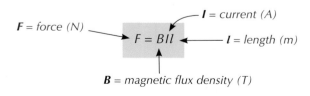

F = force (N)

I = current (A)

$$F = BIl$$

l = length (m)

B = magnetic flux density (T)

A 10 cm length of wire carrying a current of 3 A sits inside a magnetic field. The current flows at 90° to the direction of the magnetic field. It experiences a force of 0.12 N from the motor effect.

Calculate the magnetic flux density of the magnet.

First, convert the length into metres.

$$l = 10 \text{ cm} = 0.1 \text{ m}$$

You're looking for the magnetic flux density, so rearrange $F = BIl$ to find B, then substitute in the values you're given.

$$F = BIl, \text{ so } B = F \div (l \times I)$$
$$= 0.12 \div (3 \times 0.1) = 0.4 \text{ T}$$

Fleming's left-hand rule

If a current is flowing at 90° to a magnetic field, you can tell which way the force acting on the conductor due to the motor effect will act using **Fleming's left-hand rule**.

Here's what you do:

- Using your left hand, point your **F**irst finger in the direction of the **F**ield.

- Point your se**C**ond finger in the direction of the **C**urrent.

- Stick your thu**M**b out so it's at 90° to the other two fingers (see Figure 5). It will then point in the direction of the force (**M**otion).

If the direction of the current or magnetic field is reversed, then the direction of the force is reversed too (try it).

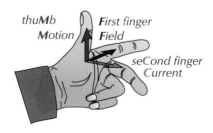

thu**M**b
Motion
First finger
Field
se**C**ond finger
Current

Figure 5: *A diagram showing how Fleming's left-hand rule can be used to find the direction of the force experienced by a current-carrying wire at 90° to a magnetic field.*

Tip: H You can use Fleming's left-hand rule to find the missing direction of any of these three quantities — as long as you know the other two.

Exam Tip H
You need to practise this before you get into the exam — you might need to use it to answer an exam question. It's no good pointing all over the place and ending up with the wrong answer because you can't remember which hand you're supposed to be using or what each finger represents.

Draw in the direction of the force acting on this wire.

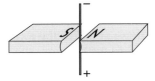

- Start by drawing in the current arrows and the magnetic field lines. Current goes from positive to negative and magnetic fields go from north to south. Then use Fleming's left-hand rule to work out the direction of the force (motion).

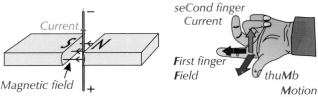

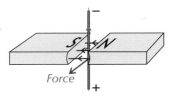

- Finally, draw in the direction of the force.

Practice Questions — Fact Recall

Q1 For the motor effect, give two ways the force on a current-carrying wire at 90° to a magnetic field can be increased.

Q2 What is the size of the force due to the motor effect on a current-carrying wire if it's parallel to a magnetic field?

Q3 State the equation which gives the size of the force due to the motor effect, and give the units for each quantity. State the condition that is required for this equation to work.

Q4 In Fleming's left-hand rule, what do the middle finger, index finger and thumb each represent?

Practice Questions — Application

Tip: 🄷 You'll have to work out the direction of the current and magnetic field yourself for part c).

Q1 In each of the situations below, the current-carrying wire is at 90° to the magnetic field. Give the direction of the force on the wire.

a) Current 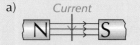   b) Current 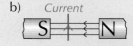   c) Current

Q2 Give the direction of the force on the wire in Q1 c) if the direction of the current is swapped and the poles of the magnets are swapped.

Q3 A wire carrying a current of 5.0 A through a 0.20 T magnetic field (at 90° to the field) experiences a force of 0.25 N.
Calculate the length of the wire, in cm, inside the magnetic field.

4. Using the Motor Effect Higher

The motor effect has many useful applications. It becomes really handy once you start using it to turn an axle.

Learning Objectives:

- **H** Understand how the motor effect can be used to make a coil of conductor rotate in a magnetic field.
- **H** Know that the rotation of a current-carrying coil in a magnetic field is the basis for many simple motors.

Specification Reference 6.7.2.3

The simple dc electric motor

You know from page 221 that the motor effect is when a current-carrying wire experiences a force in a magnetic field. Electric motors use the motor effect to produce rotation — and that rotation is the basis of an awful lot of appliances.

How it works

A loop of wire that's free to rotate about an axis is placed in a magnetic field (see Figure 1).

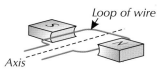

Figure 1: *A loop of wire in a magnetic field free to rotate about its axis.*

When a direct current flows through the loop, the two side arms, which are at 90° to the field, each experience a force due to the motor effect. They experience forces in opposite directions because the direction of the current in each arm is opposite (see Figure 2). The loop will start to rotate around its axis because the forces act one up and one down.

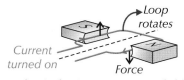

Figure 2: *A loop of wire in a magnetic field rotating when current flows through it.*

Tip: Remember, direct current (dc) is current that only flows in one direction, see page 86.

Tip: **H** Fleming's left-hand rule can be used to find the direction of each force — see page 223 if you need a reminder.

When the wire loop reaches a vertical position the forces will still be acting one up and one down on the same arms of the loop, so the loop gets stuck (see Figure 3).

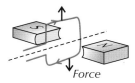

Figure 3: *A loop of wire getting stuck in the same position due to the forces acting on it.*

Tip: **H** The loop will actually vibrate back and forth slightly as it'll have some momentum, but you don't need to worry about that.

For the motor to keep rotating in the same direction, the forces acting on the arms of the loop need to swap direction.

Reversing the direction of the current reverses the direction of the force (see page 223). A **split-ring commutator** is a clever way of doing this — it swaps the contacts of the loop every half turn, reversing the current — see Figures 4 and 5.

A split-ring commutator is just a conducting ring with a gap between the two halves. As it rotates, the part of the commutator that is touching each contact changes every half turn.

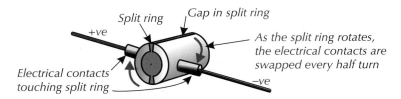

Figure 4: A split-ring commutator.

By linking each end of the loop to one half of a split-ring commutator, you change the electrical contacts of the loop (and so the direction of the current) every half turn. This means that the force acting on each arm of the loop will swap every half turn, allowing rotation to continue in the same direction.

Tip: H You can have an ac (alternating current) electric motor too, in which case you don't need a split-ring commutator — it just has to rotate at or close to the frequency of the current.

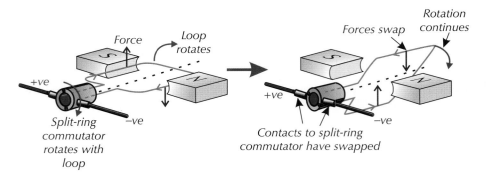

Figure 5: A dc electric motor using a split-ring commutator to swap the direction of the current, and so the forces, every half turn.

And that's it — a simple dc electric motor. Make sure you understand how it uses the motor effect to work.

Speed of a simple electric motor

The speed of an electric motor can be increased in two main ways:

- by increasing the current.

- by increasing the strength of the magnetic field.

Both of these factors increase the force experienced by the wire due to the motor effect, so it rotates faster.

Using a coil of wire instead of a single loop will also increase the force caused by the motor effect. It's simple really — the sides of each individual loop experience a force, so the more loops you have, the larger the total force on the sides of the coil. So, if you're calculating the force on a coil of wire in a magnetic field, you need to first calculate the force on a single loop (using the equation on p. 222) and then multiply it by the number of loops in the coil.

Direction of a simple electric motor

The direction that a motor turns in can be found using Fleming's left-hand rule, and can be reversed either by:

- swapping the polarity of the direct current (dc) supply, or
- swapping the magnetic poles over.

Example — **Higher**

Is the electric motor turning clockwise or anticlockwise?

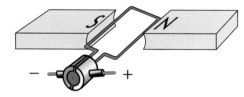

- Start by drawing in the magnetic field lines from north to south, and the direction of the current from positive to negative.

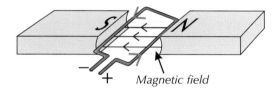

Magnetic field

- Then use Fleming's left-hand rule on one side of the loop to work out the direction of the force (motion). Let's use the right side of the loop.

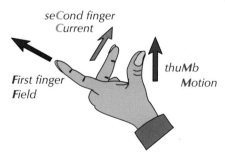

seCond finger
Current

First finger
Field

thuMb
Motion

- Finally, draw in the direction of the force.

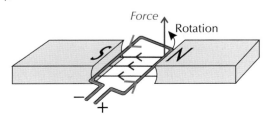

Force
Rotation

- So — the motor is turning anticlockwise.

Tip: **H** The first step of this method should look familiar — it's the same one that was used on page 224 to find the direction of the force on a straight wire in a magnetic field.

Q1 Why is a split-ring commutator needed in an electric motor that uses direct current?

Q2 Give two ways the direction of rotation of a simple electric motor can be reversed.

Practice Question — Application

Q1 Look at this diagram of a simple electric motor.

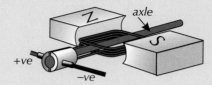

a) Which direction is the axle turning — clockwise or anticlockwise?

b) What will happen to the speed of the axle if the current is increased?

c) What will happen if the magnetic poles are reversed?

Topic 7 Checklist — Make sure you know...

Magnetic Fields

☐ That magnets have a magnetic field — a region in which other magnets, magnetic materials and wires carrying a current experience a non-contact force.

☐ That all magnets have two poles, north and south, where the magnetic field is strongest.

☐ That the strength of a magnetic field decreases with distance from the magnet.

☐ That magnetic field lines point away from north poles and towards south poles, and how to draw the magnetic field pattern of a bar magnet.

☐ That like poles repel each other and unlike poles attract each other.

☐ That compasses work due to magnetism, and provide evidence that the Earth's core is magnetic.

☐ How to use a compass to plot a magnetic field.

☐ What an induced magnet is, and the difference between permanent and induced magnets.

☐ That the force on induced magnets (like all magnetic materials) in a magnetic field is always attractive.

Electromagnetism

☐ That a current flowing through a conductor generates a magnetic field.

☐ That you can demonstrate the existence of the magnetic field around a current-carrying conductor using a compass.

cont...

☐ That the direction of the magnetic field generated by a current can be found using the right-hand thumb rule.

☐ That the strength of the magnetic field generated by a current increases with the size of the current, and decreases with distance from the wire.

☐ Why bending a current-carrying conductor into a coil increases the magnetic field strength.

☐ How to draw the magnetic fields of a current-carrying wire and a solenoid.

☐ That the magnetic field inside a solenoid is strong and uniform, and the field outside resembles that of a bar magnet.

☐ That the strength of the magnetic field of a solenoid can be increased by adding an iron core, and that this forms a simple electromagnet.

The Motor Effect

☐ H That a current flowing through a conductor in a magnetic field causes a force between the magnet producing that field and the conductor — this is the motor effect.

☐ H That the size of the force depends on the size of the current, the length of conductor inside the magnetic field, and the magnetic flux density of the magnetic field.

☐ H How to calculate the size of the force when the current is at 90° to the magnetic field using $F = BIl$.

☐ H That the direction of the force depends on the direction of the current and the direction of the magnetic field, and how to use Fleming's left-hand rule.

Using the Motor Effect

☐ H How the motor effect can cause a coil of current-carrying wire to rotate inside a magnetic field.

☐ H How this is the basis of a simple electric motor, and how the speed and direction of an electric motor can be changed.

Exam-style Questions

1   A student designs a simple battery-powered screwdriver, as shown. The coil of wire is placed in a uniform magnetic field between two permanent bar magnets. The coil is supplied with direct current (dc), and a split-ring commutator is used to reverse the direction of the current flowing through the coil of wire every half turn.

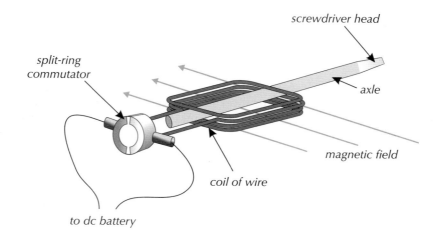

1.1   Describe what is meant by the motor effect.

(1 mark)

1.2   The screwdriver uses the motor effect to produce rotation of the axle. Usually, the screwdriver head rotates clockwise. A reverse switch rotates the position of the magnets so that the direction of the magnetic field is reversed.

Explain why this causes the screwdriver head to rotate anticlockwise.

(2 marks)

1.3   The current flowing through the wire is 3 A. The coil forms a square with sides 0.5 cm long and four wires tall. The magnetic flux density of the magnet is 0.2 T.
Calculate the total force on one of the two sides perpendicular to the magnetic field.
Give your answer in newtons.
Use the correct equation from the equations listed on page 284.

(2 marks)

The bar magnets used by the drill lose their magnetism over time, so the drill becomes gradually less powerful. One way of avoiding this is using electromagnets in place of the bar magnets. The electromagnets are made of a coil of wire, connected to a dc supply, that is wrapped around an iron core.

1.4   Explain how turning on the dc supply to the electromagnets produces a magnetic field around them.

(2 marks)

1.5   Explain why an ac supply would not be suitable to power an electromagnet in the screwdriver.

(3 marks)

1. Apparatus and Techniques

For the physics part of GCSE Combined Science, you'll have to do at least eight practicals, called Required Practical Activities. You'll need to know how to use various pieces of apparatus and carry out different scientific techniques. And not only do you need to carry out the practicals, you could also be asked about them in the exams. Luckily, all the physics Required Practical Activities are covered in this book, and the next few pages cover some of the techniques that you'll need to know about.

Measuring mass

Mass should be measured using a balance. For a solid, set the balance to zero, place your object onto the scale and read off the mass.

If you're measuring the mass of a liquid (or a granular solid, like sand) start by putting an empty container onto the balance. Next, reset the balance to zero, so you don't include the mass of the container in your measurement. Then just pour the substance you want to measure the mass of into the container and record the mass displayed. Easy peasy.

Measuring weight

Remember not to get weight and mass confused. Mass is the amount of 'stuff' in an object. Weight is the force acting on the object due to gravity (p. 129).

You could calculate the weight of an object by measuring its mass (see above) and then multiplying by the gravitational field strength (p. 130). But to measure the weight of an object directly, you should use a newtonmeter (see Figure 1). Make sure that whatever you're measuring is securely attached to the hook of the newtonmeter and can hang freely. Remember to wait until it's stopped swinging or bouncing before you read off the value.

Measuring length

In most cases a standard centimetre ruler can be used to measure length. It depends on what you're measuring though — metre rulers are handy for large distances, while micrometers (which have smaller divisions than a standard ruler) are used for measuring tiny things like the diameter of a wire. If you're dealing with something where it's tricky to measure just one accurately (e.g. water ripples, p. 193), you can measure the length of ten of them and then divide by ten to find the length of one.

If you're taking multiple measurements of the same object (e.g. to measure changes in length) then make sure you always measure from the same point on the object. It can help to draw or stick small markers onto the object to line up your ruler against — see Figure 2.

The ruler should always be parallel to what you want to measure. You should also make sure the ruler and the object are always at eye level when you take a reading. This stops parallax affecting your results (see next page).

Tip: The Required Practical Activities in this book are marked with a big stamp like this...

REQUIRED PRACTICAL **1**

The practicals that you do in class might be slightly different to the ones in this book (as it's up to your teacher exactly what method you use), but they'll cover the same principles and techniques.

Figure 1: *Measuring weight using a newtonmeter.*

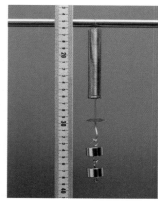

Figure 2: *A red marker being used to help read a length measurement from a ruler.*

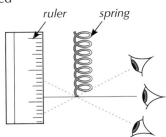
Tip: Whenever you're reading off a scale, use the value of the nearest mark on the scale (the nearest graduation).

Measuring angles

You should use a protractor to measure angles. First align the vertex (point) of the angle with the mark in the centre of the protractor. Line up the base line of the protractor with one line that forms the angle and then measure the angle of the other line using the scale on the protractor (see Figure 4).

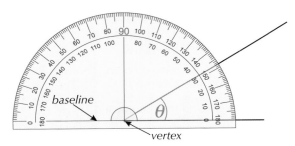

Figure 4: A protractor, correctly aligned to measure angle θ. The angle is 32°.

If the lines creating the angle are very thick, align the protractor and measure the angle using the centre of the lines. Using a sharp pencil to trace light rays or draw ray diagrams (page 195) helps to reduce errors when measuring angles.

If the lines are too short to measure easily, you may have to extend them. Again, make sure you use a sharp pencil and a ruler to do this.

Figure 5: The bulb of a thermometer fully submerged in the liquid it is measuring.

Measuring temperature

You measure temperature with a thermometer. To ensure you measure the temperature accurately, make sure the bulb of your thermometer is completely submerged in any substance you're measuring if it's a fluid (see Figure 5), or held directly against what you're measuring if it's a solid.

If you're taking a single measurement, wait for the temperature to stabilise before you take your reading. If you're measuring how the temperature of a substance is changing, take readings at regular time intervals (e.g. every 10 s).

Again, read your measurement off the scale on a thermometer at eye level.

Measuring time

You should use a stopwatch to measure time in most experiments — they're more accurate than regular watches. You can start and stop the timer whenever you need, or you can set an alarm so you know exactly when to stop an experiment or take a reading.

For some time measurements, you might be able to use a light gate. This will reduce the errors in your experiment. Have a look at page 167 for an example of a light gate being used.

A light gate sends a beam of light from one side of the gate to a detector on the other side. When something passes through the gate, the beam of light is interrupted. The light gate measures how long the beam was interrupted for. Light gates can use their measurements of time to calculate speed and acceleration, given the right information.

Tip: You can input data into light gate software, for example, the length of the thing that interrupts the beam. This allows it to calculate other quantities such as speed.

Measuring volume

Measuring the volume of a liquid

Measuring cylinders are the most common way to measure the volume of a liquid. They come in all different sizes. Make sure you choose one that's the right size for the measurement you want to make. It's no good using a huge 1 dm³ (1000 cm³) cylinder to measure out 2 cm³ of a liquid — the graduations (markings for scale) will be too big and you'll end up with massive errors. It'd be much better to use one that measures up to 10 cm³.

You can also use a pipette to measure volume. Pipettes are used to suck up and transfer volumes of liquid between containers. Graduated pipettes are used to transfer accurate volumes. A pipette filler is attached to the end of a graduated pipette, to control the amount of liquid being drawn up.

Whichever method you use, always read the volume from the bottom of the meniscus (the curved upper surface of the liquid) when it's at eye level — see Figure 6.

Figure 6: *The meniscus of a fluid in a measuring cylinder, viewed at eye level. This one reads 32.*

Measuring the volume of a solid

Eureka cans (or displacement cans) are used in combination with measuring cylinders to find the volumes of solids. A eureka can is essentially a beaker with a downward spout. A solid object will displace an amount of water equal to its volume, which can then be measured using a measuring cylinder.

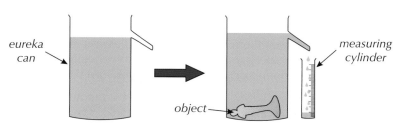

Figure 7: *A eureka can being used to measure volume.*

This method is particularly useful for irregularly shaped objects, where you can't simply measure its dimensions and calculate the volume mathematically. However, this method will only work for objects that sink. If the object floats, it will only displace a volume of water equal to the volume of the object that is submerged. You can see more on how to use a eureka can on page 98.

Good laboratory practice

Tip: For lots more info on doing experiments, see the Working Scientifically section at the start of this book.

When it comes to actually doing an experiment, it's important that you use good laboratory practice. This means working safely and accurately. To ensure you get good results, make sure you do the following:

- Measure all your quantities carefully — the more accurately you measure things the more accurate your results will be.

- Try to be consistent — for example, if you're using a piece of apparatus, make sure you use the same one throughout the experiment.

- Don't let yourself get distracted by other people — if you're distracted by what other people are doing you're more likely to make a mistake or miss a reading.

- As you're going along, make sure you remember to fill in your table of results — it's no good doing a perfect experiment if you forget to record the data.

Working safely

There are always hazards in any experiment, so before you start a practical you should do a risk assessment first. A risk assessment identifies all possible hazards in an experiment and lists the precautions you'll take to deal with them. You should also read and follow any safety precautions provided with the apparatus or by your teacher to do with your method or the apparatus you're using.

The hazards will depend on the experiment and the apparatus you're using, but the examples given here should give you some ideas of things to think about.

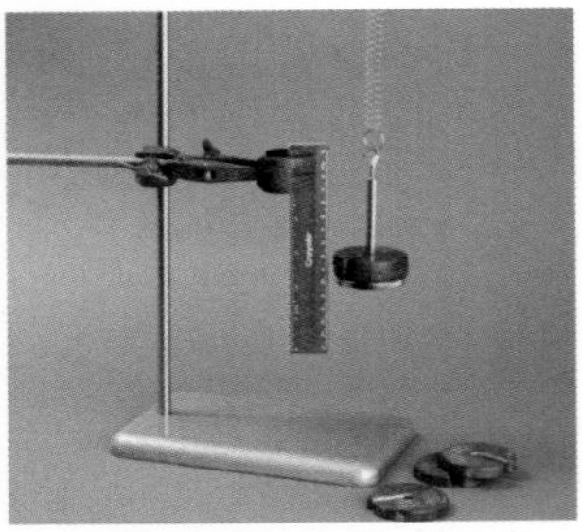

Figure 8: *A clamp stand being used in a hanging mass experiment.*

Figure 9: *A scientist wearing laser safety goggles while working with lasers.*

Examples

- Stop masses and equipment falling by using clamp stands. Make sure masses are of a sensible weight so they don't break the equipment they're used with, and use pulleys of a sensible length. That way, any hanging masses won't hit the floor during the experiment.

- When heating materials, make sure to let them cool before moving them, or wear insulated gloves while handling them.

- When working with water, clean up any spillages immediately to avoid a slip hazard, and be extra careful when using water around electricity.

- If you're using a laser, there are a few safety rules you must follow. Always wear laser safety goggles and never look directly into the laser or shine it towards another person. Make sure you turn the laser off if it's not needed to avoid any accidents.

- When working with electronics, make sure you use a low enough voltage and current to prevent wires overheating (and potentially melting) and avoid damage to components, like blowing a filament bulb.

You also need to be aware of general safety in the lab — handle glassware carefully so it doesn't break, don't stick your fingers in sockets and avoid touching frayed wires. That kind of thing.

2. Working with Electronics

You'll have to do a lot of experiments using electrical circuits. Here's a run down of some of the measurements you'll need to make most often and the equipment you'll need to use to do so.

Circuit diagrams

You need to be able to interpret circuit diagrams. Before you get cracking on an experiment involving any kind of electrical devices, you have to plan and build your circuit using a circuit diagram. Make sure you know all of the circuit symbols on page 60 so you're not stumped before you've even started.

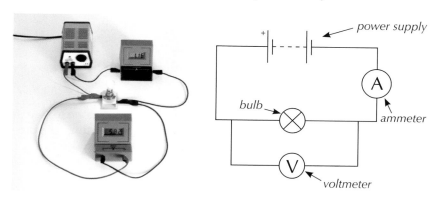

Tip: Make sure you draw wires as straight lines, and don't let them cross each other unless there's a connection. This makes your circuit diagrams a lot clearer.

Figure 1: *A photo of a simple electrical circuit, alongside a circuit diagram of the same electrical circuit.*

Making measurements in circuits

Using voltmeters

A voltmeter measures potential difference (see page 62). If you're using an analogue voltmeter, choose the voltmeter with the most appropriate unit for what you're measuring (e.g. V or mV). If you're using a digital voltmeter, you'll most likely be able to switch between them.

Figure 2: *An example of an analogue voltmeter (left) and a digital voltmeter (right).*

Connect the voltmeter in parallel (p. 72) across the component you want to test. The voltmeter will usually have red (positive) and black (negative) ports, to help you connect them to a circuit correctly. If you get them backwards, your voltage reading will be negative. Once everything's set up, simply read the potential difference from the scale (or from the screen if it's digital).

Using ammeters

Ammeters measure electrical current (see page 61). Just like with voltmeters, choose the ammeter with the most appropriate unit (usually A or mA), unless it's a digital one.

Connect the ammeter in series (p. 68) with the component you want to test, making sure they're both on the same branch. Again, they usually have red and black ports to show you where to connect your wires. Then simply read off the current shown on the scale or by the screen.

Tip: You should turn your circuit off between readings to prevent wires overheating and affecting your results or damaging the equipment.

Using multimeters

Figure 3: *An example of a digital multimeter.*

Instead of having a separate ammeter and voltmeter, many circuits use multimeters (see Figure 3). These are devices that measure a range of properties — usually potential difference, current and resistance.

One wire should always be plugged into the black (negative) port. If you want to find potential difference, make sure the other wire is plugged into the red (positive) port that says 'V' (for volts), and connect it like a voltmeter. To find the current, use the red (positive) port labelled 'A' or 'mA' (for amps), and connect it like an ammeter.

The dial on the multimeter should then be turned to the relevant section, e.g. to 'A' to measure current in amps (on Figure 3, the 'DCA' section measures direct current, dc). The screen will display the value you're measuring in the units you've chosen with the dial.

Oscilloscopes

An oscilloscope is basically a snazzy voltmeter. You can use one to 'see' how the potential difference of an electricity supply changes over time. Figure 4 shows an oscilloscope and how it can be used.

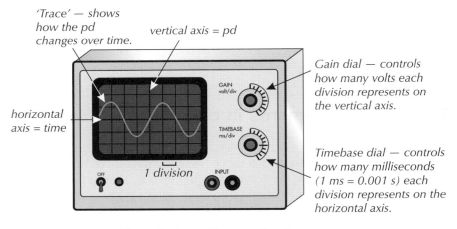

Figure 4: *An oscilloscope showing a trace.*

To use an oscilloscope, simply connect it up as you would any voltmeter. You can then read values of the potential difference from the trace displayed.

Each main division (or square) on the screen is usually divided into five smaller divisions so it can be read to a higher resolution. So each minor division is 0.2 of a major division. You'll probably want to adjust the 'gain' and 'timebase' dials to make sure each division represents a sensible value for what you want to measure.

Maths skills for GCSE Combined Science

Maths crops up quite a lot in GCSE Combined Science so it's really important that you've mastered all the maths skills needed before sitting your exams. Maths skills are covered throughout this book but here's an extra little section, just on maths, to help you out with the physics exams.

1. Calculations

Sometimes the numbers you use in physics are just plain awkward — they're either too big, too small or go on forever. The next few pages show how calculations can be made a lot easier.

Standard form

You need to be able to work with numbers that are written in **standard form**. Standard form is used for writing very big or very small numbers in a more convenient way. Standard form must always look like this:

This number must always be between 1 and 10. ⟶ $A \times 10^n$ ⟵ *This number is the number of places the decimal point moves.*

You can write a standard form number out in full by moving the decimal point. Which direction to move the decimal point, and how many places to move it depends on 'n'. If 'n' is positive, the decimal point needs to move to the right. If 'n' is negative the decimal point needs to move to the left.

Example

Here's how to write out 9.3×10^4 in full.

▪ Work out which way the decimal point needs to move, by looking at the 'n' number. Here it's a positive number (4) so the decimal point needs to move four places to the right:

$$9.3 \times 10^4 = 9\,3\,0\,0\,0.$$

▪ So 9.3×10^4 is the same as 93 000.

Here's how to write out 5.6×10^{-5} in full.

▪ 'n' is a negative number (–5) so the decimal point needs to move five places to the left.

$$5.6 \times 10^{-5} = .0\,0\,0\,0\,5\,6$$

▪ So 5.6×10^{-5} is the same as 0.000056.

Tip: If a number isn't written in standard form, it's said to be in decimal form — e.g. 0.00012 or 34 500.

Tip: You need to add a zero into any space left by the decimal point moving.

Figure 1: *The 'Exp' or '×10ˣ' button is used to input standard form on calculators.*

The key things to remember with numbers in standard form are...

- When 'n' is positive the number is big. The bigger 'n' is, the bigger the number is.

- When 'n' is negative the number is small. The smaller 'n' is (the more negative), the smaller the number is.

- When 'n' is the same for two or more numbers, you need to look at the start of each number to work out which is bigger. For example, 4.5 is bigger than 3.0, so 4.5×10^5 is bigger than 3.0×10^5.

There's a special button on your calculator for using standard form in a calculation — it's the 'Exp' button. So if, for example, you wanted to type in 2×10^7, you'd only need to type in: '2' 'Exp' '7'. Some calculators may have a different button that does the same job, for example it could say 'EE' or '×10ˣ' instead of 'Exp' — see Figure 1.

Ratios, fractions and percentages

You need to be able to use ratios, fractions and percentages, and know what they mean.

Fractions and ratios

Fractions and ratios are two different things in maths, but they are used to express relationships between quantities in physics in very similar ways.

A fraction is just one number divided by another number, written as $\frac{x}{y}$. They're used all over the place in physics:

Tip: When using the equation $E_k = \frac{1}{2}mv^2$, you could type 0.5 into your calculator instead. Either will work, as $\frac{1}{2} = 0.5$.

Example 1

- $E_k = \frac{1}{2}mv^2$ uses the fraction $\frac{1}{2}$, or 1 divided by 2.

- $\text{Power} = \dfrac{\text{Energy transferred}}{\text{time}}$ uses a fraction to express power as energy transferred over time.

Tip: Calculating power is covered on page 32.

A ratio is a proportional relationship between two quantities. It tells you how the two quantities are related to each other.

Tip: For a given efficiency, total input energy transfer and useful output energy transfer are proportional to each other.

Example 2

Efficiency is a ratio. It is the relationship between the amount of energy you transfer to a device, and the amount of energy it transfers usefully:

$$\text{efficiency} = \dfrac{\text{useful output energy transfer}}{\text{total input energy transfer}}$$

But it is also a fraction. This is an example of 'ratio' and 'fraction' being used to describe similar things.

Usually in maths, ratios are expressed in a special form when comparing two quantities.

A colon separates one quantity from the other. ⟶ $x : y$ ⟵ x and y stand for the two quantities.

To write a ratio in this form, first write down the numbers you have of each thing, separated by a colon. Then divide the numbers by the same amount until they're the smallest they can be whilst still being whole numbers — this is called simplifying the ratio. You can also find what a ratio simplifies to using your calculator.

Example 3

To find the ratio 120 : 150 in its simplest form using your calculator, just type in $\frac{120}{150}$ as a fraction and press equals. Your calculator will give you the most simplified version, which in this case is $\frac{4}{5}$.

So the ratio in its simplest form is 4 : 5.

If your calculator gives a decimal, use the button on your calculator that swaps between fractions and decimals — it'll probably look like one of these:

      CHANGE

Percentages

Percent means 'out of 100'. A percentage is really just a fraction out of 100, so 62% means 62 out of 100. In physics, percentages are mostly used to express one number as a percentage of another number. For example, useful output energy transfer as a percentage of total input energy transfer is efficiency (see page 38). To find one number as a percentage of another, divide the first number by the second and multiply by 100.

Example

1092 J of energy is transferred to a motor. 819 J of this transferred usefully by the motor. Calculate the efficiency of the motor as a percentage.

To find 819 as a percentage of 1092, first divide 819 by 1092:
819 ÷ 1092 = 0.75

Then multiply this by 100:
0.75 × 100 = 75%

So efficiency of motor = 75 %

Tip: Take a look at page 38 for more on calculating efficiencies.

Estimating

Estimating can be a really useful tool in physics. You've already seen that you can use typical values (e.g. speed and mass, see pages 148 and 165) in calculations to give estimates.

You can also use estimating to check if your final answer is sensible or not.

Example 1

A spring with spring constant 12.05 N/m is extended by 0.98 m. Calculate the energy transferred to its elastic potential energy store? Use the equation: $E_e = \frac{1}{2}ke^2$.

First estimate what the answer should be:
elastic potential energy = $0.5 \times 12.05 \times 0.98^2 \approx 0.5 \times 10 \times 1^2 \approx 5$ J

The actual answer is 5.8 J (to 2 s.f.). From the estimated calculation, 5.8 J is a sensible answer. If your answer was 5800 J, you would know that your calculation had gone wrong somewhere.

Estimating can also be useful for choosing apparatus to use in an experiment.

Example 2

The apparatus for measuring the volume of an awards statue is shown on the right.

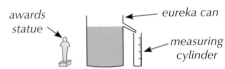

When the statue is put in the eureka can, the water level rises, which causes water to flow into the measuring cylinder. The volume of the statue is equal to the volume of water displaced. To decide what measuring cylinder to use, you should estimate the volume of the object.

An estimate for the volume of the statue can be found if the statue is considered to be a cuboid with a height of 20 cm and a base of 7 cm by 7 cm.

Volume of a cuboid = $w \times h \times d$
$$= 7 \times 20 \times 7$$
$$= 980 \text{ cm}^3$$

The measuring cylinder should be able to hold about 1000 cm³.

Tip: You need to be able to find the volume of an irregularly shaped object in order to find its density. See page 98.

2. Algebra

Physics involves a lot of rearranging equations and substituting values into equations. It can be easy to make simple mistakes, so here's a few things to remember...

Algebra symbols

Here's a reminder of some of the symbols that you may come across:

Symbol	Meaning
=	is equal to
<	is less than
<<	is much less than
>	is greater than
>>	is much greater than
$\propto$	is directly proportional to
~	is approximately
Δ	change in (a quantity)
$\approx$	is approximately equal to

Tip: An example of using $\propto$ can be found on page 130.

Tip: Δ is the Greek capital letter 'delta'. An example of using Δ can be found on page 150.

Rearranging equations

Being able to rearrange equations is a must in physics — you'll often need to change the subject of an equation. The subject of an equation is just the value that the rest of the equation is equal to (usually a single letter on the left-hand side of the equals sign). For rearranging equations, remember the golden rule — whatever you do to one side of the equation, you must do to the other side.

Figure 1: *It can be easy to make a mistake rearranging equations when you're stressed in an exam. It's a good idea to double check rearrangements, especially if it's a tricky one where you've had to combine and rearrange equations.*

Example 1

Rearrange the equation for momentum, $p = mv$, to make v the subject.

$p = mv$

Divide by m to get v by itself.

$\dfrac{p}{m} = v$

So $v = \dfrac{p}{m}$.

Example 2

For an object travelling with a uniform acceleration, the equation that links the initial velocity, final velocity, acceleration and distance travelled is: $v^2 - u^2 = 2as$. Rearrange the equation to make v the subject.

$v^2 - u^2 = 2as$

Add u^2 to both sides to get v^2 on its own.

$v^2 = 2as + u^2$

Take the square root

$v = \sqrt{2as + u^2}$

Tip: There's an example of substituting into this equation on the next page.

Tip: Remember — two letters written next to each other means they're being multiplied, so $mv = m \times v$.

Substituting into equations

Take a look at pages 17-18 for how to convert between different units.

Once you've rearranged your equation, you'll probably need to substitute values into it to find your answer. Pretty easy stuff — make sure your values are in the right units — getting this wrong is a common mistake. Take a look at pages 17-18 for how to convert between different units.

Tip: Rounding to the correct number of significant figures is covered on page 14.

Tip: Your values you put into an equation should be in the units given throughout the book, unless you're asked to give your answer in different units.

Tip: Converting all the values into the correct units <u>before</u> putting them into the equation stops you making silly mistakes.

Tip: Rounding to the correct number of significant figures is covered on page 14.

Example

A train pulls out of a station and is initially travelling at 2.0 m/s. The train accelerates with a constant acceleration over a distance of 3.4 km. At this distance, the train reaches a final velocity of 150 km/h. Calculate the acceleration of the train. Use the equation $v^2 - u^2 = 2as$. Give your answer in m/s².

Your answer needs to be in m/s², so you need to be using metres and seconds. Some of the given values are in different units, so you need to convert them.

$u = 2.0$ m/s

$s = 3.4$ km $= 3.4 \times 1 \times 10^3$ m $= 3400$ m

$v = 150$ km/h $= 150 \times 1 \times 10^3$ m/h $= 150\,000$ m/h
$$= 150\,000 \div 3600 \text{ m/s} = 41.66... \text{ m/s}$$

Rearrange the equation $v^2 - u^2 = 2as$ to make a the subject:

$$a = \frac{v^2 - u^2}{2s} = \frac{41.66...^2 - 2.0^2}{2 \times 3400} = 0.254... \text{ m/s}^2 = 0.25 \text{ m/s}^2 \text{ (to 2 s.f.)}$$

Formula triangles

Tip: The word formula is sometimes used instead of the word equation, e.g. the formula for power is $\frac{\text{energy transferred}}{\text{time}}$.

If three terms are related by a formula that looks like $v = f\lambda$ or $f = \frac{v}{\lambda}$, then you can put them into a formula triangle like this:

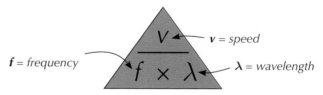

Figure 2: The formula triangle for $v = f\lambda$ —
v on the top and $f \times \lambda$ on the bottom.

Tip: For an equation with two terms multiplied together, these go on the bottom of the formula triangle (and so the other must go on the top). For an equation with one term divided by another, the one on top of the division goes on top in the formula triangle and the others go on the bottom (in any order).

- To use the triangle, put your thumb over the term you want to find and write down what's left showing. This gives you your formula (for example $f = \frac{v}{\lambda}$).
- Then put in the values for the other terms and work out the term you want.

Example

Tip: Alternatively, you could work this out using the method for rearranging equations given on the previous page.

Give the equation for power (P) in terms of energy transferred (E) and time (t) given the formula $E = Pt$.

- As P is multiplied by t, E goes on top, leaving $P \times t$ on the bottom.

- Covering P leaves $\frac{E}{t}$.
- So, power = energy transferred ÷ time.

---

3. Graphs

Results are often presented using graphs, as you've seen on pages 15-16. They make it easier to work out relations between variables and can also be used to calculate other quantities.

Linear graphs

You will most often come across **linear graphs**. A linear graph means that the two variables plotted on the axes produce a straight line. If the line goes through the origin (0,0), then the two variables are directly proportional. An example of a linear graph is shown in Figure 1.

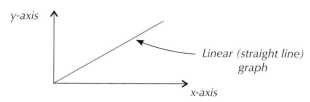

Figure 1: A linear graph, which passes through the origin.

Tip: The origin of a graph is the point (0,0) on the graph, i.e. it's the point at which the x-axis and y-axis meet.

Tip: A non-linear graph is just any graph that's curved.

Finding the gradient

The **gradient** (slope) of a graph tells you how quickly the variable on the y-axis changes if you change the variable on the x-axis. It is calculated using:

$$\text{gradient} = \frac{\text{change in } y}{\text{change in } x}$$

Tip: If the value on the x-axis is time, then the gradient will be equal to the rate of change of the value on the y-axis. For example, on a distance-time graph, the gradient is the rate of change of distance, which is speed.

Example

This linear graph shows the force acting on a spring against its extension. The gradient of the line is equal to the spring constant of the spring.

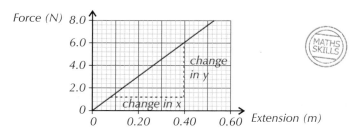

Tip: There's more on force-extension graphs on page 141.

To calculate the gradient, pick two points on the line that are easy to read and a good distance apart. Draw a line down from one of the points and a line across from the other to make a triangle. The line drawn down the side of the triangle is the change in y and the line across the bottom is the change in x.

Change in y = 6.0 – 1.2 = 4.8 N   Change in x = 0.40 – 0.08 = 0.32 m

Tip: You can use this method to calculate the rate of change from a graph, so long as the x-axis is time.

Spring constant = gradient = $\dfrac{\text{change in } y}{\text{change in } x} = \dfrac{4.8}{0.32}$ = 15 N/m

y = mx + c

The equation of a straight line is given by:

y = y-axis variable

c = y-intercept

$$y = mx + c$$

m = gradient

x = x-axis variable

The y-intercept is the point at which the line crosses the y-axis. If the straight line passes through the origin of the graph, then the y-intercept is just zero. You can use this equation to work out what the gradient and y-intercept values of a graph represent.

Example

A student is heating a block of aluminium with an electric heater in order to find its specific heat capacity. The expected shape of the graph from his experiment is shown. The change in temperature is the y-axis variable and the energy transferred to the aluminium is the x-axis variable.

Tip: Take a look at pages 30-31 for more about this experiment and the graph.

temperature change (°C)

energy transferred (J)

MATHS SKILLS

The equation that relates temperature change and energy transferred is $\Delta E = mc\Delta\theta$, where ΔE = energy transferred, m = mass of the aluminium, c = specific heat capacity of the aluminium and $\Delta\theta$ = temperature change.

This equation can't be compared to the equation of a straight line yet — the subject of the equation (see page 241) needs to be the y-axis variable, which in this case is $\Delta\theta$. So divide both sides of the equation by mc, to get:

Tip: You won't always need to rearrange an equation before you compare it to the equation of a straight line. For example, the gradient of a distance-time graph is equal to speed, which can be seen from the equation $s = vt$ (see page 152).

$$\Delta\theta = \frac{1}{mc}\Delta E$$

When you compare this to the equation of the straight line, you can see that the gradient is equal to $\frac{1}{mc}$:

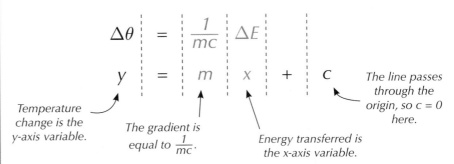

$$\Delta\theta \quad = \quad \frac{1}{mc} \quad \Delta E$$

$$y \quad = \quad m \quad x \quad + \quad c$$

Tip: You'll often find that the y-intercept is equal to zero, and that the graph passes through the origin. If c wasn't equal to zero, then the straight line would be shifted up or down, to pass through the y-axis at the value of c.

Temperature change is the y-axis variable.

The gradient is equal to $\frac{1}{mc}$.

Energy transferred is the x-axis variable.

The line passes through the origin, so c = 0 here.

Once the student has plotted his data on a graph he can find the gradient, which can then be used to calculate the unknown value of c, as gradient = $\frac{1}{mc}$.

Curved graphs

For a curved graph, the gradient is always changing. So you can't use the same method as the one on page 243 to calculate the gradient — you would end up with an average gradient between the two points chosen.

To find the gradient of a curve at a point, you need to draw a **tangent** to the curve at that point. A tangent is a straight line that touches the curve at that point, but doesn't cross it. So to draw one, you position a ruler so that it just touches the curve at the point you're interested in, and draw a straight line. Then you just find the gradient of the tangent using the method for straight lines on page 243.

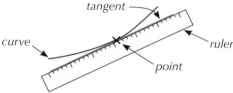

Figure 3: *Drawing the tangent to a curve.*

Figure 2: *Make sure you use a really sharp pencil and a ruler whenever you're drawing graphs and tangents.*

Example	**Higher**

The velocity-time graph of a cyclist is shown below. Find the acceleration of the cyclist at 70 s.

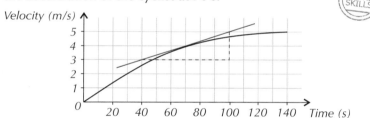

A tangent to the curve at 70 s is drawn on the graph. Its gradient is:

$$\frac{\text{change in } y}{\text{change in } x} = \frac{5-3}{100-40} = \frac{2}{60} = 0.03333... = 0.03 \text{ (to 1 s.f.)}$$

The rate of change of velocity is acceleration.
So the gradient of a velocity-time graph is acceleration.

So the acceleration at 70 s = 0.03 m/s² (to 1 s.f.)

Tip: **H** Another example of finding the gradient of a tangent is shown on page 153.

Tip: Just like with linear graphs, if the variable of the x-axis is time, the gradient at a point is rate of change of the quantity on the y-axis.

Area under a graph

Sometimes the area between the curve or line and the horizontal axis of a graph represents a quantity. For example:

- **H** The area under a velocity-time graph of an object is equal to the distance travelled by the object (page 156).

- The area under a linear force-extension graph for a stretched spring is equal to the energy transferred to the spring's elastic potential energy store.

To find an area under a graph, you'll either need to work it out exactly by breaking it up into triangles and rectangles or estimate the area by counting squares. Which method you use depends on the graph's shape. You'll have to count squares for a curved graph, but you can work it out exactly for a straight line graph. There are examples of both methods on pages 156-157.

Tip: The formulas for the area of a triangle and a rectangle are on the next page.

4. Geometry

You'll be expected to be comfortable with working out measurements of 2D and 3D shapes, such as areas, surface areas and volumes, in physics contexts.

Area

Make sure you remember how to calculate the areas of triangles and rectangles.

> **Tip:** These come in handy when calculating the area under a graph.

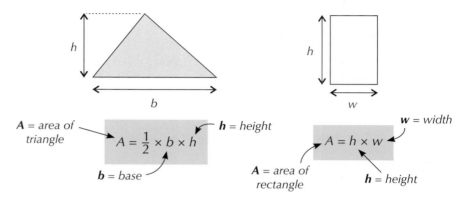

A = area of triangle

$A = \frac{1}{2} \times b \times h$

h = height

b = base

w = width

$A = h \times w$

A = area of rectangle

h = height

Surface area and volume

If you need to work out the surface area of a 3D shape, you just need to add up the areas of all the 2D faces of the shape. So, for example, if you need to work out the surface area of a cuboid, you just find the area of each rectangular face and then add them together.

> **Tip:** Make sure you don't forget any sides when finding the surface area. For a cube or cuboid, there should be 6.

Make sure you remember how to calculate the volume of a cuboid:

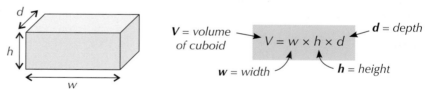

V = volume of cuboid

$V = w \times h \times d$

d = depth

w = width

h = height

> **Tip:** You need to be able to calculate volumes to calculate densities (see page 96).

Example

A block of copper is shown. Calculate the volume and surface area of the copper.

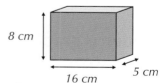

8 cm

16 cm   5 cm

Volume = $w \times h \times d$ = 16 × 8 × 5 = 640 cm³.

Surface area of front face = $h \times w$ = 8 × 16 = 128 cm².
Therefore the surface area of back face = 128 cm².

Surface area of right face = $h \times w$ = 8 × 5 = 40 cm².
Therefore the surface area of left face = 40 cm².

Surface area of top face = $h \times w$ = 5 × 16 = 80 cm².
Therefore the surface area of bottom face = 80 cm².

Total surface area = 128 + 128 + 40 + 40 + 80 + 80 = 496 cm².

1. The Exams

Unfortunately, you'll need to sit some exams for GCSE Combined Science. And that's what this page is about — what to expect in your exams.

Assessment for GCSE Combined Science

To get your GCSE in Combined Science you'll have to do some exams that test your science knowledge, your understanding of the Required Practical Activity experiments and how comfortable you are with Working Scientifically. You'll also be tested on your maths skills.

All the physics content that you need to know is in this book. All the physics Required Practical Activities are also covered in detail and clearly labelled, examples that use maths skills are marked up, and there are even dedicated sections on Working Scientifically (p. 1-20), Maths Skills (p. 237-246) and Practical Skills (p. 231-236). You'll also need to know all the biology and chemistry content, which isn't covered in this book.

The exams

You'll sit six separate exams at the end of Year 11 — two for each of biology, chemistry and physics.

In the physics exams, you'll be tested on maths skills in at least 30% of the marks, and could be asked questions on the Required Practical Activities and Working Scientifically requirements in either of them. You're allowed to use a calculator in all of your GCSE Combined Science exams, so make sure you've got one.

The structure of the physics exams is shown below:

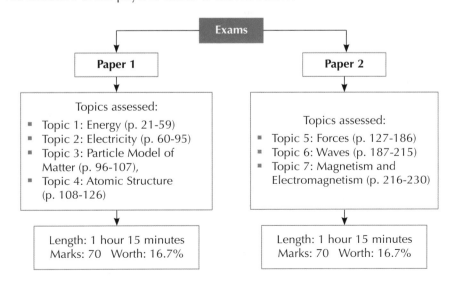

> **Exam Tip**
> Make sure you have a good read through these pages. It might not seem all that important now but you don't want to get any surprises just before an exam.

> **Exam Tip**
> As well as a calculator, you should make sure you've got a ruler for both exams. And don't forget the basics — a couple of black pens and sharp pencils.

> **Exam Tip**
> Use these topic lists as a guide, but be aware that they may expect you to use basic physics knowledge from any part of the course in either exam. In particular, you'll probably need to apply your knowledge of energy stores and transfers (from Topics 1 and 2) in Paper 2.

2. Exam Technique

Knowing the science is vitally important when it comes to passing your exams. But having good exam technique will also help. So here are some handy hints on how to squeeze every mark you possibly can out of those examiners.

Time management

Exam Tip
You shouldn't really be spending more time on a 1 mark question than on a 4 mark question. Use the marks available as a rough guide for how long each question should take to answer.

Good time management is one of the most important exam skills to have — you need to think about how much time to spend on each question. Check out the length of your exams (you'll find them on the previous page and on the front of your exam papers). These timings give you about 1 minute per mark. Try to stick to this to give yourself the best chance to get as many marks as possible.

Don't spend ages struggling with a question if you're finding it hard to answer — move on. You can come back to it later when you've bagged loads of other marks elsewhere. Also, you might find that some questions need a lot of work for only a few marks, while others are much quicker — so if you're short of time, answer the quick and easy questions first.

Exam Tip
Don't forget to go back and do any questions that you left the first time round — you don't want to miss out on marks because you forgot to do the question.

> **Example**
>
> The questions below are both worth the same number of marks but require different amounts of work.
>
> **1.1**   Name **two** renewable energy resources.
>
> *(2 marks)*
>
> **2.1**   Sketch a graph of activity against time for a radioactive isotope.
>
> *(2 marks)*
>
> Question 1.1 only asks you to write down the names of two energy resources — if you can remember them this shouldn't take you too long.
>
> Question 2.1 asks you to sketch a graph — this may take you a bit longer than writing down a couple of names, and it might take a couple of attempts to get right.
>
> So if you're running out of time, it makes sense to do questions like 1.1 first and come back to 2.1 if you've got time at the end.

Reading the question

You've probably heard it a million times before, but make sure you always read the whole question carefully. It can be easy to look at a question and read what you're expecting to see rather than what it's actually asking you. Read it through before you start answering, and read it again when you've finished, to make sure your answer is sensible and matches up to what the question is asking.

Remember to pay attention to the marks available too. They can often give you a sense of how much work is needed to answer the question. If it's just a 1 mark question, it'll often only need a single word or phrase as an answer, or a very simple calculation. Questions worth more marks are likely to be longer questions, which need to be clearly structured and may involve writing a short paragraph or a more complicated calculation.

Exam Tip
The amount of space given for your answer should also give you an idea about how much you need to write.

Making educated guesses

Make sure you answer all the questions that you can — don't leave any blank if you can avoid it. If a question asks you to tick a box, circle a word or draw lines between boxes, you should never, ever leave it blank, even if you're short on time. It only takes a second or two to answer these questions, and even if you're not absolutely sure what the answer is you can have a good guess.

Example

Look at the question below.

1.1   Which of the following are types of ionising radiation?
        Tick **two** boxes.

        Radio waves   ☐   Gamma rays   ☐

        Microwaves   ☐   Alpha particles ☐

                                                (2 marks)

Say you know that radio waves aren't a type of ionising radiation and gamma rays definitely are, but aren't sure about the other two answers.

You can tick gamma rays — you know it's a type of ionising radiation. You know radio waves is wrong, so leave that box blank. That leaves you with microwaves and alpha particles. If you're not absolutely sure which is ionising and which isn't, just have a guess. You won't lose any marks if you get it wrong and there's a 50% chance that you'll get it right.

Exam Tip
If you're asked, for example, to tick two boxes, make sure you only tick two. If you tick more than two, you won't get the marks even if some of your answers are correct.

Calculations

Calculations can seem daunting if you're not so keen on maths, but they're often where a load of marks are hiding. And there are some dead easy ways to make sure you don't miss out on them.

You'll be given an Equation Sheet in the physics exams that tells you some of the equations you might need. There are plenty of other equations you won't be given though — you'll be expected to remember them. Make sure you always write down any equation you use before you put any numbers into it.

Make sure you write down all your working. Getting the final answer is only one part of the question — if it's all you write down, and you get it wrong, that's all the marks gone. But if you write down all the steps that lead to the answer, and you've used the correct method, you'll be awarded marks for your working. Then you'll be able to pick up most of the marks, regardless of whether your final answer's correct or not.

Exam Tip
Take a look at p. 284 to see which equations will be given on the Equation Sheet in the exam.

Exam Tip
You can do an estimate to check that your answers to calculations are a sensible number. Check out page 240 for more on estimates.

3. Question Types

If all questions were the same, exams would be mightily boring. So really, it's quite handy that there are lots of different question types. Here are just a few...

Command words

Command words are just the bits of a question that tell you what to do. You'll find answering exam questions much easier if you understand exactly what they mean, so here's a brief summary of the most common ones:

Exam Tip

When you're reading an exam question, you might find it helpful to underline the command words. It can help you work out what type of answer to give.

Exam Tip

It's easy to get <u>describe</u> and <u>explain</u> mixed up, but they're quite different. For example, if you're asked to describe some data, just state the overall pattern or trend. If you're asked to explain data, you'll need to <u>give reasons</u> for the trend.

Command word:	What to do:
Give / Name / Identify / State / Write	Give a brief one or two word answer, or a short sentence.
Choose	Select your answer from a range of options.
Complete	Write your answer in the space given. This could be a gap in a sentence or table, or you might have to finish a diagram.
Describe	Write about what something's like, e.g. describe the trend in a set of results.
Suggest	Use your scientific knowledge to work out what the answer might be.
Determine	Use the data or information you've been given to reach your answer.
Explain	Make something clear, or give the reasons why something happens. The points in your answer need to be linked together, so you should include words like because, so, therefore, due to, etc.
Calculate / Work out	Use the numbers in the question to work out an answer.
Show	Give clear evidence, and state a conclusion which this evidence supports.
Compare	Give the similarities and differences between two things.
Evaluate	Give the arguments both for and against an issue, or the advantages and disadvantages of something. You may also need to give an overall judgement.
Sketch	Draw without a lot of detail, e.g. for a graph you just need the general shape and correct axes.

Some questions will also ask you to answer 'using the information provided' (e.g. a graph, table or passage of text) — if so, you must refer to the information you've been given or you won't get the marks. You'll often need to use information or diagrams that are provided for you when answering questions with command words such as 'measure' or 'plot'.

Required Practical Activities

The Required Practical Activities are eight specific physics experiments that you need to cover during your lessons. You'll be asked about them in the exams too. At least 15% of the total marks in your exams will test your understanding of these experiments and the apparatus and techniques involved. There are a lot of different types of question you could be asked on these experiments. Here are some basic areas they might ask you about:

- Carrying out the experiment — e.g. planning or describing a method, describing how to take measurements or use apparatus.

- Risk assessment — e.g. identifying or explaining hazards associated with the experiment, or safety precautions which should be taken.

- Understanding variables — e.g. identifying control, dependent and independent variables.

- Data handling — e.g. plotting graphs or doing calculations using some sample results provided.

- Analysing results — e.g. making conclusions based on sample results.

- Evaluating the experiment — e.g. making judgements on the quality of results, identifying where mistakes may have been made in the method, suggesting improvements to the experiment.

Required Practical Activity questions won't be pointed out to you in the exam, so you'll need to make sure you know the practicals inside out, and can recognise them easily. For an example of a question testing your understanding of a practical, see page 146.

Tip: There are Required Practical Activities in biology and chemistry too, but they're not covered in this book.

Exam Tip
The Required Practical Activity questions are likely to have some overlap with Working Scientifically, so make sure you've brushed up on pages 1-20.

Levels of response questions

Some questions are designed to assess your ability to present and explain scientific ideas in a logical and coherent way, as well as your scientific knowledge. These questions often link together different topics, and are worth more marks than most other question types. You'll be told which questions these are on the front of your exam paper.

This type of question is marked using a 'levels of response' mark scheme. Your answer is given a level depending on the number of marks available and its overall quality and scientific content. Here's an idea of how the levels may work out for a 6 mark question:

Exam Tip
Make sure your writing is legible, and be careful with your spelling, punctuation and grammar.

Example

Level 0

A Level 0 answer has no relevant information, and makes no attempt to answer the question. It receives no marks.

Level 1

A Level 1 answer usually makes one or two correct statements, but does not fully answer the question. For instance, when asked to describe and explain the differences between two materials, it might state one or two correct properties of the materials, but not explain them or attempt to compare the two. These answers receive 1 or 2 marks.

Level 2

A Level 2 answer usually makes a number of correct statements, with explanation, but falls short of fully answering the question. It may miss a step, omit an important fact, or not be organised as logically as it should be. These answers receive 3 or 4 marks.

Level 3

A Level 3 answer will answer the question fully, in a logical fashion. It will make a number of points that are explained and related back to the question. Any conclusions it makes will be supported by evidence in the answer. These answers receive 5 or 6 marks.

Make sure you answer the question fully, and cover all points indicated in the question. You also need to organise your answer clearly — the points you make need to be in a logical order. Use specialist scientific vocabulary whenever you can. For example, if you're talking about the structure of the atom, you need to use scientific terms like 'the nuclear model'. Obviously you need to use these terms correctly — it's no good knowing the words if you don't know what they actually mean.

There are some exam-style questions that use this type of mark scheme in this book (marked up with an asterisk, *). You can use them to practise writing logical and coherent answers. Use the worked answers given at the back of this book to mark what you've written. The answers will tell you the relevant points you could've included, but it'll be down to you to put everything together into a full, well-structured answer.

Answers

Topic 1 — Energy

Topic 1a — Energy Transfers

1. Energy Stores and Transfers

Page 24 — Fact Recall Questions

Q1 Thermal (or internal) energy store, kinetic energy store, gravitational potential energy store, elastic potential energy store, chemical energy store, magnetic energy store, electrostatic energy store and nuclear energy store.

Q2 A closed system is a system where neither matter nor energy can enter or leave.

Q3 Energy can be transferred usefully, stored or dissipated, but can never be created or destroyed.

Page 24 — Application Question

Q1 a) Energy is transferred mechanically from the elastic potential energy store of the bow to the kinetic energy store of the arrow.

b) Energy is transferred by heating from the chemical energy store of the gas to the thermal energy stores of the soup and the surroundings.

c) Energy is transferred electrically from the chemical energy store of the battery to the kinetic energy store of the motor / the blades of the fan.

2. Kinetic and Potential Energy Stores

Page 28 — Fact Recall Questions

Q1 The large dog has more energy in its kinetic energy store, because the energy in this store is related to mass and speed by $E_k = \frac{1}{2}mv^2$.

Q2 $E_k = \frac{1}{2}mv^2$. E_k is the energy in the kinetic energy store in J, m is mass in kg and v is speed in m/s.

Q3 $E_p = mgh$. E_p is the energy transferred to the gravitational potential energy store in J, m is mass in kg, g is gravitational field strength in N/kg and h is height in m.

Q4 $E_e = \frac{1}{2}ke^2$. E_e is the energy in the elastic potential energy store in J, k is the spring constant in N/m and e is extension (or compression) in m.

Page 28 — Application Questions

Q1 $E_p = mgh = 25\,000 \times 9.8 \times 12\,000 = \textbf{2 940 000 000 J}$

Q2 $E_e = \frac{1}{2}ke^2$ so,
$k = 2E_e \div e^2 = (2 \times 18) \div 0.6^2 = \textbf{100 N/m}$

Q3 Rearranging $E_k = \frac{1}{2}mv^2$,
$$v = \sqrt{\frac{2E_k}{m}} = \sqrt{\frac{2 \times 40}{0.0125}} = \textbf{80 m/s}$$

Q4 Due to conservation of energy, the energy lost from the potato's g.p.e. store is all transferred to its kinetic energy store, so $E_p = E_k = 450$ J
Rearranging $E_k = \frac{1}{2}mv^2$,
$$v = \sqrt{\frac{2E_k}{m}} = \sqrt{\frac{2 \times 450}{1}} = \textbf{30 m/s}$$

If there had been air resistance, some energy would have been transferred to other stores, such as the thermal energy store of the air.

3. Specific Heat Capacity

Page 31 — Fact Recall Question

Q1 The amount of energy needed to change the temperature of 1 kg of a substance by 1°C.

Page 31 — Application Questions

Q1 $\Delta\theta = 100.0\ °C - 20.0\ °C = 80.0\ °C$
$\Delta E = mc\Delta\theta.$
$= 0.20 \times 4200 \times 80.0 = \textbf{67 200 J}$

Q2 $m = 400$ g $= 0.4$ kg
$\Delta\theta = 113\ °C - 25\ °C = 88\ °C$
$\Delta E = mc\Delta\theta$
$c = \Delta E \div (m\Delta\theta) = 70\,400 \div (0.4 \times 88)$
$= \textbf{2000 J/kg°C}$

4. Power

Page 33 — Fact Recall Questions

Q1 Power is the rate of doing work — i.e. how much work is done per second.
Remember, you can also define power in terms of energy transferred. Energy transferred and work done are the same thing.

Q2 $P = \frac{E}{t}$ and $P = \frac{W}{t}$. P is power in watts, E is energy transferred in joules, W is work done in joules and t is time in seconds.

Page 33 — Application Questions

Q1 a) $P = E \div t = 150 \div 37.5 = \textbf{4 W}$

b) 79.8 kJ = 79 800 J
$P = E \div t = 79\,800 \div 42 = \textbf{1900 W}$

c) 6 840 kJ = 6 840 000 J
9.5 minutes = 570 s
$P = E \div t = 6\,840\,000 \div 570 = \textbf{12 000 W}$

Q2 Lift B will lift the load in the least time. Since both lifts need to supply the same amount of energy to perform the task, the lift with the larger power, B, will perform the task in less time, as it supplies more energy per second.

Q3 a) $P = W \div t$, so $t = W \div P$
$t = 1344 \div 525 = \textbf{2.56 s}$

b) 2.86 kW = 2860 W
$P = E \div t$, so $t = E \div P$
$t = 1430 \div 2860 = \textbf{0.5 s}$

Q4 a) $P = E \div t$, so $E = Pt$
        $E = 1240 \times 35 = \textbf{43 400 J}$
    b) 17 minutes = 1020 s
        $E = Pt = 1500 \times 1020 = \textbf{1 530 000 J}$

5. Conduction and Convection
Page 35 — Fact Recall Questions
Q1 The transfer of energy by heating through a substance by vibrating particles colliding. The particles of the part of the substance that is heated have more energy in their kinetic energy stores and vibrate more. The particles collide with their neighbouring particles and pass on some of this energy, causing energy eventually to be spread out through the substance.
Q2 Convection is the transfer of energy by the movement of more energetic particles in a gas or liquid from a hotter to a cooler region.
Q3 Solids
    The particles in a solid can only vibrate about their fixed positions — they can't move from one place to another and take their energy with them.

6. Reducing Unwanted Energy Transfers
Page 37 — Fact Recall Questions
Q1 a) Foam squirted into the gap between the bricks of a cavity wall stops convection currents being set up in the gap.
    b) An insulating material laid on a loft floor reduces conduction through the loft floor and prevents convection currents forming in the loft space, which helps reduce energy transferred out of thermal energy stores in the house.
    c) Double-glazed windows have a double layer of glass separated by an air gap. Because air conducts poorly it will reduce energy loss by conduction through the window.
Q2 E.g. A lubricant (e.g. oil) can be used on an axle in a fan to decrease the friction between the axle and its support and so decreases the unwanted energy transfers to thermal energy stores due to friction.

7. Efficiency
Page 40 — Fact Recall Questions
Q1 $\text{efficiency} = \dfrac{\text{useful output energy transfer}}{\text{total input energy transfer}}$

    $\text{efficiency} = \dfrac{\text{useful power output}}{\text{total power input}}$
Q2 An electric heater.
Q3 It is transferred to thermal energy stores.

Page 40 — Application Questions
Q1 a) $\text{efficiency} = \dfrac{\text{useful power output}}{\text{total power input}}$

        $= \dfrac{54}{90}$

        $= \textbf{0.6}$

    b) Useful energy out = 800 – 280 = 520 J
        $\text{efficiency} = \dfrac{\text{useful output energy transfer}}{\text{total input energy transfer}}$

        $= \dfrac{520}{800}$

        $= \textbf{0.65}$
Q2 a) $\text{efficiency} = \dfrac{\text{useful power output}}{\text{total power input}}$

        $= \dfrac{12.6}{36}$

        $= 0.35$
        percentage efficiency = 0.35 × 100 = **35%**

    b) $\text{efficiency} = \dfrac{\text{useful output energy transfer}}{\text{total input energy transfer}}$

        $= \dfrac{4.5}{7.5}$

        $= 0.6$
        percentage efficiency = 0.6 × 100 = **60%**
        The energy transferred by heating to thermal energy stores and emitted as sound isn't useful — only the light is.
Q3 a) useful output energy transfer = 298 + 197 = **495 kJ**
        The energy emitted as light and as sound is useful.
    b) wasted energy = 660 – 495 = **165 kJ**

    c) $\text{efficiency} = \dfrac{\text{useful output energy transfer}}{\text{total input energy transfer}}$

        $= \dfrac{495}{660}$

        $= \textbf{0.75}$
Q4 convert percentage efficiency into decimal efficiency
    efficiency = 68 % = 0.68
    Rearrange $\text{efficiency} = \dfrac{\text{useful output energy transfer}}{\text{total input energy transfer}}$

    $\text{total input energy transfer} = \dfrac{\text{useful output energy transfer}}{\text{efficiency}}$

    $= \dfrac{816}{0.68}$

    $= \textbf{1200 J}$
Q5 E.g. lubricate the workings to reduce friction in the motor, and therefore energy transferred to 'wasted' thermal stores. Reduce the amount of sound the vacuum makes, therefore reducing energy transferred to 'wasted' stores in the surroundings.

Pages 43-44 — Energy Transfers
Exam-style Questions
1.1 E.g. From the chemical energy store of the gas to the thermal energy store of the pot (and surroundings).
     From the thermal energy store of the pot to the thermal energy store of the water.
     From the thermal energy store of the water (or pot) to the thermal energy stores of the surroundings.
     (3 marks — 1 mark for each correct answer)

1.2 The second pan's material could have a higher thermal conductivity *(1 mark)*.

1.3 Air is an insulator / is a poor conductor / has a low thermal conductivity *(1 mark)* so energy is transferred across the gap slowly by conduction *(1 mark)*.

2.1 $E_p = mgh$
$E_p = (85.0 + 10.0) \times 9.8 \times 10.0$ *(1 mark)*
$= 9310$ J *(1 mark)*

2.2 $P = E \div t$
$P = 9310 \div 7.0$ *(1 mark)* $= 1330$ W *(1 mark)*
(Allow follow-through from part 2.1)
If you got 2.1 wrong, you still get all the marks for 2.2 if you've done everything else right.

2.3 $E_k = \frac{1}{2}mv^2$, so,
$v = \sqrt{\dfrac{2E_k}{m}}$ *(1 mark)* $= \sqrt{\dfrac{2 \times 153.9}{85.0 + 10.0}}$ *(1 mark)*
$= 1.8$ m/s *(1 mark)*

2.4 Assume there is no air resistance so all energy in g.p.e. store is transferred to the kinetic energy store, *(1 mark)*,
so by conservation of energy, $mgh = \frac{1}{2}mv^2$, so
$v = \sqrt{2gh}$ *(1 mark)* $= \sqrt{2 \times 9.8 \times 1.25}$ *(1 mark)*
$= 4.949... = 4.9$ m/s (to 2 s.f.) *(1 mark)*

3.1 $P = W \div t$ *(1 mark)*

3.2 $P = 4 \div 0.5$ *(1 mark)* $= 8$ W *(1 mark)*

3.3 Work done $= 4$ J $=$ energy transferred to elastic potential energy store *(1 mark)*,
$E_e = \frac{1}{2}ke^2$, so $k = 2E_e \div e^2 = (2 \times 4) \div 0.4^2$ *(1 mark)*
$= 50$ N/m *(1 mark)*

3.4 First, convert percentage efficiency to a decimal, $62.5\% = 0.625$
$\text{efficiency} = \dfrac{\text{useful power output}}{\text{total power input}}$ so,
total power input = useful power output ÷ efficiency
$= 25 \div 0.625$ *(1 mark)*
$= 40$ W *(1 mark)*

3.5 E.g. Friction between the wheel axle and its supports causes energy from the kinetic energy store of the car to be dissipated into thermal energy stores *(1 mark)*

3.6 E.g. The wheel axle of the car could be lubricated to decrease the friction *(1 mark)*.

4.1 How to grade your answer:
Level 0: There is no relevant information.
(No marks)
Level 1: There is a brief description of an experiment that could be used to calculate the specific heat capacity of water. *(1 to 2 marks)*
Level 2: There is a clear description of an experiment that could be used to calculate the specific heat capacity of water. A method describing how to process the results of this experiment to calculate the specific heat capacity is described briefly. *(3 to 4 marks)*
Level 3: There is a clear and detailed description of an experiment that could be used to calculate the specific heat capacity of water. A method describing how to process the results of this experiment to calculate the specific heat capacity is clearly described. *(5 to 6 marks)*

Here are some points your answer may include:
Put the beaker on a mass balance and zero the balance.
Fill the beaker with water and record the mass of the water.
Place the thermometer into the beaker and measure the temperature of the water.
Place the heating element into the water.
Turn on the heating element to heat the water.
As the water is heated, record the temperature of the water and current through the heating element periodically.
The current through the circuit shouldn't change.
Using the potential difference of the power supply, calculate the energy transferred by the heater at the time of each temperature reading using $P = VI$ and $E = Pt$.
Plot a graph of change in temperature against energy transferred.
Calculate the gradient (of the straight line part) of the graph, and calculate the specific heat capacity using:
specific heat capacity = 1 ÷ (gradient × mass of water)

4.2 E.g. Care must be taken when handling the heating element and hot water to avoid being burnt *(1 mark)*.

4.3 $\Delta\theta = 100.0\ °C - 10.0\ °C = 90.0\ °C$
$\Delta E = mc\Delta\theta$, so
$c = \Delta E \div (m\Delta\theta)$ *(1 mark)*
$= 189\ 000 \div (0.50 \times 90.0)$ *(1 mark)*
$= 4200$ J/kg°C *(1 mark)*

Topic 1b — Energy Resources

1. Energy Resources and Their Uses
Page 46 — Fact Recall Questions
Q1 Coal, oil and (natural) gas.
Q2 a) Any four from: wind, the Sun (solar), water waves, geothermal, tides, hydroelectricity, bio-fuels.
b) E.g. they often produce much less energy than non-renewable resources / a lot of them are less reliable because they depend on the weather.
Q3 E.g. renewable: bio-fuels
non-renewable: petrol/diesel/coal
Q4 Electromagnetic radiation from the Sun is used to heat water which is then pumped into radiators in the building.

2. Wind, Solar and Geothermal
Page 49 — Fact Recall Questions
Q1 The wind turns the blades of the turbine, which are connected to an electrical generator inside the turbine. This generates electricity as it turns.
Q2 E.g. they generate no electricity when there's no wind / they generate no electricity when the wind is too strong.
Q3 Supplying a device in a remote location with another source of energy could be very difficult and expensive.
Q4 Hot underground rocks (thermal energy stores).

Q1 a) E.g. Solar cells, because the street light is remote,
will get lots of sunshine during the day and
requires a fairly small amount of electricity.
   b) E.g. Wind power, because the sign will be exposed
to wind and requires a fairly small amount of
electricity.
   c) E.g. Geothermal power, because the area is
volcanic, so there will be hot rocks close to the
surface that can be used to heat homes directly.

3. Hydroelectricity, Waves and Tides
Page 52 — Fact Recall Questions

Q1 Water is held behind a dam and allowed out through
turbines. This turns the turbines, that are connected
to generators which generate electricity.
Q2 E.g. flooding of a valley can result in rotting
vegetation which releases methane and carbon
dioxide.
Hydroelectric power stations can have a large impact
on local habitats (and wildlife).
Q3 Remote areas can be difficult to supply with fuel or
connect to the national grid. Having a hydroelectric
power station in a remote location to provide
electricity avoids these problems, as it can be more
easily connected to homes and needs no fuel to run.
Q4 Using wave-powered turbines on the coastline.
When a wave reaches the coastline, the motion of the
wave forces air up through a turbine which drives a
generator and generates electricity. (When the wave
retreats, the air is forced back out through the same
turbine, generating more electricity.)
Q5 E.g. the electricity supply is not very reliable, as no
electricity can be generated when the sea is calm.
Q6 Tidal barrages are dams with turbines in them. They
stop the tide flowing into and out of a river estuary, so
that a height difference of water builds up between
the sides. The tide water is then allowed to flow
through turbines from the higher side to the lower
side. The motion of the turbines turns a generator,
which produces electricity.

4. Bio-fuels and Non-renewables
Page 55 — Fact Recall Questions

Q1 a) If a process is carbon neutral, it removes as much
CO_2 from the atmosphere as it releases.
   b) E.g. the plants used to make bio-fuels absorb CO_2
from the atmosphere as they grow. If they absorb
the same amount as is released when they burn
they are said to be carbon neutral. The process
may not be carbon neutral if the bio-fuel plants
aren't being grown at the same rate as they are
being used.
Q2 E.g. carbon dioxide and sulfur dioxide.
Q3 a) nuclear fuel
   b) E.g. highly radioactive waste is produced, which is
difficult to dispose of.
Possibility of nuclear disasters that can
dramatically harm people/the environment.

5. Trends in Energy Resource Use
Page 57 — Fact Recall Questions

Q1 Appliances are being made more efficient, and
people are more concerned about the amount of
electricity they use.
Q2 Any two from: e.g. they're not as reliable as non-
renewables / they can have large initial setup costs
/ a number of power stations that use renewable
resources can only be built in certain locations /
a lot of renewable resources cannot easily have
their power output increased to meet demand /
some renewables don't produce as much energy as
non-renewables.

Page 59 — Energy Resources
Exam-style Questions

1.1 Non-renewable energy sources:
Coal (49.9%), Oil (2.4%), Gas (20.3%) and Nuclear
(19.6%).
Total percentage = 49.9 + 2.4 + 20.3 + 19.6
= **92.2%**
*(2 marks for correct answer, otherwise 1 mark for
correctly identifying all of the non-renewable energy
sources in the table)*
1.2 E.g. coal, oil and gas are the energy sources listed that
emit the most harmful gases (e.g. CO_2, sulfur dioxide)
when burned to generate electricity *(1 mark)*. A far
greater percentage of Country 1's electricity comes
from using these sources, so this country will produce
more pollution *(1 mark)*.
*The reservoirs in hydroelectric power stations release a
small amount of methane. This is nothing in comparison
to the amount of harmful gases released by burning fossil
fuels.*
1.3 Any one from: e.g. burning coal releases CO_2 into
the atmosphere (which contributes to the greenhouse
effect) / burning coal releases sulfur dioxide (which
causes acid rain) / coal mining destroys the landscape
(1 mark).
1.4 E.g. crops used to make bio-fuels have to be grown,
so they can't respond to immediate energy demands
(1 mark).
2.1 A non-renewable energy resource is one that is not
being replenished at the same rate as it is being used,
so it will eventually run out *(1 mark)*.
2.2 E.g. coal is burnt in fireplaces to heat homes *(1 mark)*.
2.3 Any one from: e.g. burning coal produces greenhouse
gases which contribute to global warming / burning
coal produces sulfur dioxide which causes acid rain /
coal mining makes a mess of the landscape *(1 mark)*.
2.4 E.g. Wind power could be an alternative *(1 mark)*.
The winds and exposed hills would allow wind
turbines to generate electricity *(1 mark)*. Wave power
could be an alternative *(1 mark)*. It is an island, so
it has a coastline, and the regular strong winds will
produce powerful waves, allowing generation of
electricity from wave power *(1 mark)*.
2.5 E.g. the renewable alternatives are not reliable, as
the wind doesn't always blow, so there may be times
when they generate no electricity *(1 mark)*.

Topic 2 — Electricity

Topic 2a — Circuits

1. Circuits, Current and Potential Difference
Page 62 — Fact Recall Questions

Q1 a)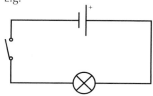
b)
c)
d)
e)

Q2 A circuit is incomplete if you can't follow a wire from one end of the battery (or other power supply), through any components to the other end of the battery.

Q3 Current flows from positive to negative.

Q4 $Q = It$, where Q = charge in coulombs (C), I = current in amps (A) and t = time in seconds (s).

Q5 A source of potential difference.

Page 62 — Application Questions

Q1 E.g.

This is just one example of a correct circuit diagram — you could have the components in a different order in the circuit.

Q2 E.g.

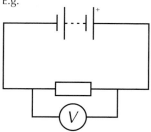

Remember that voltmeters are always connected across a component.

Q3 E.g.

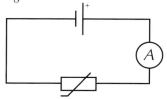

Remember that ammeters are always connected in series with a component.

Q4 Circuit B.
In the rest of the circuits, the lamp is in an incomplete part of the circuit. Don't worry about the extra bits coming off the circuit — as long as there's a complete cycle containing the lamp, current will flow through it and the lamp will light.

Q5 $I = 0.2$ A, $Q = 50$ C
$Q = It$, so
$t = Q \div I = 50 \div 0.2 = \textbf{250 s}$

Q6 $t = 1$ minute $= 60$ seconds
$Q = It$, so
$I = Q \div t = 102 \div 60 = \textbf{1.7 A}$

2. Resistance and *I-V* Characteristics
Page 67 — Fact Recall Questions

Q1 Resistance is anything in a circuit that opposes the flow of current. It is measured in ohms, Ω.

Q2 $V = IR$ (potential difference = current × resistance)

Q3 E.g.

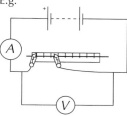

Q4 Wire length and resistance are directly proportional — as wire length increases, so does resistance.

Q5 E.g.

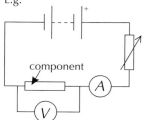

Q6 Read off the values of current and potential difference at a single point on the graph, and use $R = V \div I$ to calculate the resistance.

Q7 a) E.g.

b) E.g.

Q8 a) The resistance is initially high but drops as V increases, allowing current to flow.
b) The resistance is very high, so current can't flow through a diode in this direction.

Page 67 — Application Questions

Q1 A diode.

Q2 $V = IR = 0.015 \times 2.0 = \textbf{0.03 V}$

Q3 $R = V \div I = 14.4 \div 0.60 = \textbf{24 } \Omega$

Q4 $R = V \div I$. The graph is a straight line, so the resistance is constant, so just pick a point on the line and use the values of V and I to work out the resistance:
E.g. $R = V \div I = 2 \div 0.25 = \textbf{8 } \Omega$

3. Series Circuits

Page 71 — Fact Recall Questions

Q1 Components are connected all in a line, end to end.

Q2 Ammeter

Q3 In series and in the same direction as each other (and any other cells in the circuit).

Q4 False, it is shared between all components.

Q5 It is always the same.

Q6 When a resistor is added in series, it has to take a share of the pd. This decreases the pd through each component, and hence decreases the current ($V = IR$). In a series circuit, the current is constant through each component, therefore the total current decreases, so the total resistance increases.

Page 71 — Application Question

Q1 a) 1.5 A
b) $V_1 = IR = 1.5 \times 7.0 = \textbf{10.5 V}$
c) $V = V_1 + V_2$ so $V_2 = V - V_1 = 12 - 10.5 = \textbf{1.5 V}$
d) $V = IR$ so $R = V \div I = 1.5 \div 1.5 = \textbf{1 } \Omega$

4. Parallel Circuits

Page 76 — Fact Recall Questions

Q1 Components are connected to the battery separately to the other components (on their own branches).

Q2 Each branch/component can be turned on and off separately, whereas in series circuits, turning off one component will turn them all off.

Q3 It is the same across each component and across the power supply.

Q4 By adding up the current in every branch.

Page 76 — Application Questions

Q1 a) Find the pd across the branch with the resistor in, and it will be the same as the pd shown by the voltmeter. The current through the branch is 0.75 A and the resistance is 8.0 Ω.
$V = IR = 0.75 \times 8.0 = \textbf{6.0 V}$
Remember, the resistance of an ammeter is so small that you don't need to consider it — you can pretend it's not there.
b) The total current in the circuit is 2.0 A, and the current through the branch with the resistor is 0.75 A. So the current through the bulb is 2.0 A – 0.75 A = 1.25 A. The voltage across the bulb is 6.0 V so the resistance can be found by rearranging $V = IR$.
$R = V \div I = 6.0 \div 1.25 = \textbf{4.8 } \Omega$

c) The total resistance is less than the answer to b).
Remember, the total resistance of a parallel circuit is always less than the resistance of any of the individual branches.

Q2 a) With the switch open, the circuit is just a simple series circuit with two resistors and an ammeter. The current in the circuit is 0.70 A and the total resistance is $12 + 8.0 = 20 \ \Omega$.
$V = IR = 0.70 \times 20 = \textbf{14 V}$
b) i) The potential difference is the same on each branch of the parallel part of the circuit. So you can just find the voltage on the lower branch by using the resistance of, and current through resistor R_1.
$V = IR_1 = 0.50 \times 8.0 = \textbf{4.0 V}$
ii) The total potential difference of the circuit is shared between resistor R_2 and the parallel loop with the other components on it. The potential difference across the parallel loop is 4.0 V and the total potential difference is 14 V, so the potential difference across resistor R_2 is $14 - 4.0 = \textbf{10 V}$.

5. Investigating Resistance

Page 79 — Application Question

Q1 a) E.g.

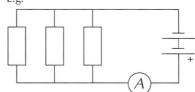

b)

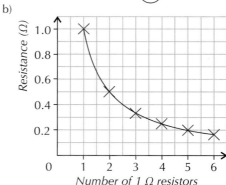

c) The total resistance of the circuit decreases as the number of resistors connected in parallel increases. When a resistor is added in parallel, it has the same potential difference across it as the source. But by adding another branch, the current has more than one direction to go in. This increases the amount of current flowing. Using $V = IR$, an increase in current at a constant pd means a decrease in the total resistance.

6. LDRs and Thermistors
Page 82 — Fact Recall Questions
Q1 Increase the light intensity.
An LDR is a light dependent resistor — its resistance decreases as the light hitting it gets brighter.

Q2 E.g.

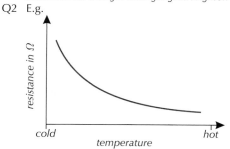

Q3 a) E.g. automatic night lights / outside lighting / burglar detectors.
b) E.g. thermostats / temperature sensors.

Page 82 — Application Question
Q1 a) A light-dependant resistor (LDR).
b) The cat blocks the light incident on the LDR, so the light intensity drops and the resistance increases, causing the alarm to sound.

Pages 84-85 — Circuits
Exam-style Questions
1.1 The ammeter should be connected in series with the filament lamp *(1 mark)* because the current is constant in a series loop, so it will measure the same current as is passing through the lamp *(1 mark)*.

1.2 E.g.

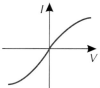

(1 mark)

1.3 No, the filament lamp is not an ohmic conductor as the current is not directly proportional to the voltage / the relationship between current and voltage is not linear *(1 mark)*.

1.4 E.g.

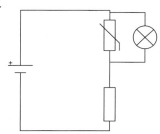

(1 mark for correct symbols for all components, 1 mark for cell, thermistor and resistor connected in series, 1 mark for filament lamp connected in parallel with the thermistor only.)

When the temperature drops, the thermistor's resistance will increase. So it'll take a higher share of the source pd. This means that putting the lamp across the thermistor will result in it getting brighter when the temperature decreases.

1.5 The student should move the filament lamp to be connected in parallel with the resistor *(1 mark)*.

2.1 The rate of flow of charge *(1 mark)*.

2.2 The potential difference across the battery is the same as the potential difference across the motor.
$V = 14$ V *(1 mark)*

2.3 $Q = It$, so the current passing through the motor is found by:
$I_{motor} = Q \div t$ *(1 mark)* $= 15 \div 30$ *(1 mark)*
$= 0.5$ A *(1 mark)*
The components are in parallel, so the sum of their currents is equal to the total current:
$I_{total} = I_{motor} + I_{lamp}$
$1.2 = 0.5 + I_{lamp}$ *(1 mark)*
$I_{lamp} = 1.2 - 0.5 = \textbf{0.7 A}$ *(1 mark)*

2.4 The potential difference through the filament bulb is the same as the power supply, $V = 14$ V. *(1 mark)*
$V = IR$
$R = V \div I$ *(1 mark)*
$= 14 \div 0.7$ *(1 mark)* $= \textbf{20 } \Omega$ *(1 mark)*

3.1 The resistance of the variable resistor can be increased or decreased, which will decrease or increase the current in the circuit *(1 mark)*.

3.2 A resistor OR a wire *(1 mark, accept 'an ohmic conductor')*.

3.3 Choose a point on the graph and read off the values — e.g. $I = 0.2$ A when $V = 1$ V.
$V = IR$
So $R = V \div I$ *(1 mark)*
$= 1 \div 0.2$ *(1 mark)* $= \textbf{5 } \Omega$ *(1 mark)*

3.4 Graph B *(1 mark)*. In graph B, Y has a lower value of I for each value of V, which means the resistance is higher *(1 mark)*.
Remember — a higher resistance means less current will flow for a given pd.

Topic 2b — Domestic Electricity

1. Electricity in the Home
Page 87 — Fact Recall Questions
Q1 Direct current is current that only flows in one direction.

Q2 Alternating current. The direction of ac is constantly changing whereas dc always flows in one direction.

Q3 The live wire is brown, the neutral wire is blue and the earth wire is green and yellow.

Q4 a) The live wire has a high potential difference (around 230 V). The blue neutral wire is around 0 V.
b) The earth wire protects the wiring of an appliance and has a safety role — it stops the appliance from becoming live.

2. Power and Energy Transfer
Page 91 — Fact Recall Questions
Q1 a) E.g. any two of: a motor, a kettle, a speaker.
   b) E.g. any two of:
      motor — kinetic energy store
      kettle — thermal energy store
      speaker — kinetic energy store
      There are loads of options you could give here — these are just a few common examples.
Q2 It is transferred to the thermal energy store of the components and the surroundings.
Q3 $E = Pt$. E in energy transferred in joules, P is power in watts and t is time in seconds.
Q4 $P = VI$. Power (P) is measured in watts, potential difference (V) is in volts and current (I) is in amps.

Page 91 — Application Questions
Q1 Cooker B will use the most energy in 20 minutes because it has the highest power.
Q2 $P = VI = 230 \times 3.0 =$ **690 W**
Q3 $P = 2.0$ kW $= 2000$ W, $t = 30$ minutes $= 1800$ s
   $E = Pt = 2000 \times 1800 =$ **3 600 000 J**
Q4 $E = QV$, so $V = E \div Q = 22 \div 4.0 =$ **5.5 V**
Q5 $P = I^2R$
   $R = P \div I^2 = 40 \div (0.2)^2 =$ **1000 Ω**
Q6 Microwave A:
   $E = Pt = 900 \times (4 \times 60) = 216\ 000$ J
   Microwave B:
   $E = Pt = 650 \times (6 \times 60) = 234\ 000$ J
   So **microwave B** transfers the most energy.
   Remember to convert the time into seconds before carrying out any calculations.

3. The National Grid
Page 93 — Fact Recall Questions
Q1 a) A transformer changes the potential difference of an electrical supply.
   b) When electricity is transmitted, energy is lost through heating in the cables. This energy loss is greater for a higher current. Transmitting electricity at a high voltage reduces the current for the same amount of power, so transformers are used to increase the voltage, decrease the current and reduce the energy loss. Transformers are also used to decrease the voltage to safe levels again before the electricity reaches users.
Q2 A — power station
   B — step-up transformer
   C — pylons / electricity cables
   D — step-down transformer
   E — consumers
Q3 a) E.g. any two from: when people wake up in the morning / when it starts to get dark / when people get home from school or work / when it starts to get cold.
   b) E.g. Powers stations usually run below their maximum power output, so there's capacity to cope with higher demand. Smaller power stations which can be started quickly are kept on standby.

Page 95 — Domestic Electricity
Exam-style Questions
1.1 brown *(1 mark)*.
1.2 Power = potential difference × current / $P = VI$ *(1 mark)*
1.3 $I = P \div V$ *(1 mark)*
    $= 575 \div 230$ *(1 mark)* $= 2.5$ A *(1 mark)*
1.4 The exposed wire could provide a link to earth *(1 mark)* causing a huge current to flow *(1 mark)* which could heat the wire enough to start a fire *(1 mark)*.
2.1 Pd = 230 V *(1 mark)*, frequency = 50 Hz *(1 mark)*.
2.2 To transmit a high power, either a high current or high pd must be used *(1 mark)*. A high current would result in lots of energy being lost to thermal energy stores *(1 mark)*. Transmitting at a high voltage means a lower current can be used, which reduces energy loss and makes transmission more efficient *(1 mark)*.
2.3 Energy transferred = power × time / $E = Pt$ *(1 mark)*
2.4 Power = 2.55 kW = 2550 W
    $t = E \div P$ *(1 mark)*
    $= 7\ 038\ 000 \div 2550$ *(1 mark)*
    $= $ **2760 s** *(1 mark)*
2.5 Energy transferred = charge × potential difference / $E = QV$ *(1 mark)*
2.6 $Q = E \div V$ *(1 mark)*
    $= 7\ 038\ 000 \div 230$ *(1 mark)*
    $= $ **30 600 C** *(1 mark)*
2.7 $P = 1150$ W, $V = 230$ V
    $P = VI$
    $I = P \div V$ *(1 mark)*
    $= 1150 \div 230$ *(1 mark)*
    $= $ **5.00 A** *(1 mark)*

Topic 3 — Particle Model of Matter

1. Density and States of Matter
Page 99 — Fact Recall Questions
Q1 density = mass ÷ volume ($\rho = m \div v$)
Q2 Solid, liquid and gas.
Q3 The particles in a solid are held close together by strong forces in a fixed, regular arrangement. The particles don't have much energy and so can't move around — they can only vibrate about fixed positions.
Q4 The particles in a liquid have more energy than in a solid. They are still close to each other, but unlike in a solid, they're able to move past each other and form irregular arrangements.
Q5 Gas
Q6 Eureka can, measuring cylinder and mass balance.

Page 99 — Application Questions

Q1 The volume of the block is:
$0.030 \times 0.045 \times 0.060 = 0.000081 \text{ m}^3$
$\rho = m \div v = 0.324 \div 0.000081 = \textbf{4000 kg/m}^3$
Don't forget to convert the lengths into metres, or convert the mass to g if you want to find the answer in g/cm³.

Q2 a) E.g. The balls represent the particles of a solid — they don't swap positions, they're close together and are arranged in a (fairly) regular pattern.
b) A gas.
c) The particles in a solid are packed closely together without much of a gap between them, like the balls in the box when the fan is switched off. So solids are generally quite dense (relative to the other states of matter). In a gas, the particles are spread much further apart, with large gaps between them, like the balls in the box when the fan is switched on. This means that gases are much less dense than solids.

2. Internal Energy and Changes of State
Page 102 — Fact Recall Questions

Q1 The internal energy of a system is the total energy that its particles have in their kinetic and potential energy stores.
Q2 By heating the system.
Q3 E.g. freezing, melting, boiling/evaporating, condensing and sublimating.
Q4 A physical change means that you don't end up with a new substance — it's the same substance as you started with, just in a different form.
Q5 Yes, a change of state does conserve mass. The number of particles in a substance doesn't change when the substance changes state. Only the arrangement and energy of the particles changes.
Q6

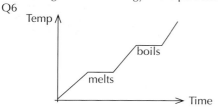

Page 102 — Application Questions

Q1 As the kettle heats the liquid, energy is transferred into the kinetic energy stores of the liquid's particles. The particles start to move around more. Eventually the particles have enough energy in their kinetic energy stores to be able to break the bonds between them. At this point the liquid starts to boil and become a gas.
Q2 When the steam reaches the cold window, it cools down. Energy is transferred away from the kinetic energy stores of the steam's particles. The particles move around less until bonds can form between them. At this point the steam condenses and becomes a liquid (water).

3. Specific Latent Heat
Page 103 — Fact Recall Questions

Q1 E.g. the specific latent heat of fusion is the amount of energy needed to change 1 kg of a solid to a liquid without changing its temperature. The specific latent heat of vaporisation is the amount of energy needed to change 1 kg of a liquid to a gas without changing its temperature.
Q2 J/kg

Page 103 — Application Questions

Q1 $E = mL$ and $25.0 \text{ g} = 0.0250 \text{ kg}$
$E = 0.0250 \times 334\,000 = \textbf{8350 J}$
Q2 $E = mL$ so $m = E \div L = 4\,960\,000 \div 1\,550\,000$
$= \textbf{3.20 kg}$

4. Particle Motion in Gases
Page 104 — Fact Recall Questions

Q1 Random motion / random directions and speeds.
Q2 The particles move about at high speeds and collide with the walls of the container, exerting a force on them. Pressure is force per unit area, so the particles exert a pressure.
Q3 The higher the temperature of a gas, the higher the average energy in the kinetic stores of its particles (heating the gas will transfer energy into the kinetic stores of its particles). This means the particles will collide with the walls of a container more often and with greater speed, so they will exert a higher force. This means the pressure will be greater.

Pages 106-107 — Particle Model of Matter
Exam-style Questions

1.1 Density = mass ÷ volume / $\rho = m \div V$ *(1 mark)*
1.2 $V = m \div \rho$ *(1 mark)*
$= 450 \div 9$ *(1 mark)* $= \textbf{50 cm}^3$ *(1 mark)*
1.3 It is a liquid *(1 mark)*. It started off as a solid, but the flat spot on the graph shows the point at which it changes state and melts into a liquid *(1 mark)*.
If there was a second flat spot on the graph, this would show another change of state, so the substance would've changed from liquid into gas.
1.4 The mass is 450 g *(1 mark)*. This is because a change of state conserves mass (the number of particles doesn't change, they're just arranged differently) *(1 mark)*.
2.1 $\rho = m \div V$
So $m = \rho V$ *(1 mark)*
$= 0.025 \times 0.08$ *(1 mark)*
$= \textbf{0.002 kg}$ *(1 mark)*
2.2 $E = mL$
So $L = E \div m$ *(1 mark)*
$= 5000 \div 0.002$ *(1 mark)*
$= \textbf{2 500 000}$ *(1 mark)* **J/kg** *(1 mark)*
If you got the mass wrong in part 2.1, you'll still get the marks in part 2.2 as long as you've done everything else correctly.

2.3 The density will be greater than 0.025 kg/m³ *(1 mark)*. Liquids are denser than gases, as their particles are more tightly packed together *(1 mark)*.

3.1 E.g. Place a measuring cylinder on a balance and zero the balance *(1 mark)*. Pour some liquid into the measuring cylinder and record the liquid's volume using the scale on the measuring cylinder *(1 mark)*. Record the mass of the liquid as shown on the balance *(1 mark)*. Use the formula $\rho = m \div v$ to find the density *(1 mark)*.

3.2 85 °C is the boiling point of the liquid *(1 mark)*. At this point, any energy transferred will go into breaking the bonds between particles, rather than raising temperature *(1 mark)*. The liquid will then change state, as it boils into a gas *(1 mark)*.

4.1 The specific latent heat of fusion of a substance is the amount of energy needed to change 1 kg of it from solid to liquid *(1 mark)* form without changing its temperature *(1 mark)* / the amount of energy released when 1 kg of it changes from liquid to solid *(1 mark)* without changing its temperature *(1 mark)*.

4.2 $E = mL$
So $m = E \div L$ *(1 mark)* = 67 500 ÷ 450 000 *(1 mark)*
= **0.15 kg** *(1 mark)*

4.3 If the solid was not already at its melting temperature, then some of the 67 500 J transferred would've gone into increasing the solid's temperature *(1 mark)*, rather than all of it being used to change the state *(1 mark)*.

5.1

 (1 mark)   *(1 mark)*

Water   Water vapour

5.2 Water and water vapour have particles that can move past each other, so they can both flow *(1 mark)*. Ice is a solid, so its particles can only vibrate about their fixed positions, so ice can't flow *(1 mark)*.

5.3 E.g. Water vapour is easily compressible *(1 mark)*. There's lots of space between the particles, so they can be pushed closer together *(1 mark)*. Water and ice are not easily compressible *(1 mark)*, as there's no space for the particles to be pushed closer together *(1 mark)*.

Topic 4 — Atomic Structure

1. The History of the Atom
Page 109 — Fact Recall Questions
Q1 According to the model, an atom is made of a positively-charged sphere with tiny negative electrons stuck in it (like plums in a plum pudding).

Q2 It was expected that alpha particles fired at thin gold foil would be deflected at most by a very small amount by the electrons in the atoms.

Q3 Most alpha particles passed straight through and the odd one bounced straight back. The fact that most alpha particles passed straight through the foil showed that most of the atom is empty space. Some positively-charged alpha particles were deflected by the nucleus by a large angle, showing that the nucleus had a large positive charge. Very few alpha particles bounced back, showing that the nucleus is very small.

2. The Structure of the Atom
Page 113 — Fact Recall Questions
Q1 Protons, neutrons and electrons.
Q2 The electron.
Q3 The relative mass is 1 and the relative charge is 0.
Q4 They are equal. The atom has no overall charge (it's neutral), so the charges must be equal (and opposite) to cancel each other out.
Q5 Atomic number is the number of protons in the nucleus of an atom. Mass number is the number of protons and neutrons in the nucleus of an atom.
Q6 The atomic number is always the same (they have the same number of protons).
Q7 Another form of the same element which has atoms with the same number of protons (atomic number) but a different number of neutrons (mass number).

Page 113 — Application Question
Q1 a) 17 − 16 = **+1**
   Remember, electrons have a negative charge of −1 and protons have a positive charge of +1.
   b) The particle has an overall charge/the particle has more protons than electrons.
   c) They have the same number of protons but a different number of neutrons.

3. Radioactivity
Page 117 — Fact Recall Questions
Q1 It gives out radiation from the nuclei of its atoms no matter what is done to it.
Q2 You can't — it is random.
   Sorry — that was sort of a trick question...
Q3 From strongest (most ionising) to weakest (least ionising): Alpha, beta, gamma.
Q4 Alpha radiation is made up of alpha particles, which are made up of two protons and two neutrons (a helium nucleus).
   Beta radiation is made up of beta particles, which are electrons.
   Gamma radiation is made up of gamma rays, which are electromagnetic waves with a very short wavelength.
Q5 The atomic number and mass number.

Page 117 — Application Questions
Q1 a) Radiation A, as it passes through the hand and radiation B doesn't.
   b) Radiation B, as it doesn't even penetrate through the hand.
   c) Gamma radiation, as it penetrates through all of the materials.

Q2 Alpha decay.
Q3 a) Beta decay
   b) $^{228}_{88}Ra \rightarrow ^{228}_{89}Ac + ^{0}_{-1}e$
   Remember you need to balance the atomic and mass
   numbers on each side of the equation.
Q4 a) Alpha particles would be stopped by the paper.
   b) Gamma rays would pass straight through the
      paper, whatever its thickness.

4. Activity and Half-life
Page 120 — Fact Recall Questions
Q1 Because the activity never drops to zero.
Q2 Half-life is the time it takes for the number of nuclei
   of a radioactive isotope in a sample to halve.
   Half-life is the time it takes for the count rate from a
   sample containing the isotope to fall to half its initial
   level.

Page 121 — Application Questions
Q1 After 1 hour (60 minutes), it will have had 4
   half-lives because $60 \div 15 = 4$.
   So it will have halved four times.
   After one half-life: $240 \div 2 = 120$
   After two half-lives: $120 \div 2 = 60$
   After three half-lives: $60 \div 2 = 30$
   After four half-lives: $30 \div 2 = 15$
   So the count rate will be **15 cpm**.
Q2 Initial count rate = 16
   After one half-life: $16 \div 2 = 8$
   After two half-lives: $8 \div 2 = 4$
   So 2 hours is 2 half-lives. So one half-life is **1 hour**.
Q3 Initial activity = 32 Bq
   After one half-life: $32 \div 2 = 16$
   After two half-lives: $16 \div 2 = 8$
   After three half-lives: $8 \div 2 = 4$
   Therefore, it will have dropped to 4 Bq after
   3 half-lives.
Q4 The initial count rate is 120, so after one half-life it
   will have decreased to 60. Find 60 on the activity
   axis and follow across to the curve and then down
   to the time axis.

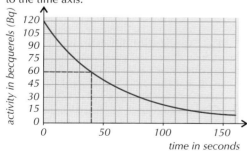

   The half-life is **40 seconds**.
Q5 Initial activity = 9600 Bq
   After one half-life, activity = $9600 \div 2 = 4800$
   After two half-lives, activity = $4800 \div 2 = 2400$
   After three half-lives, activity = $2400 \div 2 = 1200$
   So the percentage = $(1200 \div 9600) \times 100 = $ **12.5%**

5. Irradiation and Contamination
Page 122 — Fact Recall Questions
Q1 Irradiation is exposure to radiation from a radioactive
   source.
   Contamination is where unwanted atoms of a
   radioactive substance are present in or on another
   material.
Q2 Beta and gamma radiation are the most dangerous
   outside the body because they can penetrate into
   your body.
Q3 Alpha radiation is the most dangerous inside the body
   because it does damage in a localised area and is
   highly ionising.

Pages 125-126 — Atomic Structure
Exam-style Questions
1.1 The nucleus contains <u>protons</u> and <u>neutrons</u>.
    OR
    The nucleus contains <u>neutrons</u> and <u>protons</u>.
    The numbers of protons and <u>electrons</u> in a neutral
    atom are equal.
    (2 marks for all correct otherwise 1 mark for one
    correct answer.)
1.2 The atoms have the same number of protons (atomic
    number) but a different number of neutrons (mass
    numbers) *(1 mark)*.
2.1

Radiation type:	Made up of:	Stopped by:
Alpha particles	2 protons and 2 neutrons *(1 mark)* OR helium nuclei *(1 mark)*	Thin paper
Beta particles *(1 mark)*	Electrons	Thin aluminium
Gamma rays	Short-wavelength EM waves	Thick lead

2.2 Ionising means it is capable of removing an electron
    from an atom and turning it into a positive ion.
    (1 mark)
2.3 Alpha radiation is the most highly ionising radiation
    and so if emitted inside the body it can badly damage
    cells in a localised area *(1 mark)*.
2.4 Its atomic number decreases by 2 *(1 mark)* and its
    mass number decreases by 4 *(1 mark)*.
    It loses 2 protons and 2 neutrons.
2.5 A neutron changes into a proton *(1 mark)*.
3.1 The average time it takes for the number of nuclei in
    a caesium-137 sample to halve is 30 years *(1 mark)*.
    OR
    The time it takes for the count rate from a sample of
    caesium-137 to fall to half its initial level is 30 years
    (1 mark).
3.2 90 years = 3 half-lives *(1 mark)*
    Activity after 30 years = $24 \div 2 = 12$
    Activity after 60 years = $12 \div 2 = 6$
    Activity after 90 years = $6 \div 2$ *(1 mark)* = **3 Bq**
    (1 mark)

3.3 Some isotopes have very long half-lives (e.g. for caesium-137 it's 30 years) so it will take a long time for the radiation levels in affected areas to decrease to a safe level *(1 mark)*.

3.4 Beta *(1 mark)*.

3.5 $^{137}_{55}\text{Cs} \rightarrow {}^{137}_{56}\text{Ba} + {}^{0}_{-1}\text{e}$ *(1 mark)*

4 How to grade your answer:
Level 0: There is no relevant information. *(0 marks)*
Level 1: There is a brief explanation of how the method would detect cracks with no explanation of the type of radiation used. *(1 to 2 marks)*
Level 2: There is an explanation of how the method would detect cracks and some explanation of the type of radiation or of an appropriate half-life. *(3 to 4 marks)*
Level 3: There is a clear and detailed explanation of how the method would detect cracks and the radiation type and half-life are fully explained. *(5 to 6 marks)*
Here are some points your answer may include:
The radioactive isotope will give out radiation.
The detector will detect how much radiation is reaching it as it moves along above the pipe.
If there is a crack, the substance will leak out and collect outside the pipe.
This means there will be a higher concentration of the radioactive isotope around a crack.
This will be detected as a higher count rate by the detector.
So the engineer will know where the crack is located — it'll be directly below the detector when the reading increases.
The source used should be a gamma source.
Gamma radiation penetrates far into materials without being stopped and so will pass through the ground and reach the detector.
Alpha and beta radiation would be stopped by the ground as they have lower penetration levels, so they wouldn't reach the detector.
The source should have a short half-life.
This will ensure it does not continue emitting lots of radiation for a long time, which would possibly harm people that come close to the pipes or the substance.

Topic 5 — Forces

Topic 5a — Force Basics

1. Contact and Non-Contact Forces

Page 128 — Fact Recall Questions
Q1 A scalar quantity only has magnitude, but a vector quantity has magnitude and direction.
Q2 a) Vector
   b) Vector
   c) Scalar
   d) Vector
   e) Scalar
Q3 A contact force is a force between two objects due to the objects touching.

Q4 A non-contact force is a force between two objects which exists when the objects are not touching.
Q5 An interaction pair is a pair of forces that act on two interacting objects. The forces are equal and opposite.

Page 128 — Application Question
Q1

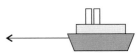

The arrow should be longer than the original arrow and be pointing in the opposite direction.

2. Weight, Mass and Gravity

Page 130 — Fact Recall Questions
Q1 Weight is the force acting on an object due to the gravitational field strength at the object's location.
Q2 The point at which the weight of the object appears to act.
Q3 A calibrated spring balance (or newtonmeter).

Page 130 — Application Question
Q1 a) $W = mg = 15 \times 9.8 = $ **147 N**
   b) Its mass would stay the same.

3. Resultant Forces

Page 134 — Fact Recall Questions
Q1 When an object has more than one force acting on it, the resultant force is a single force that has the same effect as the original forces acting altogether.
Q2 A free body diagram shows all the forces acting on an object, including the magnitude and direction of each force.
Q3 An object is in equilibrium if drawing all the forces tip-to-tail gives a complete loop.
Q4 Resolving a force means splitting the force into two component forces that are at right angles to each other. The combination of the two forces has the same effect as the original single force.

Page 134 — Application Questions
Q1 If the forward direction is the positive direction, then the resultant force = 87 − 24 = 63 N
So the resultant force is **63 N forwards**.
Q2 The boat is not in equilibrium as drawing all the forces to scale and tip-to-tail doesn't create a complete loop:

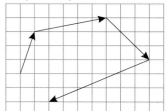

Q3   E.g.

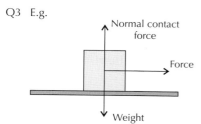

The weight and normal contact arrows should be vertical
and pointing in opposite directions to each other. They
should also be the same length. The force arrow should
be horizontal. It could point in either direction and be any
length, as you're not given its exact direction or magnitude.

Q4   First, resolve the 20 N force:

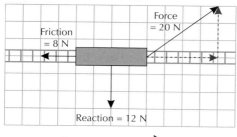

The frictional force that has a magnitude of 8 N is
2 squares long, so 1 square = 4 N.
The component of the pulling force in the direction
of motion is 4 squares long, so has a magnitude of
4 × 4 = 16 N.
Resultant force in direction of motion = 16 − 8 = **8 N**.
You don't need to worry about the 12 N reaction force
as it's at a right angle to the direction of the motion and
doesn't contribute to the resultant force you're looking for.

4. Work Done
Page 136 — Fact Recall Questions
Q1   Work done = force × distance ($W = Fs$)
     Work done is the energy transferred when a force acts
     on an object, causing it to move a certain distance.
Q2   1 joule is equal to 1 newton metre.
Q3   Doing work against friction causes energy to be
     transferred to thermal energy stores. This causes a rise
     in temperature.

Page 136 — Application Questions
Q1 $W = Fs = 24 \times 14 = $ **336 J**
Q2   a) $W = Fs = 250 \times 20 = $ **5000 J**
     b) Rearrange equation:
        $s = W \div F = 750 \div 250 = $ **3 m**

Page 138 — Force Basics
Exam-style Questions
1.1 $W = mg$
      $= 1.8 \times 9.8$ *(1 mark)*
      $= 17.64 = $ **18 N (to 2 s.f.)** *(1 mark)*
1.2   Magnitude = 5 − 1.4 = **3.6 N** *(1 mark)*

1.3 $W = Fs$
      So $s = W \div F$ *(1 mark)* $= 19.8 \div 3.6$ *(1 mark)*
      $= $ **5.5 m** *(1 mark)*
      You're given the work done by the resultant force, so make
      sure you use the value you worked out in 1.2, not the 5 N or
      1.4 N force.
2.1   Contact force *(1 mark)*
2.2   Resolve the forces of both horses:

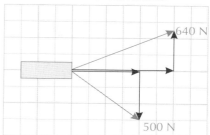

Find the scale of the diagram:
500 N = 2.5 cm, so 1 cm = 200 N
Measure the length of each component that is in the
direction of the boat's motion (East):
Horse 1: East component = 3 cm
         3 × 200 N = 600 N
Horse 2: East component = 2 cm
         2 × 200 N = 400 N
So the total force provided by the horses in the
direction of motion = 600 + 400 = **1000 N**
*(4 marks for correct answer, otherwise 1 mark for
resolving the forces, 1 mark for working out the scale
and 1 mark for finding the magnitude of the force
provided by each horse in the direction of the boat's
motion)*
2.3   Drag force = 1000 − 800 = 200 N *(1 mark)*

Topic 5b — Forces and Elasticity
1. Elastic Objects
Page 142 — Fact Recall Questions
Q1   If only one force is applied to an object, then the
     object will just move in the direction of the force.
Q2   An elastic object will return to its original shape after
     all forces have been removed from it.
Q3   force (N) = spring constant (N/m) × extension (m)
     (or $F = ke$)
Q4   The limit of proportionality is the point beyond
     which the extension of an object will no longer be
     proportional to the force applied to the object.
Q5   All the energy is released, because all the energy
     transferred ends up in the spring's elastic potential
     energy store, and all of the energy is transferred out of
     that store when the spring is released.

Page 142 — Application Questions
Q1   Extension = 0.75 − 0.50 = 0.25 m
     $F = ke = 34 \times 0.25 = $ **8.5 N**
Q2   Point B.
     The limit of proportionality is always the point at which a
     force-extension graph starts to curve.

Q3 a) Compression = 16 – 12 = 4 cm
In metres, this is 4 ÷ 100 = 0.04 m
Rearrange $F = ke$ for k:
$k = F ÷ e = 0.80 ÷ 0.04 = $ **20 N/m**
b) $E_e = ½ke^2 = ½ × 20 × 0.04^2 = $ **0.016 J**
c) Spring B's spring constant is higher than that of spring A.
You can work this out from $F = ke$. If e is smaller, then k must be larger to keep F the same.

2. Investigating Springs
Page 144 — Fact Recall Questions
Q1 A pilot experiment allows you to find the size of masses that should be used in order to record enough measurements to plot a straight line force-extension graph (the part of the graph up until the limit of proportionality is reached).
Q2 E.g. Safety goggles should be worn to protect the eyes if the spring snaps.
Q3 The gradient of the force-extension graph is equal to the spring constant of the spring.

Page 146 — Forces and Elasticity
Exam-style Questions
1.1 When a force of 0.70 N was applied to the spring, the limit of proportionality of the spring may have been passed, and so the graph would have started to curve, and the data point would be in the right position *(1 mark)*.
E.g. The student could increase the force acting on the spring to see whether the data points continue to follow the straight line of best fit, or whether the line of best fit should start to curve *(1 mark)*.
1.2 If the spring has been stretched too far *(1 mark)*, it will no longer deform elastically, and so it could not be used again for the same experiment *(1 mark)*.
1.3 Spring constant = gradient of line of best fit *(1 mark)*
gradient = $\frac{\text{change in } y}{\text{change in } x}$
E.g. spring constant = $\frac{0.80 - 0}{0.300 - 0}$ *(1 mark)*
= 2.66...
= **2.7 N/m (to 2 s.f.)** *(1 mark)*
Don't forget to convert the extension from cm to m. And remember to use as large a range of the line as possible when you're calculating the gradient.
2.1 The weight of the mass is the force that is acting on the spring, so use the equation $F = ke$.
Calculate the compression first: $e = 165 – 140$
= 25 mm *(1 mark)*
Convert the compression to m: 25 ÷ 1000 = 0.025 m
Then substitute the values into the equation for force:
$F = ke$
= 160 × 0.025 *(1 mark)*
= **4 N** *(1 mark)*
2.2 $E = ½ke^2 = ½ × 160 × 0.025^2$ *(1 mark)*
= **0.05 J** *(1 mark)*

Topic 5c — Forces and Motion
1. Distance, Displacement, Speed and Velocity
Page 149 — Fact Recall Questions
Q1 a) vector
b) scalar
c) vector
d) scalar
Q2 If an object is travelling at a constant speed but is changing direction, then its velocity is changing.
Remember — speed only has a magnitude, but velocity has magnitude and direction.
Q3 a) 6 m/s
b) 3 m/s
c) 1.5 m/s
Q4 distance travelled (m) = speed (m/s) × time (s)
(or $s = vt$)

Page 149 — Application Questions
Q1 a) Distance = 16 + 25 + 16 = **57 m**
b) The car has a displacement of 0 when it has travelled 16 m east and 16 m west, as it is travelling back on itself.
So displacement = **25 m south.**
Make sure you give both the magnitude and direction in your answer.
Q2 Typical walking speed = 1.5 m/s.
$s = vt = 1.5 × 18 = $ **27 m**
Q3 a) Use the train's speed between stations A and B and the time taken to travel between them.
$s = vt = 45 × 120 = $ **5400 m**
b) Use the speed the train is moving at between stations A and B, and the distance between them.
Change the distance into m:
16.8 × 1000 = 16 800 m
Then rearrange the distance equation:
$s = vt$, so $t = s ÷ v = 16 800 ÷ 60 = $ **280 s**
c) Total distance travelled = 5400 + 16 800 = 22 200 m
Total time taken to travel this distance = 120 + 280 = 400 s
$s = vt$, so $v = s ÷ t = 22 200 ÷ 400 = $ **55.5 m/s**

2. Acceleration
Page 151 — Fact Recall Questions
Q1 Acceleration is a measure of the rate of change of velocity.
Q2 m/s^2

Page 151 — Application Questions
Q1 Δv = final velocity – initial velocity
= 10 – 25 = –15 m/s
$a = \frac{\Delta v}{t} = –15 ÷ 5 = $ **–3 m/s²**
Q2 $a = \frac{\Delta v}{t}$, so $\Delta v = at = 4 × 5 = $ 20 m/s
The cheetah is initially at rest, so its change in velocity is equal to its final velocity, $\Delta v = v$.
So $v = $ **20 m/s**

Q3 Rearrange $v^2 - u^2 = 2as$ for acceleration:
$$a = (v^2 - u^2) \div 2s = (7.1^2 - 5.6^2) \div (2 \times 38.1)$$
$$= \textbf{0.25 m/s}^2$$

Q4 Rearrange $v^2 - u^2 = 2as$ for distance (height):
$$s = (v^2 - u^2) \div 2a = (6.0^2 - 0^2) \div (2 \times 9.8)$$
$$= 1.83...$$
$$= \textbf{1.8 m (to 2 s.f.)}$$
$u = 0$ because the apple is at rest up until the point it falls.

3. Distance-Time Graphs
Page 154 — Fact Recall Questions
Q1 The speed of the object.
Q2 It tells you that the object is stationary.
Q3 It represents acceleration (or deceleration).
Q4 Draw a tangent to the curve at the given time, and then calculate the gradient of the tangent.

Page 154 — Application Questions
Q1 A — It's increasing (the object is speeding up).
B — It's not changing (the object is moving at a steady speed).
C — It's decreasing (the object is slowing down).
D — It's zero (the object is not moving).
Q2 For the first 10 seconds the graph will be curved with an increasing gradient. For the next 5 seconds it will be a sloped straight line.
Q3 a)

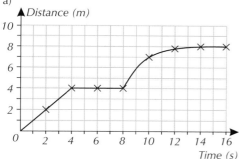

b) $s = vt$, so
$v = s \div t$
$= 4 \div 4 = \textbf{1 m/s}$
c) Speed at 10 s is equal to the gradient of the tangent to the curve at that point.
E.g.

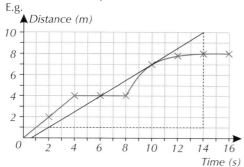

change in $y = 10 - 1 = 9$
change in $x = 14 - 2 = 12$
gradient $= 9 \div 12 = 0.75$
So, speed at 10 s = **0.75 m/s**

Tangents are difficult to draw accurately. Your answer may be slightly different to this one, but as long as it's close enough to this answer, you should be fine.

4. Velocity-Time Graphs
Page 157 — Fact Recall Questions
Q1 The acceleration (of the object).
Q2 The distance travelled (by the object).

Page 158 — Application Questions
Q1 A — It's not changing (the object has a steady acceleration).
B — It's zero (the object is moving at a steady speed).
C — It's increasing (the object is speeding up, but not at a steady rate).
D — It's not changing (the object has a steady deceleration).
Q2 a) 4 m/s
b) Between 100 and 120 seconds.
It's the part where the graph has a negative gradient (sloping downwards).
c) The acceleration is equal to the gradient, so:
$$\text{gradient} = \frac{\text{change in the vertical}}{\text{change in the horizontal}} = \frac{8 - 4}{80 - 60}$$
$$= \textbf{0.2 m/s}^2$$
d) Distance travelled between 0 and 20 s
$= \frac{1}{2} \times \text{base} \times \text{height} = \frac{1}{2} \times 20 \times 4 = 40 \text{ m}$
Distance travelled between 20 and 60 s
$= \text{base} \times \text{height} = (60 - 20) \times 4 = 160 \text{ m}$
So total distance travelled $= 40 + 160 = \textbf{200 m}$
Remember to break the area into separate shapes if you think it will make the calculation easier.
Q3

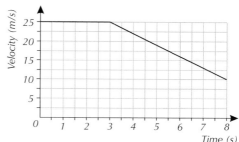

$$\text{Acceleration} = \text{gradient} = \frac{\text{change in the vertical}}{\text{change in the horizontal}}$$
$$= \frac{10 - 25}{8 - 3} = \textbf{-3 m/s}^2$$
The acceleration is negative as the car is decelerating.
Q4 Distance represented by one square
$= \text{width of one square} \times \text{height of one square}$
$= 2.5 \text{ s} \times 5 \text{ m/s} = 12.5 \text{ m}$
Number of squares under the graph between 0 and 20 s ≈ 38
Total distance travelled $= 12.5 \times 38 = \textbf{475 m}$

5. Terminal Velocity
Page 161 — Fact Recall Questions
Q1 The resistive forces must be equal to the driving force.
Q2 Drag is the friction experienced by an object moving through a fluid.

Answers

Q3 The greater the object's speed, the greater the drag force.

Q4 As an object falls, it is acted on by a gravitational force which causes it to accelerate. It is also acted on by the resistive force of air resistance. As the object accelerates, the resistive force on it increases. Eventually, the resistive force acting upwards will equal the force due to gravity acting downwards. At this point the resultant force on the object becomes zero, so the object stops accelerating and reaches a constant velocity — the terminal velocity.

Page 161 — Application Questions

Q1 On Earth, air resistance causes objects to fall at different speeds depending on their shape and size — it has a greater effect on the feather than on the rock. On the Moon there's no air, so there's no air resistance and all objects accelerate due to gravity at the same rate.

Q2 A parachute increases the resistive forces acting by increasing the skydiver's area. Because the total resistive force is greater, drag will equal the skydiver's weight at a lower speed (i.e. the terminal velocity will be lower).

6. Newton's First Law

Page 163 — Fact Recall Question

Q1 a) Nothing will happen — it will remain stationary.
   b) The object will accelerate (start moving) in the direction of the resultant force.
   c) The object will keep moving at the same velocity.
   d) The object will accelerate in the direction of its motion.
   e) The object will decelerate.

Page 163 — Application Question

Q1 The resultant force is zero.

7. Newton's Second Law and Inertia

Page 166 — Fact Recall Questions

Q1 Newton's Second Law says that the resultant force acting on an object is directly proportional to the acceleration of the object, and that the acceleration of an object is inversely proportional to the mass of the object.

Q2 $F = ma$, where F = force in N, m = mass in kg and a = acceleration in m/s^2.

Q3 Inertia is the tendency of an object to remain at a constant velocity.

Q4 Inertial mass is the ratio of the resultant force on an object to its acceleration.

Page 166 — Application Questions

Q1 The car without the rock has a smaller mass, so it will win the race. Acceleration is inversely proportional to mass ($a = F \div m$), so a larger mass means a smaller acceleration for a given driving force.

Q2 $a = F \div m = 303 \div 1.5 = $ **202 m/s^2**

Q3 No resistive forces, so driving force = resultant force.
Resultant force acting on left-hand car:
$F = ma = 1200 \times 2.3 = 2760$ N
Resultant force acting on right-hand car:
$F = ma = 820 \times 3.1 = 2542$ N
The resultant force acting on the **left-hand car** is greater, so that car's engine is providing the greater driving force.

Q4 Typical speed of a car = 25 m/s
Typical mass of a car = 1000 kg
$\Delta v = 25 - 5 = 20$ m/s
$a = \frac{\Delta v}{t} = 20 \div 20 = 1$ m/s^2
$F = ma = 1\,000 \times 1 = $ **1000 N**

8. Investigating Motion

Page 168 — Fact Recall Question

Q1 a) It would decrease.
   $a = F \div m$, so an increase in mass would give a decrease in acceleration.
   b) It would decrease.
   $a = F \div m$, so a decrease in force would give a decrease in acceleration.

9. Newton's Third Law

Page 170 — Fact Recall Questions

Q1 When two objects interact, the forces they exert on each other are equal and opposite.

Page 170 — Application Question

Q1 No, as the two forces are not of the same type and they are both acting on the ball.

Pages 173-175 — Forces and Motion
Exam-style Questions

1.1 Between 70 and 120 seconds *(1 mark)*
1.2 Acceleration = gradient *(1 mark)*
$= \dfrac{\text{change in the vertical}}{\text{change in the horizontal}} = \dfrac{10-6}{40-30}$ *(1 mark)*
$= $ **0.4 m/s^2** *(1 mark)*
You could have also used the formula $a = \Delta v \div t$, using the graph to find Δv and t.
1.3 $F = ma$
$= 980 \times 0.4$ *(1 mark)*
$= $ **392 N** *(1 mark)*
1.4 The distance travelled between 30 and 40 s is equal to the area under the graph *(1 mark)*, which can be found by splitting the area up into a triangle and a rectangle:
Area $= (\frac{1}{2} \times b \times h) + (b \times h)$
$= (\frac{1}{2} \times 10 \times 4) + (10 \times 6)$ *(1 mark)*
$= $ **80 m** *(1 mark)*

1.5 The graph between 30 and 40 s should show an acceleration (i.e. a steepening upwards curve), but it is showing that the car is stationary *(1 mark)*. The graph between 40 and 70 s should have a steeper gradient than the graph between 10 and 30 s, as the velocity is greater for this range *(1 mark)*. The graph between 70 and 120 s should show a deceleration (i.e. a levelling off curve upwards), instead of the straight line which represents a constant speed *(1 mark)*.

The graph between 70 and 120 s is also going downhill, which isn't possible for a distance-time graph.

2.1 The acceleration of the trolley is due to the weight of the hook and the masses attached to it *(1 mark)*.

2.2 The force can be decreased by moving a mass from the hook to the trolley *(1 mark)*.

2.3 The gap makes sure that the card interrupts the light gate signal twice, which allows the light gate to measure the velocity of the trolley at two different times during its motion *(1 mark)*. This information can then be used to calculate the acceleration of the trolley *(1 mark)*.

2.4 Doubling the force will double the acceleration *(1 mark)*. This is because an object's acceleration is directly proportional to the resultant force acting on it ($F = ma$) *(1 mark)*.

3.1 0 N *(1 mark)*

If it's travelling at a steady speed in a straight line, the resultant force acting on it must be zero.

3.2 $s = vt$, so:
$t = s \div v$ *(1 mark)* $= 448 \div 28$ *(1 mark)*
$= $ **16 s** *(1 mark)*

3.3 Making the truck more streamlined reduces the air resistance acting on the truck *(1 mark)*. So the speed at which resistive forces match the driving force will be greater *(1 mark)*.

3.4 First calculate the acceleration of the truck.
$F = ma$, so:
$a = F \div m = 35\ 000 \div 25\ 000$ *(1 mark)*
$= 1.4$ m/s² *(1 mark)*
Then rearrange the equation $v^2 - u^2 = 2as$:
$s = (v^2 - u^2) \div 2a = (0^2 - 28^2) \div (2 \times -1.4)$ *(1 mark)*
$= $ **280 m** *(1 mark)*

It's a deceleration, so put a = -1.4 into the equation.

4.1 Before reaching terminal velocity, the force due to gravity is **greater than** the resistive force due to air resistance. *(1 mark)*

4.2 After reaching terminal velocity, the force due to gravity is **the same as** the resistive force due to air resistance. *(1 mark)*

4.3 It will decrease *(1 mark)*

4.4 They will increase *(1 mark)*

5.1 The force is equal in size and in the opposite direction to F *(1 mark)*.

5.2 Change in velocity = 3 − 0 = 3 m/s
$a = \dfrac{\Delta v}{t} = 3 \div 1.2$ *(1 mark)*
$= $ **2.5 m/s²** *(1 mark)*

5.3 $F = ma = 100 \times 2.5$ *(1 mark)*
$= $ **250 N** *(1 mark)*

Topic 5d — Car Safety and Momentum

1. Stopping Distances

Page 179 — Fact Recall Questions

Q1 The stopping distance is the distance covered by the vehicle in the time between the driver first spotting a hazard and the vehicle coming to a complete stop. It's the sum of the thinking distance and the braking distance.
The thinking distance is the distance the vehicle travels during the driver's reaction time.
The braking distance is the distance the vehicle travels after the brakes are applied until it comes to a complete stop.

Q2 Any three from: e.g. ice (or water, oil, leaves etc.) on the road, quality of the tyres, quality of the car's brakes, weather conditions.

Q3 a) Braking
b) Thinking
c) Thinking
d) Braking

Page 179 — Application Questions

Q1 Stopping distance = 15 + 38 = **53 m**

Q2 E.g. Her colleagues could talk to her and distract her, delaying when she spots the hazard. She could be tired from the day at work, increasing her reaction time and so her thinking distance. It may be icy on the roads, increasing her braking distance.

Q3 a) 60 mph is twice 30 mph.
Thinking distance is directly proportional to speed, so new thinking distance = 9 × 2 = **18 m**
b) Braking distance increases by the square of the scale factor of the speed increase, so new braking distance = 14 × 2² = **56 m**
c) Stopping distance at 60 mph = 18 + 56 = **74 m**

2. Reaction Times

Page 181 — Fact Recall Question

Q1 Sit with your arm resting on the edge of a table. Have someone hold a ruler end-down so that the 0 cm mark hangs between your thumb and forefinger. The ruler should be dropped without warning. Grab the ruler between your thumb and forefinger as quickly as possible. Measure the distance at which you have caught the ruler. Use $v^2 - u^2 = 2as$ and $a = \Delta v \div t$ to calculate the time taken for the ruler to fall that distance. This is your reaction time.

Page 181 — Application Question

Q1 a) Average distance = (3.0 + 5.0 + 7.0) ÷ 3
$= 15.0 \div 3$
$= $ **5.0 cm**

b) $v^2 - u^2 = 2as$
$s = 5.0$ cm $= 0.050$ m
so $v = \sqrt{2as + u^2} = \sqrt{(2 \times 9.8 \times 0.050) + 0^2}$
$= 0.989...$ m/s
$a = \Delta v \div t$, so $t = \Delta v \div a = 0.989... \div 9.8$
$= 0.101...$
$= \mathbf{0.10}$ **s (to 2 s.f.)**
Remember to convert the distance from cm to m.

c) E.g. They are tired from the school day, so their reaction time is slower.

3. Braking and Energy Transfer
Page 182 — Application Questions
Q1 When the brakes are applied, work is done. This transfers energy from the kinetic energy stores of the wheels to the thermal energy stores of the brakes. This means the temperature of the brakes increases. The higher the speed of the vehicle, the greater the work done in stopping the vehicle. So stopping suddenly from a high speed causes a large energy transfer, and the brakes to overheat.

Q2 $v^2 - u^2 = 2as$ so
$a = (v^2 - u^2) \div 2s = (0^2 - 30^2) \div (2 \times 45)$
$= -10$ m/s^2
Typical car mass $= 1000$ kg
$F = ma = 1000 \times 10 = \mathbf{10\ 000\ N}$

4. Momentum
Page 184 — Fact Recall Questions
Q1 The object's mass and velocity.
Q2 $p = mv$. p is momentum in kg m/s, m is mass in kg and v is velocity in m/s.
Q3 They are the same.

Page 184 — Application Questions
Q1 a) $p = mv = 0.1 \times 0.6 = \mathbf{0.06\ kg\ m/s\ north}$
   Don't forget to give a direction.
   b) $p = mv = 0.00080 \times 12 = \mathbf{0.0096\ kg\ m/s\ left}$
   c) $p = mv = 5.2 \times 8.0 = \mathbf{42\ kg\ m/s\ down\ (2\ s.f.)}$
Q2 The total momentum before and after the event is 0. Momentum depends on mass and velocity, so if the gas canister's velocity before the explosion is zero, the momentum is 0. Assuming it's a closed system, the total momentum after the explosion will be equal to the momentum before, so it must be 0 as well.
Q3 a) Rearranging $p = mv$,
   $v = p \div m = 3.04 \div 0.95 = \mathbf{3.2\ m/s\ south}$
   b) Rearranging $p = mv$,
   $v = p \div m = 45\ 000 \div 2000 = \mathbf{22.5\ m/s\ east}$
Q4 a) Rearranging $p = mv$,
   $m = p \div v = 31.5 \div 0.75 = \mathbf{42\ kg}$
   b) Rearranging $p = mv$,
   $m = p \div v = 210 \div 7.5 = \mathbf{28\ kg}$

Page 186 — Car Safety and Momentum
Exam-style Questions
1.1 The other driver may have a different reaction time, which would result in a different thinking distance, and so a different stopping distance *(1 mark)*.
1.2 $v^2 - u^2 = 2as$
   so $a = (v^2 - u^2) \div 2s = (0^2 - 30^2) \div (2 \times 60)$ *(1 mark)*
   $= -7.5$ m/s^2 *(1 mark)*
   $F = ma = 2000 \times 7.5$ *(1 mark)*
   $= \mathbf{15\ 000\ N}$ *(1 mark)*
1.3 Work is done against friction between the brakes and the wheels *(1 mark)*. This transfers energy from the kinetic energy stores of the wheels to the thermal energy stores of the brakes, causing a decrease in speed *(1 mark)*.
1.4 The truck's wheels will have a lot of energy in their kinetic energy stores *(1 mark)*. A lot of work has to be done by the brakes to slow the truck down *(1 mark)*. This can cause the temperature of the brakes to rise too much and they overheat, which stops them from working *(1 mark)*.
1.5 E.g. poor visibility due to rainfall may increase the time it takes the driver to spot the obstacle / the stopping distance will be increased because wet roads increase braking distance *(2 marks, 1 mark for each correct answer)*.
2.1 In a closed system, the total momentum before an event is the same as after the event *(1 mark)*.
2.2 Say to the right is positive.
   The blue ball is at rest, so it has zero momentum
   Total momentum = momentum of white ball *(1 mark)*
   $p = mv$, so total momentum $= (m_{white} \times v_{white})$
   $p = [0.16 \times 0.5]$ *(1 mark)*
   $p = \mathbf{0.08\ kg\ m/s\ to\ the\ right}$ *(1 mark)*
2.3 After the collision, the blue ball has a velocity less than that of the white ball before the collision *(1 mark)*. The white ball now has a lower velocity than before *(1 mark)*. Both balls have a momentum that is lower than momentum of the white ball before the collision *(1 mark)*. Due to conservation of momentum, the sum of the momentum of each ball is equal to the momentum of the white ball before the collision *(1 mark)*.

Topic 6 — Waves

Topic 6a — Properties of Waves

1. Wave Basics
Page 188 — Fact Recall Questions
Q1 a) A wave in which the oscillations are perpendicular to the direction in which the wave travels/transfers energy.
   b) E.g. any electromagnetic wave, ripples on water, waves on a string, a slinky wiggled up and down.
   c) A wave in which the oscillations are parallel to the direction in which the wave travels/transfers energy.

Q2 In areas of compression, the particles are bunched up close together. In areas of rarefaction, the particles are more spread out.

Q3 B

Q4 No. An object will bob up and down on the ripples rather than move across the water.

2. Features of Waves

Page 190 — Fact Recall Question

Q1 a) The amplitude of a wave is the maximum displacement of a point on the wave from its undisturbed (or rest) position.
b) The wavelength is the distance between the same point on two adjacent waves.
c) The frequency is the number of waves passing a certain point per second.
d) The period is the time taken for one cycle of a wave to be completed.

Page 190 — Application Questions

Q1 The wavelength is the length of one full cycle. The distance shown on the diagram is only half a cycle, so the wavelength is twice the distance shown on the diagram, **4.0 m**.

Q2 a) Amplitude = **1 cm**, Period = **4 s**
b) $f = 1 \div T = 1 \div 4 = $ **0.25 Hz**

3. Wave Speed

Page 194 — Fact Recall Questions

Q1 $v = f\lambda$, v = speed in m/s, f = frequency in Hz, λ = wavelength in m

Q2 E.g. Use a signal generator connected to a speaker to make a sound of known frequency. Put two microphones next to the speaker. The microphones should be connected to an oscilloscope. Slowly move one microphone away from the speaker. Its wave will shift sideways on the oscilloscope. Keep moving it until the two waves on the oscilloscope are aligned once more. At this point the microphones will be exactly one wavelength apart, so measure the distance between them. You can then use the formula $v = f\lambda$ to find the speed (v) of the sound wave passing through the air, using the wavelength you measured and the frequency of the signal generator.

Q3 330 m/s

Q4 Adjust the frequency of the vibration transducer until a clear wave can be seen on the string. Record this frequency, f. Use a metre ruler to measure the length of multiple (at least 4) half-wavelengths. Divide this length by the number of half-wavelengths to get the average half-wavelength, and then double it to find the average wavelength, λ. Then use the formula $v = f\lambda$ to find the speed (v) of the waves.

Page 194 — Application Questions

Q1 $v = f\lambda = 15 \times 0.45 = $ **6.75 m/s**

Q2 $f = 3$ kHz $= 3000$ Hz
$v = f\lambda$, so $\lambda = v \div f = 1500 \div 3000 = $ **0.5 m**

Q3 $v = f\lambda$, so $f = v \div \lambda = (3.0 \times 10^8) \div (7.5 \times 10^{-7})$
$= $ **4×10^{14} Hz**

Q4 $\lambda = 1 \div 10 = 0.1$ cm, which is 0.001 m
$v = f\lambda = 100 \times 0.001 = $ **0.1 m/s**
Make sure the frequency is in Hz and the wavelength is in metres before you use the wave equation.

4. Refraction of Waves

Page 197 — Fact Recall Questions

Q1 When a wave changes direction as it passes across the boundary between two materials at an angle to the normal.

Q2 E.g.

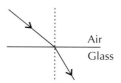

The exact angles aren't important, but it must bend towards the normal.

Q3 Its path doesn't change direction.

Q4 Its speed and wavelength will increase. Its frequency won't change.

Q5 The wavefronts are closer together.

Q6 It bends away from the normal.

Page 197 — Application Questions

Q1

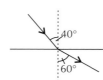

Q2 The wave in Q1 **speeds up** as it enters the new substance.

Page 199 — Properties of Waves

Exam-style Questions

1.1 $3.0 \div 2 = $ **1.5 m** *(1 mark)*

1.2 frequency *(1 mark)*

1.3 $T = 1 \div f = 1 \div 2$ *(1 mark)* $= $ **0.5 s** *(1 mark)*

1.4 wave speed = frequency × wavelength / $v = f\lambda$ *(1 mark)*

1.5 $v = 2 \times 1.5$ *(1 mark)* $= $ **3 m/s** *(1 mark)*

2.1

(1 mark for basic construction of ray diagram, with incident ray at an angle to the boundary and the refracted ray bent towards the normal, 1 mark for accurately drawn angles of incidence and refraction.)

2.2 How to grade your answer:
Level 0: There is no relevant information.
(No marks)
Level 1: There is a brief description of how the wave changes. **(1 to 2 marks)**
Level 2: There is some explanation of how the diagram relates to the changes in the wave. **(3 to 4 marks)**
Level 3: There is a clear and detailed explanation of how the diagram relates to the changes in the wave. **(5 to 6 marks)**

Here are some points your answer may include:
The wavefronts are shown closer together in the glass block. This indicates a decrease in wavelength. The frequency does not change.
Because frequency doesn't change, the speed of the wave must also decrease in the glass block. This is because the wave obeys the wave equation, $v = f\lambda$, so a decrease in wavelength at a constant frequency must mean a decrease in velocity.
The direction of the wavefronts changes in the block. The wave has bent towards the normal. This is because the part of the wave that reaches the glass block first starts slowing down before the rest of the wave.

Topic 6b — Electromagnetic Waves

1. What are Electromagnetic Waves?
Page 202 — Fact Recall Questions
Q1 Transverse
Q2 A continuous spectrum of all the possible wavelengths (or frequencies) of electromagnetic waves.
Q3 Gamma rays, X-rays, ultraviolet, visible light, infrared, microwaves, radio waves.
Q4 Gamma rays
Q5 The speed of any electromagnetic wave in a vacuum is the same (about 3×10^8 m/s).
Q6 E.g. A hot object (the source) emits infrared radiation as it cools down. This radiation is absorbed by the air around it (the absorber) and transfers energy to the thermal energy stores of the air.
Q7 Electrons falling to a lower energy level from a higher one and a nucleus releasing excess energy after a radioactive decay.
Q8 It can be absorbed, reflected or transmitted. No, the same thing won't always happen to any EM wave — different wavelengths may behave differently at the same boundary.

Page 202 — Application Question
Q1 a) The wavelength increases.
b) Radio waves

2. Radio Waves
Page 204 — Fact Recall Questions
Q1 Alternating current.
Q2 TV and radio communications.

Q3 They can be reflected back and forth between the atmospheric layers and the Earth to travel long distances.

3. More EM Waves and their Uses
Page 208 — Fact Recall Questions
Q1 Microwaves and infrared radiation.
Q2 An electric heater contains a wire that gets hot when current flows through it. The wire then emits infrared radiation, which is absorbed by the air and objects in the room / is transferred to the thermal energy stores of the air and objects in the room. This results in an increase in temperature.
Q3 It travels along the fibre by reflecting off the fibre's walls.
Q4 E.g. in sun tanning lamps and in energy efficient lamps.
Q5 They pass easily through soft tissue like flesh, but less easily through denser material like bone, so they're useful for forming an image of the body (particularly the skeleton).

Page 208 — Application Question
Q1 Image B was taken at night. In image B, the background is darker. This means the surroundings must be cooler, so the photo was taken at night-time.

4. Investigating Infrared Radiation
Page 210 — Fact Recall Questions
Q1 E.g. a hollow, metal, water-tight cube. Its vertical faces have different surfaces. It is filled with hot water and readings of the infrared radiation emitted by each vertical face are taken, at a fixed distance. This is used to determine which colour and texture of face is the best radiation emitter.
Q2 The wax and ball bearings are there to show which plate absorbs more infrared radiation. The better the absorber, the higher the rate of energy transfer to the wax and so the quicker the ball bearing will fall.

5. Dangers of EM Radiation
Page 212 — Fact Recall Questions
Q1 Any two from: sunburn, causing skin to age prematurely, damage to eyes, increased risk of skin cancer.
Q2 Radiation that has enough energy to knock electrons off atoms.
Q3 X-rays and gamma rays
Q4 They can kill cells or cause gene mutations which can lead to cancer.
Q5 The risk of harm from exposure to radiation.
Q6 How much radiation is absorbed, the type of radiation, the body tissue absorbing the radiation.

Page 212 — Application Question

Q1 a) 10 times larger

b) E.g. the body tissues exposed to radiation in the X-ray of the pelvis are more sensitive to radiation damage than the tissues exposed in a dental X-ray. / In a pelvic X-ray, more X-rays must be used as the X-rays pass through a lot more body tissue, because the pelvis is a much larger part of the body than the mouth.

Pages 214-215 — Electromagnetic Waves Exam-style Questions

1.1 Wavelength *(1 mark)*

1.2 Ultraviolet *(1 mark)*

1.3 Radio waves *(1 mark)* and microwaves *(1 mark)*

2.1 $0.7 \div 0.004$ *(1 mark)* = **175** times greater *(1 mark)*

2.2 X-rays are ionising — they can cause electrons to be removed from an atom *(1 mark)*. If this happens in a human cell, it can cause the cell to die, or mutate and cause cancer *(1 mark)*.

2.3 The radiation dose from a spinal X-ray is much higher than from one of the teeth *(1 mark)*. Having regular spinal X-rays could be very dangerous due to the high radiation dose, so the benefits would be outweighed by the risks *(1 mark)*.

3.1 Alternating current is made up of oscillating electrons — these produce radio waves of the same frequency as the current *(1 mark)*. These radio waves are emitted by a transmitter and absorbed by a receiver *(1 mark)*. The energy carried by the waves is transferred to the kinetic energy stores of electrons in the receiver *(1 mark)*. This causes the electrons to oscillate and, if the receiver is part of a complete circuit, generates an alternating current with the same frequency as the absorbed radio waves *(1 mark)*.

3.2 X-rays are absorbed by the Earth's atmosphere *(1 mark)*, so telescopes must be located outside the Earth's atmosphere to detect X-rays from space *(1 mark)*.

3.3 The microwaves used in a microwave oven have to be absorbed by water molecules to cook the food *(1 mark)*. Microwaves of these wavelengths could not be used to communicate with satellites because the Earth's atmosphere contains water, and so the microwaves would be absorbed by water molecules in the atmosphere *(1 mark)*.

4.1 41 W/m² *(1 mark)*

4.2 The whole surface of the can is the same temperature, as it is all heated by the same water, so the thermometer readings are equal *(1 mark)*. The two different surface colours emit different levels of IR radiation — shiny silver is a worse emitter than matt black, so the IR sensor readings are different *(1 mark)*.

4.3 The amount of radiation detected would be lower than before *(1 mark)*. This is because the can would have cooled/decreased in temperature during the 15 minute period, and cooler objects emit less infrared radiation *(1 mark)*.

4.4 The amount of radiation detected would be less than from the matt black side *(1 mark)* but more than from the shiny silver side *(1 mark)*. This is because matt objects are better emitters than shiny objects, but black objects are better emitters than lighter-coloured ones *(1 mark)*.

Topic 7 — Magnetism and Electromagnetism

1. Magnetic Fields

Page 217 — Fact Recall Questions

Q1 It's a region where magnetic materials (like iron and steel), and also wires carrying currents, experience a force acting on them.

Q2

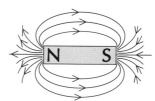

Q3 When not in the field of another magnet, the magnet in a compass points north. It is experiencing a magnetic force, so the Earth must have a magnetic field. For the Earth to have a magnetic field, its core must be magnetic.

Q4 An induced magnet is a magnetic material which becomes a magnet (with its own magnetic field) when it is placed inside another magnetic field, but which has no magnetic field otherwise.

2. Electromagnetism

Page 220 — Fact Recall Questions

Q1 In the right-hand thumb rule, your thumb represents the current. Your fingers represent the magnetic field.

Q2

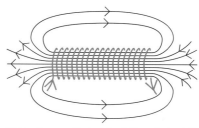

All the lines on the inside of the coil should be straight and parallel. Outside the coil, it looks just like a bar magnet.

Q3 You can increase the strength of a solenoid by placing an iron core inside the coil.
You could also increase the current in the coil.

Q4 An electromagnet is a magnet whose magnetic field can be turned on and off with an electric current. Their most common form is a coil of wire around an iron core. When a current flows through the coil of wire, a magnetic field is formed around the wire and the core is magnetised.

Q5 E.g. in scrap yard cranes used for picking up and moving scrap metal.

Page 220 — Application Questions

Q1 a) The current is flowing into the page.
Curl the fingers of your right hand in the direction of the magnetic field (i.e. clockwise). Your thumb should point into the page.
b) The magnetic field lines would also change direction — i.e. they'd point anti-clockwise.

3. The Motor Effect
Page 224 — Fact Recall Questions

Q1 By increasing the strength of the magnetic field and increasing the current in the wire.

Q2 Zero
The wire won't feel any force if it's parallel to the magnetic field — it'll experience the greatest force when it's at 90° to the magnetic field.

Q3 $F = BIl$. F is in N (newtons), B is in T (tesla), I is in A (amperes) and l is in m (meters) This equation is only valid when the current is flowing at 90° to the direction of the magnetic field.

Q4 The first finger is the field, the second finger is the current and the thumb is the force (or motion).

Page 224 — Application Questions

Q1 a) Out of the page.
b) Out of the page.
c) Into the page.

Q2 Into the page.
Swapping both the current and the field will swap the direction of the force twice, with no overall effect.

Q3 $F = BIl$, so $l = F \div (B \times I)$
$l = 0.25 \div (0.20 \times 5.0) = 0.25$ m = **25 cm**

4. Using the Motor Effect
Page 228 — Fact Recall Questions

Q1 It reverses the direction of the current every half turn so that the force on each arm of the wire loop changes direction every half turn. This way the force is always acting in a direction that causes the coil to keep rotating.

Q2 By swapping the polarity of the dc supply or swapping the magnetic poles over.
It'll only be reversed if you swap one of these things. If you swap both it'll just carry on in the same direction. If you don't believe me, check it using Fleming's left-hand rule.

Page 228 — Application Question

Q1 a) anticlockwise
b) It'll increase.
c) The direction of rotation will be reversed.

Page 230 — Magnetism and Electromagnetism
Exam-style Questions

1.1 The motor effect is when a current-carrying wire in a magnetic field experiences a force *(1 mark)*.

1.2 Reversing the direction of the magnetic field reverses the direction of the force caused by the motor effect *(1 mark)*, so the motor turns in the opposite direction (anticlockwise) *(1 mark)*.

1.3 $F = BIl$
$F = 0.2 \times 3 \times 0.005$ *(1 mark)*
$F = 0.003$ N
There are 4 wires in total, and the above force on each wire, so the total force is
$F = 0.003 \times 4 = $ **0.012 N** *(1 mark)*

1.4 When the dc supply is turned on a current flows through the coil of wire *(1 mark)*. When current flows through a wire, a magnetic field is produced around it, so the electromagnet becomes magnetic *(1 mark)*.

1.5 An alternating current supply would not be suitable because the direction of the current would be constantly changing *(1 mark)*. This would cause the direction of the magnetic field to constantly change *(1 mark)*, which would cause the direction of rotation of the coil (and hence the screwdriver) to constantly change, making it unable to function as intended *(1 mark)*.

Glossary

A

Absorption
When a wave transfers energy to the energy stores of a material.

Acceleration
A measure of how quickly velocity is changing.

Accurate result
A result that is very close to the true answer.

Activity (radioactive)
The number of nuclei of a sample that decay per second.

Air resistance
The frictional force caused by air on a moving object.

Alpha decay
A type of radioactive decay in which an alpha particle is given out from a decaying nucleus.

Alpha particle
A positively-charged particle made up of two protons and two neutrons (a helium nucleus).

Alpha particle scattering experiment
An experiment in which alpha particles were fired at gold foil to see if they were deflected. It led to the plum pudding model being abandoned in favour of the nuclear model of the atom.

Alternating current (ac)
Current that is constantly changing direction.

Ammeter
A component used to measure the current through a component. It is always connected in series with the component.

Amplitude
The maximum displacement of a point on a wave from its rest position.

Angle of incidence
The angle the incident ray of a wave makes with the normal at a boundary.

Angle of refraction
The angle a refracted ray makes with the normal when a wave refracts at a boundary.

Anomalous result
A result that doesn't seem to fit with the rest of the data.

Atmosphere
A relatively thin layer of air that surrounds the Earth.

Atom
Particles that make up matter.

Atomic number
The number of protons in the nucleus of an atom.

B

Beta decay
A type of radioactive decay in which a beta particle is given out from a decaying nucleus.

Beta particle
A high-speed electron emitted in beta decay.

Bias
Unfairness in the way data is presented, possibly because the presenter is trying to make a particular point (sometimes without knowing they're doing it).

Bio-fuel
A renewable energy resource made from plant products or animal dung.

Braking distance
The braking distance is the distance a vehicle travels after the brakes are applied until it comes to a complete stop, as a result of the braking force.

C

Calibrate
Measure something with a known quantity to see if the instrument being used to measure that quantity gives the correct value.

Carbon neutral fuel
A fuel is carbon neutral if it absorbs as much CO_2 from the atmosphere (when it's produced/grown) as it releases when it's burned.

Categoric data
Data that comes in distinct categories, e.g. blood type (A+, B–, etc.), metals (copper, zinc, etc.).

Closed system
A system where neither matter nor energy can enter or leave. The net change in total energy in a closed system is always zero.

Conduction
A method of energy transfer by heating where vibrating particles transfer energy through a material by colliding with neighbouring particles and transferring energy between their kinetic energy stores.

Conductor (electrical)
A material in which electrical charges can easily move.

Conservation of energy principle
Energy can be transferred usefully from one energy store to another, stored or dissipated — but it can never be created or destroyed.

Conservation of momentum
In a closed system, the total momentum before an event is the same as the total momentum after the event.

Contamination (radioactive)
The presence of unwanted radioactive atoms on or inside an object.

Continuous data
Numerical data that can have any value within a range (e.g. length, volume or temperature).

Control experiment
An experiment that's kept under the same conditions as the rest of the investigation, but where the independent variable isn't altered.

Control group
A group that matches the one being studied, but where the independent variable isn't altered. The group is kept under the same conditions as the group in the experiment.

Control variable
A variable in an experiment that is kept the same.

Convection
A method of energy transfer by heating in liquids and gases in which energetic particles move away from hotter regions to cooler regions.

Conversion factor
A number which you must multiply or divide a unit by to convert it t‚ different unit.

Correlation
A relationship between

Current
The flow of electric charge. The size of the current is the rate of flow of charge. Measured in amperes (A).

Decommissioning
The process of shutting down a power station so that it's completely safe and poses no risk to people or the environment.

Density
A substance's mass per unit volume.

Dependent variable
The variable in an experiment that is measured.

Diode
A circuit component that only allows current to flow through it in one direction. It has a very high resistance in the other direction.

Direct current (dc)
Current that always flows in the same direction.

Discrete data
Numerical data that can only take a certain value, with no in-between value (e.g. number of people).

Displacement
The straight-line distance and direction from an object's starting position to its finishing position.

Distance-time graph
A graph showing how the distance travelled by an object changes over a period of time.

Drag
The frictional force caused by any fluid (a liquid or gas) on a moving object.

Earth wire
The green and yellow wire in an electrical cable that only carries current when there's a fault. It stops exposed metal parts of an appliance from becoming live.

Efficiency
The proportion of input energy transfer which is usefully transferred. Also the proportion of input power which is usefully output.

Elastic deformation
An object undergoing elastic deformation will return to its original shape once any forces being applied to it are removed.

Elastic object
An object which can be elastically deformed.

Elastic potential energy store
Anything that has been stretched or compressed, e.g. a spring, has energy in its elastic potential energy store.

Electromagnet
A solenoid with an iron core.

Electromagnetic (EM) spectrum
A continuous spectrum of all the possible wavelengths of electromagnetic waves.

Electron
A subatomic particle with a relative charge of −1 and a relative mass of 1/2000.

Energy store
A means by which an object stores energy. There are different types of energy store: thermal (or internal), kinetic, gravitational potential, elastic potential, chemical, magnetic, electrostatic and nuclear.

Equilibrium
A state in which all the forces acting on an object are balanced, so the resultant force is zero.

Fair test
A controlled experiment where the only thing being changed is the independent variable.

Fleming's left-hand rule
The rule used to work out the direction of the force produced by the motor effect. Your first finger points in the direction of the magnetic field, your second finger points in the direction of the current and your thumb points in the direction of the force (or motion).

Fluid
A substance that can flow — either a liquid or a gas.

Force
A push or a pull on an object caused by it interacting with something.

Fossil fuel
The fossil fuels are coal, oil and natural gas. They're non-renewable energy resources that we burn to generate electricity.

Free body diagram
A diagram that shows all the forces acting on an isolated object, the direction in which the forces are acting and their (relative) magnitudes.

Frequency
The number of complete waves passing a certain point per second, or the number of waves produced by a source per second. Measured in hertz, Hz.

Frequency density
The height of a bar on a histogram. It is found by the frequency divided by the class width.

Friction
A force that opposes an object's motion. It acts in the opposite direction to motion.

Gamma decay
A type of radioactive decay in which a gamma ray is given out from a decaying nucleus.

Gamma ray
A high-frequency, short-wavelength electromagnetic wave.

Geiger-Müller tube
A particle detector that is used with a counter to measure count rate.

Geothermal power
A renewable energy resource where energy is transferred from the thermal energy stores of hot rocks underground and is used to generate electricity or to heat buildings.

Gradient
The slope of a line graph. It shows how quickly the variable on the y-axis changes with the variable on the x-axis.

Gravitational potential energy (g.p.e) store
Anything that has mass and is in a gravitational field has energy in its gravitational potential energy store.

Greenhouse effect
The process by which gases in the Earth's atmosphere block radiation from the Sun from leaving the atmosphere. This causes the overall temperature of the atmosphere to rise (i.e. global warming).

Half-life
The time it takes for the number of nuclei of a radioactive isotope in a sample to halve.
OR
The time it takes for the count rate (or activity) of a radioactive sample to fall to half its initial level.

Hazard
Something that has the potential to cause harm (e.g. fire, electricity, etc.).

Hydroelectric power station
A power station in which a dam is built across a valley or river which holds back water, forming a reservoir. It allows water to flow out of the reservoir through turbines at a controlled rate. This turns the turbines, which are attached to generators and can generate electricity.

Hypothesis
A possible explanation for a scientific observation.

Independent variable
The variable in an experiment that is changed.

Induced magnet
A magnetic material that only has its own magnetic field, and behaves as a magnet, while it is inside another magnetic field.

Inelastic deformation
An object undergoing inelastic deformation will not return to its original shape once the forces being applied to it are removed.

Inertia
The tendency of an object to remain stationary or continue travelling at a constant velocity.

Inertial mass
The ratio between the resultant force acting on an accelerating object and its acceleration.

Infrared (IR) radiation
A type of electromagnetic wave that is given out by all objects. It can also be absorbed by objects which makes the object hotter.

Internal energy
The total energy that a system's particles have in their kinetic and potential energy stores.

Ion
An atom in which the number of electrons is different to the number of protons, giving it an overall charge.

Ionising radiation
Radiation that has enough energy to knock electrons off atoms.

Irradiation
Exposure to radiation.

Isotope
A different form of the same element, which has atoms with the same number of protons (atomic number), but a different number of neutrons (and so different mass number).

I-V characteristic
A graph of current against potential difference for a component.

Kinetic energy store
Anything that's moving has energy in its kinetic energy store.

Latent heat
The energy required to change the state of a substance without changing its temperature.

Light-dependent resistor (LDR)
A resistor whose resistance is dependent on light intensity. The resistance decreases as light intensity increases.

Limit of proportionality
The point beyond which the force applied to an elastic object is no longer directly proportional to the extension of the object.

Line of action (of a force)
A straight line passing through the point at which the force is acting in the same direction as the force.

Linear graph
A straight line graph for which $y = mx + c$, where m = gradient and c = y-intercept.

Live wire
The brown wire in an electrical cable that carries an alternating potential difference from the mains.

Longitudinal wave
A wave in which the oscillations are along the same line as the direction of energy transfer.

Lubricant
A substance (usually a liquid) that can flow easily between two objects. Used to reduce friction between surfaces.

Magnetic field
A region where magnetic materials (like iron and steel) and current-carrying wires experience a force.

Magnetic flux density
The number of magnetic field lines per unit area. Its symbol is B and it is measured in tesla, T.

Magnetic material
A material (such as iron, steel, cobalt or nickel) which can become an induced magnet while it's inside another magnetic field.

Mass number
The number of neutrons and protons in the nucleus of an atom.

Mean (average)
A measure of average found by adding up all the data and dividing by the number of values there are.

Median (average)
A measure of average found by selecting the middle value from a data set arranged in ascending order.

Medical tracer
A radioactive isotope that can be injected into or swallowed by people. Their progress around the body can be followed using an external detector and can diagnose medical conditions.

Microwave
A type of electromagnetic wave that can be used for cooking and satellite communications.

Mode (average)
A measure of average found by selecting the most frequent value from a data set.

Model
Used to describe or display how an object or system behaves in reality.

Momentum
A property of a moving object that is the product of its mass and velocity.

Motor effect
When a current-carrying wire in a magnetic field experiences a force.

National grid
The network of transformers and cables that distributes electrical power from power stations to consumers.

Neutral wire
The blue wire in an electrical cable that carries away current from the appliance. It is around 0 V.

Neutron
A subatomic particle with a relative charge of 0 and a relative mass of 1.

Newton's First Law
An object will remain at rest or travelling at a constant velocity unless it is acted on by a resultant force.

Newton's Second Law
The acceleration of an object is directly proportional to the resultant force acting on it, and inversely proportional to its mass.

Newton's Third Law
When two objects interact, they exert equal and opposite forces on each other.

Non-contact force
A force that can act between objects that are not touching.

Non-renewable energy resource
An energy resource that is non-renewable cannot be made at the same rate as it's being used, so it will run out one day.

Normal (at a boundary)
A line that's perpendicular (at 90°) to a surface at the point of incidence (where a wave hits the surface).

Nuclear model
A model of the atom that says that the atom has a small, central positively-charged nucleus with negatively-charged electrons moving around the nucleus, and that most of the atom is empty space. The nucleus is made up of protons and neutrons.

Nucleus (atom)
The centre of an atom, containing protons and neutrons.

Ohmic conductor
A conductor with resistance that is constant at a constant temperature. It has a linear *I-V* characteristic.

P

Parallel circuit
A circuit in which every component is connected separately to the positive and negative ends of the battery.

Peer-review
The process in which other scientists check the results and explanations of an investigation before they are published.

Period (of a wave)
The time taken for one full cycle of a wave to be completed.

Permanent magnet
A magnetic material that always has its own magnetic field around it.

Physical change
A change where you don't end up with a new substance — it's the same substance as before, just in a different form. (A change of state is a physical change.)

Potential difference
The driving force that pushes electric charge around a circuit, measured in volts (V). Also known as pd or voltage.

Power
The rate of transferring energy (or doing work). Normally measured in watts (W).

Precise result
When all the data is close to the mean.

Prediction
A statement that can be tested and is based on a hypothesis.

Pressure
The force per unit area exerted on a surface.

Proton
A subatomic particle with a relative charge of +1 and a relative mass of 1.

Radiation dose
A measure of the risk of harm to your body due to exposure to radiation.

Radio wave
A type of electromagnetic wave mainly used for radio and TV signals.

Radioactive decay
The random process of a radioactive substance giving out radiation from the nuclei of its atoms.

Radioactive substance
A substance that spontaneously gives out radiation from the nuclei of its atoms.

Radiotherapy
A treatment of cancer that uses ionising radiation (such as gamma rays and X-rays) to kill cancer cells.

Random error
A difference in the results of an experiment caused by unpredictable events, e.g. human error in measuring.

Range
The difference between the smallest and largest values in a set of data.

Ray
A straight line showing the direction of energy transfer of a wave, indicating the path along which the wave moves.

Ray diagram
A diagram that shows the path of light waves.

Reaction time
The time taken for a person to react after an event (e.g. seeing a hazard).

Reflection
When a wave bounces back as it meets a boundary between two materials.

Refraction
When a wave changes direction as it passes across the boundary between two materials at an angle to the normal.

Reliable result
A result that is repeatable and reproducible.

Renewable energy resource
An energy resource that is renewable is one that is being, or can be, made at the same rate (or faster) than it's being used, and so will never run out.

Repeatable result
A result that will come out the same if the experiment is repeated by the same person using the same method and equipment.

Reproducible result
A result that will come out the same if someone different does the experiment, or a slightly different method or piece of equipment is used.

Resistance
Anything in a circuit that reduces the flow of current. Measured in ohms, Ω.

Resolution
The smallest change a measuring instrument can detect.

Resultant force
A single force that can replace all the forces acting on an object to give the same effect as the original forces acting altogether.

Right-hand thumb rule
The rule to work out the direction of the magnetic field around a current-carrying wire. Your thumb points in the direction of the current, and your fingers curl in the direction of the magnetic field.

Risk
The chance that a hazard will cause harm.

Scalar
A quantity that has magnitude but no direction.

Scaling prefix
A word or symbol which goes before a unit to indicate a multiplying factor (e.g. 1 km = 1000 m).

Series circuit
A circuit in which every component is connected in a line, end to end.

S.I. unit
A unit recognised as standard by scientists all over the world.

Significant figure
The first significant figure of a number is the first non-zero digit. The second, third and fourth significant figures follow on immediately after it.

Solar cell
A device that generates electricity directly from the Sun's radiation.

Solenoid
A coil of wire often used in the construction of electromagnets.

Specific heat capacity
The amount of energy (in joules) needed to raise the temperature of 1 kg of a material by 1°C.

Specific latent heat (SLH)
The amount of energy needed to change 1 kg of a substance from one state to another without changing its temperature. (For cooling, it is the energy released by a change in state.)

Specific latent heat of fusion
The specific latent heat for changing between a solid and a liquid (melting or freezing).

Specific latent heat of vaporisation
The specific latent heat for changing between a liquid and a gas (evaporating, boiling or condensing).

Split-ring commutator
A ring with gaps in it that swaps the electrical contacts of a device every half-turn.

Standard form
A number written in the form $A \times 10^n$, where A is a number between 1 and 10.

State of matter
The form which a substance can take — e.g. solid, liquid or gas.

Stopping distance
The distance covered by a vehicle in the time between the driver spotting a hazard and the vehicle coming to a complete stop. It's the sum of the thinking distance and the braking distance.

System
The object, or group of objects, that you're considering.

Systematic error
An error that is consistently made throughout an experiment.

Tangent
A straight line that touches a curve at a point but doesn't cross it.

Terminal velocity
The maximum velocity a falling object can reach without any added driving forces. It's the velocity at which the resistive forces (drag) acting on the object match the force due to gravity (weight).

Theory
A hypothesis which has been accepted by the scientific community because there is good evidence to back it up.

Thermal conductivity
A measure of how quickly an object transfers energy by heating through conduction.

Thermal insulator
A material with a low thermal conductivity.

Thermistor
A resistor whose resistance is dependent on the temperature. The resistance decreases as temperature increases.

Thinking distance
The distance a vehicle travels during the driver's reaction time (before the brakes have been applied).

Three-core cable
An electrical cable containing a live wire, a neutral wire and an earth wire.

Tidal barrage
A dam built across a river estuary with turbines connected to generators. When there's a difference in water height on either side, water flows through the dam, turning the turbines and generating electricity.

Transformer
A device which can change the potential difference of an ac supply.

Transmission (of a wave)
When a wave passes through a boundary from one material into another and continues travelling.

Transverse wave
A wave in which the oscillations are perpendicular (at 90°) to the direction of energy transfer.

Trial run
A quick version of an experiment that can be used to work out the range of variables and the interval between the variables that will be used in the proper experiment.

Ultraviolet (UV) radiation
A type of electromagnetic wave, the main source of which is sunlight.

Uncertainty
The amount by which a given result may differ from the true value.

Valid result
A result that is repeatable, reproducible and answers the original question.

Vector
A quantity which has both magnitude (size) and a direction.

Velocity
The speed and direction of an object.

Velocity-time graph
A graph showing how the velocity of an object changes over a period of time.

Visible light
The part of the electromagnetic spectrum that we can see with our eyes.

Voltmeter
A component used to measure the potential difference across a component. Always connected in parallel with the component.

W

Wave
An oscillation that transfers energy without transferring any matter.

Wavefront
A line perpendicular to the direction of energy transfer of a wave. It is used to represent a crest (or trough) of a wave in a wavefront diagram.

Wavelength
The length of a full cycle of a wave, e.g. from a crest to the next crest.

Weight
The force acting on an object due to gravity.

Work done
The energy transferred when a force moves an object through a distance, or by a moving charge.

X

X-ray
A high-frequency, short-wavelength electromagnetic wave. It is mainly used in medical imaging and treatment.

Z

Zero error
A type of systematic error caused by using a piece of equipment that isn't zeroed properly.

Acknowledgements

Cover image **KTSDesign**/Science Photo Library, p 4 **Alastair Philip Wiper**/Science Photo Library, p 5 **Frank Zullo**/Science Photo Library, p 6 **Belmonte**/Science Photo Library, p 7 **Trevor Clifford Photography**/Science Photo Library, p 8 **Philippe Plailly**/Science Photo Library, p 11 iStock.com/**tunart**, p 22 **Martyn F. Chillmaid**/Science Photo Library, p 30 **Tony McConnell**/Science Photo Library, p 35 **Martyn F. Chillmaid**/Science Photo Library, p 36 (top) Science Photo Library, p 36 (bottom) **Mark Sykes**/Science Photo Library, p 39 **Sheila Terry**/Science Photo Library, p 40 **Mark Sykes**/Science Photo Library, p 46 **Ashley Cooper**/Science Photo Library, p 47 **Chris Hellier**/Science Photo Library, p 48 (top) **Paul Rapson**/Science Photo Library, p 48 (bottom) **Martin Bond**/Science Photo Library, p 49 **Martin Bond**/Science Photo Library, p 50 **David Parker**/Science Photo Library, p 51 **Martin Bond**/Science Photo Library, p 52 **Martin Bond**/Science Photo Library, p 53 **Matteis/Look At Sciences**/Science Photo Library, p 54 **U.S. Coast Guard**/Science Photo Library, p 55 **Martin Bond**/Science Photo Library, p 56 iStock.com/**AMR_Photos**, p 57 **David Woodfall Images**/Science Photo Library, p 65 **Trevor Clifford Photography**/Science Photo Library, p 66 (top) **Andrew Lambert Photography**/Science Photo Library, p 66 (bottom) **Lawrence Lawry**/Science Photo Library, p 69 **Cordelia Molloy**/Science Photo Library, p 73 **Philippe Psaila**/Science Photo Library, p 80 (top) **Martyn F. Chillmaid**/Science Photo Library, p 80 (bottom) **Martyn F. Chillmaid**/Science Photo Library, p 81 **Andrew Lambert Photography**/Science Photo Library, p 87 **Martyn F. Chillmaid**/Science Photo Library, p 89 **Martyn F. Chillmaid**/Science Photo Library, p 97 **Mehau Kulyk**/Science Photo Library, p 98 Science Photo Library, p 101 (top) **Charles D. Winters**/Science Photo Library, p 101 (bottom) **GIPhotoStock**/Science Photo Library, p 109 **Emilio Segre Visual Archives/American Institute of Physics**/Science Photo Library, p 120 **Trevor Clifford Photography**/Science Photo Library, p 127 iStock.com/**Hallgerd**, p 129 **Martyn F. Chillmaid**/Science Photo Library, p 131 iStock.com/**ideabug**, p 136 **Lee Powers**/Science Photo Library, p 140 **Sputnik**/Science Photo Library, p 148 **Andy Williams**/Science Photo Library, p 150 **Alan and Sandy Carey**/Science Photo Library, p 159 iStock.com/**bsnider**, p 160 (top) **Gustoimages**/Science Photo Library, p 160 (bottom) **NASA**/Science Photo Library, p 161 **Sputnik**/Science Photo Library, p 163 **NASA/Joel Kowsky**/Science Photo Library, p 165 **Ashley Cooper**/Science Photo Library, p 167 **Martyn F. Chillmaid**/Science Photo Library, p 169 **Sheila Terry**/Science Photo Library, p 177 (top) **Ton Kinsbergen**/Science Photo Library, p 177 (bottom) **David Woodfall Images**/Science Photo Library, p 180 **Sputnik**/Science Photo Library, p 184 **Sputnik**/Science Photo Library, p 188 **David Weintraub**/Science Photo Library, p 190 **Tek Image**/Science Photo Library, p 195 iStock.com/**AlistairCotton**, p 201 **Ton Kinsbergen**/Science Photo Library, p 202 **David Parker**/Science Photo Library, p 204 **Alex Bartel**/Science Photo Library, p 205 **Chris Martin-Bahr**/Science Photo Library, p 206 (top right) **Tony McConnell**/Science Photo Library, p 206 (top left) **Sputnik**/Science Photo Library, p 206 (bottom) **Mark Sykes**/Science Photo Library, p 207 (top) **Alfred Pasieka**/Science Photo Library, p 207 (middle) Science Photo Library, p 207 (bottom) **Jim West**/Science Photo Library, p 208 **Du Cane Medical Imaging Ltd**/Science Photo Library, p 209 **Cordelia Molloy**/Science Photo Library, p 211 **Sue Ford**/Science Photo Library, p 211 **BSIP, Laurent**/Science Photo Library, p 212 **Public Health England**/Science Photo Library, p 217 **Dorling Kindersley/UIG**/Science Photo Library, p 219 (top) **Andrew Lambert Photography**/Science Photo Library, p 219 (middle) **CERN**/Science Photo Library, p 219 (bottom) **Alex Bartel**/Science Photo Library, p 222 **Trevor Clifford Photography**/Science Photo Library, p 231 (top) **Andrew Lambert Photography**/Science Photo Library, p 231 (bottom) **GIPhotoStock**/Science Photo Library, p 232 **Charles D. Winters**/Science Photo Library, p 233 **GIPhotoStock**/Science Photo Library, p 234 (top) **Trevor Clifford Photography**/Science Photo Library, p 234 (bottom) **Crown Copyright/Health & Safety Laboratory**/Science Photo Library, p 235 (top) Science Photo Library, p 235 (bottom) **Martyn F. Chillmaid**/Science Photo Library, p 236 Science Photo Library, p 241 iStock.com/**Wavebreak**, p 245 iStock.com/**sorendls**

Index

Physics Equations List

In each physics paper you have to sit for your Combined Science GCSE, you'll be given an equations sheet listing some of the equations you might need to use. That means you don't have to learn them (hurrah), but you still need to be able to pick out the correct equations to use and be really confident using them. The equations sheet won't give you any units for the equation quantities — so make sure you know them inside out.

The equations you'll be given in the exam are all on this page. You can use this page as a reference when you're doing the exam-style questions at the end of each section.

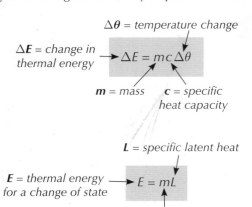

$\Delta\theta$ = temperature change
ΔE = change in thermal energy
$$\Delta E = mc\Delta\theta$$
m = mass c = specific heat capacity

L = specific latent heat
E = thermal energy for a change of state
$$E = mL$$
m = mass

v = final velocity a = acceleration
$$v^2 - u^2 = 2as$$
u = initial velocity s = distance

E_e = elastic potential energy
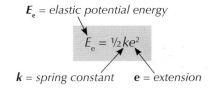
$$E_e = \tfrac{1}{2}ke^2$$
k = spring constant e = extension

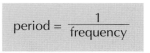
$$\text{period} = \frac{1}{\text{frequency}}$$

B = magnetic flux density l = length
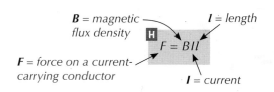
$$F = BIl$$
F = force on a current-carrying conductor I = current

AN INTRODUCTORY GUIDE TO

Anatomy
&Physiology

LOUISE TUCKER

GENERAL EDITORS JANE FOULSTON, FAE MAJOR & MARGUERITE WYNNE

EMS
Publishing

Published by EMS Publishing
2nd Floor Chiswick Gate,
598-608 Chiswick High Road, London, W4 5RT
0845 017 9022

Designed for the publishers by Idego Media Limited
Book, brochure, catalogue and magazine design specialists for print and digital.
More information can be found at www.idegomedia.co.uk

First published March 2000
Reprinted October 2000
Reprinted October 2001
Second edition October 2002
Reprinted October 2003
Reprinted March 2005
Third edition March 2008
Revised August 2009
Fourth edition July 2011

ISBN 978 1903348345

Printed by Scotprint

Introduction

This book provides an introduction to the anatomy and physiology of the body. An understanding of anatomy and physiology is essential for all those working in beauty therapy, complementary therapy, sports therapy, nursing and paramedicine. When treating patients and clients, knowledge of the structure and function of the various systems of the body ensures that the correct treatment is administered and contraindications are recognised. Professionals, as well as ITEC, CIDESCO, CIBTAC, Edexcel, City and Guilds and NVQ students will find it an invaluable learning and reference tool.

AUTHOR
Louise Tucker
Louise Tucker is a freelance writer and teacher. She has written and published several books and articles.

GENERAL EDITORS
Jane Foulston
Jane Foulston, the Chief Executive of ITEC, has been working in the in the beauty industry for over 28 years and has edited many best selling textbooks. Jane has always had a passion for education and the need to provide the highest standards of education in the beauty and spa industry.

Fae Major
Fae Major has worked in the beauty therapy industry for 23 years. Her experience has included working for Steiner's, alternative medicine clinics as well as private beauty salons in the UK and Barbados. Fae has 15 years' teaching experience and as a result became a practical examiner for ITEC in 1992. As well as continuing to examine, Fae is currently working for ITEC as part of the Qualifications Development team.

Marguerite Wynne
Marguerite Wynne began her career in one of London's foremost beauty salons and went on to teach in the College of Beauty Therapy in the West End. Subsequently she owned her own salon and school in Buckinghamshire and at the same time worked as Chief Examiner for ITEC. In 2005 Marguerite was appointed Education Manager for ITEC where she now monitors the standards and consistency of ITEC examinations.

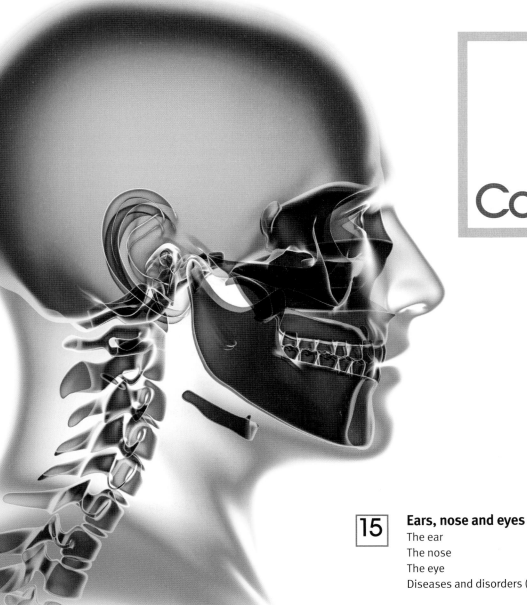

Contents

KEY TO ANATOMICAL LANGUAGE

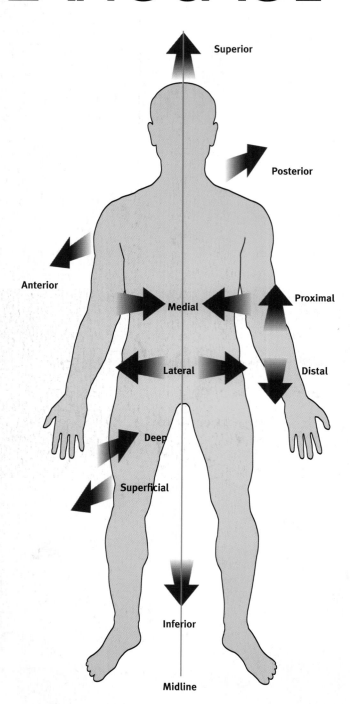

Anatomy means the study of the body's structure. In order to avoid confusion when referring to parts of the body, it is necessary to have a standardised system of anatomical descriptions and positions. The definitions used on diagrams are explained below. All of these terms refer to what is known as the standard anatomical position: the body is standing erect, facing the observer, with arms extended and the palms of the hands facing forwards (see diagram). Learning these terms will help you to understand the diagrams in the book as well as help you describe your own.

Anterior:	Towards front e.g. the quadriceps are anterior to the hamstrings
Posterior:	Towards rear e.g. the vertebrae are posterior to the sternum
Superficial:	Nearer to surface e.g. skin is superficial to bone
Deep:	Further from surface e.g. transversus abdominus is deep to rectus abdominus
Proximal:	Nearer to source e.g. the biceps femoris origin is proximal to its insertion
Distal:	Further from source e.g. the toes are distal to the knee
External:	Outer e.g. the skin is our external covering
Internal:	Inner e.g. the heart is an internal organ
Inferior:	Towards lower part e.g. infraspinatus is inferior to supraspinatus
Superior:	Towards upper part e.g. the head is superior to the feet
Medial:	Towards midline e.g. the tibia is medial to the fibula
Lateral:	Away from midline e.g. swinging the arm out sideways is moving it laterally
Midline:	Vertical line through the centre of the body from head to feet

The Cell

The cell is the basis of all life. To understand the structure and function of the body, we need to understand the structure and function of its tiniest part – the cell.

A cell is the smallest unit of matter that can live independently and reproduce itself. Cells exist in all shapes and sizes — elongated, square, star-shaped and oval — and have many different functions. A group of cells form tissue.
The study of the structure and form of cells and tissues is called histology.

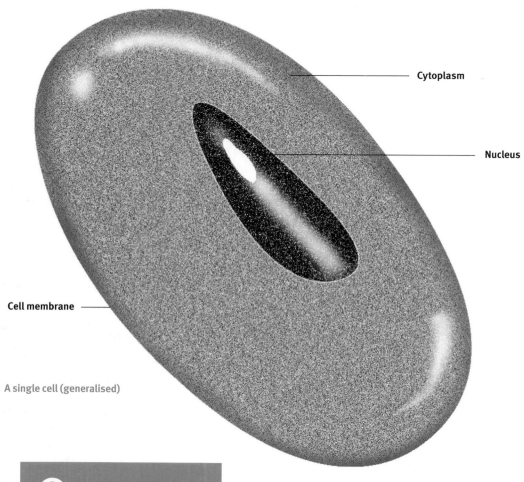

Cytoplasm

Nucleus

Cell membrane

A single cell (generalised)

LEARNING OBJECTIVES
The target knowledge of this chapter is:
- the structure of a cell
- the function of a cell
- mitosis – how cells reproduce
- meiosis – how humans are reproduced from cells
- the different tissue types made from cells.

TOPIC 1: STRUCTURE OF THE CELL

WHAT IS A CELL MADE OF?

Protoplasm, a slightly opaque, colourless jelly-like substance. It is 70% water plus

- organic and inorganic salts
- carbohydrates
- lipids (fatty substance)
- nitrogenous substances; these are amino acids obtained from protein
- compounds of all of the above substances.

WHAT DOES A CELL LOOK LIKE?

The diagram below is of a generalised cell, i.e. it shows you all the parts that exist in different types of cell. It is meant as a guide not as an exact replica. The cell is a living structure, thus it is only possible to show a general picture. It is worth remembering that cells constantly move and change.

The cell and its organelles

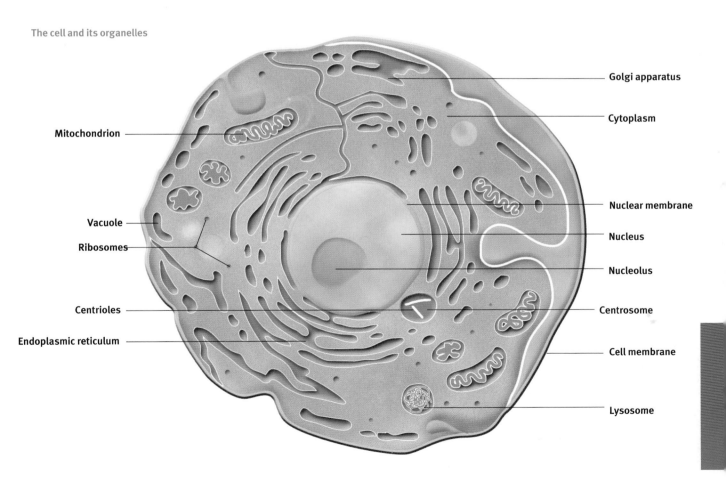

Mitochondrion

Vacuole

Ribosomes

Centrioles

Endoplasmic reticulum

Golgi apparatus

Cytoplasm

Nuclear membrane

Nucleus

Nucleolus

Centrosome

Cell membrane

Lysosome

The following list explains the function of all the structures named on the diagram on page 9.

CELL MEMBRANE

A fine, semi-permeable membrane made of protein threads and lipids (fats), which has two functions: to keep the nucleus and the cytoplasm in the cell but to let other substances, like fats and proteins, out. It works as a filter between the fluid inside the cell and the tissue fluid outside it. Some substances can cross this membrane but others are blocked. Substances go in and out of cells in several different ways:

Diffusion

Cell (semi-permeable) membrane

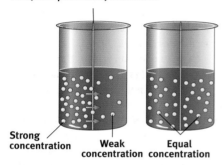

Strong concentration   Weak concentration   Equal concentration

- **diffusion:** the membrane has tiny holes, or pores, between its proteins and lipids through which small molecules, like oxygen and carbon dioxide, can pass.

- **osmosis:** the process of transferring water across the membrane by osmotic pressure — when the concentration or pressure of a solution is greater on one side of the membrane, water passes through to that side until the concentration is equal on both sides. When both sides of the membrane have solutions of the same pressure, it is called isotonic pressure.

- **dissolution (or dissolving):** fatty substances are too big to diffuse through the membrane's tiny pores, so they dissolve into the fatty or lipid part of the membrane.

Dissolution

Cell (semi-permeable) membrane

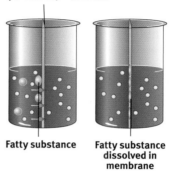

Fatty substance   Fatty substance dissolved in membrane

- **active transport:** when substances are too large to pass directly through the membrane, or are not soluble in fat, a carrier substance in the cell membrane takes them from the outside to the inside. Glucose and amino acids are both transferred by active transport. It is active because energy is used.

- **filtration:** the movement of water and soluble substances across a membrane caused by the difference in pressure either side of the membrane. The force of a fluid's weight pushes against a surface and the fluid is thus moved through the membrane. This is called hydro-static pressure which is the process responsible for the formation of urine in the kidneys. Waste products are filtered out of the blood into the kidney tubules because of a difference in hydrostatic pressure.

Osmosis

Cell (semi-permeable) membrane

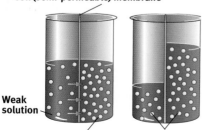

Weak solution

Strong solution   Equal strength solution

Active transport

Cell (semi-permeable) membrane

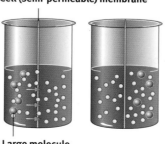

Large molecule

Filtration

Cell (semi-permeable) membrane

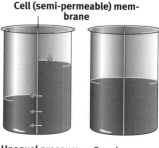

Unequal pressure   Equal pressure

CYTOPLASM

Cytoplasm is the protoplasm inside the cell but outside the nucleus. It contains several different structures and substances:

Mitochondria

These organelles (little organs) are sometimes referred to as the 'power houses' of the cell, since they supply the cell with energy. Cell survival depends upon the chemical reactions that take place within the mitochondria, which result in a release of energy and the formation of ATP (adenosine triphosphate), the main energy transporter within the cell.

Ribosomes

The 'protein factories' of a cell. They produce enzymes and other protein compounds; protein is used for the growth and repair of a cell.

Endoplasmic reticulum

A network of membranes that forms the 'circulatory system' of a cell. Rough Endoplasmic Reticulum, so named because of the ribosomes present on its surface, is most prevalent and transports the protein made by the ribosomes throughout the cell. The less widespread Smooth Endoplasmic Reticulum is involved in lipid and steroid production.

Golgi apparatus

Golgi apparatus is formed at one end from vesicles which bud off from the endoplasmic reticulum, and at the other end vesicles are released into the cell. This process forms a communication network from deep within the cell to its membrane. Golgi vesicles are also used to make lysosomes.

Lysosomes

These organelles contain digestive enzymes which destroy worn-out parts of a cell and bacteria. They break down parts of food allowing them to be used for energy transfer within the cell.

Vacuoles

These are spaces within the cytoplasm. They contain waste materials or secretions formed by the cytoplasm and are used for storage or digestion purposes in different kinds of cells.

Centrioles

These are paired, rod-like organelles that lie at right angles to each other. They are made of fine tubules which play an important role in mitosis (cell reproduction).

Centrosomes

Dense areas of cytoplasm containing the centrioles.

NUCLEUS

The largest organelle, the nucleus, controls the cell's processes of growth, repair and reproduction. It contains nucleoli, chromatin and nucleoplasm all enclosed by the nuclear membrane.

Nucleolus

A small body within the nucleus (usually 1-2 per nucleus) that controls the formation of ribosomes which then move into the cytoplasm of the cell.

Chromatin and Chromosomes

Chromatin is loosely coiled strands of DNA (deoxyribonucleic acid). Just prior to cell division, the chromatin becomes more tightly coiled, forming chromosomes.

Chromosomes consist of two chromatids, each comprising one DNA molecule, held together by a centromere. DNA is organised into functional units called genes which control cell activities and inheritance. Each species is determined by the number of chromosomes in the nucleus. Human cells contain 46 chromosomes, 23 from each parent.

Nucleoplasm

Specialised protoplasm, in which the nucleoli and chromatin/chromosomes are suspended along with nutrients and other necessary chemicals.

YOU NOW KNOW

the structure of a cell and the names of all its different parts. The next sections explain how cells function and reproduce.

TOPIC 2:
CELL FUNCTION

WHAT DOES A CELL DO?

It lives! The human body is made of cells, which form organs, tissues, and fluid. Blood, for example, is a liquid tissue made of several different types of cells. What a cell does is reproduced on a larger scale throughout the body and throughout human life: breathing, digesting, excreting, reproducing, sensing, growing, moving, dying.

When a cell goes wrong, if it is not replaced or repaired, the body goes wrong since cell failure and a subsequent inability to perform its usual functions is the origin of disease and illness.

If you want to understand a cell's relationship to the rest of the body think of this:

- a group of cells of similar type and function join to form a tissue
- a group of tissues of related function join to form an organ (e.g. stomach, lung, heart)
- a group of organs of related function join to form a system (e.g. digestive, respiratory, vascular)
- a group of systems join together to form an organism (e.g. a human body).

● REMEMBER

A useful way of remembering the functions of a cell is to remember the first letter of each function as "Mrs Grem"

Summary
of functions

- **Movement:** whole cells, like blood cells, can move and parts of cells move, like the cilia of ciliated cells, but only in one direction.
- **Respiration:** this is controlled absorption of oxygen that combines with nutrients in an oxidative reaction. This results in energy production and the formation of ATP. The waste produced is carbon dioxide.
- **Sensitivity:** cells are able to respond to stimuli, which can be mechanical, electrical, thermal or chemical.
- **Growth:** cells grow and repair themselves by making protein.
- **Reproduction:** all cells grow to maturity and the majority then reproduce themselves. This can be simple cell division (mitosis) or sexual reproduction (meiosis).
- **Excretion:** waste which might be harmful to the cell in large amounts, e.g. urea or carbon dioxide, is removed.
- **Metabolism:** the chemical reactions that occur inside the cell.
- **Anabolism:** the chemical activity involved in the process of making new products (usually proteins) for growth and repair.
- **Catabolism:** the chemical activity involved in the breakdown of substances into simple forms, which results in the production of energy and waste. The energy is used to perform various cell functions.

TOPIC 3:
CELL REPRODUCTION

HOW DO CELLS GROW/REPRODUCE?

Cells grow in number through a process called mitosis whereby exact replicas of chromosomes in parent cells are duplicated to form daughter cells. Cells reproduce sexually through meiosis, a process which produces genetic variation.

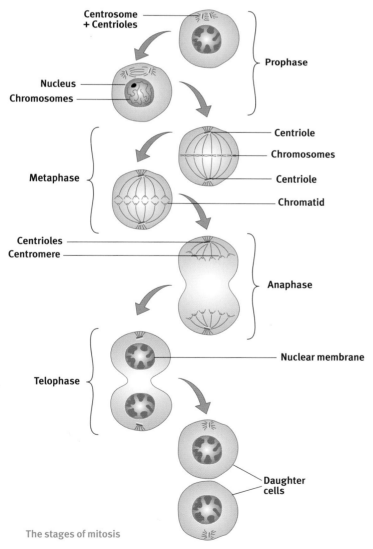

The stages of mitosis

Mitosis

Mitosis is the multiplication of cells i.e. the continuous process of making new cells for growth and repair, and in order for life to continue when old cells die. Mitosis is faster in children and slows in later life. There are four main stages of mitosis during which the cell is actively dividing, and one resting stage.

1) Prophase

- The centrosome divides into two centrioles. These move away from each other, though still joined by the spindle-like threads of the centrosome.
- Towards the end of the prophase the chromatin in the cell's nucleus shortens and thickens, forming into visible pairs of rods called chromosomes (made of condensed chromatin and DNA).
- Each chromosome consists of two chromatids joined by a centromere.
- The nucleolus disappears.

2) Metaphase

- The nuclear membrane of the nucleus disappears.
- The chromosomes arrange themselves at the centre of the cell, each attached to the spindle by its centromere.
- By the end of the metaphase, each individual chromosome can be seen distinctly as two chromatids starting to pull apart.

3) Anaphase

- The centromere stretches as the centrioles are drawn further apart.
- Pairs of chromatids divide and identical halves of the pairs move to each end of the cell.
- At the end of the anaphase, the spindle threads of the centrioles divide to form new centromeres and the cell membrane begins to constrict in the centre.

4) Telophase
■ A new nuclear membrane appears around each set of chromosomes.
■ The spindle fibres disintegrate and the centrioles replicate.
■ The cell membrane continues to constrict until two cells are formed. These two daughter cells will be identical copies of the original single parent cell. Eventually, the daughter cells will also divide and the whole process continues throughout life.

Interphase
■ The interval in the cell cycle between two cell divisions when the individual chromosomes cannot be distinguished.
■ It is the time when DNA is replicated in the cell nucleus.
■ The cell carries out normal metabolic activities.
■ Nuclear protein is synthesized.
■ Cell increases in size.

MEIOSIS
Meiosis is the reproduction of cells that results in a gamete/ sex cell. In the first stage of meiosis, the centromeres do not split and so whole

● DID YOU KNOW?
Inside a single, microscopic zygote, is all the information needed to make a new human being.

chromosomes move to opposite poles on the spindle. This results in daughter cells with half the number of chromosomes of the parent cell. In humans this is 23 chromosomes in the male sperm and 23 chromosomes in the female ovum. When a male sperm fuses with a female ovum, a zygote with 46 chromosomes is created. If the halving didn't occur, doubling of chromosome numbers would result in each new generation. The zygote will divide by mitosis, and the organism that results from the cell division is an embryo which develops into a foetus.

YOU NOW KNOW
the structure and function of cells and how they reproduce.
The following section explains the different tissues made from cells found in the body.

TOPIC 4: TISSUE TYPES MADE FROM CELLS

Cells make tissue. There are four types of tissue: epithelial, connective, nervous and muscular.

EPITHELIAL TISSUE
(also known as epithelium)
Simple epithelium usually functions as a covering or lining for organs and vessels. Compound epithelium provides external protection, for example fingernails, and internal elasticity, for example the lining of the mouth.

Simple epithelium
Simple epithelium consists of a single layer of cells attached to a basement membrane. Goblet cells are often found in simple epithelium. These cells secrete mucus. There are four types of simple epithelium: squamous or pavement, cuboidal, columnar and ciliated.

Squamous
Structure: single layer of flattened cells attached to a basement membrane
Function: forms a thin, often permeable lining for the heart, blood and lymph vessels, and alveoli of the lungs; allows diffusion and filtration.

Squamous

Cuboidal
Structure: single layer of cube-shaped cells attached to a basement membrane.
Function: forms lining of kidney tubules as well as some glands; can secrete

Cuboidal

Columnar
Structure: single layer of tall, rectangular cells attached to a basement membrane; resilient.
Function: forms lining in very active parts of the body such as the stomach, intestines and urethra; some of the cells secrete mucus and some absorb mucus, depending on where they are in the body.

Columnar

Ciliated
Structure: single layer of mostly columnar cells (sometimes combined with squamous or cuboidal cells) attached to a basement membrane. Tiny hair-like projections, or cilia, stick out from the cell membrane.
Function: the cilia work in waves, all moving together in the same direction. They help to remove mucus, foreign matter and debris, keeping passageways and linings clear. The respiratory system is lined with these cells.

Ciliated columnar

COMPOUND EPITHELIUM
Compound epithelium has many layers of cells and no basement membrane. It is formed from a combination of deep layers of columnar cells plus flatter cells towards the surface. It protects delicate parts of the body. There are two types: stratified and transitional.

Stratified
■ Keratinised (dry)

Structure: compound epithelium with dry surface cells; forms a dead layer e.g. hair, skin, nails. It is keratinised (i.e. the surface layer has dried out into keratin, a fibrous protein which creates a waterproof layer). Skin is stratified, keratinised, squamous epithelium.

Function: the keratinisation prevents deeper layers from drying out and protects them.

■ Non-keratinised (wet)

Structure: compound epithelium with wet surface cells e.g. inside mouth, lining of oesophagus, conjunctiva (mucous membrane) of eyes.

Function: provides lubrication.

Transitional
Structure: similar to stratified epithelium except that the surface cells are not flattened and thus can change shape when necessary; cube-shaped surface cells and deeper pear-shaped cells.

Function: found in organs that need waterproof and expandable lining e.g. bladder and ureters.

NERVOUS TISSUE
Structure: arranged in bundles of fibres, composed of nerve cells and neuroglia. The cells have long fibrous processes.

On a nerve cell these processes are called dendrites and axons.

Function: capable of transmitting signals to and from the brain; protective.

MUSCULAR TISSUE
There are three types of muscle tissue:
■ Skeletal – striated and voluntary
■ Smooth – non-striated and involuntary
■ Cardiac – striated and involuntary

Structure: all muscle is made of 75% water, 20% protein, 5% mineral salts, glycogen, glucose and fat.

Function:
skeletal: to help support and move the body;
smooth: to carry out involuntary functions, e.g. peristalsis;
cardiac: heart muscle to pump blood.

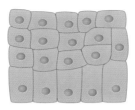

Stratified

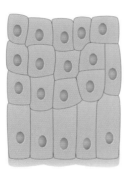

Transitional

CONNECTIVE TISSUE
Connective tissues are the supporting tissues of the body; they have mostly mechanical functions and connect more active tissues (like bones and muscles).

Structure: can be semi-solid, solid or liquid; can have fibres present or not.

Function: mainly mechanical connecting other more active tissues.

There are eight types:
■ areolar
■ adipose
■ lymphoid
■ yellow elastic
■ white fibrous
■ bone
■ blood
■ cartilage.

AREOLAR
This is loose connective tissue, the most general connective tissue found in the human body.

Structure: semi-solid and permeable thus allowing fluids to pass through; it contains yellow elastic and white fibres as well as fibrocytes and mast cells which produce histamine (protection) and heparin (anti-coagulant, prevents clotting).

Function: found all over the body connecting and supporting other tissues e.g. under the skin, between muscles, supporting blood vessels and nerves and in the alimentary canal.

ADIPOSE
This is also known as fatty tissue.

Structure: made up of fat cells containing fat globules; found between muscle fibres and, with areolar tissue, under the skin giving the body a smooth, continuous outline; also found around the kidneys and the back of the eyes.

Function: protective and insulatory properties: helps retain body heat because it is a poor conductor of heat; also a food reserve.

LYMPHOID
Structure: semi-solid tissue; has some white fibres but not in bundles; lots of cells, the majority are lymphocytes and reticular cells which have a disease control function – the cell engulfs bacteria and destroys it.

Function: forms lymphatic system cells and blood cells and thus protects against disease; found in lymph nodes, thymus, the spleen, the tonsils, in the wall of the large intestine, the appendix and the glands of the small intestine.

YELLOW ELASTIC
Structure: mainly composed of elastic fibres and very few cells; this tissue is capable of considerable extension and recoil.
Function: to enable stretch and recoil e.g. forms lung tissue, bronchi and trachea, arteries especially the large ones, stomach, bladder and any other organs that need to stretch and recoil.

WHITE FIBROUS
Structure: strongly connective but not very elastic; consists mainly of closely packed bundles of collagen fibres with only a few cells in rows between the fibres; the fibres run in the same direction.
Function: connection and protection of parts of the body e.g. forms ligaments and the periosteum of bone; forms the outer protection of organs e.g. around the kidneys, the dura of the brain, the fascia of muscles and the tendons.

BONE
Structure: hardest structure in the body; two types, compact and cancellous – compact is dense bone for strength, cancellous for structure bearing and cellular development; composition of bone is 25% water, 30% organic material, 45% inorganic salts.
Function: to support and protect the body and all its organs, as well as produce cells in bone marrow.

BLOOD
Structure: fluid connective tissue, containing 45% cells and 55% plasma. Cell content is erythrocytes (red blood cells), leucocytes (white blood cells) and thrombocytes (platelets).
Function: to transport food and oxygen to all the cells of the body and to remove waste from them (erythrocytes), to fight infection (leucocytes) and to clot (thrombocytes).

CARTILAGE
Structure: firm, tough tissue; solid and contains cells called chondrocytes; there are three types:

Hyaline
Structure: bluish-white, smooth; chondrocyte cells are grouped together in nests in a solid matrix; particularly resilient.
Function: connecting and protecting: found on articular surfaces of joints i.e. parts of bone which form joints; forms costal cartilages and parts of the larynx, trachea and bronchi.

Yellow elastic cartilage
Structure: yellow elastic fibres running through a solid matrix. Contains fibrocyte and chondrocyte cells which lie between multidirectional fibres.
Function: flexibility; found in parts of the body that need to move freely like the pinna (cartilage part of the ear) and epiglottis.

White fibrocartilage
Structure: white fibres closely packed in dense masses; contains chondrocyte cells; extremely tough and slightly flexible.
Function: to absorb shock e.g. it forms intervertebral discs as well as the semi-lunar cartilages, the shock absorbers positioned between the articulating surfaces of the knee joint bones; also found in hip and shoulder sockets.

Summary
The cell:
- is a microscopic building block
- is a microcosm of body functions: ingesting, excreting, breathing, reproducing, moving, dying
- reproduces by division
- makes tissues; there are four main tissue types in the body.

DON'T FORGET
TO LOGIN TO GAIN ACCESS TO YOUR **FREE** MULTI-MEDIA LEARNING RESOURCES

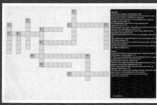

☐ Test your knowledge with crosswords

☐ Test your knowledge with fill in the gaps

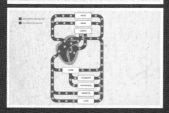

☐ Test your knowledge with interactive animations and diagrams

To login to use these resources visit

www.emspublishing.co.uk/anatomy and follow the onscreen instructions.

The Skin

The skin is an outer protective layer, also known as an integument.

The Skin

The skin is the largest organ. It covers the whole body and is water-resistant. There are two layers: the epidermis and the dermis. It has many functions including protecting and shaping the body.

Cross-section of skin

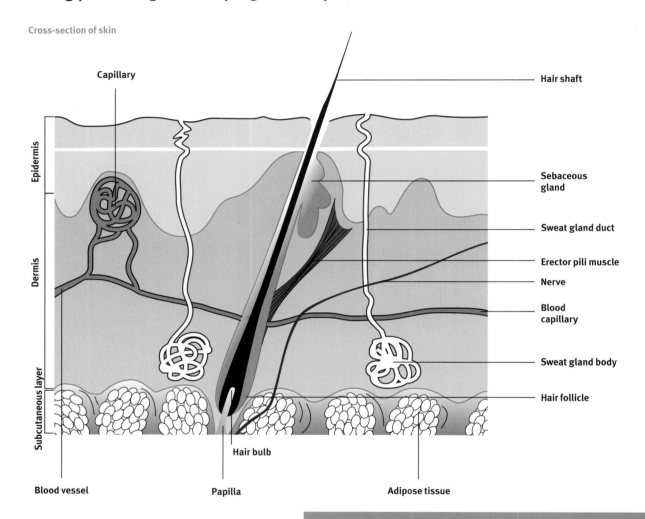

Capillary

Hair shaft

Epidermis

Dermis

Sebaceous gland

Sweat gland duct

Erector pili muscle

Nerve

Blood capillary

Sweat gland body

Subcutaneous layer

Hair follicle

Hair bulb

Blood vessel

Papilla

Adipose tissue

LEARNING OBJECTIVES

The target knowledge of this chapter is:
- the structure of the skin (epidermis and dermis)
- the functions of the skin
- diseases and disorders of the skin.

TOPIC 1:
STRUCTURE

WHAT IS THE EPIDERMIS?

The epidermis is the layer of skin that we can see. It varies in thickness, depending on the part of the body e.g. it is thickest on the soles of the feet and palms of the hand and thinnest on eyelids and nipples. The cells on the surface are constantly coming off (shedding): this is called desquamation. They are also constantly replaced from below as cells in the basal layer of the epidermis multiply and are pushed up to the surface. The basal layer of the epidermis received its blood supply, nutrients and fluids from the dermis. There is hardly supply to this layer. In total there are five layers in the epidermis.

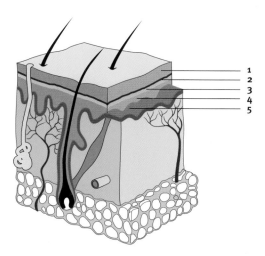

1. **Stratum corneum**
2. **Stratum lucidum**
3. **Stratum granulosum**
4. **Stratum spinosum**
5. **Stratum germinativum – basal**

STRUCTURE OF EPIDERMIS

1. Stratum corneum – surface
- hardened, flattened dead cells
- constantly being shed – desquamation
- cell membrane is not visible.

2. Stratum lucidum - clear layer
- denucleated cells but not completely hard
- most easily visible under a microscope (only on palms and soles)
- cell membranes becoming less visible

3. Stratum granulosum – granular layer
- cells have a distinct nucleus but cell membranes are dying
- tissue after trauma.

4. Stratum spinosum – prickle cell layer
- cells are living and membranes are intact; they have fibrils which interlock
- capable of mitosis under friction or pressure i.e. on soles of feet or palms of hands.

5. Stratum germinativum – basal layer
- the primary site of cell division/ reproduction (mitosis) in the skin
- cells are living. It is in this layer that cells are made. They take about 28–30 days to move up from here through the five layers of the epidermis before being shed.
- this layer contains a pigment known as melanin that gives skin its natural colour, whether red, yellow or black. Melanin is produced by cells called melanocytes.

THE DERMIS?

The dermis is commonly known as the true skin. Unlike the epidermis, this layer is connected to the blood and lymph supply as well as the nerves. The dermis contains sweat and sebaceous glands, hair follicles and many living cells. It is made of connective tissue, mainly areolar tissue which is tough and elastic, and contains white collagen fibres and yellow elastic tissue known as elastin. Collagen plumps the skin and elastin keeps it supple and elastic. Both diminish with age.

The dermis contains eight main types of structure:

1) Specialised cells
- **fibroblasts:** responsible for the production of areolar tissue, collagen and elastin. Fibroblasts can be damaged by ultraviolet light.
- **mast cells:** produce histamine as an allergic response and heparin, an anti-coagulant
- **histiocytes:** also produce histamine
- **leucocytes:** white blood cells which help to fight infection and disease.

2) Nerve endings:
- alert the brain and thus the body to heat, cold, pressure and pain
- part of the defence system of the body.

3) Sweat glands
Sweat glands which stretch from deep in the dermis to the outer layer of the epidermis. Sweat contains mainly water, urea and salts (mostly sodium chloride), and is produced by two kinds of gland:

- **eccrine:** these excrete watery sweat and control body temperature, and are found all over the body, but especially on the palms of the hands and the soles of the feet.

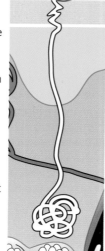

• DID YOU KNOW?
The surface of a blister is made of raised epidermis and the fluid inside it is serum. It can be painlessly peeled or cut away because the epidermis has no nerves to feel pain.

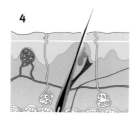

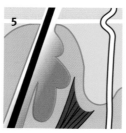

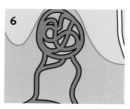

- **apocrine:** these are found in the groin and axillae (armpits), and excrete a milky fluid which, when it mixes with bacteria on the surface of the skin, produces body odour.

4) Hair follicles:
- travel through the epidermis and the dermis.
- tiny muscles, called erector pili, are attached to each hair and help with the temperature control of the body by pulling the hair upright and trapping a layer of air – goose pimples.

5) Sebaceous glands:
- connected with hair follicles, and produce sebum, a fatty acid which keeps the skin moist and which lubricates the hair shaft. They are therefore found in hairy areas, not on the palms of the hands or soles of the feet.
- sweat and sebum combine on the surface of the skin to form the acid mantle, a protective shield which helps to control bacteria levels and prevents infections and disease and also acts as a natural moisturiser. The pH balance of the skin is 4.5–5.6 and this acid environment helps to prevent bacterial growth.

6) Blood supply:
- a system of blood vessels including microscopic capillaries which are one cell thick.

7) Lymphatic capillary:
- works in conjunction with the blood supply to carry waste products away from the area.

8) Papilla:
- small conical projections at the base of the hair
- contain blood vessels and nerves which supply the hair with nutrients.

YOU NOW KNOW
the structure of both layers of the skin. The following section describes the skin's functions.

TOPIC 2: FUNCTIONS

SECRETION

The skin secretes sebum from the sebaceous glands. This fatty substance lubricates the hair shafts and when combined with perspiration on the surface of the skin, it creates a natural moisturiser which acts as a protective barrier against bacteria.

HEAT REGULATION

Body temperature is maintained in healthy humans at 37ºC (98.6ºF). Organs involved in heat production are the muscles, liver and digestive organs. Heat is absorbed and maintained in the subcutaneous layer of adipose tissue. Heat regulation is controlled in the following ways:

■ Cooling

Vasodilation: when the body becomes hot, the capillaries dilate allowing more blood to reach the surface of the skin. The pores dilate allowing the heat to be lost from the body. This causes the skin to flush – this is known as hyperaemia. Sweating will occur simultaneously and the evaporation of perspiration from the surface has a cooling effect on the body.

■ Warming

Vasoconstriction: when cold, the body protects itself by moving blood from the extremities to the major organs, thus ensuring that they are kept warm. With the blood diverted to the deeper parts of the body, the capillaries contract as do the pores. As a result, the skin appears pale and heat loss is inhibited.

The erector pili muscles contract, causing body hair to stand on end, trapping air against the surface of the skin, which is then warmed by body heat. Shivering occurs, caused by rapid and repeated muscle contractions which work to raise body temperature.

● USEFUL TIP

To remember the skin's functions think of SHAPES Very Much – SHAPES VM are the first letters of the eight functions.

● WHAT DOES BEING SHED MEAN

If you look around any room you will see dust. Dust, amongst other things, contains millions of shed, or desquamated skin cells that have fallen off the body. Whereas dead blood cells are destroyed inside the body, dead skin cells are destroyed outside the body that is on the outer layer, the skin. Once they are dead, they exfoliate – peel off. This is known as desquamation. Try rubbing your skin when it is very dry and you will see small particles coming away from the surface. These are dead skin cells.

ABSORPTION

The skin is a waterproof covering but some chemical substances, such as drugs and essential oils, can penetrate the skin through the layers, the hair follicles and sweat glands. The amount of penetration is affected by the health and condition of the skin.

PROTECTION

The skin acts as a barrier to the body's invasion by micro-organisms like bacteria. The naturally acid pH of the skin's surface inhibits bacterial production. Splits, cuts, tears and irregularities caused by disease or disorder increase the risk of infection. Melanin, the pigment produced by the melanocytes in the basal layer of the epidermis, has a protective function. It helps to protect against ultraviolet light damage to tissues. Sensory nerve endings found at differing levels in the dermis warn of possible trauma and, by reflex action, prevent greater damage to the body.

ELIMINATION

Some toxins are eliminated from the body through the skin via the sweat glands. The toxins normally take the form of waste salts and water.

SENSATION

Specialised nerve endings found in the dermis make the body aware of its surroundings. They warn of pain, cold, heat, pressure and touch. Different receptors lie at different levels in the skin. Pain and touch receptors are closer to the surface. All receptors warn of and help prevent trauma to the skin and underlying structures.

VITAMIN D FORMATION

Vitamin D is essential for the formation and maintenance of bone. Vitamin D production is stimulated by ultraviolet light which converts 7-dehydro-cholesterol in the sebum into vitamin

D. This circulates in the blood and any excess is stored in the liver. Lack of Vitamin D can result in rickets in children.

MELANIN FORMATION

In the sun, the hormone MSH stimulates the melanocytes in the basal layer of the epidermis to produce melanin, a substance which produces a darkening of the skin to protect the underlying structures. The pigment protects the body from harmful effects of the sun's rays since dark colours absorb radiation.

YOU NOW KNOW

You now know all about the structure and functions of skin. The next section explains the diseases and disorders that can affect this organ.

● DID YOU KNOW?

The skin is the largest organ in the human body. If you stretched it out flat it would measure from eleven to eighteen square metres in area and total about 12% of the weight of a human.

TOPIC 3: DISEASES AND DISORDERS (PATHOLOGIES)

CONGENITAL

■ **Eczema:** found all over the body but most often on the inside of the knee (in the popliteal space) and elbow joints, on the face, hands and scalp. The skin becomes extremely dry and itchy causing great discomfort. Skin has scaly dry patches with bleeding at points. Not contagious.

■ **Psoriasis:** chronic inflammatory skin disease characterised by red patches covered with silvery scales that are constantly shed. Size of scales vary from minute spots to quite large sheets of skin. Points of bleeding may occur beneath scales. Affects whole body or specific areas, like face and scalp. Not infectious.

BACTERIAL

■ **Acne rosacea:** gives a flushed, reddened appearance. Occurs on the face, this condition can be aggravated by anything causing vasodilation – heat, sunshine, spicy food, alcohol, cold. Affects both men and women especially menopausal women. Not related to acne vulgaris. Not contagious.

■ **Acne vulgaris:** normally caused by hormonal imbalances which increase sebum production leading to blocked glands and infection. The skin has a shiny, sallow appearance with papules, pustules and comedones. It is prone to open pores. Where pustules have cleared there is often pitting and scarring. The main sites for infection are the face, back, chest and shoulders. Not contagious.

■ **Boils:** a bacterial infection of the skin, causing inflammation around a hair follicle.

■ **Carbuncles:** Is a skin infection that often involves a group of hair follicles. The infected material forms a lump which occurs deep in the skin.

■ **Folliculitis:** bacterial infection of the pilo-sebaceous duct (sebaceous gland and hair follicle) causing inflammation. Common in adolescence. Possible link with acne vulgaris.

■ **Impetigo:** a bacterial infection causing thin-roofed blisters which weep and leave a thick, yellow crust. Highly contagious.

VIRAL

■ **Warts:** a small horny tumour found on the skin, often on fingers and thumbs. Caused by viral infection. Highly contagious.

■ **Verrucas:** warts found on the feet. Highly contagious.

■ **Herpes simplex:** a viral infection commonly known as cold sores; not confined to the mouth, can spread over the face and other parts of the body. Appears as small blisters which if left alone will dry up leaving a crust which falls off. Highly contagious when active.

■ **Herpes zoster:** a viral infection commonly known as shingles. Adult form of chicken pox. Usually affects spinal nerves and one side of the thorax. Highly contagious.

FUNGAL

■ **Tinea corporis, pedis:** infections which attach themselves to keratinised structures like the skin. Tinea corporis is commonly known as ringworm and can be found anywhere on the body. Tinea pedis is commonly known as athlete's foot. Highly infectious.

PARASITICAL INFESTATION

■ **Pediculosis:** The infestation with lice resulting in severe itching. This can occur on the head (capitis), body (corporis) and pubic (pubis) areas.

■ **Scabies:** A contagious skin infection caused by the itch mite; characterized by persistent itching and skin irritation

● DID YOU KNOW?

The colour of your hair is affected by the amount of melanin in your body. For example, grey hair is caused by a decrease in melanin production. Instead of the pigment (providing colour), there are air bubbles in the hairs and to the naked eye the hair now looks grey.

PIGMENTATION DISORDERS

■ **Dermatosis Papulosa Nigra:** Is a condition of many small, benign skin lesions, characterized by dark-brown papular lesions on the face and upper body, mainly found on a black skin.

■ **Papilloma -** A benign epithelial tumour forming a rounded mass.

■ **Vitiligo:** a complete loss of colour in well-defined areas of the face and limbs. A form of leucoderma (an abnormal whiteness of the skin due to absence of pigmentation); begins in patches but may converge to form fairly large areas; most obvious in darker skins.

■ **Albinism:** complete lack of melanocytes resulting in lack of pigmentation in skin, hair and eyes. Sufferers have poor eyesight and extreme ultraviolet sensitivity. This is an inherited condition.

■ **Chloasma:** butterfly mask often caused by pregnancy and the contraceptive pill; a hyper pigmentation condition involving the upper cheeks, nose and occasionally forehead. Discolouration usually disappears spontaneously at the end of pregnancy.

■ **Ephelides:** freckles; small pigmented areas of skin which become more evident on exposure to sunlight and are found in greatest abundance on the face, arms and legs; fair-skinned individuals suffer most from the condition.

■ **Lentigo:** also known as liver spots; dark patches of pigmentation which appear more distinct than freckles and have a slightly raised appearance and more scattered distribution.

■ **Moles (papilloma):** a common occurrence on the face and body and present in several different forms, varying in size, colour and vascular appearance. Flat moles are called sessile whilst those raised above the surface, or attached by a stalk are pedunculated.

■ **Naevae:** birth mark; if pigmented may occur on any part of the body and are often found on the neck and face, being sometimes associated with strong hair growth. Vary in size from pinhead to several centimetres and in rare cases may be extremely large. Pigmentation varies from light brown to black. Strawberry naevae (pink or red birth marks) often affect babies, eventually disappearing after a few years.

■ **Port wine stain:** a large area of dilated capillaries causing a pink to dark red skin colour which makes it contrast vividly with the surrounding skin. The stain is commonly found on the face.

GENERAL

■ **Blisters -** An elevation of the skin filled with serous fluid.

■ **Cyst -** Is a closed sac having a distinct membrane and division on the nearby tissue. It may contain air, fluids, or semi-solid material.

■ **Keloid scars -** Is a type of scar which results in an overgrowth of tissue at the site of a healed skin injury. Keloids are firm, rubbery lesions or shiny, fibrous nodules and can vary in colour.

■ **Striae -** Are also known as stretch marks.

■ **Verrucae filliformis -** Are soft, small, flesh-coloured skin flaps on the neck, armpits, or groin which are often known as skin tags.

■ **Xanthomas -** Is a deposit of yellowish cholesterol-rich material in tendons and other body parts.

■ **Burns -** An injury caused by exposure to heat, flame or friction leaving a sore mark on the skin.

■ **Cellulitis -** An inflammation of body tissue (especially that below the skin) characterized by fever, swelling, redness and pain.

■ **Methicillin-resistant Staphylococcus aureus (MRSA) -** A serious and potentially fatal infection caused by Staphylococcus aureus bacteria (often called "Staph") that is resistant to the broadspectrum antibiotics commonly used to treat it.

■ **Pressure sores/bed sores -** Ulcers that occur on areas of the skin that are under pressure from lying in bed, sitting in wheelchairs, wearing a cast, or being immobile for a long period of time.

■ **Broken capillaries:** dilated capillaries on a fine skin texture often affecting large areas of the face. The skin responds fiercely to stimulation and permanent dilated vessels are apparent, particularly on the upper cheeks and nose. Ruptured blood vessels assume a line-like appearance in surface tissues and can become bulbous and blue in colour due to the congestion in the blood vessels of the area.

■ **Crow's feet:** fine lines around the eyes caused by habitual expressions and daily movement, associated with ageing of muscle tissue. Premature formation may be due to eye strain and is often associated with oedema (swelling) around and under the eyes.

■ **UV damage:** UV rays stimulate rapid production of basal cells. This causes the stratum corneum to thicken. Over- exposure to UVA may cause premature ageing whereas over-exposure to UVB may cause skin cancer.

■ **Urticaria – hives, nettle rash:** often an allergic reaction. Characterised by weals or welts of pinkish colour produced by extreme dilation of capillaries. Very itchy. Can lead to secondary infection by bacteria through scratching.

■ **Allergic reaction:** when irritated, the body produces histamine (part of the defence mechanism) in the skin. This can cause red, blotchy patches on skin, watery, stinging eyes, swellings and runny nose. Can be slight or intense, depending on each body's reaction.

■ **Comedones:** commonly known as blackheads, these are caused by a build-up of sebaceous secretions which have become trapped in the hair follicles and have subsequently dried out and hardened. The colour comes from oxidation. Common in puberty.

Dermatitis: an allergic inflammation of the skin characterised by erythema – redness of the skin, itching and various skin lesions. Commonly known as contact dermatitis, there are many causes including plants, drugs, clothing, cosmetics and chemicals. Not contagious.

Milia: commonly present as tiny white bumps or whiteheads, these form when sebum becomes trapped in a blind duct with no surface opening. The condition is most common on dry skin and milia appear on the obicularis oculi muscle area and between the eyebrows. Milia can form after injury, e.g. sunburn on the face or shoulders, and are sometimes widespread.

SUDIFEROUS GLAND DISORDERS -

Bromidrosis/osmidrosis - Fetid or foul-smelling perspiration which is caused by decomposition of the sweat and cellular debris by the action of bacteria and yeasts.

Anhidrosis - The reduced ability or inability to sweat.

Hyperhidrosis - Is the condition characterized by abnormally increased perspiration.

SKIN CANCER

Basal cell carcinoma
Occurs on exposed parts of the skin, especially face, nose, eyelid, cheek.

Squamous cell carcinoma
Squamous cells are those found on the surface of the body, on the top layer of the skin. Squamous cell carcinoma is said to be caused by sunlight, chemicals or physical irritants. It starts very small but grows rapidly, becoming raised.

Malignant melanoma
A malignant tumour of melanocytes. It usually develops in a previously benign mole. The mole has become larger and darker, ulcerated and the tumour eventually spreads.

Summary

The skin:

- Skin is composed of two layers, the epidermis and the dermis
- The skin has eight functions: secretion; heat regulation; absorption; protection; elimination; sensation; Vitamin D production; melanin production.
- The skin is affected by seven different types of disease: congenital; bacterial; viral; fungal; pigmentation disorders and skin cancers and other general conditions

DON'T FORGET
TO LOGIN TO GAIN ACCESS TO YOUR **FREE** MULTI-MEDIA LEARNING RESOURCES

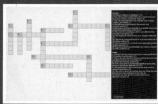

☐ Test your knowledge with crosswords

☐ Test your knowledge with fill in the gaps

☐ Test your knowledge with interactive animations and diagrams

To login to use these resources visit
www.emspublishing.co.uk/anatomy and follow the onscreen instructions.

03

The Skeletal system

The skeleton or skeletal system consists of the bones and the joints of the body.

The Skeletal system

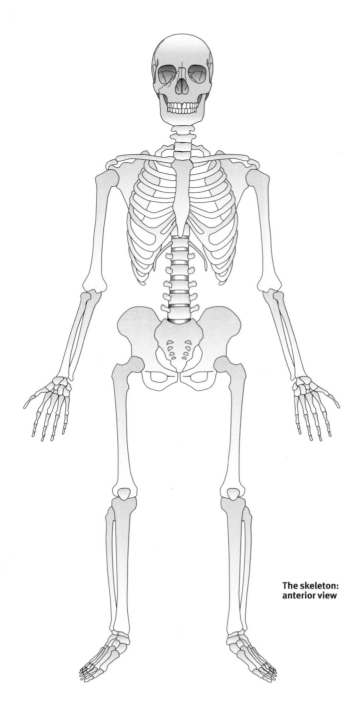

The skeleton is a hard framework of 206 bones that supports and protects the muscles and organs of the human body. It is divided into two parts:

the axial skeleton: this supports the head, neck and trunk (also known as torso). It consists of the skull, the vertebral column, the ribs and the sternum

the appendicular skeleton: this supports the appendages or limbs and attaches them to the rest of the body. It consists of the shoulder girdle, the upper limbs, the pelvic girdle and the lower limbs.

The skeleton: anterior view

LEARNING OBJECTIVES
The target knowledge of this chapter is:
- the structure of the skeleton including names and position of all bones
- the function of the skeleton
- the types of bone and bone tissue
- types of deformity, fracture and disease affecting the skeleton.

TOPIC 1: STRUCTURE AND FUNCTION

STRUCTURE

The skeleton is made up of bones. There are 206 individual bones in the human body and five different types, defined according to their shape:

- **long bones:** the body's levers, they allow movement, particularly in the limbs e.g. the femur (thigh bone), tibia and fibula (lower leg bones), clavicle (collar bone), humerus (upper arm bone), the radius and the ulna (lower arm), metacarpals (hand bones), metatarsals (foot bones) and phalanges (finger and toe bones).

- **short bones:** strong and compact bones, usually grouped in parts of the body where little movement is required e.g. tarsals (ankle bones) and carpals (wrist bones).

- **flat bones:** protective bones with broad flat surfaces for muscle attachment e.g. occipital, parietal, frontal, nasal, vomer, lacrimal (all of these are in the skull), scapula (shoulder bone), innominate bones (pelvis), sternum (breastbone), ribs.

- **irregular bones:** bones that do not fit into the above categories and have different characteristics e.g. vertebrae, including the sacrum and coccyx (backbone), maxilla (upper jaw), mandible (lower jaw), ethmoid, palatine, sphenoid, zygomatic (cheek) and temporal (all bones of the face and head).

- **sesamoid bones:** bones within tendons. There are two main sesamoid bones in the human body, the patella (kneecap), and the hyoid (base of the tongue). The hyoid is sometimes classified as an irregular bone because it is attached by ligaments and not 'floating' in a tendon like the patella.

FUNCTIONS

- supports the body: all body tissues (apart from cartilage and bone) are soft so without the skeleton the body would be jelly-like and could not stand up. The bones and their arrangement give the body its shape.
- allows and enables movement
- protects delicate body organs e.g. the cranium, or skull, is a hard shell surrounding the soft brain and the thoracic cage (ribs and sternum) covers the heart and lungs
- forms blood cells (in the red bone marrow)
- forms joints which are essential for the movement of the body
- **provides attachment for muscles which move the joints:** muscles are attached to bones and pull them into different positions, thus moving the body
- provides a store of calcium salts and phosphorus.

THE SKELETON

An easy way to remember the differences between the axial and appendicular parts of the skeleton is to think of axes (i.e. the centre) versus appendage (i.e. the added bits). The centre is the head, neck and torso, the added bits are the arms and legs and the bones that attach them to the body.

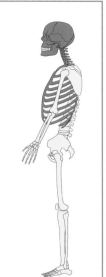

 Axial skeleton
☐ appendicular

WHAT ARE BONES MADE OF?

Bones are living tissue made from special cells called osteoblasts and osteoclasts. The tissue varies considerably in density and compactness: the closer to the surface of the bone the more compact it is. Many bones have a central cavity containing marrow, a tissue which is the source of most of the cells of the blood and is also a site for the storage of fats. There are two main types of bone tissue:

- **compact:** to the naked eye this looks like a solid structure but under a microscope it looks like honeycomb, i.e. full of holes. Haversian canals (see below) are passageways containing blood vessels, lymph capillaries and nerves which run through the tissue. Compact bone is found on the outside of most bones and in the shaft of long bones.

- **cancellous:** this type of bone looks like a sponge and it is found at the ends of long bones and in irregular, flat and sesamoid bones. Bone marrow only exists in cancellous bone.

All bones have both types of tissue.
The amount of each depends on the type of bone.

WHAT ARE HAVERSIAN CANALS?

Haversian canals run lengthways through compact bone and contain blood and lymph capillaries and nerves. The larger the canal the less dense and compact the bones.

YOU NOW KNOW
What a skeleton is, what types of bone make a skeleton, what a bone is and what bones are made of. The following series of detailed diagrams illustrate and name the major bones in the skeleton starting with the axial section.

Cross-section of long bone

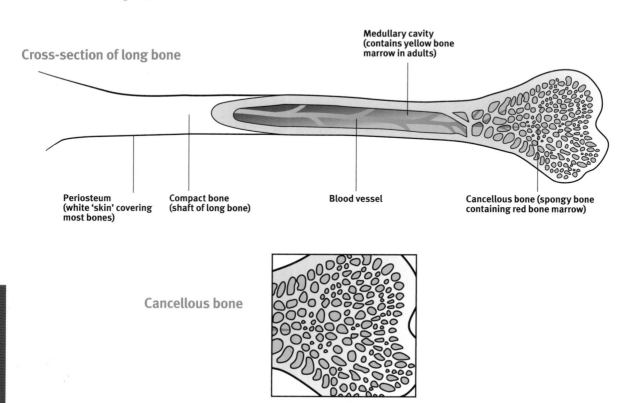

Medullary cavity (contains yellow bone marrow in adults)

Periosteum (white 'skin' covering most bones)

Compact bone (shaft of long bone)

Blood vessel

Cancellous bone (spongy bone containing red bone marrow)

Cancellous bone

SECTION 1: THE AXIAL SKELETON

Skull: anterior view

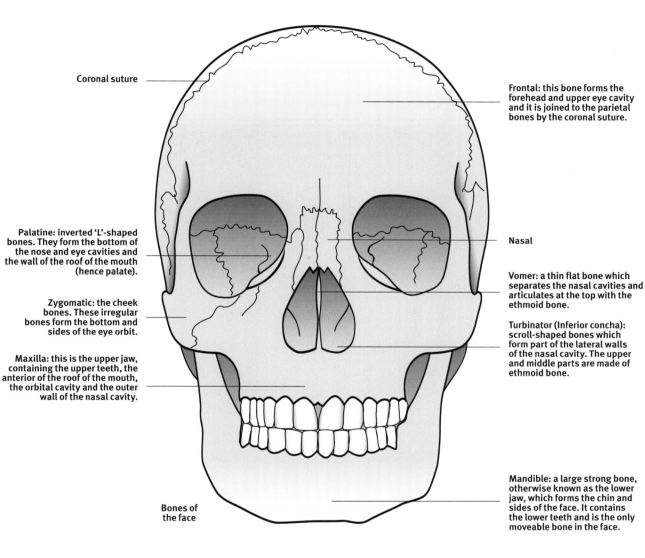

Coronal suture

Frontal: this bone forms the forehead and upper eye cavity and it is joined to the parietal bones by the coronal suture.

Palatine: inverted 'L'-shaped bones. They form the bottom of the nose and eye cavities and the wall of the roof of the mouth (hence palate).

Nasal

Vomer: a thin flat bone which separates the nasal cavities and articulates at the top with the ethmoid bone.

Zygomatic: the cheek bones. These irregular bones form the bottom and sides of the eye orbit.

Turbinator (Inferior concha): scroll-shaped bones which form part of the lateral walls of the nasal cavity. The upper and middle parts are made of ethmoid bone.

Maxilla: this is the upper jaw, containing the upper teeth, the anterior of the roof of the mouth, the orbital cavity and the outer wall of the nasal cavity.

Mandible: a large strong bone, otherwise known as the lower jaw, which forms the chin and sides of the face. It contains the lower teeth and is the only moveable bone in the face.

Bones of the face

The axial skeleton includes:
Skull: cranium 8 bones; face 14 bones
hyoid: 1 bone
Vertebral column: 33 vertebrae, some fused, so 26 bones in total
Sternum: 3 bones
Ribs: 12 pairs (24 bones)

Skull: side view

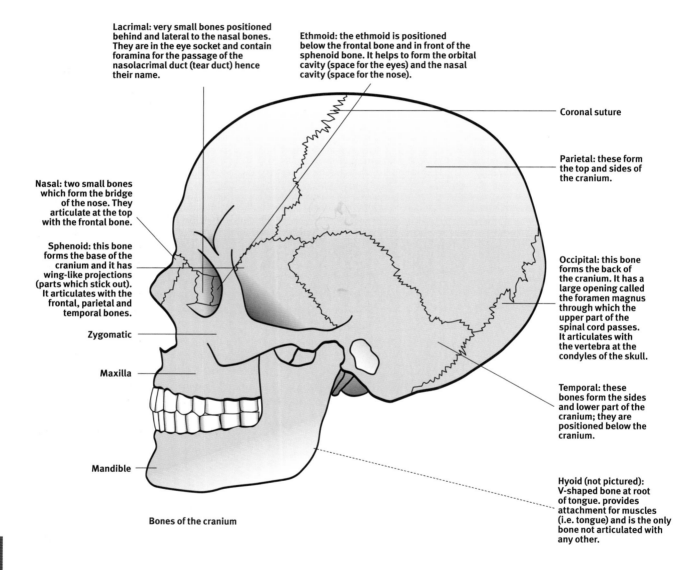

Lacrimal: very small bones positioned behind and lateral to the nasal bones. They are in the eye socket and contain foramina for the passage of the nasolacrimal duct (tear duct) hence their name.

Ethmoid: the ethmoid is positioned below the frontal bone and in front of the sphenoid bone. It helps to form the orbital cavity (space for the eyes) and the nasal cavity (space for the nose).

Coronal suture

Parietal: these form the top and sides of the cranium.

Nasal: two small bones which form the bridge of the nose. They articulate at the top with the frontal bone.

Sphenoid: this bone forms the base of the cranium and it has wing-like projections (parts which stick out). It articulates with the frontal, parietal and temporal bones.

Zygomatic

Maxilla

Mandible

Occipital: this bone forms the back of the cranium. It has a large opening called the foramen magnus through which the upper part of the spinal cord passes. It articulates with the vertebra at the condyles of the skull.

Temporal: these bones form the sides and lower part of the cranium; they are positioned below the cranium.

Hyoid (not pictured): V-shaped bone at root of tongue. provides attachment for muscles (i.e. tongue) and is the only bone not articulated with any other.

Bones of the cranium

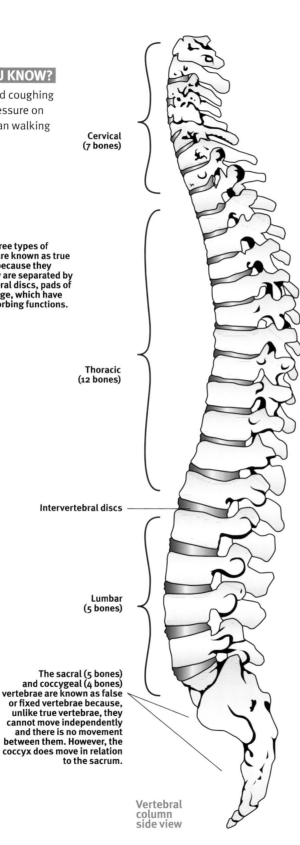

Cervical
(7 bones)

The first three types of vertebrae are known as true vertebrae because they move. They are separated by intervertebral discs, pads of fibrocartilage, which have shock-absorbing functions.

Thoracic
(12 bones)

Intervertebral discs

Lumbar
(5 bones)

The sacral (5 bones) and coccygeal (4 bones) vertebrae are known as false or fixed vertebrae because, unlike true vertebrae, they cannot move independently and there is no movement between them. However, the coccyx does move in relation to the sacrum.

Vertebral column side view

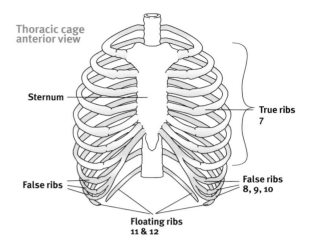

Thoracic cage anterior view

Sternum

True ribs 7

False ribs

False ribs 8, 9, 10

Floating ribs 11 & 12

WHAT IS THE VERTEBRAL COLUMN?

A more common name for the vertebral column is the spine. It is the central part of the skeleton, supporting the head and enclosing the spinal cord and it is constructed to combine great strength with a moderate degree of mobility. It is made of 33 vertebrae — irregular, interlocking bones. Some of these are fused so there are only 26 individual bones. There are 5 different types of vertebrae:

- cervical (7 bones in the neck)
- thoracic (12 bones carrying the ribs in the centre of the body)
- lumbar (5 bones in the lower back)
- sacral (5 bones in the pelvis, fused to form the sacrum)
- coccygeal (4 bones below the sacrum, forming the coccyx).

YOU NOW KNOW

The positions and names of all the major bones in the axial skeleton. The next section covers the appendicular skeleton, the shoulder and pelvic girdles, arms and legs.

SECTION 2:
THE APPENDICULAR SKELETON
The appendicular skeleton includes:
Shoulder girdle: 2 scapulae and 2 clavicles
Arm: 1 humerus, 1 ulna, 1 radius (each arm)
Wrist: 8 carpal bones (each wrist)
Hand: 5 metacarpal bones (each palm of hand)
Fingers: 14 phalanges in each hand, 2 in a thumb
and 3 each in the other fingers
Pelvic girdle: 2 innominate bones (each one
including an ilium, ischium and pubis)
Leg: 1 femur, 1 tibia, 1 fibula and 1 patella
(each leg)
Ankle and foot: 7 tarsals and 5 metatarsals
(each foot)
Toes: 14 phalanges in each foot, 2 in a big toe and
3 each in the other toes.

● DID YOU KNOW?
A woman's pelvis is shallower and broader than a
man's so that the body of a baby may be cradled
and protected before birth.

● DID YOU KNOW?
Pelvis means basin.

THE SHOULDER GIRDLE
The shoulder girdle consists of two scapulae
(shoulder blades) and two clavicles (collar bones).
These four bones form an incomplete ring,
articulating with the manubrium – the flat part at
the top of the sternum (breast bone) – at the front,
hence the name girdle.

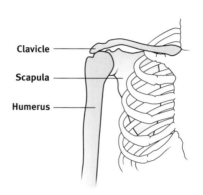

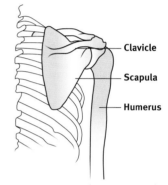

Shoulder girdle (posterior view)   Shoulder girdle (anterior view)

THE PELVIC GIRDLE
The pelvic girdle is formed by two large innominate
bones which meet in front at the symphysis pubis
and articulate with the sacrum in the back to
form a ring of bone. The innominate bones, with
the sacrum and coccyx, form the pelvis which
surrounds the pelvic cavity. The pelvis of the
female is wider and shallower than that of the
male. Each innominate bone is formed by the
fusion of three parts – an ilium, an ischium and a
pubis. At the junction of these is a socket for the
head of the femur.

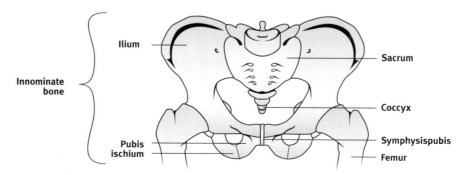

The pelvic girdle anteriorview

TOPIC 2: THE LIMBS

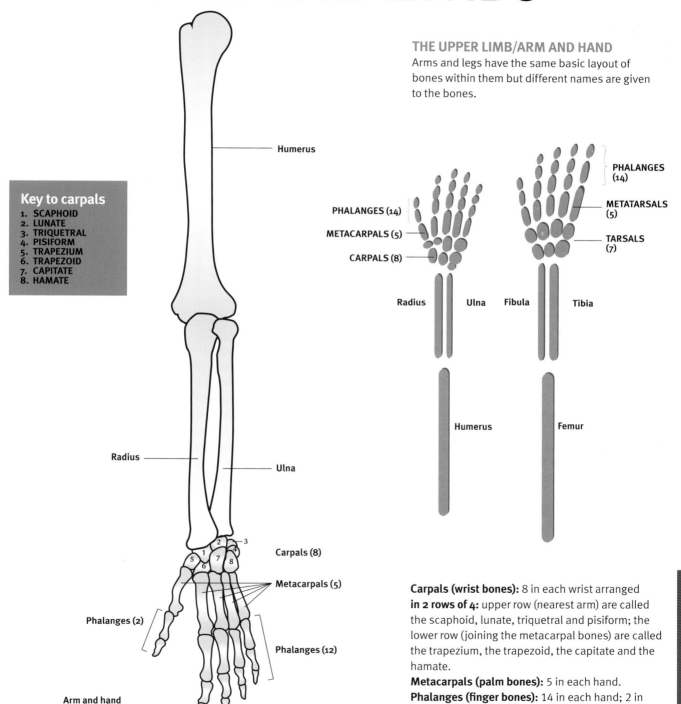

THE UPPER LIMB/ARM AND HAND
Arms and legs have the same basic layout of bones within them but different names are given to the bones.

Key to carpals
1. SCAPHOID
2. LUNATE
3. TRIQUETRAL
4. PISIFORM
5. TRAPEZIUM
6. TRAPEZOID
7. CAPITATE
8. HAMATE

Humerus

PHALANGES (14)
METATARSALS (5)
TARSALS (7)

PHALANGES (14)
METACARPALS (5)
CARPALS (8)

Radius   Ulna   Fibula   Tibia

Humerus   Femur

Radius
Ulna
Carpals (8)
Metacarpals (5)
Phalanges (2)
Phalanges (12)

Arm and hand (anterior view)

Carpals (wrist bones): 8 in each wrist arranged **in 2 rows of 4:** upper row (nearest arm) are called the scaphoid, lunate, triquetral and pisiform; the lower row (joining the metacarpal bones) are called the trapezium, the trapezoid, the capitate and the hamate.
Metacarpals (palm bones): 5 in each hand.
Phalanges (finger bones): 14 in each hand; 2 in each thumb and 3 in each of the other fingers.

THE LOWER LIMB/LEG AND FOOT

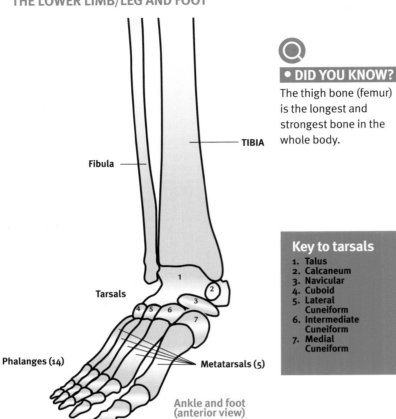

TIBIA

Fibula

Tarsals

Phalanges (14)

Metatarsals (5)

Ankle and foot
(anterior view)

● DID YOU KNOW?
The thigh bone (femur) is the longest and strongest bone in the whole body.

Key to tarsals
1. Talus
2. Calcaneum
3. Navicular
4. Cuboid
5. Lateral Cuneiform
6. Intermediate Cuneiform
7. Medial Cuneiform

Tarsals: 7 in each ankle/heel: the talus joins the foot to the leg and is a principal part of the ankle joint, the calcaneus (the heel bone) projects backwards; the navicular bone lies between the talus and cuneiform bones, there are 3 wedge-shaped cuneiform bones, the medial, intermediate and lateral and finally the cuboid bone on the lateral side of the foot, which is between the calcaneus and the metatarsals.
Metatarsals: 5 in each foot.
Phalanges: 14 in each foot, 2 in each big toe and 3 in each of the other toes.

YOU NOW KNOW
The names of, number of and position of all the major bones in the body. The next section covers joints, the hinges that join bones and enable movement of the limbs.

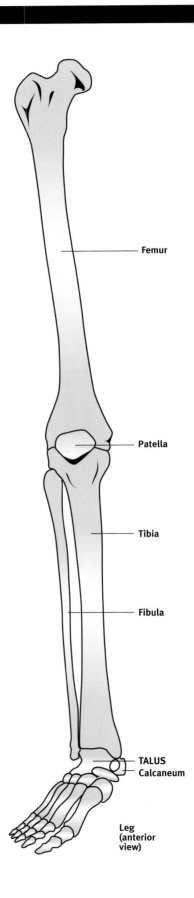

Femur

Patella

Tibia

Fibula

TALUS
Calcaneum

Leg
(anterior view)

TOPIC 3: JOINTS

WHAT ARE JOINTS?

Joints are the body's hinges. There are three types:

- Freely moveable, or synovial joints.
- Slightly moveable, or cartilaginous joints
- Fixed, or fibrous joints

FREELY MOVEABLE, OR SYNOVIAL JOINTS

Characteristics: varied degrees of movement depending on sub-type

Structure: All contain hyaline (articular) cartilage, a joint capsule, synovial membrane and synovial fluid. Some may also have bursae, fat pads and/or ligaments blending with the capsule.

Five different types: ball and socket; hinge; gliding; pivot; saddle.

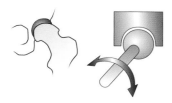

Ball and socket: most moveable of all joints. Allow flexion, extension, adduction, abduction, rotation and circumduction e.g. shoulder and hip joints.

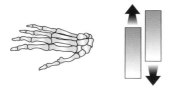

Gliding: the bones glide over each other; the least moveable of joints e.g. between tarsals and carpals.

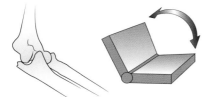

Hinge: movement in one direction (plane) only. Movements are flexion and extension e.g. elbow, knee, ankle, joints between phalanges of fingers and toes.

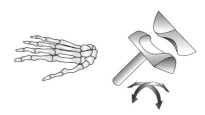

Saddle: movement around two axes allowing flexion, extension, adduction, abduction, circumduction. Found between trapezium of carpus (wrist) and metacarpal of thumb.

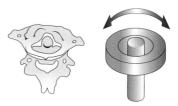

Pivot: movement around one axis only and a rotary movement e.g. first two cervical vertebrae (atlas and axis) which allow the head to rotate and proximal ends of radius and ulna.

SLIGHTLY MOVEABLE, OR CARTILAGINOUS JOINTS

Characteristics: slightly moveable, moves by compression of the cartilage

Structure: pad of white fibrocartilage between the bones, e.g. spine.

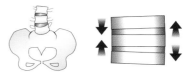

Slightly moveable, or cartilaginous joints

FIXED, OR FIBROUS JOINTS

Chararacteristics: no movement

Structure: fibrous tissue between the ends of the bones e.g. sutures in the skull, innominate (pelvic girdle) bones.

Fixed or fibrous

YOU NOW KNOW
What joints are and how they work. The final section explains postural deformities, fractures and certain bone diseases.

WHAT ARE POSTURAL DEFORMITIES?

The spine has two natural curves: an inward curve in the lower back (lumbar area: put your hand there and try it) and a slight outward curve in the upper back (the thoracic area). In certain cases, the spine's natural curves become exaggerated, causing unnatural curves, or postural deformities. There are three causes for these:

- **congenital:** those which are present at birth or are hereditary.
- **environmental:** sitting and standing incorrectly can cause long-term damage to the spine. Many people in sedentary work are affected by these causes.
- **traumatic:** caused by accidents.

What do postural deformities look like?

Kyphosis: an exaggerated outward (toward the posterior) curvature of the cervical spine.
Scoliosis: a sideways curvature of the spine
Lordosis: an exaggerated inward (towards the anterior) curvature of the lumbar spine

WHAT IS A FRACTURE?

A fracture is the breakage of a bone due either to injury or disease. There are six main types:

- **simple:** (sometimes called closed) a bone has broken in one place and not damaged the tissue around it
- **compound:** (sometimes called open) a fracture in which the broken bone pierces the skin and/ or communicates with the surface of the skin through an open wound
- **comminuted:** a bone broken in several places
- **greenstick:** more common in soft and flexible bones, especially children's, this is an incomplete fracture of a long bone
- **impacted:** a bone which has been broken and then one end is driven into the other (like one car shunting into the back of another)
- **complicated (not pictured):** broken bone which damages tissue and/or organs around it.

DID YOU KNOW?

The fictional Hunchback of Notre Dame is probably the most famous of all sufferers of kyphosis!

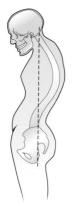
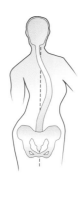
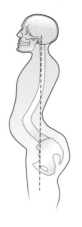

Kyphosis   **Scoliosis**   **Lordosis**

Simple

Compound

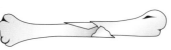

Comminuted

Greenstick

Impacted

TOPIC 4: DISEASES AND DISORDERS (PATHOLOGIES)

ARTHRITIS

Arthritis is an inflammation of the joints. Mono-articular arthritis is an inflammation of one joint and poly-arthritis is an inflammation of many. It can be acute or chronic:

- **acute:** symptoms are heat, redness, and visible inflammation of the affected joints accompanied by severe pain.
- **chronic:** involves loss of cartilage, deposition of bone tissue around the joint margins and lesser degrees of pain and inflammation.

GOUT

A form of arthritis that can occur in any part of the body but often affects the big toe; more common in men than women.
Cause: deposition of uric acid crystals within the joint capsule and cartilage.
Effect: attacks of acute gouty arthritis, chronic destruction of joints.

OSTEO-ARTHRITIS

(also known as degenerative)
Cause: may be injury of the joint or, if widespread, may be associated with the ageing process.
Effect: chronic arthritis of degenerative type – cartilage of joint breaks down; usually affects weight-bearing joints like knees, feet and back.

RHEUMATOID ARTHRITIS

(type of poly-arthritis)
Cause: an auto immune disease that attacks the synovial membranes and goes on to degrade and malform the articular surfaces of the bones.
Effect: acute and chronic phases with varying degrees of damage and deformity.

Ankylosing spondylitis: type of arthritis with acute and chronic phases which results in fusion of the joints of the spine causing severe deformity and immobility.

FRACTURES

- **Simple -** When the bone is cracked and then separates, causing little damage to the soft tissue.
- **Compound -** A bone fracture associated with lacerated soft tissue or an open wound.
- **Comminuted -** A fracture in which the bone is splintered or crushed.
- **Greenstick -** A partial fracture of a bone (usually in children); the bone is bent but broken on one side only.
- **Complicated -** A fracture in which the broken bone penetrates an organ or important structures surrounding it.
- **Loss of limb -** Prosthesis - Is an artificial extension that replaces a missing body part.
- **Osteomalacia -** Abnormal softening of bones caused by deficiencies of phosphorus, calcium or vitamin D. This can also be known as rickets.
- **Osteogenesis imperfecta -** A disorder of connective tissue characterzised by brittle bones that fracture easily.
- **Psoriatic Arthritis -** An immune system disorder that includes both psoriatic skin lesions and joint inflammation, although they may not necessarily occur at the same time.
- **Paget's disease -** A condition characterized by excessive overgrowth of bone, especially in the spine, pelvis, skull and femur caused by an increase in the osteoclastic and osteoblastic activity of the bone cells.
- **Rickets -** A bone softening and deforming disease, particularly in children, caused by a deficiency of vitamin D and sunlight associated

with impaired metabolism of calcium and phosphorus that causes bowed legs, knock-knees, or other deformities of the skeleton.

- **Scleroderma -** A chronic auto-immune disease characterized by a hardening or sclerosis in the skin or other organs.
- **Spinal stenosis -** A medical condition in which the spinal canal narrows and compresses the spinal cord and nerves.
- **Systemic Lupus Erythematosus (SLE) -** An inflammatory disease of connective tissue with variable features including fever, weakness, fatigue, joint pains and skin lesions.

OSTEOPOROSIS

(also known as brittle bone disease)
Cause: calcium deficiency; accelerated bone loss especially in post-menopausal women.
Effect: porosity and brittleness of bones.

SLIPPED DISC

Cause: the weakening or tearing of one of the intervertebral discs.
Effect: disc bulges or sticks out and this may press on the spinal nerve causing pain.

STRESS

Stress is any factor which affects mental or physical health. When stressed, muscle tension increases and this causes poor posture (for example hunched shoulders or a clenched jaw), stiff joints and problems with the spinal vertebrae.

GENERAL

- **Carpal Tunnel Syndrome -** A painful disorder caused by compression of a nerve in the carpal tunnel; characterized by discomfort and weakness in the hands and fingers and by sensations of tingling, burning or numbness.
- **Cervical spondylitis -** Is degenerative arthritis of the joints between cervical vertebrae. If severe, it may cause pressure on nerve roots with subsequent pain or parasthesia in the limbs.
- **Synovitis -** An inflammation of the synovial membrane that lines a synovial joint; results in pain and swelling.
- **Whiplash -** An injury to the neck (the cervical vertebrae) resulting from rapid acceleration or deceleration (as in an automobile accident).

Interrelationships
Skeletal system links to:

Muscular: muscles always cross joints and thus rely on the framework of the skeleton for leverage and movement.
Circulatory: erythrocytes are produced in the bone marrow of long bones.
Nervous: muscles require a nerve impulse to contract which produces movement in the skeleton.
Digestive: breaks down foodstuffs and works with the circulatory system to transport nutrients to bone tissues.
Urinary: a hormone produced by the kidneys helps to stimulate the production of bone marrow in long bones.

Summary

The skeletal system:

- The skeleton is composed of bones and joints which form the axial (central head, neck and torso) skeleton and the appendicular (appendages – arms and legs) skeleton.
- It protects and supports the body, allows movement, produces blood cells (in red bone marrow), stores calcium and provides attachment for muscles.
- The skeleton is susceptible to breakage (fractures), and postural deformities caused by congenital or environmental factors.

The Muscular system

Muscles are the body's movers and shakers. These tissues are attached to other parts of the body and when they relax and contract they enable movement.

The Muscular system

The muscular system comprises the muscles of the body and their attachments — tendons and fascia. When muscle fibres contract the muscles change shape and move whichever part of the body they are attached to. This can be a voluntary (conscious) movement such as lifting an arm or an involuntary movement such as shivering.

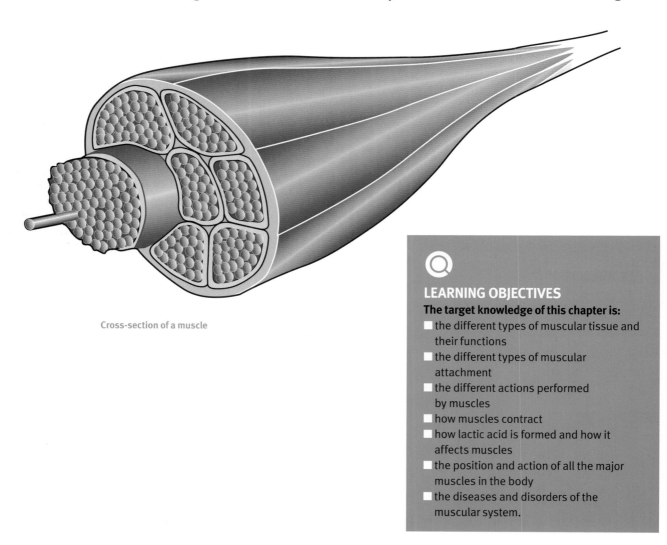

Cross-section of a muscle

LEARNING OBJECTIVES

The target knowledge of this chapter is:
- the different types of muscular tissue and their functions
- the different types of muscular attachment
- the different actions performed by muscles
- how muscles contract
- how lactic acid is formed and how it affects muscles
- the position and action of all the major muscles in the body
- the diseases and disorders of the muscular system.

TOPIC 1: STRUCTURE

WHAT IS A MUSCLE?

A muscle is a group of specialised, elastic tissues. More of the human body is made of muscle than any other tissue: 23% of a woman's body weight and about 40% of a man's.

Structure: muscle tissue is bound together in bundles and contained in a sheath (sometimes called a fascia), the end of which extends to form a tendon that attaches the muscle to other parts of the body. Muscle is 75% water, 20% proteins, 5% fats, mineral salts and glycogen.

Function: a muscle's function is to contract and by doing so start a movement in the surrounding structures (the tendons, ligaments and eventually bones). The muscle contracts in reaction to a nerve stimulus sent by the brain through a motor nerve. The muscle then shortens becoming fatter at the centre.

Summary of muscular functions

1 contract and thereby produce movement e.g. to move joints
2 stabilise joints
3 maintain postural tone
4 aid in temperature control e.g. shivering and dilation of capillaries (see Skin).

WHAT DOES MUSCLE LOOK LIKE?

There are three types of muscular tissue, each with a different structure.

Skeletal muscle

(striated and voluntary)

Function: these are the muscles which we consciously control e.g. our arms and legs. If we want to walk we do so.

Structure: skeletal muscle has cylindrical cells which make up fibres. Each fibre has several nuclei (multi-nucleated cells) and is surrounded by a sheath (sarcolemma).The muscle fibres form bundles and they all run in the same direction. Under a microscope voluntary muscle looks stripy. The stripes or striations are formed by actin and myosin protein filaments which run across the fibre in transverse bands. Where the actin and myosin cross a darker 'stripe' is created, where they do not cross the appearance is lighter. When the muscle contracts the actin filaments slide between the myosin filaments which causes a shortening and thickening of the fibres.

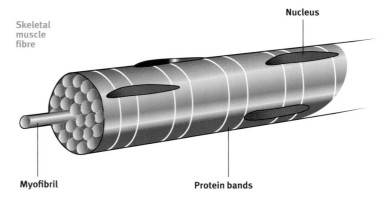

Skeletal muscle fibre

Nucleus

Myofibril

Protein bands

Smooth muscle

(non striated and involuntary)

Function: these are the muscles we do not consciously control e.g. those that are found in the walls of blood and lymphatic vessels, in respiratory, digestive and genito-urinary systems. These muscles work automatically whether we want them to or not!

Structure: smooth muscles have spindle-shaped cells with no distinct membrane and only one nucleus. Bundles of the fibres form the muscle we see with the naked eye.

Cardiac muscle

Function: to power the pump action of the heart.

Structure: cardiac muscle only exists in the heart; it is involuntary muscle tissue but its fibres are striated and each cell has one nucleus so, in structure, it resembles skeletal muscle. Each cell or fibre has a nucleus.

Smallest and largest

- The smallest skeletal muscle (i.e. a muscle attached to a bone) is the stapedius in the ear. It activates the stapes, the stirrup-shaped bone in the middle ear which sends vibrations from the eardrum to the inner ear.
- The largest muscle in the body is the Lattisimus Dorsi, the flat back muscle which covers the central and lower back.
- The strongest muscle in the body is the gluteus maximus which forms the main bulk of the buttock. This muscle is responsible for lifting the torso after bending down or leaning over.

Smooth muscle

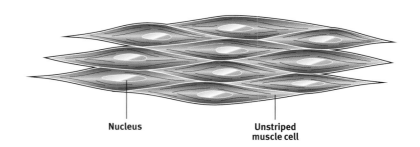

Nucleus

Unstriped muscle cell

Cardiac muscle

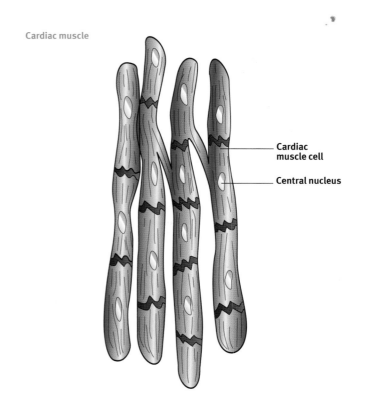

Cardiac muscle cell

Central nucleus

YOU NOW KNOW

what a muscle is and the structure and function of the three types of muscular tissue. The following section explains how muscles work and the names of the different muscle parts.

TOPIC 2: FUNCTION

HOW DO MUSCLES WORK?

By contraction: the fibres become shorter and thicker and the parts attached to the fibres (periosteum, bone, tendons and fascia) are pulled by the contraction and move. When a muscle fibre contracts it follows the 'all or nothing' law i.e. it contracts completely or not at all. Varying forces (strengths) of contraction are produced depending upon the number of fibres recruited. The greater the number of fibres that contract, the greater the force produced. Smooth muscle and cardiac muscle contract independently of our conscious will. Skeletal muscles, however, move because we want them to. There are two types of contraction:

- **isometric:** as the muscle contracts, its length remains the same whilst the tension increases in an attempt to overcome the opposing force, e.g pushing against an object that is too heavy to move (such as a wall) or holding a glass of water still in front of you

- **isotonic:** as the muscle contracts, its length changes whilst the tension remains constant or develops to overcome the opposing force, pushing an object over or lifting a glass of water to your mouth and lowering it back to the table.

HOW DOES MOVEMENT HAPPEN?

In skeletal muscle (those attached to bones) a muscle needs to pass over a joint to create movement. Muscle contraction pulls one bone towards another and thus moves the limb. Muscles never work alone: any movement results from the actions of several muscles. In general, muscles work in pairs. Each pair contains an agonist (the contracting muscle) and an antagonist (the opposing, relaxing muscle). The agonist and the antagonist must contract and relax equally to ensure a smooth and not jerky movement.

● DID YOU KNOW?

Human babies, unlike some other mammals, are not born knowing how to control the voluntary muscles that help us stand and move. They learn to control and co-ordinate muscles in the following order: first the head, then the neck, the shoulders and arms, and then the lower parts of the body. When a baby finally learns to stand and walk, it has mastered all the muscles of movement because the last ones in the learning process are the pelvis and legs.

● DID YOU KNOW?

The adductor muscles, which take the limb towards the medial line, are also found in bivalve seashells — those with two hinged parts like clams, oysters, mussels and cockles. The muscle closes the shell.

HOW DOES A MUSCLE KNOW WHEN TO CONTRACT?

The stimulus to contract comes from the nervous system through the nerves. Motor nerves enter the muscles and break into many nerve endings, each one stimulating a single muscle fibre.

WHERE DOES A MUSCLE GET ENERGY FROM?

In order for contraction (and therefore movement) to take place, there must be an adequate blood supply to provide oxygen and nutrients and to remove carbon dioxide and waste products from energy production. Muscles receive their nutrients and oxygen from the arterial capillaries. This is converted into energy by chemical changes. The nutrients and oxygen are used up by the muscle and the waste product, lactic acid, is then excreted into the venous blood stream.

A muscle's ability to contract is affected by the following factors:

- energy available
- strength of the stimulus from the nerve
- time muscle has been contracting
- adequate blood supply bringing enough oxygen and nutrients
- strength of inhibitory nerve supply
- temperature of muscle (warmth increases response)
- presence of waste products like lactic acid.

DIFFERENT STAGES OF CONTRACTION

Tone: slight degree of contraction by some fibres as others are relaxing. In normal healthy muscles there will always be a few muscle fibres contracting at any one time, even during sleep. This action gives normal posture to the body.

Relaxation: a lessening of tension, so a reduction in the number of fibres contracting at any one time. Muscle tension can be affected by conscious effort and thought and relaxation can be taught.

PROBLEMS WITH OVER-CONTRACTION

Muscle tension: this is over-stimulation of muscle fibres. More fibres contract than are necessary to maintain postural tone.

Muscle fatigue: when stimulated a muscle will need oxygen and fuel for its energy. This fuel is mainly glucose, stored in the muscle as glycogen and fats and transported by the blood. The muscle burns the glucose and fats by combining them with oxygen from the blood.

If a muscle continues to contract without enough rest (e.g. if someone does too much exercise without breaks), the muscle will run out of oxygen and a by-product of this deficiency, lactic acid, will build up. This acid causes a burning sensation in the muscle, the muscle begins to quiver and soon stops contracting. The exerciser will feel stiffness and pain in the affected muscle.

TERMS OF DESCRIPTION FOR MUSCLES

- **origin:** the fixed end of a muscle. This end of the muscle barely moves during muscle action.
- **insertion:** the moving end of a muscle, the point to which the force of the muscle is directed. A muscle always works from its insertion towards its origin.
- **attachment:** at their origin and insertion muscles attach to bone via tendons to produce movement of joints. They sometimes take attachment from other connective tissue such as cartilage or the fascia of other muscles.
- **belly:** thickest part or main body of muscle; usually the middle part away from insertion and origin.

YOU NOW KNOW
what muscles are and how they work. The following section explains how muscles fit into the rest of the body and details the movements (actions) and positions of all the main muscles in the human body.

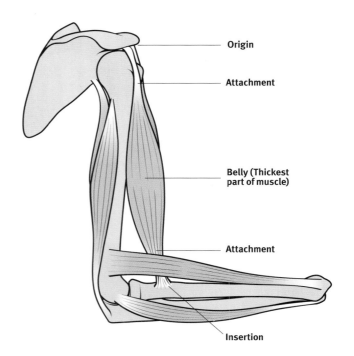

- Origin
- Attachment
- Belly (Thickest part of muscle)
- Attachment
- Insertion

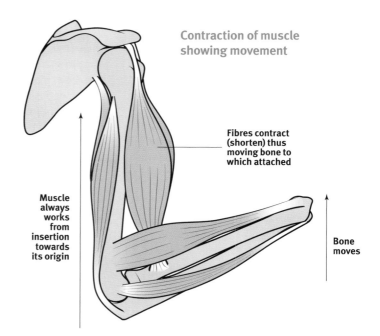

Contraction of muscle showing movement

Fibres contract (shorten) thus moving bone to which attached

Muscle always works from insertion towards its origin

Bone moves

● DID YOU KNOW?
That shivering is caused by muscle contraction?
When you're cold your body starts producing body heat by making muscles contract and relax quicker than usual. This is shivering.

TOPIC 3: HOW ARE MUSCLES ATTACHED TO THE REST OF THE BODY

Muscles are attached by tendons and the fascia.

TENDON

Structure: white fibrous cords (an extension of the fascia) with no elasticity which are of different lengths and thickness and are very strong. They have few, if any, blood vessels or nerves.

Function: it connects muscle to bone.

FASCIA

Structure: white, fibrous connective tissue. It is found in all parts of the body, in different lengths and thicknesses.

Function:

- superficial fascia – beneath the skin; found over almost the whole surface of the body; facilitates the movement of the skin; serves as a medium for the passage of nerves and blood vessels; helps retain body warmth; connects skin with deep fascia.

- deep fascia – dense, inelastic, stiff membrane which forms a sheath (covering) for muscles and broad surfaces for attachment. Made of shiny tendinous fibres it is thicker in unprotected areas and assists muscle action through tension and pressure.

DO ALL MUSCLES WORK IN THE SAME WAY?

All muscles work by contraction but each muscle performs a specific action (type of movement) in order to move the body. There are several different actions:

Flexion: bend or flex a limb inwards

Extension: bend or extend a limb outwards

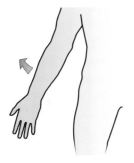

Abduction: move a limb away from the midline

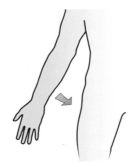

Adduction: move a limb towards the midline

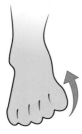

Inversion: turning towards centre e.g. sole of foot

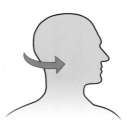

Rotation: rotate head at neck

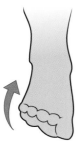

Eversion: turning outwards away from centre e.g. sole of foot

Supination: turn a limb to face upwards

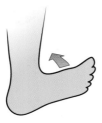

Dorsiflexion: flexing/bending foot up (with toe up, heel down)

Pronation: turn a limb to face downwards

• DID YOU KNOW?

The advent of more and more jobs involving the use of computers has resulted in new diseases caused by constant keyboard work. These are known as 'repetitive- strain injuries' or RSIs. The most common repetitive strain injury is 'carpal-tunnel syndrome'. It has been called the 'secretary's disease' but it can affect anyone whose job requires lots of wrist flexion (hence 'carpal' bones of the wrist) or prolonged finger extension. There are different symptoms including wrist pain, swelling and numbness or 'pins-and-needles' in the index and middle fingers.

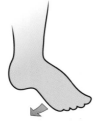

Plantarflexion: flexing/bending foot down towards the ground (with toe down, heel up) e.g. as in walking

THE PRINCIPAL MUSCLES OF THE BODY

There are thousands of muscles in the body. The following series of diagrams show the principal muscles of the body, detailing their position and their action.

Key: P: position   A: action

1. OCCIPITOFRONTALIS
P: THE OCCIPITALIS AND FRONTALIS ARE COLLECTIVELY KNOWN AS OCCIPITOFRONTALIS
A: LIFTS EYEBROWS AND WRINKLES SKIN OF FOREHEAD; CREATES LOOKS OF SURPRISE AND HORROR

2. OCCIPITALIS
P: FIBROUS SHEET OVER OCCIPITAL BONE
A: MOVES SCALP BACKWARDs

3. FRONTALIS
P: FIBROUS SHEET OVER FRONTAL AND PARIETAL BONES
A: MOVES SCALP FORWARDS

4. PROCERUS
P: CONTINUATION OF FRONTALIS DOWN MIDLINE OF NOSE BETWEEN EYEBROWS
A: WRINKLES AT BRIDGE OF NOSE (DISG USTED EXPRESSION)

5. NASALIS
P: SIDES OF THE NOSE
A: COMPRESSES AND DILATES NASAL OPENING (PRODUCES ANNOYED EXPRESSION AND SNIFFING)

6/7. LEVATOR LABII SUPERIORIS
P: THIN BAND OF MUSCLE FROM EYE TO MOUTH
A: LIFTS UPPER LIP; PRODUCES CHEERFUL EXPRESSION

8. LEVATOR ANGULI ORIS
P: THIN BAND OF MUSCLE BELOW LEVATOR LABII SUPERIORIS
A: RAISES CORNER OF MOUTH; PRODUCES CHEERFUL EXPRESSION

9. ZYGOMATICUS
P: THIN MUSCLE ANGLED ACROSS FACE SUPERFICIAL TO MASSETER
A: MOVES ANGLE OF MOUTH UP, BACK AND OUT (SMILING)

10. ORBICULARIS ORIS
P: SPHINCTER MUSCLE AROUND MOUTH
A: PURSES LIPS

11. MENTALIS
P: ABOVE MENTAL TUBEROSITY ON CHIN
A: LIFTS SKIN ON CHIN AND TURNS LOWER LIP OUTWARDS

12. DEPRESSOR LABII INFERIORIS
P: MID-LINE OF CHIN TO LOWER LIP
A: PULLS LOWER LIP STRAIGHT DOWN

13. DEPRESSOR ANGULI ORIS
P: FROM MODIOLUS TO MANDIBLE
A: PULLS DOWN CORNERS OF MOUTH

14. BUCCINATOR
P: BROAD THIN MUSCLE DEEP TO MASSETER
A: COMPRESSES CHEEK AGAINST TEETH TO MAINTAIN TENSION; AIDS IN MASTICATION

15. RISORIUS
P: BETWEEN MASSETER AND CORNER OF MOUTH
A: RETRACTS ANGLE OF MOUTH AND LIFTS UPPER LIP (PRODUCES GRINNING EXPRESSION)

16. MEDIAL PTERYGOID
P: INNER SURFACE OF MANDIBLE
A: RAISES THE MANDIBLE

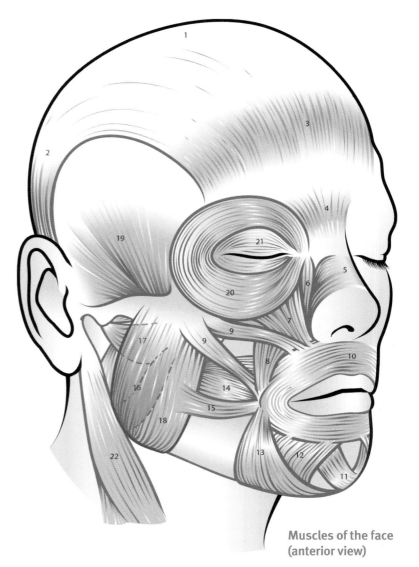

Muscles of the face (anterior view)

17. LATERAL PTERYGOID
P: BEHIND THE ZYGOMATIC ARCH (CHEEK BONE)
A: PUSHES MANDIBLE OUT AND OPENS MOUTH

18. MASSETER
P: FROM ZYGOMATIC ARCH TO MANDIBLE
A: RAISES LOWER JAW; CHIEF MUSCLE OF MASTICATION

19. TEMPORALIS
P: FROM TEMPORAL BONE TO MANDIBLE
A: RAISES AND RETRACTS LOWER JAW

20. ORBICULARIS OCULI
P: SPHINCTER MUSCLE AROUND EYE
A: CLOSES EYELID

21. LEVATOR PALPEBRAE SUPERIORIS
P: EXTENDS FROM THE POSTERIOR PORT OF THE ORBITAL CAVITY TO THE UPPER EYE LID
A: RAISES THE EYELID

22. STERNOCLEIDOMASTOID
P: ROPE-LIKE MUSCLE RUNNING AT AN ANGLE UP SIDES OF NECK
A: FLEXES HEAD AND TURNS FROM SIDE TO SIDE

Key: P: **position**   A: **action**   Muscles of the head and neck (side view)

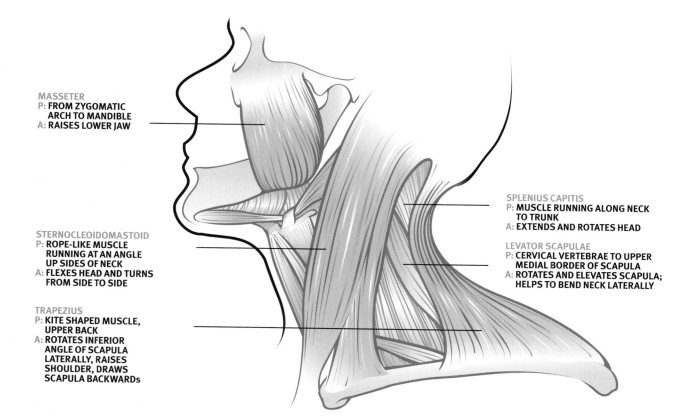

MASSETER
P: **FROM ZYGOMATIC ARCH TO MANDIBLE**
A: **RAISES LOWER JAW**

STERNOCLEOIDOMASTOID
P: **ROPE-LIKE MUSCLE RUNNING AT AN ANGLE UP SIDES OF NECK**
A: **FLEXES HEAD AND TURNS FROM SIDE TO SIDE**

TRAPEZIUS
P: **KITE SHAPED MUSCLE, UPPER BACK**
A: **ROTATES INFERIOR ANGLE OF SCAPULA LATERALLY, RAISES SHOULDER, DRAWS SCAPULA BACKWARDs**

SPLENIUS CAPITIS
P: **MUSCLE RUNNING ALONG NECK TO TRUNK**
A: **EXTENDS AND ROTATES HEAD**

LEVATOR SCAPULAE
P: **CERVICAL VERTEBRAE TO UPPER MEDIAL BORDER OF SCAPULA**
A: **ROTATES AND ELEVATES SCAPULA; HELPS TO BEND NECK LATERALLY**

Key: P: **position**   A: **action**

Muscles of the trunk – neck, chest and abdomen – anterior view

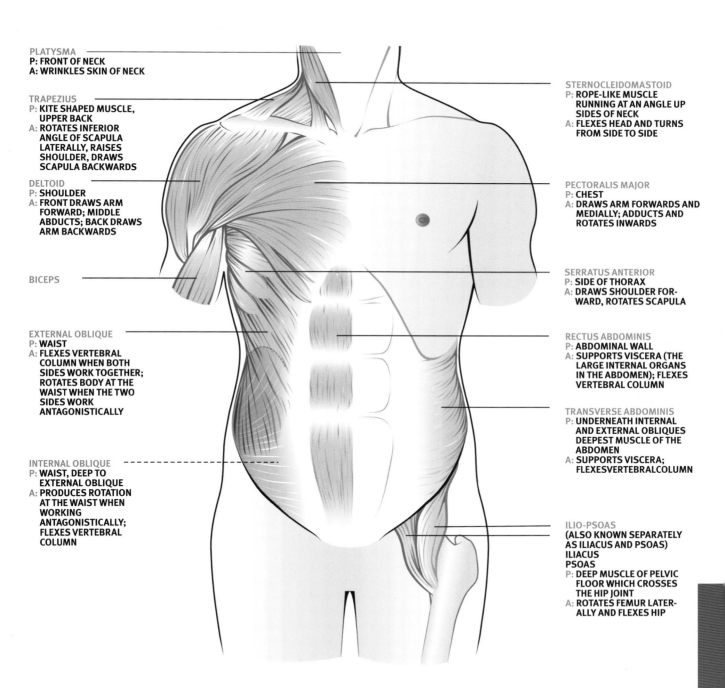

PLATYSMA
P: **FRONT OF NECK**
A: **WRINKLES SKIN OF NECK**

TRAPEZIUS
P: **KITE SHAPED MUSCLE,
UPPER BACK**
A: **ROTATES INFERIOR
ANGLE OF SCAPULA
LATERALLY, RAISES
SHOULDER, DRAWS
SCAPULA BACKWARDS**

DELTOID
P: **SHOULDER**
A: **FRONT DRAWS ARM
FORWARD; MIDDLE
ABDUCTS; BACK DRAWS
ARM BACKWARDS**

BICEPS

EXTERNAL OBLIQUE
P: **WAIST**
A: **FLEXES VERTEBRAL
COLUMN WHEN BOTH
SIDES WORK TOGETHER;
ROTATES BODY AT THE
WAIST WHEN THE TWO
SIDES WORK
ANTAGONISTICALLY**

INTERNAL OBLIQUE
P: **WAIST, DEEP TO
EXTERNAL OBLIQUE**
A: **PRODUCES ROTATION
AT THE WAIST WHEN
WORKING
ANTAGONISTICALLY;
FLEXES VERTEBRAL
COLUMN**

STERNOCLEIDOMASTOID
P: **ROPE-LIKE MUSCLE
RUNNING AT AN ANGLE UP
SIDES OF NECK**
A: **FLEXES HEAD AND TURNS
FROM SIDE TO SIDE**

PECTORALIS MAJOR
P: **CHEST**
A: **DRAWS ARM FORWARDS AND
MEDIALLY; ADDUCTS AND
ROTATES INWARDS**

SERRATUS ANTERIOR
P: **SIDE OF THORAX**
A: **DRAWS SHOULDER FOR-
WARD, ROTATES SCAPULA**

RECTUS ABDOMINIS
P: **ABDOMINAL WALL**
A: **SUPPORTS VISCERA (THE
LARGE INTERNAL ORGANS
IN THE ABDOMEN); FLEXES
VERTEBRAL COLUMN**

TRANSVERSE ABDOMINIS
P: **UNDERNEATH INTERNAL
AND EXTERNAL OBLIQUES
DEEPEST MUSCLE OF THE
ABDOMEN**
A: **SUPPORTS VISCERA;
FLEXESVERTEBRALCOLUMN**

ILIO-PSOAS
**(ALSO KNOWN SEPARATELY
AS ILIACUS AND PSOAS)
ILIACUS
PSOAS**
P: **DEEP MUSCLE OF PELVIC
FLOOR WHICH CROSSES
THE HIP JOINT**
A: **ROTATES FEMUR LATER-
ALLY AND FLEXES HIP**

Key: **P: position   A: action**   Muscles of the trunk – neck, chest and abdomen – posterior view

SUPERFICIAL MUSCLES

STERNOCLEIDOMASTOID

TRAPEZIUS
P: **KITE-SHAPED MUSCLE, UPPER BACK**
A: **ROTATES INFERIOR ANGLE OF SCAPULA LATERALLY, RAISES SHOULDER, DRAWS SCAPULA BACKWARDS**

DELTOID
P: **SHOULDER**
A: **FRONT DRAWS ARM FORWARD; MIDDLE ABDUCTS; BACK DRAWS ARM BACKWARDS**

TRICEPS

LATISSIMUS DORSI
P: **COVERS BACK**
A: **DRAWS ARM BACKWARDS, ADDUCTS AND ROTATES IT MEDIALLY**

EXTERNAL OBLIQUES

GLUTEUS MEDIUS
P: **HIGHER ON THE PELVIS CONTINUING DEEP TO GLUTEUS MAXIMUS**
A: **ABDUCTS AND ROTATES FEMUR MEDIALLY**

GLUTEUS MAXIMUS
P: **MAIN BULK OF BUTTOCK**
A: **EXTENDS THE HIP, RAISES TRUNK AFTER STOOPING, LATERAL ROTATION OF HIP/FEMUR**

DEEP MUSCLES

SPLENIUS CAPITIS
P: **MUSCLE RUNNING ALONG NECK TO TRUNK**
A: **EXTENDS AND ROTATES HEAD**

LEVATOR SCAPULAE

RHOMBOIDS
P: **BETWEEN SCAPULA AND SPINE**
A: **ADDUCTS SCAPULA**

SUPRASPINATUS
P: **TOP OF SCAPULA (ABOVE SPINE)**
A: **ABDUCTS ARM, HOLDS HUMERUS IN SOCKET**

INFRASPINATUS
P: **SCAPULA (BELOW SPINE)**
A: **LATERAL ROTATION OF HUMERUS; STABILISES HUMERUS IN SOCKET**

TERES MINOR
P: **SIDE OF SCAPULA TO HUMERUS**
A: **LATERAL ROTATION OF HUMERUS; STABILISES HUMERUS IN SOCKET**

TERES MAJOR
P: **SIDE OF SCAPULA TO HUMERUS**
A: **ADDUCTS AND MEDIALLY ROTATES HUMERUS; EXTENDS SHOULDER JOINT**

P: **SIDE OF THORAX**
A: **DRAWS SHOULDER FORWARD, ROTATES SCAPULA**

ERECTOR SPINAE
P: **RIBBON-SHAPED GROUP OF MUSCLES EITHER SIDE OF SPINE**
A: **EXTENDS VERTEBRAL COLUMN**

GLUTEUS MINIMUS
P: **FAN SHAPED MUSCLE UNDERNEATH GLUTEUS MEDIUS**
A: **ABDUCTS AND ROTATES FEMUR MEDIALLY**

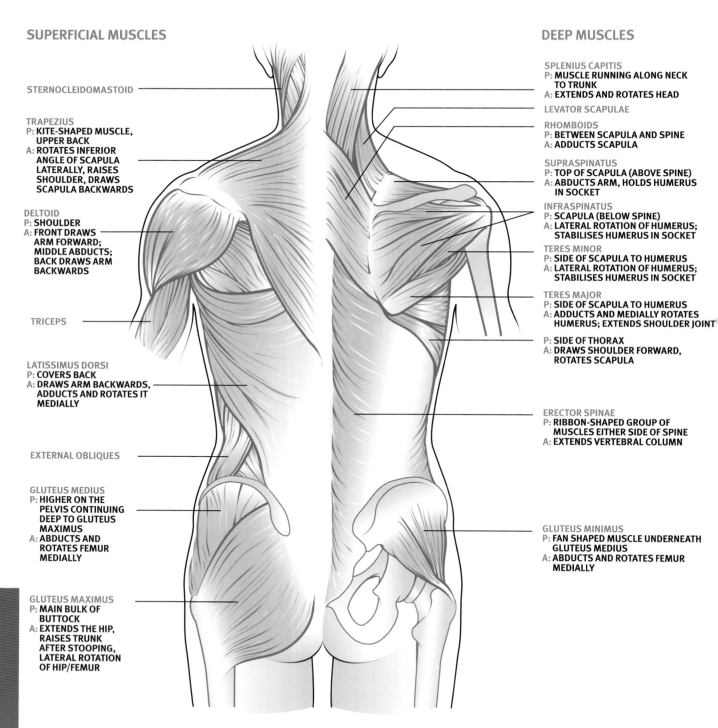

Key: P: **position**   A: **action**

Muscles of the shoulder and arm – anterior view

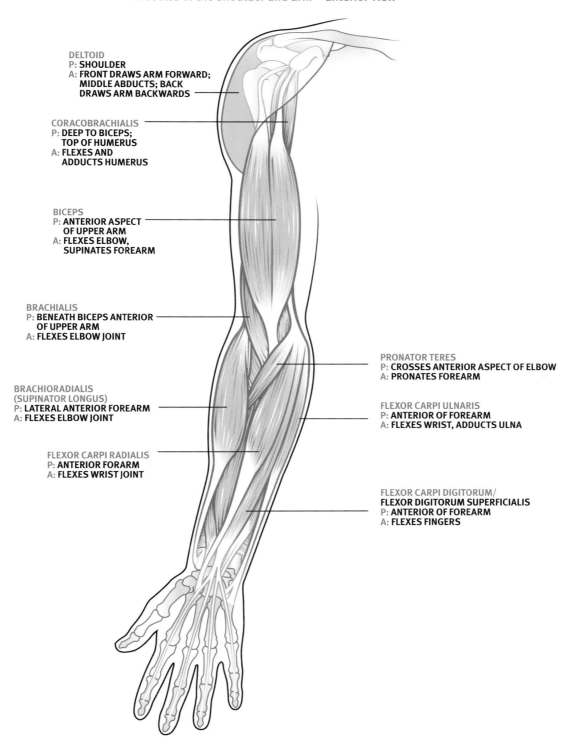

DELTOID
P: **SHOULDER**
A: **FRONT DRAWS ARM FORWARD;
MIDDLE ABDUCTS; BACK
DRAWS ARM BACKWARDS**

CORACOBRACHIALIS
P: **DEEP TO BICEPS;
TOP OF HUMERUS**
A: **FLEXES AND
ADDUCTS HUMERUS**

BICEPS
P: **ANTERIOR ASPECT
OF UPPER ARM**
A: **FLEXES ELBOW,
SUPINATES FOREARM**

BRACHIALIS
P: **BENEATH BICEPS ANTERIOR
OF UPPER ARM**
A: **FLEXES ELBOW JOINT**

BRACHIORADIALIS
(SUPINATOR LONGUS)
P: **LATERAL ANTERIOR FOREARM**
A: **FLEXES ELBOW JOINT**

FLEXOR CARPI RADIALIS
P: **ANTERIOR FOREARM**
A: **FLEXES WRIST JOINT**

PRONATOR TERES
P: **CROSSES ANTERIOR ASPECT OF ELBOW**
A: **PRONATES FOREARM**

FLEXOR CARPI ULNARIS
P: **ANTERIOR OF FOREARM**
A: **FLEXES WRIST, ADDUCTS ULNA**

FLEXOR CARPI DIGITORUM/
FLEXOR DIGITORUM SUPERFICIALIS
P: **ANTERIOR OF FOREARM**
A: **FLEXES FINGERS**

Key: P: position   A: action

Muscles of the shoulder and arm – posterior view

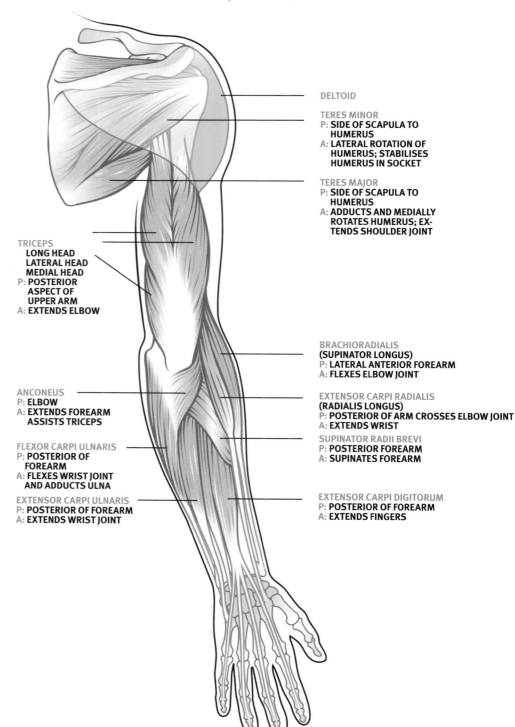

DELTOID

TERES MINOR
P: **SIDE OF SCAPULA TO HUMERUS**
A: **LATERAL ROTATION OF HUMERUS; STABILISES HUMERUS IN SOCKET**

TERES MAJOR
P: **SIDE OF SCAPULA TO HUMERUS**
A: **ADDUCTS AND MEDIALLY ROTATES HUMERUS; EXTENDS SHOULDER JOINT**

TRICEPS
**LONG HEAD
LATERAL HEAD
MEDIAL HEAD**
P: **POSTERIOR ASPECT OF UPPER ARM**
A: **EXTENDS ELBOW**

BRACHIORADIALIS
(SUPINATOR LONGUS)
P: **LATERAL ANTERIOR FOREARM**
A: **FLEXES ELBOW JOINT**

ANCONEUS
P: **ELBOW**
A: **EXTENDS FOREARM ASSISTS TRICEPS**

EXTENSOR CARPI RADIALIS
(RADIALIS LONGUS)
P: **POSTERIOR OF ARM CROSSES ELBOW JOINT**
A: **EXTENDS WRIST**

SUPINATOR RADII BREVI
P: **POSTERIOR FOREARM**
A: **SUPINATES FOREARM**

FLEXOR CARPI ULNARIS
P: **POSTERIOR OF FOREARM**
A: **FLEXES WRIST JOINT AND ADDUCTS ULNA**

EXTENSOR CARPI ULNARIS
P: **POSTERIOR OF FOREARM**
A: **EXTENDS WRIST JOINT**

EXTENSOR CARPI DIGITORUM
P: **POSTERIOR OF FOREARM**
A: **EXTENDS FINGERS**

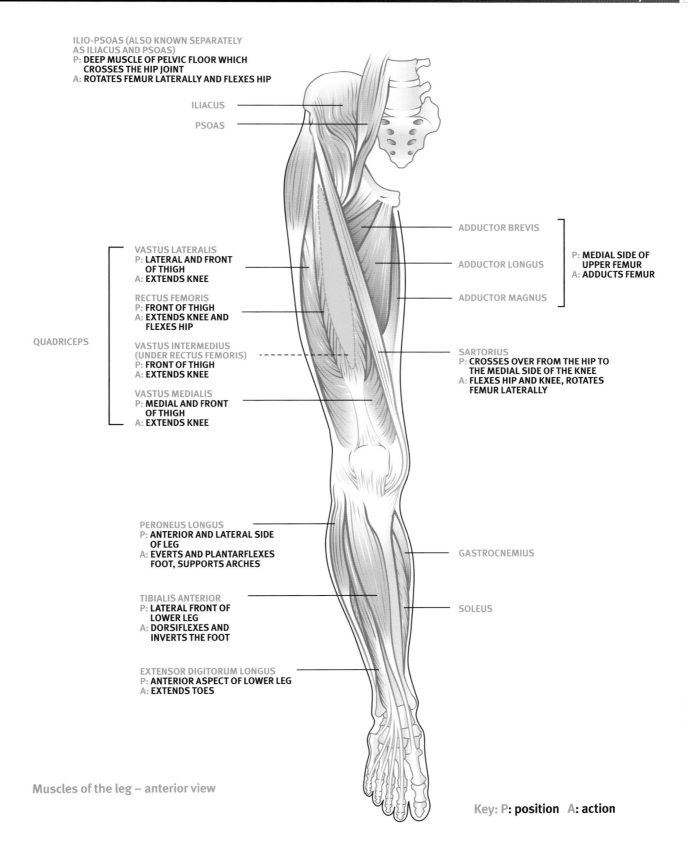

ILIO-PSOAS (ALSO KNOWN SEPARATELY AS ILIACUS AND PSOAS)
P: DEEP MUSCLE OF PELVIC FLOOR WHICH CROSSES THE HIP JOINT
A: ROTATES FEMUR LATERALLY AND FLEXES HIP

ILIACUS

PSOAS

ADDUCTOR BREVIS

ADDUCTOR LONGUS

ADDUCTOR MAGNUS

P: MEDIAL SIDE OF UPPER FEMUR
A: ADDUCTS FEMUR

VASTUS LATERALIS
P: LATERAL AND FRONT OF THIGH
A: EXTENDS KNEE

RECTUS FEMORIS
P: FRONT OF THIGH
A: EXTENDS KNEE AND FLEXES HIP

QUADRICEPS

VASTUS INTERMEDIUS (UNDER RECTUS FEMORIS)
P: FRONT OF THIGH
A: EXTENDS KNEE

VASTUS MEDIALIS
P: MEDIAL AND FRONT OF THIGH
A: EXTENDS KNEE

SARTORIUS
P: CROSSES OVER FROM THE HIP TO THE MEDIAL SIDE OF THE KNEE
A: FLEXES HIP AND KNEE, ROTATES FEMUR LATERALLY

PERONEUS LONGUS
P: ANTERIOR AND LATERAL SIDE OF LEG
A: EVERTS AND PLANTARFLEXES FOOT, SUPPORTS ARCHES

GASTROCNEMIUS

SOLEUS

TIBIALIS ANTERIOR
P: LATERAL FRONT OF LOWER LEG
A: DORSIFLEXES AND INVERTS THE FOOT

EXTENSOR DIGITORUM LONGUS
P: ANTERIOR ASPECT OF LOWER LEG
A: EXTENDS TOES

Muscles of the leg – anterior view

Key: P: position   A: action

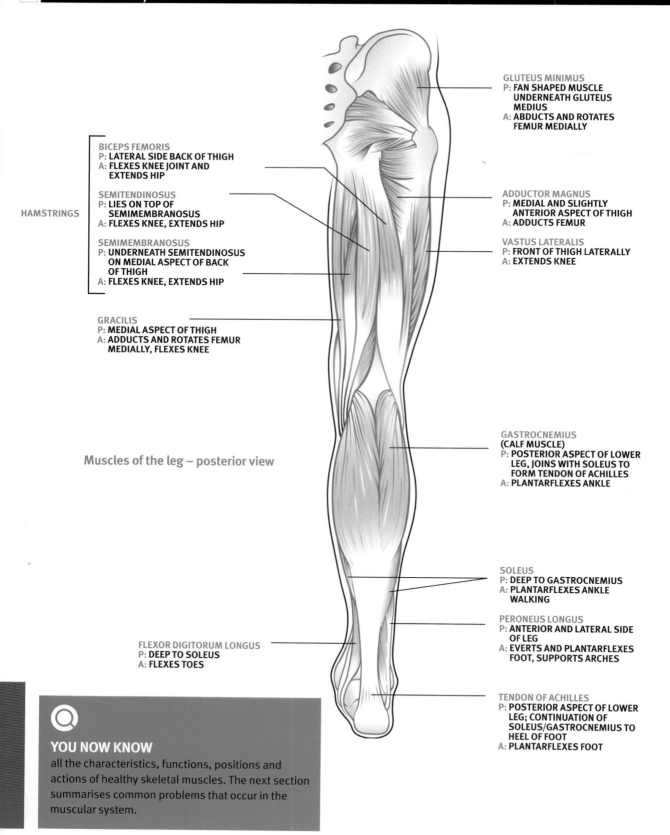

Muscles of the leg – posterior view

GLUTEUS MINIMUS
P: **FAN SHAPED MUSCLE UNDERNEATH GLUTEUS MEDIUS**
A: **ABDUCTS AND ROTATES FEMUR MEDIALLY**

ADDUCTOR MAGNUS
P: **MEDIAL AND SLIGHTLY ANTERIOR ASPECT OF THIGH**
A: **ADDUCTS FEMUR**

VASTUS LATERALIS
P: **FRONT OF THIGH LATERALLY**
A: **EXTENDS KNEE**

HAMSTRINGS

BICEPS FEMORIS
P: **LATERAL SIDE BACK OF THIGH**
A: **FLEXES KNEE JOINT AND EXTENDS HIP**

SEMITENDINOSUS
P: **LIES ON TOP OF SEMIMEMBRANOSUS**
A: **FLEXES KNEE, EXTENDS HIP**

SEMIMEMBRANOSUS
P: **UNDERNEATH SEMITENDINOSUS ON MEDIAL ASPECT OF BACK OF THIGH**
A: **FLEXES KNEE, EXTENDS HIP**

GRACILIS
P: **MEDIAL ASPECT OF THIGH**
A: **ADDUCTS AND ROTATES FEMUR MEDIALLY, FLEXES KNEE**

GASTROCNEMIUS (CALF MUSCLE)
P: **POSTERIOR ASPECT OF LOWER LEG, JOINS WITH SOLEUS TO FORM TENDON OF ACHILLES**
A: **PLANTARFLEXES ANKLE**

SOLEUS
P: **DEEP TO GASTROCNEMIUS**
A: **PLANTARFLEXES ANKLE WALKING**

PERONEUS LONGUS
P: **ANTERIOR AND LATERAL SIDE OF LEG**
A: **EVERTS AND PLANTARFLEXES FOOT, SUPPORTS ARCHES**

FLEXOR DIGITORUM LONGUS
P: **DEEP TO SOLEUS**
A: **FLEXES TOES**

TENDON OF ACHILLES
P: **POSTERIOR ASPECT OF LOWER LEG; CONTINUATION OF SOLEUS/GASTROCNEMIUS TO HEEL OF FOOT**
A: **PLANTARFLEXES FOOT**

YOU NOW KNOW
all the characteristics, functions, positions and actions of healthy skeletal muscles. The next section summarises common problems that occur in the muscular system.

TOPIC 4: DISEASES AND DISORDERS (PATHOLOGIES)

FIBROMYALGIA
Cause: unknown.
Effect: pain, stiffness and tenderness of the muscles, tendons and joints. Most common in the back, neck, shoulders and feet.

CRAMP
Cause: vigorous exercise and over-exertion; also extreme heat; sodium and/or water depletion.
Effect: painful localised and involuntary contraction of one or more muscles.

ATONY
Lack of normal tone or tension in a muscle.

ATROPHY
Cause: undernourishment; lack of use.
Effect: wasting away, or failure to reach normal size, of bulk of muscle.

MYOSITIS
Inflammation of a muscle.

RUPTURE
Burst or tear in the fascia or sheath surrounding muscles.

SPASM
A more than usual number of muscle fibres in sustained contraction, usually in response to pain. Fibres contract for much longer than is usually necessary.

SPASTICITY
Cause: inhibitory nerves have been cut.
Effect: spinal reflexes cause sustained contraction.

SPRAIN
Cause: sudden twist or wrench of the joint's ligaments
Effect: an injury or damage to a joint; painful swelling of the joint; the most commonly sprained joint is the ankle (often called a 'twisted ankle'). A sprained ankle is usually caused by the joint 'going over', thus putting all the body weight on the ankle.

STRAIN
Cause: overexertion, over-stretching, over-use; failure to warm up before strenuous activity, especially sport.
Effect: an injury to a muscle or its tendon; may occasionally involve rupture (tearing) of muscle fibres, muscle sheath or tendon.

STRESS
Cause: stress is any factor which affects physical or mental well-being.
Effect: excessive muscle tension and subsequent muscle pain, especially in the back and neck.

ADHESIONS
Are fibrous bands that form between tissues and organs, often as a result of injury.

ADHESIVE CAPSULITIS (FROZEN SHOULDER)
Is a disorder in which the connective tissue surrounding the shoulder becomes inflamed and stiff, and grows together with abnormal bands of tissue greatly restricting motion and causing chronic pain.

ACHILLES TENDONITIS

Is an injury to the achilles tendon generally precipitated by overuse of the affected limb and is more common among athletes training under less than ideal conditions.

LUMBAGO

Is backache affecting the lumbar region or lower back; can be caused by muscle strain or arthritis.

CRAMP

Is an unpleasant, often painful sensation caused by contraction or over-shortening of muscles. Cramps can be caused by cold, overexertion or low calcium levels in blood.

LATERAL EPICONDYLITIS (TENNIS ELBOW)

Is a painful inflammation of the tendon at the outer border of the elbow resulting from overuse of lower arm muscles.

MEDIAL EPICONDYLITIS (GOLFER'S ELBOW)

Is an inflammatory condition of the elbow which in some ways is similar to tennis elbow.

MICROTRAUMA

Is the general term given to small injuries to the body.

MUSCLE FATIGUE

Is a direct term for the inability to exert force with one's muscles to the degree that would be expected given the individual's general physical fitness.

REPETITIVE STRAIN INJURY/SYNDROME

Pain with associated loss of function in a limb resulting from its repeated movement.

RUPTURE

Is a forcible tearing or disruption of a tissue.

SHIN SPLINTS

A painful inflammation of the muscles around the shins; frequent among runners.

TENDONITIS

Is an inflammation in or around tendons (bands of strong fibrous tissue that hold muscle to bone).

ACHILLES BURSITIS

Is the inflammation of one or more bursae (small sacs) of synovial fluid in and around the Achilles.

MUSCULAR DYSTROPHY

Any of several hereditary diseases of the muscular system characterized by weakness and wasting of skeletal muscles.

TETANUS

An acute and serious infection of the central nervous system caused by bacterial infection of open wounds.

BURSITIS

Is the inflamation of one or more bursae (small sacs) of synovial fluid in the body.

HOUSEMAIDS KNEE

Is when the bursa in the knee becomes inflamed, it swells up, forming a large egg like protrusion over the knee cap.

INTERRELATIONSHIPS
Muscular system links to:
Nervous: relies upon nerve impulses to produce a contraction in the muscle. Without nerve stimulus movement would not be possible.
Skeletal: muscles always cross a joint and thus rely on the skeletal system for leverage and movement.
Digestive: nutrition/energy in the form of glucose is received from the digestive system. If it is not immediately used it is converted to glycogen and stored in the muscle fibres for energy production later.
Circulatory and respiratory: muscles receive oxygen from the vascular and respiratory system.

Summary

The muscular system:

- [ ] There are three types of muscle: voluntary, involuntary and cardiac.
- [ ] There are two types of muscle attachment: tendon and fascia.
- [ ] Voluntary muscles have a variety of actions.
- [ ] Muscles work by contraction.
- [ ] Over-contraction without enough oxygen can cause lactic acid to form, which prevents muscles from functioning correctly.

Muscles of the torso	Origin	Insertion	Main actions
Sternocleidomastoid	Sternum & clavicle	Mastoid process	One side only – flexes neck laterally and rotates it. Both – side flexion
Scalenus	Transverse processes of 2nd to 6th cervical	Upper surfaces of ribs 1 and 2	Raises first two ribs, flexes and rotates the neck
Splenius capitis	First six thoracic vertebrae	Mastoid process and occipital bone	Extends the neck. Slight rotation
Levator scapulae	Upper four cervical vertebrae	Superior medial border of scapula	Elevates shoulder, rotates scapula
Supraspinatus	Supraspinous fossa of scapula	Greater tuberosity of humerus	Abducts arm
Infraspinatus	Inferior spinous fossa of scapula	Greater tuberosity of humerus	Rotates arm outwards (laterally)
Subscapularis	Subscapular fossa of scapula	Lesser tuberosity of humerus	Rotates arm inwards
Teres minor	Axillary border of scapula	Greater tuberosity of humerus	Rotates arm outwards (laterally)
Teres major	Inferior angle of scapula	Medial lip of bicipital groove of humerus	Draws arm backwards, adducts and medially rotates it
Rhomboid major & minor	7th cervical and 1st to 5th thoracic vertebrae	Medial border of scapula	Adducts (draws towards spine) and rotates scapula downwards
Trapezius	Occipital bone, cervical and thoracic vertebrae	Clavicle and spine of scapula Acromion process	Elevates and braces shoulder, rotates scapula
Latissimus dorsi	Lower six thoracic and lumbar vertebrae, sacrum and illiac crest	Bicipital groove of humerus	Draws arm backwards, adducts and rotates it inwards
Erector spinae	Sacrum and iliac crest, ribs and lower vertebrae	Ribs, vertebrae and mastoid process	One side only – flexes trunk laterally. Both – extends trunk
Quadratus lumborum	Iliac crest	12th rib and transverse processes of upper four lumbar vertebrae	One side only – flexes trunk laterally and rotates it Both – extends trunk
Pectoralis major	Clavicle, sternum, upper six costal cartilages	Lateral lip of bicipital groove of humerus	Draws arm forwards (flexes) and adducts and rotates it inwards (medial rotation)
Pectoralis minor	3rd to 5th ribs	Coracoid process of scapula	Draws shoulder forwards and downwards
Serratus anterior	Upper nine ribs	Anterior surface of vertebral border of scapula	Draws shoulder forwards and rotates scapula
Rectus abdominus	Pubis	Ribs and sternum	Flexes the trunk
Abdominus tranversalis	Inguinal ligament, iliac crest, lumbar fascia, cartilages of lower six ribs	Conjoint tendon and linea alba through abdominal aponeurosis, pubis	Supports the viscera, compresses abdomen
Internal obliques	Inguinal ligament, iliac crest and lumbar fascia	Costal cartilages of ribs 9–12 and linea alba	Lumbar flexion, side flexion and rotation
External obliques	Lower eight ribs	Iliac crest and linea alba through abdominal aponeurosis	Lumbar flexion, side flexion and rotation

Muscles of the torso (cont)	Origin	Insertion	Main actions
Internal Intercostals	Lower borders of upper eleven pairs of ribs	From the cartilages to the angles of the upper eleven ribs	Draw ventral part of ribs downward, decreasing the volume of the thoracic cavity for expiration
External Intercostals	Lower margin of upper eleven ribs	Superior border of rib below (each muscle fibre runs obliquely and Inserts toward the costal cartilage)	Draw ventral part of ribs upward, increasing the volume of the thoracic cavity for inspiration

Muscles of the arm	Origin	Insertion	Main actions
Deltoid	Clavicle, acromion process and spine of scapula	Deltoid tuberosity of humerus	Front draws arm forwards, Middle abducts the arm, Back draws arm backwards
Coracobrachialis	Coracoid process of scapula	Shaft of humerus	Adducts and flexes the arm, horizontally adducts the shoulder
Biceps brachii	Long head – supra glenoid tubercle of scapula, Short head – coracoid process of scapula	Tuberosity of radius	Flexes elbow, supinates forearm
Brachialis	Shaft of humerus	Coronoid process of ulna	Flexes elbow
Brachioradialis	Lateral condyloid ridge of humerus	Distal part of radius	Flexes elbow
Triceps brachii	Long head – scapula, Medial head – humerus Lateral head – humerus	Olecranon process of ulna	Extends elbow
Anconeus	Lateral epicondyle of humerus	Olecranon process of ulna	Extends elbow
Pronator teres	Above medial epicondyle of humerus and coronoid process of ulna	Middle of shaft of radius	Pronates forearm and hand
Supinator	Lateral epicondyle of humerus	Lateral surface of radius	Supinates forearm and hand
Extensor digitorum	Lateral epicondyle of humerus	Metacarpals and phalanges	Extends wrist and fingers
Extensor carpi radialis brevis & longus	Lateral epicondyle of humerus	2nd and 3rd metacarpals	Extends and abducts wrist
Extensor carpi ulnaris	Lateral epicondyle of humerus	5th metacarpal	Extends wrist
Extensor pollicus longus	Middle third of dorsal surface of ulna, interosseous membrane	Base of distal phalanx of thumb	Extends thumb
Palmaris longus	Medial epicondyle of the humerus through the common tendon	Front of the flexor retinaculum and apex of the palmar aponeurosis	Flexes the hand
Flexor digitorum profundus	Upper three-fourths of anterior and medial surfaces of shaft of ulna and medial side of the coronoid process, interosseous membrane	Front of base of distal phalanges of fingers	Flexes distal phalanges

(Muscles of the arm cont)	Origin	Insertion	Main actions
Flexor carpi radialis	Medial epicondyle of humerus	2nd and 3rd metacarpals	Flexes wrist
Flexor carpi ulnaris	Medial epicondyle of humerus and ulna	5th metatcarpal, pisiform and hamate	Flexes wrist
Flexor digitorum superficialis	Humeroulnar head - medial epicondyle of the humerus through common tendon. Radial head - anterior surface of shaft of radius	Four tendons divide into two slips each and these insert into the sides of the middle phalanges of four fingers	Flexes the middle phalanges of the fingers
Palmar aponeurosis (palmaris brevis)	Flexor retinaculum, palmar aponeurosis	Skin of the palm	Corrugates skin of palm
Thenar eminence Abductor pollicis brevis	Tubercle of scaphoid, tubercle of trapezium, flexor retinaculum	Base of proximal phalanx of thumb	Abducts thumb and moves it anteriorly
Flexor pollicis brevis	Flexor retinaculum and trapezium and first metacarpal bone	Base of proximal phalanx of thumb	Flexes metacarpophalangeal joint of thumb, assists in abduction and rotation of thumb
Opponen pollicis	Flexor retinaculum, tubercle of trapezium	Lateral border of first metacarpal bone	Rotates thumb into opposition with fingers
Hypothenar eminence Abductor digiti minimi	Pisiform bone, tendon of flexor carpi ulnaris	Medial side of base of proximal phalanx of the little finger	Abducts little finger
Flexor digita minimi brevis	Anterior surface of flexor retinaculum, hook of hamate	Medial side of base of proximal phalanx of little finger	Flexes little finger at metacarpophalangeal
Opponens digiti minimi	Anterior surface of flexor retinaculum, hook of hamate	Whole length of medial border of fifth metacarpal bone	Rotates fifth metacarpal bone, draws fifth metacarpal bone forward
Muscles of the leg	**Origin**	**Insertion**	**Main actions**
Iliopsoas Psoas Iliacus	12th thoracic and all lumbar vertebrae, iliac fossa and front of sacrum	Lesser trochanter of femur	Flexes and medially rotates hip
Gluteus maximus	Posterior crest of ilium, posterior surface of sacrum and coccyx	Gluteal tuberosity of femur	Tenses fascia lata and extends hip, raises trunk after stooping
Gluteus medius	Posterior surface of ilium	Greater trochanter of femur	Abducts and medially rotates femur
Gluteus minimus	Lateral surface of ilium	Greater trochanter of femur	Abducts and medially rotates femur
Piriformis	Front of sacrum	Greater trochanter of femur	Laterally rotates femur
Tensor fascia lata	Anterior iliac crest	Fascia lata	Abducts and rotates the femur

(Muscles of the leg cont)	Origin	Insertion	Main actions
Biceps femoris	Long head – ischium Short head – linea aspera	Head of fibula and lateral condyle of tibia	Extends hip, flexes knee
Semimembranosus	Ischial tuberosity	Medial condyle of tibia	Extends hip, flexes knee
Semitendinosus	Ischial tuberosity	Below medial condyle of tibia	Extends hip, flexes knee
Rectus femoris	Above acetabulum	Through patella and patellar tendon on to tibial tuberosity	Extends knee, flexes hip
Vastus lateralis	Greater trochanter and linea aspera	Through patella and patellar tendon on to tibial tuberosity	Extends knee
Vastus intermedius	Shaft of femur	Through patella and patellar tendon on to tibial tuberosity	Extends knee
Vastus medialis	Whole length of linea alba and medial condyloid ridge	Through patella and patellar tendon on to tibial tuberosity	Extends knee
Sartorius	Anterior superior iliac spine	Below medial condyle of tibia	Flexes, abducts and rotates femur laterally, flexes knee
Gracilis	Pubis and ischium	Below medial condyle of tibia	Adducts and medially rotates femur, flexes knee
Adductors – longus, brevis & magnus	Pubis and ischium	Linea aspera and supra-condylar line	Adducts femur
Pectineus	Pubis	Close to lesser trochanter of femur	Adducts femur, flexes hip
Popliteus	Lateral condyle of femur	Tibia	Internally rotates and flexes the knee
Gastrocnemius	Medial and lateral condyles of femur	Through Achilles tendon to calcaneum	Plantarflexes the foot, flexes the knee
Soleus	Fibula and tibia	Calcaneum	Plantarflexes the foot
Peroneus longus	Tibia	Medial cuneiform and 1st metatarsal	Everts foot and plantarflexes ankle
Peroneus brevis	Tibia	5th metatarsal	Everts foot and plantarflexes the knee
Tibialis anterior	Shaft of tibia	Medial cuneiform and 1st metatarsal	Dorsiflexes and inverts the foot
Tibialis posterior	Tibia and fibula	Navicular and 2nd to 5th metatarsals	Inverts and plantarflexes the foot
Extensor digitorum longus	Tibia and fibula	Distal phalanges of toes	Extends toes, dorsiflexes the ankle and everts foot
Flexor digitorum longus	Posterior of tibia	Distalphalanges of toes	Flexes toes, plantarflexes the ankle and inverts foot
Extensor hallucis longus	Middle half of anterior surface of fibula and interosseous membrane	Base of distal phalanx of big toe	Extends big toe, dorsiflexes and inverts foot
Peroneous tertius	Lower third of anterior surface of fibula and interosseous membrane	Dorsal surface of base of fifth metatarsal bone	Dorsiflexes and everts foot
Extensor digitorum brevis	Anterior and lateral surfaces of calcaneus, lateral talocalcaneal ligament, inferior extensor retinaculum	Into base of proximal phalanx of big toe, into lateral sides of tendons of extensor digitorum longus of second, third and fourth toes	Extends the four toes

(Muscles of the leg cont)	Origin	Insertion	Main actions
Flexor digitorum brevis	Tuberosity of calcaneus, plantar aponeurosis	Sides of middle phalanges of second to fifth toes	Flexes proximal phalanges and extends distal phalanges of second through fifth toes
Adductor hallucis	Oblique head - second, third and fourth metatarsal bones and sheath of peroneus longus tendon Transverse head - plantar metatarsophalangeal ligaments of third, fourth and fifth toes and transverse metatarsal ligaments	Lateral side of base of proximal phalanx of big toe	Adducts big toe
Flexor Hallucis longus	Lower two-thirds of posterior surface of shaft of fibula, posterior intermuscular septum, interosseous membrane	Base of distal phalanx of big toe	Flexes distal phalanx of big toe, assists in plantar flexing foot, inverts foot
Muscles of the head, neck and chest	**Origin**	**Insertion**	**Main actions**
Occipitalis	Lateral two-thirds of superior nuchal line of occipital bone, mastoid process of temporal bone	Galea aponeurotica (an intermediate tendon leading to frontal belly)	Moves scalp backwards
Frontalis	Galea aponeurotica	Fascia of facial muscles and skin above nose and eyes	Moves scalp forwards
Temporalis	Fascia over ear	Lateral border of galea aponeurotica	Raises and retracts lower jaw
Procerus	Fascia over nasal bone and lateral nasal cartilage	Skin between eyebrows	Wrinkles at bridge of nose (disgusted expression)
Nasalis	Middle of maxilla	Muscle of opposite side over bridge of nose	Compresses and dilates nasal opening (produces annoyed expression and sniffing)
Levator labii superioris	Frontal process of maxilla and zygomatic bone	Greater alar cartilage and skin of nose, upper lip	Lifts upper lip; produces cheerful expression
Levator anguli oris	Canine fossa of maxilla	Angle of mouth	Raises corner of mouth; produces cheerful expression
Zygomaticus	Zygomatic bone	Angle of mouth and upper lip lateral to levator labii superioris	Moves angle of mouth up, back and out (smiling)
Orbicularis oris	Lateral band - alveolar border of maxilla Medial band - septum of nose Inferior portion - lateral midline of mandible	Becomes continuous with other muscles at angle of mouth	Purses lips

Muscles of the head, neck and chest (cont)	Origin	Insertion	Main actions
Mentalis	Incisive fossa of mandible	Skin of chin	Lifts skin on chin and turns lower lip outwards
Depressor anguli oris	Oblique line of the mandible	Angle of the mouth	Pulls down corners of mouth
Depressor labii inferioris	Mandible, between symphysis and mental foramen	Skin of lower lip	Pulls lower lip straight down
Buccinator	Outer surface of maxilla and mandible over molars and along pterygomandibular raphe	Deep part of muscles of lips	Compresses cheek against teeth to maintain tension and aids in mastication
Risorius	Fascia over masseter	Skin at angle of mouth	Retracts angle of mouth and lifts upper lip (produces grinning expression)
Medial pterygoid	Medial surface of lateral pterygoid plate of sphenoid bone, palatine bone and tuberosity of maxilla	Medial surface of ramus and angle of mandible	Raises the mandible
Lateral pterygoid	Superior head - lateral surface of greater wing of sphenoid Inferior head - lateral surface of lateral pterygoid plate	Condyle of mandible, tempormandibular joint	Pushes mandible out and opens mouth
Masseter	Zygomatic process of maxilla, medial and inferior surfaces of zygomatic arch	Angle and ramus of mandible, lateral surface of coronoid process of mandible	Raises lower jaw; chief muscle of mastication
Orbicularis oculi	Frontal bone, maxilla and lacrimal bone	Continues around orbit and returns to origin	Closes eyelid
Sternocleidomastoid	Sternum and medial part of clavicle	Mastoid process of temporal bone and nuchal line of occipital bone	Flexes head and turns from side to side
Platysma	Subcutaneous fascia of upper one-fourth of chest	Subcutaneous fascia and muscles of chin, jaw and mandible	Depresses and draws lower lip laterally, draws up skin of chest
Digastricus	Posterior belly - mastoid notch of temporal bone Anterior belly - inner side of inferior border of mandible near symphysis	Intermediate tendon attached to hyoid bone	Raises hyoid bone, assists in opening jaws, moves hyoid forward or backward

DON'T FORGET
TO LOGIN TO GAIN ACCESS TO YOUR **FREE** MULTI-MEDIA LEARNING RESOURCES

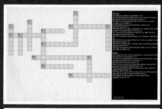

☐ Test your knowledge with crosswords

☐ Test your knowledge with fill in the gaps

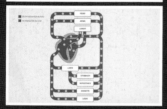

☐ Test your knowledge with interactive animations and diagrams

To login to use these resources visit

www.emspublishing.co.uk/anatomy and follow the onscreen instructions.

05

The Cardiovascular system

The Cardiovascular System is composed of the blood, the heart and the arteries and veins. It refers to two main systems - the pulmonary circulatory system and the systemic circulatory system.

The Cardiovascular system

Blood is pumped from the heart around the body through a transport system of arteries and veins. It distributes oxygen and essential nutrients to the whole body as well as removing potentially damaging waste products and carbon dioxide.

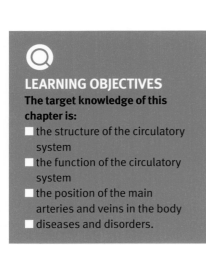

LEARNING OBJECTIVES
The target knowledge of this chapter is:
- the structure of the circulatory system
- the function of the circulatory system
- the position of the main arteries and veins in the body
- diseases and disorders.

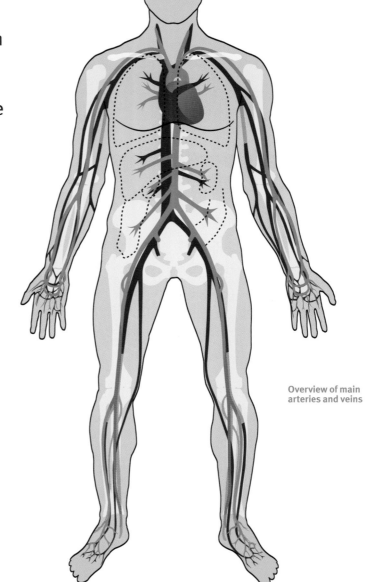

Overview of main arteries and veins

Key

- Oxygenated blood
- Deoxygenated

TOPIC 1:
WHAT IS BLOOD?

A fluid connective tissue made up of plasma and cells. Adult bodies contain approximately 4-5 litres whereas a new-born baby has only 300millitres.It is alkaline (pH7.4).

WHAT DOES BLOOD DO?
- transports oxygen, nutrients, hormones and enzymes around the body.
- transports carbon dioxide and waste materials from the body to the organs of excretion.
- helps fight infection (with leucocytes and antibodies – see opposite for more detail).
- prevents the loss of body fluids after accidents by clotting.
- regulates body temperature.

WHAT IS BLOOD MADE OF?
A: Plasma
Plasma makes up 55% of blood volume. It is a slightly thick, straw-coloured fluid. It is mostly water (90-92%) and the rest
is plasma proteins (albumin, globulin, fibrinogen and prothrombin).

Plasma helps to transport the following essential substances around the body:
- **mineral salts** – sodium chloride, commonly known as table salt, sodium carbonate and the salts of potassium, magnesium, phosphorus, calcium, iron, copper, iodine – which help nerve conduction and ensure that tissue cells keep the right acid balance.
- **nutrients** – amino acids, fatty acids, glucose, glycerol, vitamins. Most of these come from digested food and are absorbed (by the plasma proteins in blood) from the intestines to be used by cell tissues for energy, repair and cell reproduction.
- **waste** – waste products, for example urea, are transported to the liver for breakdown, and then to the kidneys to be excreted as urine

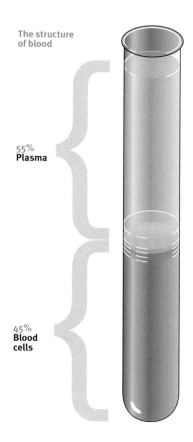

The structure of blood

55%
Plasma

45%
Blood cells

- **hormones** – chemical messengers produced by the endocrine glands. Plasma transports them to various organs and their job is then to change or influence that organ's activity or behaviour.
- **enzymes** – the chemical catalysts in the body. They produce or speed up chemical changes in other substances but remain unchanged themselves.
- **gases**– oxygen (O_2) and carbon dioxide (CO_2) are dissolved in plasma.
- **antibodies** – the body's protectors. These complex proteins are produced by lymphocytes in response to the presence of antigens, such as viruses and bacteria, in the body.

B: Cells

There are three types of blood cells:

Erythrocytes

(also known as Red Blood Cells/ Red Corpuscles)

Structure: small biconcave cells with no nucleus or other organelles.

Function: transport oxygen bound to haemoglobin (oxyhaemoglobin) – for which iron and vitamin B12 are required.

General characteristics:

- approximately 5,000,000 per millilitre of blood
- produced in red bone marrow
- life span of about 120 days
- broken down in the spleen and then the liver (where any spare iron is retrieved and recycled)
- oxyhaemoglobin gives blood its characteristic red colour

Leucocytes

(also known as White Blood Cells/ White Corpuscles)

Structure: large irregularly shaped cells which contain a nucleus

Function: to protect the body from infection

General characteristics:

- approximately 8000 per millilitre of blood in a healthy body
- number can increase rapidly when infection is present
- produced in bone marrow

- life span varies from hours to years depending on type and usage
- can pass through capillary walls into tissues

Thrombocytes

(also known as Platelets)

Structure: small, fragile cell fragments, contain mitochondria but no nucleus

Function: contain various elements that are responsible for blood clotting

General characteristics:

- approximately 250,000 per millilitre of blood
- produced in bone marrow from parts that break off large cells
- life span approximately 10 days

YOU NOW KNOW

You now know what blood is made of and what it does. The next section explains how it moves around the human body, starting with the heart.

**Erythrocytes
(red blood cells)**

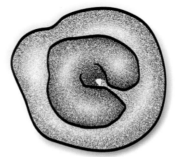

**Leucocyte
(white blood cell)**

**Thrombocytes
(platelets)**

TOPIC 2:
THE HEART & SYSTEMS OF CIRCULATION

Section A: the structure and function of the heart

HOW DOES BLOOD CIRCULATE?

Blood is pumped from the heart (a muscular organ) around the body through a transport system of arteries, veins and capillaries.

The blood circulation is two closed systems.
- Pulmonary circulation is the transport of blood from the heart to the lungs and back again
- Systemic circulation is the transport of blood from the heart to the rest of the body and back.

WHAT IS THE HEART?

The heart is the centre of the circulatory system (hence the use of the word heart to mean centre in English). If blood is the body's fuel, the heart is its engine.

WHAT DOES THE HEART LOOK LIKE?

It is a hollow red organ, approximately the size of its owner's fist, positioned in the centre of the thorax and divided into four chambers. These are the right and left atria (or auricles) in the upper part, and the right and left ventricles in the lower part. Atria and ventricles are connected by the atrioventricular opening. The septum, a muscular wall, separates the right and left sides of the heart. This prevents the blood from the veins know as deoxygenated blood on the right coming into contact with blood going to the arteries know as oxygenated blood on the left.

• USEFUL TIP

In order to remember which chambers are atria and which are ventricles, and how blood moves between them, think of their position in the alphabet: a comes before v just as blood enters the atrium before the ventricle.

• REMEMBER

Diagrams of the heart are drawn as if you are looking at someone facing you – so the right of the diagram as you look at it is actually the left of the heart.

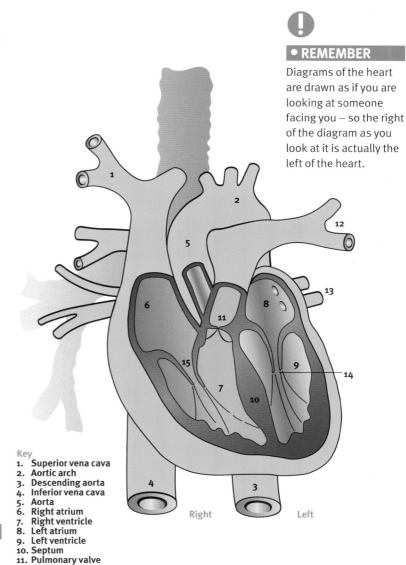

Key
1. Superior vena cava
2. Aortic arch
3. Descending aorta
4. Inferior vena cava
5. Aorta
6. Right atrium
7. Right ventricle
8. Left atrium
9. Left ventricle
10. Septum
11. Pulmonary valve
12. Pulmonary arteries
13. Pulmonary veins
14. Mitral (bicuspid) valve
15. Tricuspid valve

Right   Left

The heart has a muscular wall with membranes covering and lining it. The wall is divided into three layers:

- **endocardium:** the inner layer, is the thin serous membrane, composed of endothelial tissue, that lines the interior of the heart.

- **myocardium:** the middle layer. This is the thickest layer and it is made of cardiac muscle

- **pericardium:** the outer layer, is a double-walled sac that contains the heart and the roots of the great vessels. The inner layer is serous pericardium, while the outer layer is fibrous pericardium, a structure which helps to keep the heart in the right position in the chest.

WHAT DOES THE HEART DO?
The heart is the pump that drives the whole circulatory system. It receives and propels blood, rhythmically contracting, forcing the blood through a system of vessels. The heart's action is controlled by the autonomic nervous system.

WHAT IS A HEARTBEAT?
The heartbeat, or cardiac cycle, is the pattern of muscular contraction of the heart wall:
- both the atria contract, forcing their contents into the ventricles
- the atria relax but the ventricles contract, emptying their contents into the arteries
- the ventricles relax and the heart is at rest.
While resting the heart dilates and fills with blood. The period of rest (diastole) equals the period of contraction (systole).

• DID YOU KNOW?
Most adults heartrate is 72-80 beats per minute whereas most babies have a rate of 130 times a minute.

• DID YOU KNOW?
In one lifetime, a heart will beat approximately 2,700,000,000 times.

Artificial pacemakers are implanted to help the heart maintain a regular heartbeat. these provide an electrical or battery powered impulse to provoke a contraction

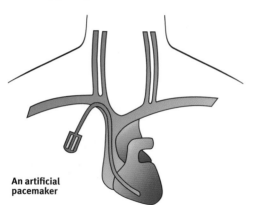

An artificial pacemaker

The heartbeat (or cycle) starts at a point in the right atrium called the pacemaker (sino-atrial node). This consists of specialised neuromuscular tissue which is supplied by the autonomic nervous system. From here, the contraction of the heart muscle spreads through the atria and then down the septum to the walls of the ventricles.

WHAT IS A PULSE?
The number of times the heart beats in one minute is known as the heart rate. When you feel your pulse this is what you are feeling – the rate at which your heart is pumping blood through your circulatory system. Technically, it is a wave of artery wall distension. When blood is pumped from the left ventricle into the aorta, the aorta distends, i.e. swells. The elastic wall of the aorta then recoils thus forcing the blood to move on. This sets up a wave of swelling and contracting which continues along all the elastic arteries. What we think of as a pulse is in fact this wave, which can be felt wherever an artery passes close to the surface of the skin and over a bone. Since the pulse varies with the heart rate, the pulse is taken to check if a heart is beating normally.

IS THE HEARTRATE ALWAYS THE SAME?
The heart rate changes in both healthy and unhealthy bodies, for a variety of reasons. The following all affect it:
- **exercise:** increases the rate of the heartbeat (and rest slows it down again)
- **age:** heart rate is faster in infants and slows gradually as age increases
- **size of the heart:** a smaller heart may have a faster heart rate and a larger heart a slower heart rate
- **emotions and excitement:** increase the heart rate, first through nervous stimuli and then through an increase in the level of adrenaline
- **temperament:** a placid, slow heart rate is not easily varied whereas an excitable person will have a quicker heart rate which changes easily
- **disease:** the heart rate is quickened by fever, haemorrhage, hyper-thyroidism and slowed by jaundice, heart blockages and pressure on the brain.

Section B: the circulation in the heart – pulmonary and coronary

WHAT IS PULMONARY CIRCULATION?

The circulation of blood from the heart to the lungs and back. Deoxygenated blood travels from the heart to the lungs in the pulmonary artery. The blood gets rid of its carbon dioxide (CO_2) and replaces it with oxygen (O_2). It then returns to the heart via the pulmonary veins (from lungs to heart) ready to be pumped around the body.

HOW DOES THIS HAPPEN?

The right atrium receives deoxygenated blood from the superior vena cava (the vein from the upper body) and the inferior vena cava (the vein from the lower body). The blood then flows into the right ventricle from where it is pumped into the pulmonary artery which divides into the right and left pulmonary arteries (which go to the right and left lungs). Blood reaches the lungs via tiny vessels called capillaries which are porous to gases (see The Respiratory System p. 116). The lungs remove the carbon dioxide (CO_2) from the blood in the capillaries, replace it with oxygen and return the oxygenated blood to the left atrium of the heart through the four pulmonary veins. The blood is pushed by the contraction of the left atrium through the bicuspid valve into the left ventricle. The left ventricle then contracts and pumps the blood through the aorta, which branches to form the ascending and descending aorta, for distribution around the body.

HOW IS THE DIRECTION OF THE BLOOD CORRECTLY MAINTAINED?

The direction of blood is maintained by valves. The atrioventricular openings each have a valve: the tricuspid valve on the right and the bicuspid valve on the left. Both these valves allow blood to flow

● DID YOU KNOW?

If you take a heart out of a human body it will continue to beat, even if it is cut into pieces...!

from the atria into the ventricles, but block the atria when the ventricles contract, ensuring that blood continues to circulate in the correct direction. The semi-lunar valves (three pocket-shaped flaps at the vessel's entrance) in the aorta and the pulmonary artery, ensure that there is no back flow from the aorta to the left ventricle or from the pulmonary artery into the right ventricle.

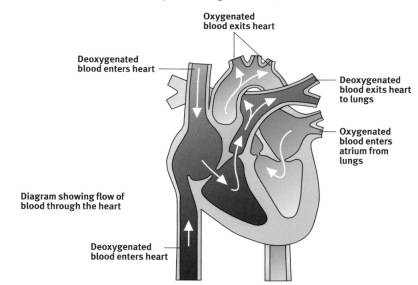

Oxygenated blood exits heart

Deoxygenated blood enters heart

Deoxygenated blood exits heart to lungs

Oxygenated blood enters atrium from lungs

Diagram showing flow of blood through the heart

Deoxygenated blood enters heart

WHAT IS CORONARY CIRCULATION?

The heart is, of course, a muscle which needs the benefits of circulation like every other muscle and organ in the body. It has its own circulatory system called coronary circulation. Right and left coronary arteries leave the beginning of the aorta and branch within the heart wall to form a network of capillaries to feed the tissue cells. The blood is then collected back into the coronary veins which empty into the right atrium of the heart.

YOU NOW KNOW

You now know how blood is pumped into and out of the heart. The following section explains how it travels from the heart around the body.

Section C: circulation in the body – systemic and portal

WHAT IS SYSTEMIC CIRCULATION?

Systemic circulation is the circulation of blood from the heart to the body. Blood leaves the heart by the aorta, the largest artery in the body, travels throughout the body and returns to the heart through the inferior and superior venae cavae (two of the largest veins). An extensive network of arteries, veins and capillaries transports blood to every cell in the body.

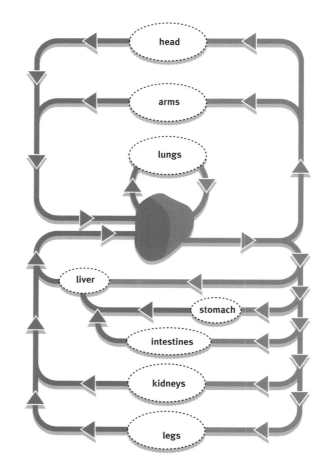

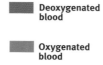

Deoxygenated blood

Oxygenated blood

WHAT IS PORTAL CIRCULATION?

The veins from the stomach, spleen, pancreas and intestines join to form the hepatic-portal vein which carries blood into the liver.

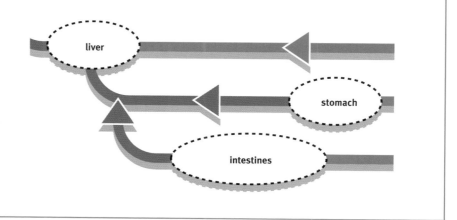

WHAT DO ARTERIES AND VEINS DO?

Arteries carry oxygenated blood from the heart and veins carry deoxygenated blood to the heart, except in the pulmonary system.

ARTERIES

Structure: arteries are thick-walled, hollow tubes. They all have the same basic construction:
- a fibrous outer covering
- a middle layer of muscle and elastic tissue
- an endothelial layer made of squamous epithelial tissue.

The quantity of muscle and elastic tissue in the middle layer depends on the size of the artery and its distance from the heart because arteries need to expand in order to propel blood along. Small arteries further from the heart have more muscle – to maintain blood pressure and keep the blood moving around the body, and less elastic tissue – because blood has been distributed to organs and so the flow has decreased and there is less stretching force placed on the vessels. The movement of the blood maintains potency (the openness of the vessel). Large arteries branch into small arteries which branch into arterioles which branch into capillaries.

Function: systemic arteries carry oxygenated blood from the heart to the body. The pulmonary artery carries deoxygenated blood to the lungs.

ARTERIOLES

Structure: arterioles are a smaller version of arteries. They have a similar structure, though the middle layer of the walls is mainly muscle tissue with less elastic tissue than arteries. Under normal conditions all the arterioles are slightly contracted which helps to maintain blood pressure.

Functions: when more oxygen and nutrients are required by an active organ, the arterioles relax and dilate to increase blood supply to it (e.g. muscles during exercise, the stomach and intestines after eating and the skin when the body temperature rises). They contract when an organ is at rest.

DID YOU KNOW?

During a 24-hour period an adult human heart pumps 36,000 litres of blood through 20,000 km of blood vessels.

General characteristics:
- the hormones adrenaline, noradrenaline and vasopressin (antidiuretic hormone) may cause the arterioles to contract
- in cases of shock, all the arterioles relax and blood pressure is very low. This is a dangerous condition.

CAPILLARIES

Structure: capillaries are the smallest blood vessels. Their walls are one cell thick (i.e. microscopic) and porous, thus allowing the passage of gases (like oxygen and carbon dioxide) and nutrients. A large amount of water, plus the solutions dissolved in it, filters out through the capillary walls and bathes the body tissues. This liquid is called interstitial fluid. It carries food, vitamins, mineral salts and hormones out to the tissues and collects waste products, especially carbon dioxide and urea, from them. Most of the fluid then returns to the capillaries before they join up to become venules.

Function: to distribute essential oxygen and nutrients to most parts of the body. Capillaries supply every part of the body except the deep brain, the hyaline cartilage and the epidermis.

VENULES

Structure: venules are small veins.
These have a thin wall with a large lumen (the passage in the centre in which the blood travels). They are easily collapsed under pressure.

Function: they carry deoxygenated blood from the capillaries to the larger veins.

DID YOU KNOW?

A bruise is caused by dead blood cells. When capillaries burst, the blood cells leak out into surrounding tissue and die off. The various colours in a bruise show the different stages of the cells' breakdown and finally the body gets rid of them and normal skin colour returns.

VEINS

Structure: veins have three-layered walls and though the basic structure is similar to that of arteries, their walls are much thinner and the lumen is much larger. They vary in size, the largest being the venae cavae (from the body into the heart) and the pulmonary vein (from the lungs to the heart). The action of skeletal muscles pushes blood through the vessels. Valves in the endothelial layer of the veins prevent a back flow of blood. Blood pressure in veins is very low so these valves are essential.

Function: systemic veins carry deoxygenated blood back to the heart. Pulmonary veins carry oxygenated blood to the heart.

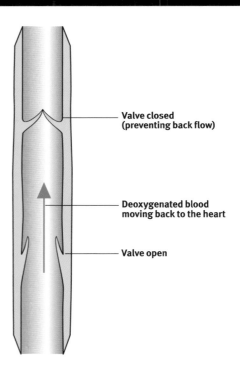

Valve closed
(preventing back flow)

Deoxygenated blood
moving back to the heart

Valve open

The table shows the different characteristics of arteries and veins

Characteristics of arteries	Characteristics of veins
Transport blood from heart	Transport blood to the heart
Oxygenated blood (not pulmonary)	Deoxygenated blood (not pulmonary)
Lumen (passage) is small	Lumen (passage) is large
Pumped by heart and muscle tissue in artery wall	Pumped by skeletal muscle pump and the presence of valves
Thick, muscular and elastic walls	Thin walls, not muscular or elastic
Oxygenated blood contains a high concentration of nutrients	Deoxygenated blood contains a high concentration of waste products

Main veins and arteries

The circulations begin at the heart. The inferior and superior venae cavae bring deoxygenated blood into the right atrium, the pulmonary veins bring oxygenated blood into the left atrium. The pulmonary arteries take blood to the lungs. The aorta, the main artery in the body, carries oxygenated blood to the body. It branches upwards to form the ascending aorta, which takes blood to the upper body (arms and head) and downwards, to form the descending aorta, taking blood to the rest of the body. Usually the names of veins correspond to the names of the arteries and they generally follow the same course, albeit in a different direction. When the blood reaches the various branches it is distributed through a network of arteries, arterioles and capillaries. The capillaries, the last vessels to distribute oxygenated blood, join the first vessels to collect deoxygenated blood, also called capillaries, which link up to form venules which feed into a network of veins taking the blood back to the heart where it travels to the lungs for reoxygenation.

YOU NOW KNOW

You now know what blood is, how it moves and where it goes. The following section shows the different parts of the body and the names of the main veins and arteries which feed each one.

TOPIC 3: MAIN ARTERIES AND VEINS OF THE BODY

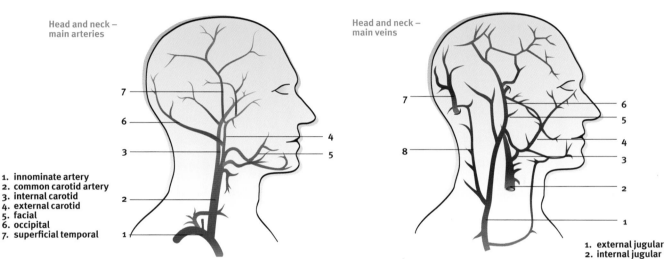

Head and neck – main arteries

1. innominate artery
2. common carotid artery
3. internal carotid
4. external carotid
5. facial
6. occipital
7. superficial temporal

Head and neck – main veins

1. external jugular
2. internal jugular
3. common facial
4. anterior facial
5. maxillary
6. superficial temporal
7. occipital
8. posterior external jugular

Trunk – main arteries and veins

1. descending aorta
2. inferior vena cava
3. heart
4. left common carotid artery
5. left subclavian artery
6. right common carotid artery
7. right subclavian artery
8. 2 pulmonary arteries
9. 2 pulmonary veins
10. right hepatic vein
11. right hepatic artery
12. splenic artery
13. splenic vein
14. right renal artery
15. right renal vein
16. superior mesenteric artery
17. right iliac artery
18. right iliac vein
19. inferior mesenteric artery
20. left iliac artery
21. left iliac vein

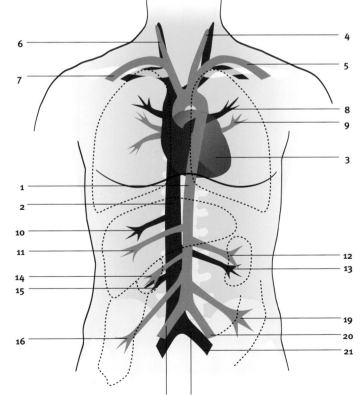

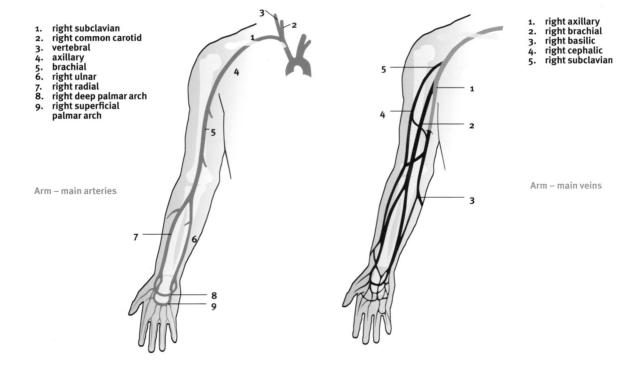

1. right subclavian
2. right common carotid
3. vertebral
4. axillary
5. brachial
6. right ulnar
7. right radial
8. right deep palmar arch
9. right superficial palmar arch

Arm – main arteries

1. right axillary
2. right brachial
3. right basilic
4. right cephalic
5. right subclavian

Arm – main veins

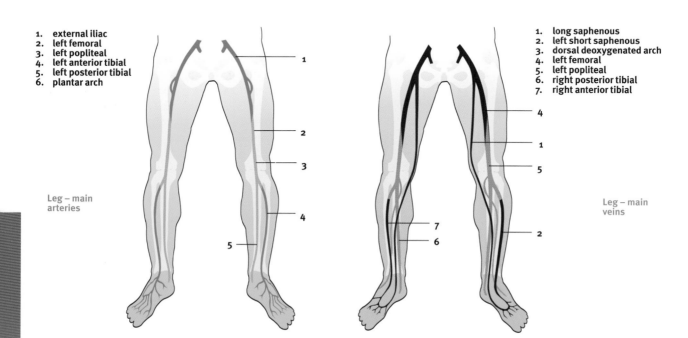

1. external iliac
2. left femoral
3. left popliteal
4. left anterior tibial
5. left posterior tibial
6. plantar arch

Leg – main arteries

1. long saphenous
2. left short saphenous
3. dorsal deoxygenated arch
4. left femoral
5. left popliteal
6. right posterior tibial
7. right anterior tibial

Leg – main veins

TOPIC 4:
BLOOD PRESSURE

If you have ever visited the doctor in the UK, you will probably have had your blood pressure checked. But what is it and how does it affect the circulation?

WHAT IS BLOOD PRESSURE?

The force that the blood exerts on the walls of the blood vessels as it is transmitted from the heart. Without pressure blood would not move at all. Blood is always under pressure but the amount of pressure varies in different types of blood vessels: high blood pressure in the arteries gradually becomes lower in the capillaries and veins. In the large veins approaching the heart there is negative pressure. The heartbeat also affects blood pressure: when the ventricle is contracting it is high, when the ventricle is dilating it is low.

WHAT FACTORS PRODUCE AND MAINTAIN PRESSURE?

- **cardiac output:** determined by the volume of blood pumped out of the heart and the heart rate. If cardiac output increases, blood pressure increases.
- **resistance offered by the arterioles:** vasoconstriction is controlled by the vasomotor nerves and by adrenaline and noradrenaline. The greater the vasoconstriction the higher the blood pressure.
- **total blood volume:** if the amount of circulating blood is reduced, blood pressure is lowered; if there is too much retention of fluid (oedema), blood pressure is raised.
- **viscosity of blood:** this depends partly on the plasma, especially the amount of plasma proteins and also on the number of erythrocytes. The lower the viscosity, the lower the blood pressure.
- **elasticity of artery walls:** if the arteries harden there is a loss of elasticity and pressure is raised. If the arteries soften, there is lower pressure.

Blood pressure is given as two readings:
- **systolic:** when the heart is contracting pressure reaches its peak level
- **diastolic:** when the heart is relaxing (dilating) pressure reaches its lowest level.

A blood pressure reading of 100/70 means that systolic pressure is 100mmHg and diastolic pressure is 70mmHg.

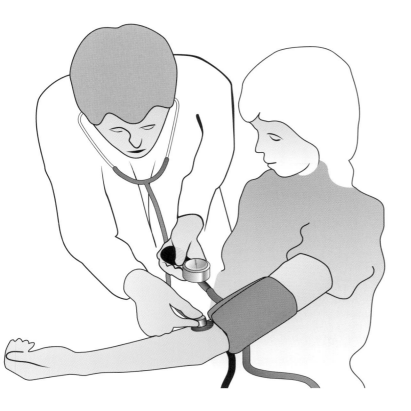

HOW ARE THEY MEASURED?

Blood pressure is measured with a sphygmomanometer. The patient's upper arm is encircled by an inflatable rubber bag contained in a cuff connected to a pressure pump and manometer. By pumping up the bag, the pressure can be raised to approximately 140+mm of mercury pressure (Hg) which is sufficient to constrict the brachial artery so no blood can pass through and the radial pulse disappears. The pressure is then lowered to a point where the pulse can be felt. At this point the pressure shown on the column of mercury is considered to be the systolic pressure. The diastolic pressure reading is taken when the sound of the pulse fades.

CAUSES AND EFFECTS OF HIGH AND LOW BLOOD PRESSURE

Hypertension (high blood pressure)

Causes: stress, medication, kidney disease, narrowing or hardening of the arteries, smoking, alcohol, diet and hereditary factors.
Effects: angina, heart attack, strokes, kidney complaints.

HYPOTENSION (LOW BLOOD PRESSURE)

Causes: underactive adrenal glands, hereditary factors; shock may cause short term hypotension.
Effects: dizziness; fainting.

● DID YOU KNOW?

How do you remember which is low and which is high blood pressure? Think of the 'o': l-o-w is hyp-o.

TOPIC 5:
BLOOD CLOTTING

HOW DOES BLOOD CLOT?

If a blood vessel (a capillary, vein or artery) is damaged (internally or externally) bleeding occurs until a clot forms. This clot stops excessive loss of blood from the system. If no blood clot forms it is called a haemorrhage. The following diagram shows the four stages of clot formation.

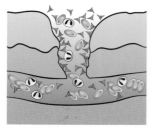 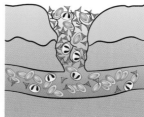 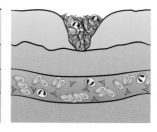 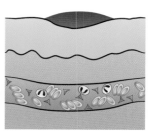

1. Thrombocytes (platelets) are easily damaged and if a blood vessel wall is broken they disintegrate and release an enzyme called thromboplastin.

2. Thromboplastin then converts a plasma protein called prothrombin into an active enzyme called thrombin. Calcium is needed for this process to work.
(Thus thromboplastin + calcium + prothrombin = thrombin).

3. Thrombin then changes another plasma protein, fibrinogen into fibrin. Fibrin is insoluble and forms a net-like covering across the damaged vessel.
(Thus thrombin + fibrinogen = fibrin).

4. As blood tries to flow through the net, the red and white cells and platelets are trapped and form a clot. The additional fluid that remains is known as serum.
(Thus fibrin + blood cells = clot).

The following are necessary for a clot to form:

- prothrombin
- calcium
- thromboplastin (produced by damaged platelets)
- fibrin
- vitamin K (necessary for formation of prothrombin)

Blood clotting can be affected by:

- a deficiency of platelets as in severe bone marrow diseases
- lack of one of the necessary components listed opposite (causing diseases such as haemophilia)
- an absence of fibrinogen
- lack of Vitamin K which is necessary for the production of prothrombin
- lack of calcium
- an excess of fibrinogen in the blood can cause thrombosis (internal and potentially dangerous blood clots).

The Rhesus factor gets its name from the Rhesus monkey which was used in Landsteiner's experiments with blood.

Finally, blood types. All human blood is the same in terms of composition and function. But four different types exist, the discovery of which made blood transfusions much more successful.

WHAT ARE BLOOD TYPES?

In 1902 an Austrian physician named Karl Landsteiner began studying why some patients died as a result of blood transfusions. He discovered the existence of different human blood types and subsequently classified them as four groups: A, B, AB and O.

Type O is known as the universal donor because type O blood can be given to patients with any blood group whereas type AB is known as the universal recipient: patients with type AB blood can receive blood from any blood group. The table shows which group is compatible with which.

Type	Can give to	Can receive from
O	Any blood group	O
AB	AB	Any blood group
A	A and AB	A and O
B	B and AB	B and O

WHAT IS THE RHESUS FACTOR?

The Rhesus factor (abbreviated as Rh) is an antigen found in the red blood cells of most people and animals. Blood that is described as rhesus positive contains this antigen, whereas rhesus negative blood does not.

The cultural and historical significance of blood

The use of the word 'blood' in the English language shows that, historically, the circulation has had a moral and social importance beyond its biological necessity, signifying family, connection and emotion. 'Blood is thicker than water' means that family duties and connections are stronger than any others. 'Blood money' refers to the compensation paid to the relatives of a murder victim in an attempt to stop them seeking revenge. If you have 'bad blood' you are likely to feel unwell and friends or relatives with 'bad blood' between them do not like each other. The term 'blue blood' comes from the Spanish sangre azul, which was used to describe aristocrats of 'purer' ancestry than those with 'mixed' blood. It is still used today to refer to the nobility and aristocracy.

Since blood has such a strong link to family and emotions it is no surprise that 'cold-blooded' means lacking feeling and 'making one's blood boil' means causing anger.

TOPIC 6: DISEASES AND DISORDERS (PATHOLOGIES)

VARICOSE VEINS

Deoxygenated blood in the lower body has to move uphill in order to return to the heart. Valves prevent the blood flowing backwards but sometimes these valves, especially those in the superficial veins of the legs, no longer work effectively.

Consequently the veins become dilated and blood collects in the veins instead of returning to the heart. The veins become distended and knobbly, showing through the skin.

Varicose veins are often caused by:
■ heredity
■ excessive periods of sitting and standing
■ pregnancy
■ obesity.

ANAEMIA

Anaemia is a reduction in the blood's ability to carry oxygen, caused either by a decrease in red blood cells, or the haemoglobin they carry, or both. It may be caused by extensive loss of blood, lack of iron in the diet, the failure of bone marrow to produce the normal level of cells or it may be inherited.

LEUKAEMIA

Leukaemia is a cancer of the blood, caused by over-production of white blood cells.

SEPTICAEMIA

Also known as blood poisoning, this is a generalised disease associated with the circulation and multiplication of toxic bacteria in the blood.

HAEMOPHILIA

The blood's inability to clot. This is an inherited disease which affects mainly men but which can be carried by women.

ARTERIOSCLEROSIS

A degenerative disease of the arteries, in which the walls of the vessels harden and lose elasticity. The loss of elasticity causes an increase in blood pressure. This condition mainly affects the elderly.

ATHEROSCLEROSIS/ATHEROMA

A build-up of fats, including cholesterol, inside the arteries which causes a narrowing of the artery passage, hardening of the vessel walls and a loss of elasticity.

BLUE BABY

A baby born with a congenital heart abnormality.

HAEMORRHOIDS

Also known as piles, these are enlarged veins in the rectum or anus which may collapse or contain blood clots.

PHLEBITIS

Inflammation of a vein. Thrombo-phlebitis is the inflammation of a vein where a blood clot has formed.

THROMBUS

A blood clot in the heart or in the blood vessels.

HIV/AIDS

Acquired Immune Deficiency Syndrome (AIDS) is a complex disease that follows infection with the Human Immuno-deficiency Virus (HIV). The virus attacks T-lymphocytes, making the immune system incapable of fighting disease. It is transmitted through blood and other body fluids.

HIGH BLOOD PRESSURE
Also known as hypertension, this is blood pressure which consistently remains above the normal level.

LOW BLOOD PRESSURE
Also known as hypotension, this is blood pressure which consistently remains below the normal level.

HIGH CHOLESTEROL
High cholesterol is an excessive build-up of a fatty substance called cholesterol, which can cause a reduction in arterial capacity (atherosclerosis – see previous page) and thus high blood pressure.

HEPATITIS A B C
Inflammations of the liver, caused by viruses, toxic substances or immunological abnormalities. Type A is spread by fecally contaminated food. Types B and C are transmitted by infected body fluids including blood. Contagious.

CORONARY THROMBOSIS
A blood clot in the coronary artery.

STRESS
Stress can be defined as any factor which affects mental or physical health. When a person is stressed, the heart beats faster, thus pumping blood more quickly. Excessive and unresolved stress can lead to high blood pressure, coronary thrombosis and heart attacks.

ANGINA
A heart condition characterized by chest pain due to reduced oxygen to the heart.

ANEURYSM
A cardiovascular disease characterized by a sac-like widening of an artery resulting from weakening of the artery wall.

HAEMATOMA
A localized swelling filled with blood.
DVT (deep vein thrombosis)
Is the formation of a blood clot ("thrombus") in a deep vein.

CARDIAC ARRHYTHMIA
Is a term for any of a large group of conditions in which there is abnormal electrical activity in the heart. The heart beat may be too fast or too slow, and may be regular or irregular.

TACHYCARDIA
An abnormally rapid heartbeat (over 100 beats per minute).

BRADYCARDIA
An abnormally slow heartbeat.

CARDIAC FAILURE
Is a condition in which a problem with the structure or function of the heart impairs its ability to supply sufficient blood flow to meet the body's needs.

EPISTAXIS (NOSE BLEEDS)
Is the relatively common occurrence of hemorrhage from the nose, usually noticed when the blood drains out through the nostrils.

GANGRENE
Is a complication of cell death characterized by the decay of body tissues, which become black (and/or green) and malodorous.

HOLE IN THE HEART (SEPTAL DEFECTS)
Are small holes in the septa between the atria and ventricles.

INTERMITTENT CLAUDICATION
Is lameness due to pain in leg muscles because the blood supply is inadequate; pain subsides with rest.

MYOCARDIAL INFARCTION
The destruction of heart tissue resulting from obstruction of the blood supply to the heart muscle.

PALPITATIONS
Is an abnormal awareness of the beating of the heart, whether it is too slow, too fast, irregular, or at its normal frequency.

PULMONARY EMBOLISM
Is a blockage of the pulmonary artery by foreign matter or by a blood clot.

RAYNAUD'S DISEASE

Is a vascular disorder that affects blood flow to the extremities (the fingers, toes, nose and ears) when exposed to cold temperatures or in response to psychological stress.

SICKLE CELL ANAEMIA

A congenital form of anaemia occurring mostly in people with black skin; characterized by abnormal blood cells having a crescent shape.

THALASSEMIA

An hereditary anaemia resulting from reduced production of either alpha or beta haemoglobin. Depending on the type, the condition can be fatal before or just after birth, or can result in varying levels of anaemia and development difficulties.

VARICOSE ULCERS

A chronic ulceration above the ankles due to varicose veins which interfere with the normal blood circulation in the affected areas.

INTERRELATIONSHIPS

Circulatory system links to:

Respiratory: carries oxygen to every cell and system of the body (internal respiration); removes waste gas from the body through diffusion between capillary/alveoli (external respiration).

Lymphatic: linked to the lymphatic system at tissue level – the circulatory system transports some waste products away from the tissues (mainly carbon dioxide) and any additional waste products are carried away by the lymphatic system. The circulatory and lymphatic systems also work together to protect the body (immunity). The lymphatic system empties back into the blood system.

Endocrine: hormones carried in blood to various target organs

Digestive: nutrients broken down in the digestive process are transported by blood from the small intestines to the liver then around the body

Muscular: blood transports glucose for energy conversion to the muscles.

Urinary: blood passes through the kidneys for purification of toxins

Skeletal: erythrocytes and leucocytes are manufactured in the bone marrow of long bones

Skin: circulation transports oxygen and nutrition to skin, hair and nails.

Summary

The cardiovascular system:

- Blood is the body's fuel, delivered by the circulatory system: it carries nutrients and oxygen to the body and collects waste and carbon dioxide from it
- The heart is the circulatory system's engine: it pumps blood around the body
- Arteries and veins are the circulatory system's pipes: they transport oxygenated blood from the heart (except the pulmonary artery) and deoxygenated blood to the heart (except the pulmonary vein).

The Lymphatic system

system

A circulatory system as complicated as that of the blood requires support.
In the human body this is provided by the lymphatic system.

The Lymphatic system

The lymphatic system is a subsidiary circulation entwined with the blood circulation. It provides a channel through which excess tissue fluid is returned to the bloodstream.

LEARNING OBJECTIVES
The target knowledge of this chapter is:

- the structure of the lymphatic system
- the function of the lymphatic system
- the position of the main lymph nodes and ducts in the body
- the connection between blood and lymph.

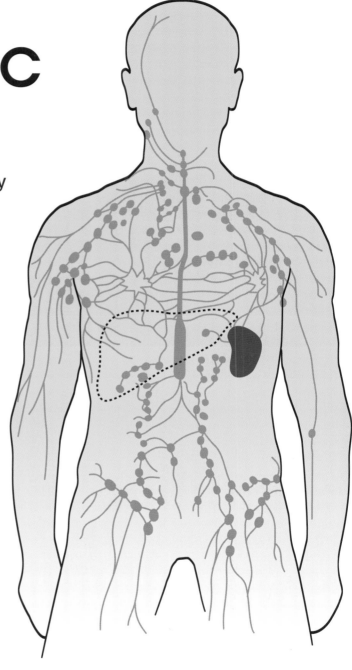

Overview of the lymphatic system showing lymph nodes and spleen

TOPIC 1: STRUCTURE AND FUNCTION

WHAT IS THE LYMPHATIC SYSTEM?

In order to understand the lymphatic system it is necessary to understand what happens in the circulatory system at tissue level. Blood travels to and from the tissues delivering nutrients and removing waste. Whole blood never leaves the capillaries but leucocytes and the 'passengers' (oxygen, food and water) can. Once outside the capillaries they are carried by a derivative of blood plasma called tissue, or interstitial, fluid. This fluid circulates throughout the tissues, delivering food, oxygen and water to the cells and collecting carbon dioxide and other waste. However, when it has finished its work and needs to return to the capillaries, not all of it can pass through the capillary walls because the pressure inside the capillaries is too high. The fluid that is left is picked up by a different set of capillaries, called the lymphatic capillaries. They have larger pores in their walls than blood capillaries and the pressure inside them is lower. Thus, excess tissue fluid, substances made of large molecules, fragments of damaged cells and foreign matter such as micro-organisms drain away into them. The fluid, known as lymph, is filtered by the lymph nodes then collected by the lymphatic ducts before entering the right and left subclavian veins and returning to the bloodstream.

WHAT IS THE STRUCTURE OF THE LYMPHATIC SYSTEM?

The lymphatic system consists of lymphatic capillaries, lymphatic vessels, lymph nodes and lymphatic ducts. The fluid in lymphatic capillaries and vessels is called lymph.

WHAT DOES IT DISTRIBUTE AND COLLECT?

Lymph, a fluid similar to blood plasma.

Structure: contains waste materials as well as leucocytes and lymphocytes (in order to ingest bacteria and cell debris) but no erythrocytes.

Function: transports excess waste (that blood cannot carry) away from tissues; adds extra leucocytes and lymphocytes to the blood.

HOW DOES LYMPH MOVE?

Several factors help to circulate lymph –
■ the contraction of skeletal muscles collapses the vessels and because there are valves present, lymph is directed towards the upper part of the body
■ a slight oncoming pressure from the tissue fluids
■ movement of the lymph towards the thorax during inspiration

Lymph collects in ducts before emptying into the right and left subclavian veins and rejoining circulation

Lymph nodes filter tissue fluid (lymph)

Lymphatic capillaries collect excess tissue fluid

Heart

Blood leaves heart in arteries and travels to tissues

Blood returns to heart in veins

Tissue

lymph circuit (simplified)

- suction: negative pressure helps to pull the lymph upwards into the lymphatic ducts, where lymph collects before being recirculated. These ducts empty into the subclavian veins which, because they are close to the heart, have negative pressure in them. This pressure pulls on the ducts and thus on the lymph vessels connected to them.

Any obstruction of the lymphatic flow results in oedema, the swelling of tissues due to the collection of excess fluid.

WHAT ARE LYMPHATIC CAPILLARIES?
The vessels which work with blood to collect excess tissue fluid. Lymphatic capillaries eventually unite to form lymphatic vessels.

Structure: fine, blind-ended permeable tubes, composed of a single layer of endothelial cells. They occur in all spaces between tissues, except in the central nervous system.

Function: carry excess tissue fluid away from tissue space.

WHAT ARE LYMPHATIC VESSELS?
These are vessels which transport lymph around the lymphatic system.

Structure: thin-walled, collapsible vessels similar to veins but carrying lymph not venous blood. They have valves (semi-lunar) to keep the lymph moving centripetally (in the direction of the heart) and prevent back flow. Consisting of a double layer of lining membrane, these valves give the vessels a knotted or beaded appearance. They have three layers:
- an outer layer of fibrous tissue
- a middle layer of muscular and elastic tissue
- an inner layer of endothelial cells.

Function: lymphatic vessels collect lymph from the lymphatic capillaries and then convey lymph towards the heart. Many lymph vessels run into the subcutaneous tissue (beneath the dermis) and all the lymphatic vessels pass through one or more lymphatic nodes.

WHAT IS THE CONNECTION BETWEEN BLOOD AND LYMPH?
The lymphatic system is a subsidiary circulation, helping the blood circulation to carry out its functions. It removes excess fluid from tissues and carries large particles that cannot pass through the smaller pores of the blood capillaries. Lymph nodes and the spleen filter lymph (the name of the fluid in the lymphatic system) and take out the waste materials it contains as well as producing antibodies and lymphocytes which are added to the lymph to be transported to the blood.

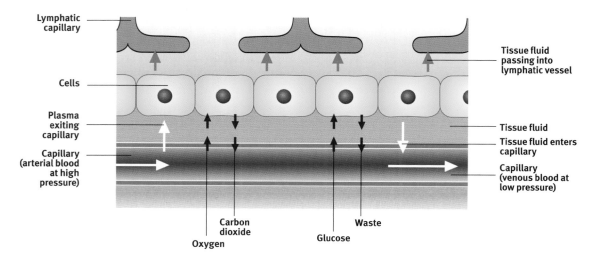

WHAT ARE LYMPH NODES?

All the small and medium-sized lymph vessels open into lymph nodes, which are strategically placed throughout the body. An afferent vessel transports lymph to the node and an efferent vessel transports the filtered lymph back to the system.

Structure: each node is made of lymphatic tissue, surrounded by a wall of tough, white fibrous tissue supported by inward strands of fibrous tissue called trabeculae. Lymph nodes vary in size.

Functions:

- to filter the lymph, remove and destroy harmful micro-organisms, tumour cells, damaged or dead tissue cells, large protein molecules and toxic substances. This filtering system prevents toxic materials from reaching the bloodstream and causing septicaemia. If this occurs, it can

● USEFUL TIP

Think of lymph Arriving and Exiting the nodes in order to remember which is an Afferent and which is an Efferent vessel.

cause the node to swell. In severe cases, this may cause cell destruction and an abscess on the node.

- to produce new lymphocytes and antibodies and add them to the lymph as necessary.
- lymphatic tissue cells within the node may become activated to form antibodies against a particular infection. They may then continue to form antibodies for several years or even a lifetime.

WHAT IS LYMPHATIC TISSUE?

Lymph nodes are made of lymphatic tissue. This contains many types of cells:

- phagocytes – white blood cells that engulf and destroy harmful (pathogenic) waste and bacteria
- lymphocytes – white blood cells that produce antibodies
- cells dividing to form new lymphocytes.

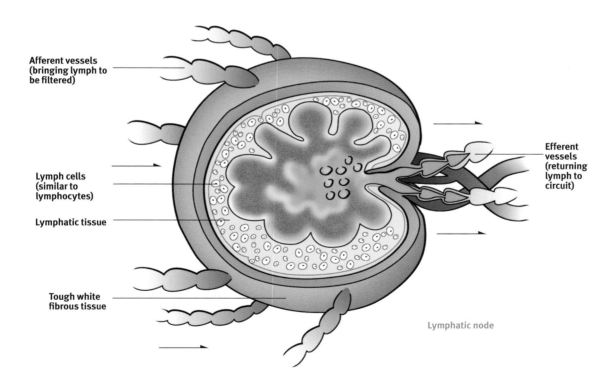

Afferent vessels (bringing lymph to be filtered)

Lymph cells (similar to lymphocytes)

Lymphatic tissue

Tough white fibrous tissue

Efferent vessels (returning lymph to circuit)

Lymphatic node

WHAT ARE LYMPHATIC DUCTS?
(shown by numbers 1-2 on the diagram)
All lymph passes into two main lymphatic vessels,
or ducts:

1. The right lymphatic duct
This is only 1.5cm long, positioned at the root of
the neck and empties into the right subclavian vein
to rejoin the circulatory system.
Function: receives all the drained lymph from the
right side of the head, chest and neck and from the
right arm.

2. The thoracic duct
This is the largest lymphatic vessel. It is 40cm long
extending from the second lumbar vertebra to the
root of the neck and empties into the subclavian
vein to rejoin the circulatory system.
Function: collects and drains lymph from the left
side of the head, the neck, both lower limbs, the
left side of the trunk and the left arm.Spleen
    The spleen is an organ which both produces
and destroys cells. It is a non-essential organ
and is sometimes removed due to damage after
accidents, as other organs can perform the same
functions. The spleen lies on the upper left-hand
side of the abdomen.

SPECIAL AREAS CONTAINING LYMPHATIC TISSUE
(shown by numbers 3-7 on the diagram)
3. tonsils
4. thymus gland
   (behind sternum)
5. Peyer's patches
   (wall of small intestine)
6. appendix
7. spleen

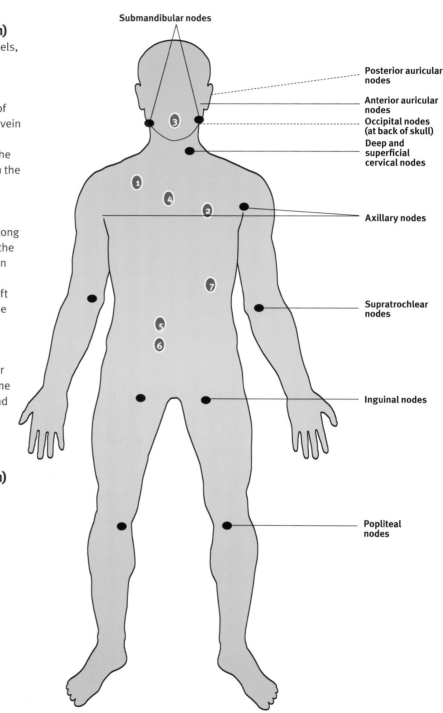

Submandibular nodes

Posterior auricular nodes

Anterior auricular nodes

Occipital nodes (at back of skull)

Deep and superficial cervical nodes

Axillary nodes

Supratrochlear nodes

Inguinal nodes

Popliteal nodes

SPLEEN

The spleen is an organ which both produces and destroys cells. It is a non-essential organ and is sometimes removed due to damage after accidents, as other organs can perform the same functions. The spleen lies on the upper left-hand side of the abdomen.

The spleen

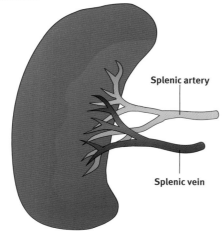

Splenic artery

Splenic vein

Structure: the spleen has an outer capsule of fibrous tissue extending into a network of fibrous strands called trabeculae. This network supports the splenic pulp which consists of several different types of cells.

Functions:
- forms new lymphocytes
- destroys thrombocytes and erythrocytes
- helps to remove foreign particles from the circulation
- helps to fight infection, becoming enlarged in certain diseases, e.g. malaria and typhoid fever
- acts as a blood reservoir. Blood sinuses within the spleen normally hold a large amount of blood which is pushed into general circulation if the spleen contracts. Contraction usually occurs two or three times a minute, but in cases of shock or even during exercise, the spleen may contract faster and for a longer period to help maintain pressure in the circulation.

TOPIC 2: DISEASES AND DISORDERS (PATHOLOGIES)

OEDEMA/WATER RETENTION
Swelling due to excess fluid in the tissue spaces and serous cavities

LYMPHOEDEMA
Oedema associated with an obstruction in the lymphatic vessels

HODGKIN'S DISEASE
Cancer of the lymphatic tissue.

CELLULITE
Lumpy deposits of body fat especially on women's thighs.

INFECTIOUS MONONUCLEOSIS (GLANDULAR FEVER)
An acute disease characterized by fever and swollen lymph nodes and an abnormal increase of mononuclear leucocytes or monocytes in the bloodstream; not highly contagious;

LYMPHADENITIS
The inflammation of lymph nodes.

NON-HODGKIN LYMPHOMA
A type of lymphoma, a cancer in the lymphatic system; causes the cells in the lymphatic system to abnormally reproduce, eventually causing tumours to grow.

HASHIMOTO'S THYROIDITIS (CHRONIC LYMPHOCYTIC THYROIDITIS)
is an autoimmune disease where the body's own T-cells attack the cells of the thyroid.

LYMPHOMA
Is a type of cancer that originates in lymphocytes of the immune system. They often originate in lymph nodes, presenting as an enlargement of the node (a tumour).

SYSTEMIC LUPUS ERYTHEMATOSUS
An inflammatory disease of connective tissue with variable features including fever, weakness, joint pains and skin lesions on the face, neck or arms.

INTERRELATIONSHIPS
Lymphatic system links to:
Circulatory: transports excess waste and toxins, which the circulatory system cannot cope with, away from the cells and tissues. Also works closely with the circulatory system to strengthen the body's immunity.
Digestive: lymphatic vessels in the small intestines (inside the lacteal of the ileum) help with the absorption of fats during digestion. These are then transported around the body in the circulatory system and distributed to cells to be used as energy.
Muscular: lactic acid formed when over-exercising muscles, or from tension and general fatigue in the muscular system, is drained away in the lymphatic system.

Summary
The lymphatic system:
- Provides a channel for transporting excess tissue fluid away from tissues and back to the blood circulation.
- Collects and transports lymph from tissue cells.
- Nodes filter lymph of harmful materials before returning it to the blood circulation.
- Produces new lymphocytes.
- Produces antibodies.
- Lymphatic capillaries in the lining of the small intestine assist in the absorption of fat droplets.

07

The Nervous system

The nervous system is a communication and instruction network.
It is composed of the brain, spinal cord and nerves.

The Nervous system

The nervous system is the control and communication centre of the body. There are two parts: the central nervous system and the peripheral nervous system. The brain is the main unit and it is connected to the rest of the body by nerve cells which function as messengers, carrying information to, and instructions from the brain. They report back on pain, sensation and danger so that the body can respond and remain in what is known as homeostasis: a stable, physiological state.

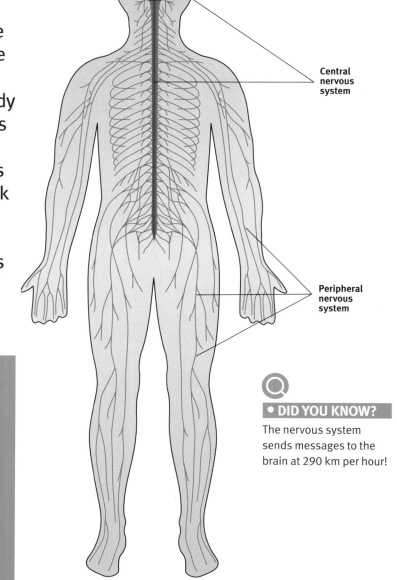

Central nervous system

Peripheral nervous system

LEARNING OBJECTIVES
The target knowledge of this chapter is:
- the structure and function of the central nervous system
- the structure and function of the peripheral nervous system
- the structure and function of the somatic and autonomic nervous systems
- what reflexes are
- diseases and disorders of the nervous system.

● DID YOU KNOW?
The nervous system sends messages to the brain at 290 km per hour!

TOPIC 1: STRUCTURE

WHAT IS THE NERVOUS SYSTEM MADE OF?

Nervous tissue which is composed of:

- nerve cells, known as neurones, with attached fibres which transmit nerve impulses
- neuroglia, a connective tissue which supports the neurones; though only found in the nervous system, neuroglia does not transmit nerve impulses.

WHAT IS A NERVE CELL?

Nerve cells are the basic unit of the system on which everything else is built. Like all cells, they have a membrane containing a nucleus and a cytoplasm but they have a particular shape: long and narrow. Some are very long (up to a metre). Nerve cells are easily damaged by toxins and lack of oxygen. Unlike other cells in the body, they are not usually replaced when they die, however, current research suggests that some may have the ability to regenerate. The main parts of a nerve cell are:

- **cell body:** the centre of the neurone, with a nucleus, cytoplasm and organelles such as mitochondria
- **dendrites:** nerve fibres, like branches, which transmit nerve impulses to the cell body; most neurones have several dendrites
- **axon:** a long single nerve fibre, which transmits nerve impulses away from the cell body; neurones generally have only one axon
- **myelin sheath:** made of a white, fatty substance, this sheath covers the axon. It insulates the axon, protects it from pressure and helps speed up nerve conduction (the speed at which messages are transmitted)
- **neurilemma:** a fine, delicate membrane which surrounds the myelin sheath and helps regenerate nerve cells; only found in peripheral nerves and not in the brain or spinal cord
- **nodes of Ranvier:** these are gaps in the myelin sheath along the nerve. They speed up the passage of nerve impulses along the fibre
- **end feet/axon terminals:** the ends of the fibrils (tiny fibres) that make the axon are expanded and called end feet or axon terminals. They pass on the axon impulse to the dendrites of the next neurone
- **synapse:** the point where one neurone meets another. A chemical messenger fills the gap between one neurone and the next, and enables the impulse to be transmitted

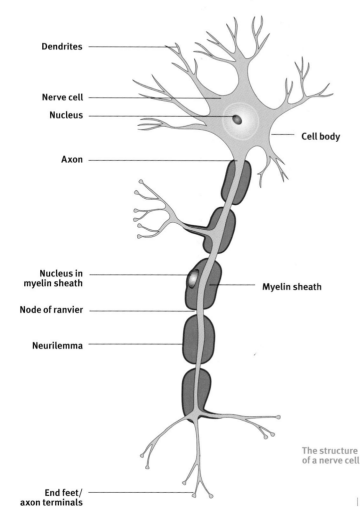

Dendrites

Nerve cell

Nucleus

Axon

Cell body

Nucleus in myelin sheath

Myelin sheath

Node of ranvier

Neurilemma

End feet/ axon terminals

The structure of a nerve cell

TOPIC 2: FUNCTION

WHAT DOES A NERVE CELL DO?

Nerve cells act as links in a chain, like relay runners, each one passing the 'baton' (information or instruction) to the next until it reaches the brain or the part of the body in question. The axon end feet of one cell are close to the dendrites of the next but they don't actually touch. The 'baton' of nerve impulses jumps across the gap via neurotransmitters, chemicals released by the nerve endings.

COLLECTIVE FUNCTION

Individual neurones have the same function throughout the body, to transmit information, but collectively they make up five different types of nerves and nervous tissue which have specific functions:

- **motor or efferent nerves:** carry impulses from the brain or spinal cord to muscles or glands which then act on the information/ instruction, producing movement or a secretion.
- **sensory or afferent nerves:** carry impulses from all parts of the body to the brain.
- **mixed:** carry both motor and sensory nerve fibres. The only place mixed nerves are found in the body is in the brain and spinal cord as cranial and spinal nerves.
- **white matter:** on the inside of the brain and the outside of the spinal cord; this is made of bundles of myelinated nerve fibres (i.e. with a sheath).
- **grey matter:** on the outside of the brain and inside of the spinal cord – this is made of cell bodies and unmyelinated axons and dendrites.

WHAT IS A NERVE IMPULSE?

Nerve cells transmit and receive impulses throughout the body. Impulses do not continually run along each nerve but are created in response to internal or external stimuli - including changes in temperature, pressure or chemicals.

Positively charged sodium and potassium ions are present inside and outside the cell. In a resting axon, the concentration of sodium ions is lower inside the cell than in the tissue fluid outside, but the concentration of potassium ions is higher inside than outside. This is maintained by differences in membrane permeability to these ions, and the sodium-potassium pump. The overall result is that the inside of the cell has a more negative charge than the outside.

Stimuli are detected by sensory receptors. The axon membrane becomes temporarily more permeable to sodium ions which rush in, making the inside of the cell more positive (depolarisation). This electrochemical charge continues in waves along the length of the nerve cell – a nerve impulse. After it has passed the resting state is restored (repolarisation)

• USEFUL TIP

How do you remember which are afferent and which are efferent nerves? Efferent exit the brain, afferent arrive in the brain.

HOW DO NERVE CELLS COMMUNICATE

Nerve impulses only travel in one direction. So the movement of nerve impulses in a single neurone is as follows: the impulse crosses the synapse from the end feet of cell A into the dendrites of cell B. The impulse travels from the dendrites to the cell body and then out again along the axon to cell B's end feet. It then jumps across the synapse, helped by the chemical messengers. This process continues until the impulse reaches either the brain or the muscle/organ concerned.

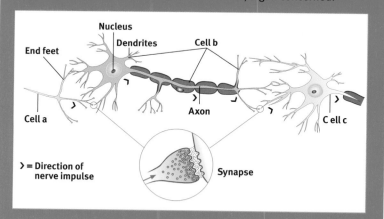

Nucleus
Dendrites
Cell b
End feet
Cell a
Axon
C ell c
> = Direction of nerve impulse
Synapse

YOU NOW KNOW

You now know the structure and function of nerve cells and what a nerve impulse is. The next section explains different systems formed by nerve cells.

TOPIC 3: DIVISIONS OF THE NERVOUS SYSTEM

The nervous system is divided into two main parts – the Central Nervous System (CNS) and the Peripheral Nervous System (PNS). The PNS acts as the lines of communication between the CNS and the rest of the body, and is further subdivided into the Somatic and Autonomic nervous systems.
The CNS is composed of the brain and the Spinal Cord.

TOPIC 3:
THE CENTRAL NERVOUS SYSTEM

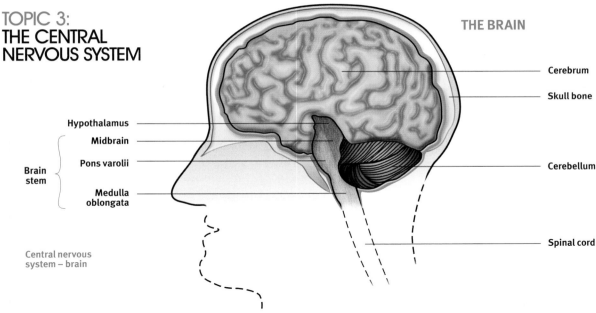

THE BRAIN

Hypothalamus
Midbrain
Pons varolii
Brain stem
Medulla oblongata

Central nervous system – brain

Cerebrum
Skull bone
Cerebellum
Spinal cord

The brain
The brain is the organ that fills the cranium (skull). It stops developing in
the 15th year of life. It is the main mass exercising control over the body and mind and it has three different sections:
- the cerebrum (also known as cerebral hemispheres)
- the cerebellum
- the brain stem.

The cerebrum
Structure: this is the largest part of the brain and is divided into two cerebral hemispheres, one on the

right and one on the left. The outer layer is made of folds of grey matter (i.e. cell bodies).
The folds increase the brain's surface area and thus the number of cell bodies. Inside the grey matter is white matter (i.e. nerve fibres). These fibres connect different parts of the brain together.

Functions:
- controlling voluntary movement (i.e. the movements we choose to make)
- interpreting and perceiving conscious sensations like pain, heat and cold
- controlling mental activity, like memory, intelligence and reasoning.

The cerebellum

Structure: the cerebellum is also known as the 'small brain'. Positioned in the posterior cranial fossa, behind the pons Varolii, below the cerebrum and over the medulla oblongata, it also consists of two hemispheres, grey matter on the surface and white matter within.

Functions:

- co-ordinating muscular activity, making sure movements are smooth and precise (damage to the cerebellum results in clumsy, uncoordinated movements).
- subconsciously controlling and maintaining muscle tone and posture.
- maintaining balance and equilibrium of body.

Hypothalamus

Structure: situated deep within the cerebrum at the top of the brainstem with the pituitary gland attached to its base.

Function: helps with the regulation of body temperature, water balance and metabolism. Centre for drives and emotions such as thirst, appetite, sex, pain and pleasure. It also regulates the pituitary gland thereby forming the main link between the nervous and endocrine systems. It secretes oxytocin and Antidiuretic Hormone (ADH) for storage in the posterior pituitary.

The brain stem

The brain stem consists of three parts, the midbrain, pons Varolii and the medulla oblongata.

Midbrain

Structure: lies between cerebrum and cerebellum and above the pons Varolii.
It is about 2cm long and consists of nerve cells and fibres.

Function: the relay station of the brain, transmitting messages to and from the spinal cord, the cerebrum and the cerebellum.

Pons Varolii

Structure: situated in front of the cerebellum, below the midbrain and above the medulla oblongata. It consists of nerve fibres, which bridge (hence pons, which means bridge in Latin) the gap between the two hemispheres of the cerebellum.

Function: like the midbrain, transmits messages to and from the spinal cord and cerebrum.

Medulla oblongata

Structure: lowest part of the brain stem, situated above the spinal cord and below the pons Varolii. Its construction is different from the cerebrum and cerebellum with white matter on the surface and grey matter in the centre. It is known as a vital centre because it controls the actions of the heart and lungs (respectively the centres of the vascular and respiratory systems). It has four centres.

Functions:

- **cardiac centre:** controls rate and force of heart contraction
- **respiratory centre:** controls rate and depth of breathing
- **vasomotor centre:** controls constriction and dilation of blood vessels
- **reflex centre:** responds to irritants thus controls vomiting, coughing, sneezing and swallowing.

THE SPINAL CORD

The spinal cord is the other main part of the central nervous system.

Structure: the spinal cord extends from the medulla oblongata through the spinal vertebrae ending at the first lumbar vertebra. It consists of white matter on the surface and grey matter inside branching off into 31 pairs of spinal nerves and part of one cranial nerve.

Function: the spinal cord carries motor and sensory nerve fibres along its length, sending messages to and from the body and brain.

TOPIC 3: OTHER IMPORTANT PARTS OF THE CENTRAL NERVOUS SYSTEM

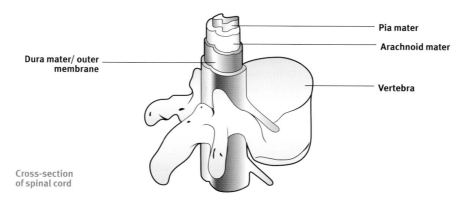

Dura mater/ outer
membrane

Pia mater

Arachnoid mater

Vertebra

Cross-section
of spinal cord

The meninges

The meninges are membranes which protect the whole of the central nervous system. There are three different layers –

- **dura mater, or outer membrane:**
  a double layer of tough, fibrous membrane: the outer layer forms the periosteum ('skin') of the skull while the inner layer, the first protective covering of the brain, continues as the spinal dura mater as far down as the sacrum.

- **arachnoid mater:** a delicate membrane positioned immediately under the dura and above the pia mater. It merges with the dura mater and thus covers the spinal cord as far as the sacrum. It connects to the sub-arachnoid space, situated between the arachnoid mater and the pia mater and is filled with cerebrospinal fluid (see below).

- **pia mater:** a thin, vascular membrane which closely covers the brain, dipping into the various surface folds of the cerebrum and cerebellum, and continues along the length of the spinal cord. It supplies blood to the brain and spinal cord.

Ventricles and cerebrospinal fluid

There are four cavities inside the brain called ventricles, all containing cerebrospinal fluid. Two of these ventricles lie laterally within the cerebrum, a third lies deep inside the brain whereas the fourth, also deep inside the brain, opens into the sub-arachnoid space.

● DID YOU KNOW?

There are more than 10 billion nerve cells in the spinal cord.

Cerebrospinal fluid

Structure: this is clear, colourless fluid, formed in special cells within choroid plexuses that are situated in the lining of the ventricles. It resembles blood plasma in composition, containing protein, glucose, salts, and other substances. It is secreted into the ventricles from where it circulates around the whole brain and spinal cord and is then reabsorbed into the venous sinuses of the body through the arachnoid mater.

Functions:

- protects the brain and spinal cord, forming a cushion between the bony cavities and the nerves and acting as a shock absorber
- keeps the pressure around the brain and spinal cord constant
- transports nutrients and removes waste and toxic substances.

YOU NOW KNOW

You now know the structure and functions of all the main parts of the central nervous system. The next section explains the peripheral nervous system and its divisions.

TOPIC 3: THE PERIPHERAL NERVOUS SYSTEM

WHAT IS THE PERIPHERAL NERVOUS SYSTEM?

The peripheral nervous system concerns all the nervous system outside the central nervous system and contains motor and sensory nerves which transmit information to and from the body and brain. It consists of 12 pairs of cranial nerves and 31 pairs of spinal nerves.

CRANIAL NERVES

Cranial nerves are divided into 12 pairs and include sensory, motor and mixed nerves. Examples of these are:

5TH TRIGEMINAL

Opthalmic – sensory nerves supplying the lacrimal glands, conjuctiva of the eyes, eye lids, forehead, anterior part of the scalp and mucous membrane of the nose

Maxillary – sensory nerves supplying the lower eye lids, upper gums, upper teeth and cheeks

Mandibular – sensory and motor nerves. Supplying the teeth and gums of the lower jaw, ear and tongue. Motor supplying the muscles of mastication

7TH FACIAL

Motor supply the muscles of facial expression and sensory supply nerves of taste from the anterior part of the tongue

11TH ACCESSORY

There are two parts, cranial and spinal.

Cranial branches joining the vagus nerve to supply the pharynx and larynx

Spinal branches supplying the trapezius and sternocleido mastoid

SPINAL NERVES

These nerves begin in the spinal cord and supply all parts of the body not covered by the cranial nerves. They are all mixed nerves. Spinal nerves are divided into 31 pairs:

- Cervical: 8 pairs
- Thoracic: 12 pairs
- Lumbar: 5 pairs
- Sacral: 5 pairs
- Coccygeal: 1 pair

The cervical and thoracic nerves are named after the vertebrae at the level at which they exit the spinal cord. The lumbar, sacral and coccygeal nerves leave the spinal cord at the level of the first lumbar vertebra and extend downwards inside the vertebral canal exiting the canal at different levels depending on their destination.

All spinal nerves except the 2nd to 12th thoracic nerves branch out and regroup to form plexuses which supply different parts of the body:

THE CERVICAL PLEXUS

This contains the first four cervical nerves and supplies the muscles of the neck, shoulder and skin and includes the phrenic nerve, which sends nerve impulses to the diaphragm telling it to contract.

THE BRACHIAL PLEXUS

This group includes the lower four cervical nerves and the first thoracic nerve. It branches out to supply the muscles from the base of the neck to the fingertips and skin.

THE THORACIC (INTERCOSTAL) NERVES

The thoracic nerves supply the chest muscles and the main part of the abdominal wall.

THE LUMBAR PLEXUS

This group includes the first three lumbar nerves and part of the fourth. It supplies the skin and muscles of the lower abdomen, thighs and groin.

THE SACRAL PLEXUS

This includes the fourth and fifth lumbar nerves and first four sacral nerves. It supplies the muscles and skin of the pelvic area. The main nerve is the sciatic nerve which supplies the hamstrings, before dividing above the knee into the tibial and common peroneal nerves to supply the lower leg.

THE COCCYGEAL PLEXUS

The coccygeal group forms a second small plexus on the back of the pelvic cavity, supplying the muscles and skin of the pelvic area such as the external sphincter of the anus, tissues of the perineum and the external genitalia.

TOPIC 3: THE SOMATIC AND AUTONOMIC NERVOUS SYSTEM

The motor division of the Peripheral Nervous System is divided into the Somatic Nervous System and the Autonomic Nervous System.

——— **Parasympathetic**

——— **Sympathetic**

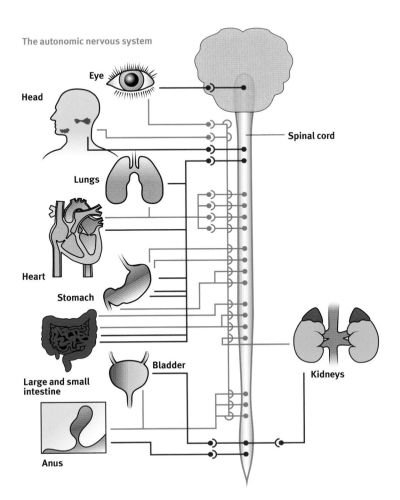

The autonomic nervous system

WHAT IS THE SOMATIC NERVOUS SYSTEM?

The Somatic Nervous System conducts impulses from the CNS to the skeletal muscle fibres. This is the voluntary branch of the PNS and allows conscious control over the contraction of skeletal muscles.

WHAT IS THE AUTONOMIC NERVOUS SYSTEM?

The Autonomic Nervous System conducts impulses from the CNS to cardiac and smooth muscles. This is an involuntary system controlled by the hypothalamus. Its nerves arise from the medulla oblongata. The Autonomic Nervous System is further divided into Sympathetic and Parasympathetic divisions. Every organ in the body has a sympathetic and parasympathetic nerve supply with one division generating the opposite effect to the other.

SYMPATHETIC

Structure: Consists of nerves that arise from the spinal cord at the thoracic and lumbar region, form ganglia (bundles of nerve fibres) just outside the CNS and then extend to the organ or tissue they supply.

Functions:

prepares body for stressful situations such as excitement or physical activity (fight or flight system). Neurones release acetylcholine and noradrenaline which have the following effects:

■ accelerates action of heart, increasing rate and force of contraction.

■ vasodilation of coronary arteries, increasing blood supply to the heart muscle.

- vasodilation of vessels supplying skeletal muscles, increasing oxygen and nutrient supply and waste removal.
- causes sustained contraction of the spleen, thus increasing volume of blood circulating.
- vasoconstriction of vessels that supply the digestive system and urinary system, increasing blood available for active muscles and brain.
- dilation of bronchioles, increasing volume of air that can be inspired and expired.

PARASYMPATHETIC

Structure: Consists of nerves that arise from the brain and sacral region of the spinal cord, form ganglia near to or inside the organ or tissue they supply.

Functions:

predominant system in non-stressful situations and keeps normal body functions running when the body is at rest. Neurones release acetylcholine.

- slows action of heart, decreasing rate and force of contraction
- vasoconstriction of coronary arteries, decreasing blood supply to the heart muscle
- vasodilation of vessels supplying the digestive system and urinary system with contraction of the bladder and rectal muscles, increasing digestion, nutrient absorption, micturition and defacation.
- constriction of the bronchi, decreasing the volume of air inspired and expired

WHAT ARE REFLEXES?

A reflex is the automatic (i.e. not controlled by the brain) movement produced by a sensory stimulus. It is instant and involuntary e.g. a finger touching boiling hot water will immediately move away.

Several structures are involved in the production of a reflex and together they constitute the 'reflex arc':

- a sense organ, like the skin or the nerve endings in muscles, tendons or organs
- a sensory nerve travelling from the sensory organ
- the spinal cord
- a motor nerve starting in the spinal cord and travelling to the motor organ.

Function: reflexes are mostly protective and designed to stimulate the quickest motor responses (movements) possible. They are reflexes which are automatic and do not require supervision, like the secretion of gastric juices when food reaches the stomach.

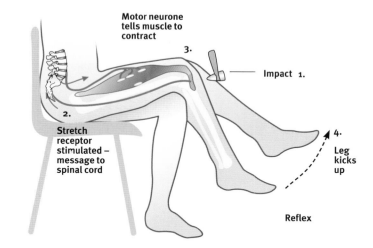

Example of a reflex action

YOU NOW KNOW

You now know the structure and function of all the different parts of the nervous system. The final section explains diseases and disorders of the systems.

TOPIC 4: DISEASES AND DISORDERS (PATHOLOGIES)

NEURITIS
Inflammation of a nerve, caused by infection, injury, poison, etc.
Effect: pain along the nerve's length and/or loss of use of the structures supplied by the nerve.

BELL'S PALSY
Injury or infection of the facial nerve which subsequently becomes inflamed
Effect: facial paralysis.

GANGLION
Is a small, usually hard bump above a tendon or in the capsule that encloses a joint. A ganglion is a non-cancerous cyst filled with a thick, jelly-like fluid. Ganglions can develop on or beneath the surface of the skin and usually occur between the ages of 20 and 40.
Effect: usually painless, but range of motion may be impaired.

NEURALGIA
Various causes
Effect: bouts of burning or stabbing pain along the course of one or more nerves.

SCIATICA
Pressure on the roots of the sciatic nerve often caused by degeneration of an intervertebral disc
Effect: pain down the back and outside of the thigh, leg and foot

PARKINSON'S DISEASE
Progressive disease caused by damage to basal ganglia of the brain and resulting in loss of dopamine (neuro-transmitter).
Effect: causes tremor and rigidity in muscles, as well as difficulty and slowness with voluntary movement.

MULTIPLE SCLEROSIS
(also known as disseminated sclerosis)
Loss of the protective myelin sheath from nerve fibres in the central nervous system.
Effect: causes muscular weakness, loss of muscular coordination, problems with skin sensation, speech and vision.

CEREBRAL PALSY
Damage to the brain, caused during birth or resulting from a pre-natal defect.
Effect: affects motor system control.

MOTOR NEURONE DISEASE
A rare progressive disorder, in which the motor neurones in the body gradually deteriorate
Effect: weakness and wasting of muscles

MYALGIC ENCEPHALOMELITIS (ME)
Also known as post-viral fatigue or chronic fatigue syndrome.
Effect: exhaustion, general aches and pains, headaches and dizziness, inflammation of the brain and spinal cord.

STRESS

Stress is any factor that affects mental or physical well-being. Emotions such as anxiety, fear and other negative feelings can affect the nervous system causing increased heart rate, breathing difficulties, sleep disturbances and stomach problems. All of these physical effects are caused by the nervous system over-working in response to stress.

DEPRESSION

Is a bipolar affective disorder - also known as manic depression, seasonal affective disorder (SAD) - also known as winter depression or winter blues, post-natal - is a form of clinical depression which can affect women, and less frequently men, after childbirth.

EPILEPSY

A disorder of the central nervous system characterized by loss of consciousness and convulsions.

MIGRAINE

A severe, disabling headache, usually affecting only one side of the head, and often accompanied by nausea, vomiting, photophobia and visual disturbances.

STROKE

A sudden loss of consciousness resulting when the rupture or occlusion of a blood vessel leads to a lack of oxygen in the brain.

TRANSIENT ISCHAEMIC ATTACK (TIA)

Sometimes called a mini-stroke: a temporary restriction of blood supply to the brain, which causes short-term symptoms such as temporary vision loss or impairment.

ALZHEIMERS DISEASE

The most common form of dementia in older people that affects many areas of cognitive function.

CONCUSSION

An injury to the brain caused by a blow; usually resulting in loss of consciousness.

DEMENTIA

The result of a brain injury, resulting in long-term decline in cognitive function due to damage or disease in the body beyond what might be expected from normal aging.

MENINGITIS

An infectious disease characterized by inflammation of the meninges (the tissues that surround the brain or spinal cord) usually caused by a bacterial infection; symptoms include headache, stiff neck, fever and nausea.

MYASTHENIA GRAVIS

A chronic progressive disease characterized by chronic fatigue and muscular weakness (especially in the face and neck).

PARALYSIS

A loss of the ability to move a body part.

PERIPHERAL NEUROPATHY

Is the term for damage to nerves of the peripheral nervous system, which may be caused either by diseases of the nerve or from the side-effects of systemic illness.

POLIOMYELITIS

An acute viral disease marked by inflammation of nerve cells of the brain stem and spinal cord.

SPINAL CORD INJURY

Is damage to white matter or myelinated fibre tracts that carry signals to and from the brain.

SPINA BIFIDA

Is a developmental birth defect involving the neural tube; a not uncommon congenital defect in which a vertebra is malformed and the backbone does not form properly.

INTERRELATIONSHIPS

Nervous system links to:

All systems: nerves from the central nervous system control and receive information from every body system.

Muscular: muscles require a nerve impulse to contract.

Skeletal: muscle contraction (caused by nerve impulses) produces movement in the skeleton.

Circulatory: nerves control the heart rate.

Respiratory: nerves control the process of respiration.

Endocrine: works closely with the endocrine system to maintain homeostasis — balance in the body.

Skin: the skin contains a variety of nerve endings, at different levels in the layers.

Summary
The nervous system

- has two parts, the central and peripheral (including autonomic) nervous systems
- informs and warns the body of environmental changes, sensations, pain and danger and initiates responses to stimuli.

DON'T FORGET
TO LOGIN TO GAIN ACCESS TO YOUR **FREE** MULTI-MEDIA LEARNING RESOURCES

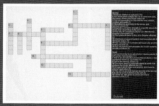

☐ Test your knowledge with crosswords

☐ Test your knowledge with fill in the gaps

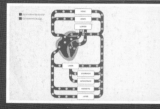

☐ Test your knowledge with interactive animations and diagrams

To login to use these resources visit
www.emspublishing.co.uk/anatomy and follow the onscreen instructions.

AN INTRODUCTORY GUIDE TO
Anatomy & Physiology

08

The Endocrine system

The endocrine system is one of the body's communication systems.
It uses hormones to tell the body what to do.

The Endocrine system

The endocrine system is composed of ductless glands which produce hormones, the body's chemical messengers.

Hormones control and affect many body functions and organs, as well as behaviour. Each gland produces specific hormones. The function of the endocrine system is closely linked to that of the nervous system.

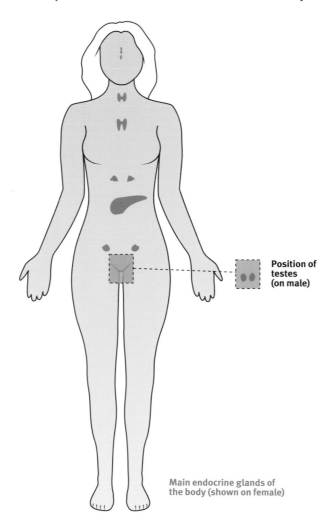

Position of testes (on male)

Main endocrine glands of the body (shown on female)

LEARNING OBJECTIVES

The target knowledge of this chapter is:

- the position of the endocrine glands
- the names and effects of hormones secreted by each gland
- the effects of hyper- and hyposecretion of hormones
- the role of sex hormones in menstruation, pregnancy and menopause
- the different stages of the menstrual cycle
- diseases and disorders of the endocrine system.

TOPIC 1: STRUCTURE AND FUNCTION

WHAT IS A HORMONE?

A hormone is a chemical messenger, which is secreted directly into the blood by a particular gland. Some hormones are made of protein (e.g. insulin), whilst others are steroids (adreno-corticoid hormones), glycoproteins (FSH, LH, TSH), and derivatives of single amino acids, (T4, T3). Hormones are produced in the gland and are then transported to the area/organ they control or affect.

WHAT IS AN ENDOCRINE GLAND?

A ductless gland which produces hormones. Ductless means that there is no separate canal or tube to transport the hormones to the blood. Hormones travel straight into the bloodstream from the gland.

WHAT DO HORMONES AND THE ENDOCRINE SYSTEM DO?

They affect the behaviour and function of different areas of the body and of the body overall, e.g. hormones are responsible for correct growth, changes during puberty, the menstrual cycle, pregnancy, the menopause, responses to stress and danger and the proper functioning of the kidneys and digestive system.

THE MAIN GLANDS OF THE BODY

The diagram opposite displays the main endocrine glands of the body and lists the hormones secreted. The following section explains the function and malfunction of each hormone. If too much of a hormone is produced it is known as hypersecretion; too little is known as hyposecretion.

YOU NOW KNOW

What an endocrine gland is, what a hormone is and what they do. The following section explains all the main endocrine glands, the hormones they secrete, their functions and malfunctions.

TOPIC 2: GLANDS AND HORMONES

PITUITARY

Location: Situated at the base of the brain, closely connected to the hypothalamus; has two hormone-secreting lobes, the anterior and posterior.

Anterior lobe hormones

■ **Human growth hormone (HGH)**
Function: regulates height and growth; main controller along with genes of final height of a person
Malfunctions: hypersecretion causes gigantism or acromegaly; hyposecretion causes dwarfism.

■ **Melanocyte-stimulating hormone (MSH)**
Function: stimulates production of melanin in basal layer of the skin.

■ **Thyrotrophin (TSH)**
Function: controls thyroid gland
Malfunctions: see thyroid gland.

■ **Adrenocorticotrophin (ACTH)**
Function: controls adrenal cortex
Malfunction: see adrenal cortex.

■ **Prolactin or lactogenic hormone (LTH)**
Function: production of milk during lactation.

■ **Gonadotrophins (gonad/sex organ hormones)**
Function: control sexual development and organs (ovaries and testes)

■ *Follicle-stimulating hormone (FSH)*
Function: stimulates ovaries to produce oestrogen and to ovulate in women and stimulates sperm production in men.

■ *Luteinising hormone (LH)*
Function: stimulates ovaries to produce the corpus luteum from ruptured follicle and produce progesterone.

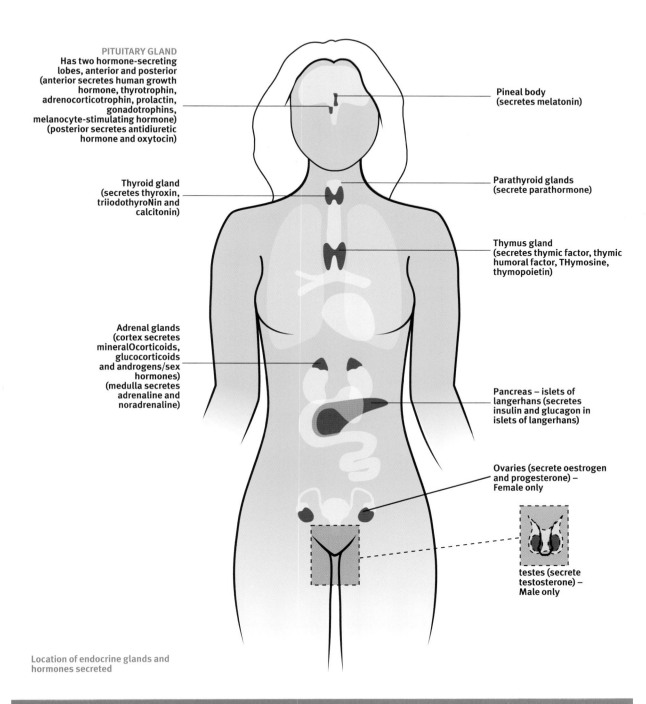

PITUITARY GLAND
Has two hormone-secreting lobes, anterior and posterior (anterior secretes human growth hormone, thyrotrophin, adrenocorticotrophin, prolactin, gonadotrophins, melanocyte-stimulating hormone) (posterior secretes antidiuretic hormone and oxytocin)

Pineal body (secretes melatonin)

Thyroid gland (secretes thyroxin, triiodothyroNin and calcitonin)

Parathyroid glands (secrete parathormone)

Thymus gland (secretes thymic factor, thymic humoral factor, THymosine, thymopoietin)

Adrenal glands (cortex secretes mineralOcorticoids, glucocorticoids and androgens/sex hormones) (medulla secretes adrenaline and noradrenaline)

Pancreas – islets of langerhans (secretes insulin and glucagon in islets of langerhans)

Ovaries (secrete oestrogen and progesterone) – Female only

testes (secrete testosterone) – Male only

Location of endocrine glands and hormones secreted

YOU NOW KNOW
The location of all the main endocrine glands in the body and the names of the hormones they secrete. The following table explains the functions and malfunctions of the glands and hormones.

FUNCTIONS AND MALFUNCTIONS OF THE GLANDS AND HORMONES

■ *Interstitial cell-stimulating hormone (ICSH)/ luteinising hormone in men*
Function: stimulates sperm production and secretion of testosterone.
Malfunctions (of gonadotrophin):
Polycystic ovarian syndrome
Endometriosis
Fibroids
See also adrenal cortex.

Posterior lobe hormones
■ **Antidiuretic hormone (ADH or vasopressin)**
Function: regulation of water absorption in kidneys
Malfunctions: hyposecretion: diabetes insipidus; hypersecretion: oedema (swelling).

■ **Oxytocin**
Function: contracts mammary glands when suckling begins, to release milk secreted into ducts; contraction of muscles of uterus to begin childbirth and during it.

THYROID GLANDS
Location: either side of the neck
Hormones:
■ **Thyroxin, and Triiodothyronine**
(produced in response to TSH from anterior lobe of Pituitary Gland).
Functions: stimulate tissue metabolism; maintain BMR (basic metabolic rate).
Malfunctions: hypersecretion known as Graves disease or thyrotoxicosis (hyper-thyroidism — increase in metabolic rate, heart rate, anxiety, intolerance of heat plus raised temperature, frequent bowel action); hyposecretion — body systems slow below normal speed, cretinism (at birth) or myxoedema (disorder caused later in life by untreated cretinism), goitre – thyroid enlargement.
■ **Calcitonin**
Function: maintenance of calcium and phosphorus balance.
Malfunction: hypersecretion causes lowering of blood calcium level by inhibiting loss of calcium from bone.

PARATHYROID GLANDS
Location: four, two either side behind thyroid
Hormone:
■ **Parathormone**
Functions: maintenance of calcium level in plasma; stimulates calcium reabsorption in kidneys; activates Vitamin D.
Malfunctions: hypersecretion – hyper-parathyroidism. Softened bones and thus spontaneous bone fractures; hyposecretion — hypoparathyroidism: abnormally low blood calcium levels; tetany (spasms in hands and feet caused by over-contraction in muscles); convulsions (from over-stimulated nerves).

ADRENAL GLANDS
Location: one on top of each kidney NB: split into two parts, adrenal cortex and adrenal medulla

Adrenal cortex
Hormones:
■ **Mineralocorticoids – aldosterone (steroids)**
Function: regulates salts in body, especially sodium chloride and potassium.
Malfunctions: hypersecretion — kidney failure, high blood pressure, too much potassium in blood causing abnormal heart beat; hyposecretion: Addison's disease; muscular atrophy and weakness; body systems slow down.
■ **Glucocorticoids (steroids)**
(cortisol and cortisone)
Functions: produced in response to ACTH (from pituitary, anterior lobe); metabolises carbohydrates, fats and proteins.
Malfunctions: stunted growth;
hypersecretion: Cushing's syndrome; hypertension; moon-shaped face; muscular atrophy; diabetes mellitus;
■ **Sex hormones (steroids)**; female: oestrogen and progesterone (some normal in male); male: testosterone (small amounts secreted in the ovaries in females)

Functions: sexual development and maturity; ovulation; hair growth in pubic and axillary (armpit) areas.
Malfunctions: many, including hirsutism, amenorrhoea (hypersecretion of testosterone in women); muscle atrophy and breast growth (hypersecretion of oestrogen in men); hyposecretion: Addison's disease.

Adrenal medulla
The adrenal medulla functions to support the sympathetic nervous system.
Hormones:
■ **Adrenaline and noradrenaline**
Function: often known as the stress hormones, they prepare the body for 'fight or flight' by speeding up heart rate, slowing digestive and urinary systems, increasing blood pressure and blood sugar level. Adrenaline is a powerful vasoconstrictor i.e. it constricts blood vessels in order to increase blood pressure.

PANCREAS
(specifically in the islets of Langerhans, specialised cells that form the endocrine part of the pancreas)
Location: behind and slightly below stomach, between duodenum and spleen, connected to duodenum by pancreatic duct
Hormones:
■ **Insulin and glucagon**
Function: helps glucose enter cells thus regulating blood sugar levels.
Malfunctions: hyposecretion: diabetes mellitus (high blood sugar level and high urine production); fatigue; weight loss; coma; hypersecretion: hypoglycaemia (low blood sugar level) including symptoms of hunger, sweating; in serious cases may lead to coma.

OVARIES
Location: either side of the uterus
Hormones:
■ **Oestrogen and Progesterone** (female sex hormones, small amount produced in male testes)

Functions: responsible for female sexual characteristics e.g. breast growth, widening of hips, pubic and axillary hair growth.

Malfunctions: Cause unknown. In women can lead to polycystic ovarian syndrome (known as Stein-Leventhal syndrome); in males can lead to muscle atrophy and breast growth.

TESTES

Location: within the scrotum, behind the penis

Hormone:

■ **Testosterone** (male sex hormone, small amount produced in female ovaries)

Functions: responsible for male sexual characteristics thus sperm production, changes at puberty — voice breaking, pubic, facial and axillary hair growth, increased muscle mass.

Malfunctions: though a low level of testosterone is normal in females, hypersecretion can lead to virilism, hirsutism and amenorrhoea.

PINEAL BODY

Location: centre of the brain

Hormone:

■ **Melatonin** (derived from serotonin)

Function: controls body rhythms — responds to sunlight

Malfunctions: jet-lagged feeling; depression, SAD – seasonal affective disorder.

THYMUS

Location: in the thorax

Hormone:

■ **Thymic Factor (TF), Thymic Humoral Factor (THF), Thymosine, Thymopoietin**

Functions: Part of immune system, appear to promote development of T Lymphocytes in the thymus gland.

Malfunction: lowered immunity and/or stress.

YOU NOW KNOW

The location of all the main endocrine glands in the body and the names of the hormones they secrete. The following table explains the functions and malfunctions of the glands and hormones.

TOPIC 3: THE ROLE OF SEX HORMONES

PUBERTY

Puberty is the age at which the internal reproductive organs of boys and girls reach maturity and become functional. Although the effect on these organs cannot be seen, the effect on the rest of the body can, in the form of secondary sexual characteristics. The average age for girls to reach puberty is 10-14, though in some cases it begins as early as 8-9. For boys the average age is 13–16.

THE EFFECTS OF HORMONES IN PUBERTY

In girls, the ovaries are stimulated by two hormones: follicle-stimulating hormone (FSH) and luteinising hormone (LH). These are known as gonadotrophins and they are secreted by the anterior lobe of the pituitary. They have the following effects:

■ uterus, fallopian tubes and ovaries reach maturity and become functional

■ ovulation and the menstrual cycle begin

■ growth of pubic and axillary hair

■ glandular tissue in the breasts enlarges and develops

■ increase in height and pelvic width

■ increase in amount of subcutaneous fat.

In boys, the same gonadotrophins are produced (follicle-stimulating hormone (FSH) and luteinising hormone (LH), though luteinising hormone is called interstitial cell-stimulating hormone (ICSH) in men and it stimulates the testes to produce testosterone. Most of the changes produced are caused by testosterone and the effects are:

■ growth of muscle and bone

■ noticeable height increase

■ voice breaks and larynx enlarges

■ growth of pubic, facial, axillary, abdominal and chest hair

■ sexual organs develop

■ seminiferous tubules (in the testes; produce testosterone and sperm) become functional and semen can be produced

■ sperm production begins.

THE MENSTRUAL CYCLE

One of the most important functions of hormones is to prepare the body for reproduction. In a male this involves sperm production. In a female, it involves producing ova (eggs) and preparing the womb so that a fertilised egg can grow into a baby. Whether an egg is fertilised or not, the process of preparing a woman's body for having a baby happens every month. This is known as the menstrual cycle. The start of menstruation (for the first time) is called the menarche. Every 28 days from puberty to menopause (approximately 35 years) the body will prepare itself for a baby and if fertilisation does not take place the body will undo its preparations before starting again a few weeks later. There are three stages:

- ☐ first (menstrual) phase
- ☐ second (proliferative) phase
- ☐ third (secretory) phase.

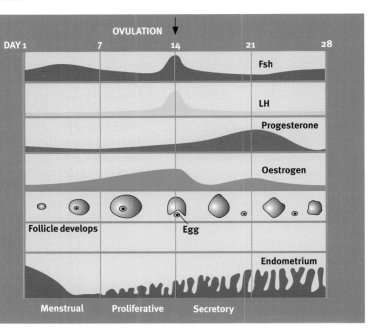

FIRST (MENSTRUAL) PHASE

This lasts for approximately five days. Progesterone produced by the corpus luteum enters the bloodstream and the pituitary gland responds by producing less luteinising hormone. But less luteinising hormone means the corpus luteum begins to break down, the progesterone level falls which stops the endometrium from holding fluid and it starts to break down as well. Menstruation begins as a result of the breakdown of the endometrium. Menstrual flow contains:

- ■ the extra mucus secretions
- ■ the cells lining the uterus
- ■ blood from broken capillaries in endometrium
- ■ the unfertilised ovum.

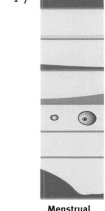

Day 1–7

Menstrual

SECOND (PROLIFERATIVE) PHASE

This lasts for approximately 7 days. Follicle-stimulating hormone (FSH) is produced in the anterior lobe of the pituitary gland and this stimulates the follicles of the ovaries to produce oestrogen. These follicles are small structures on the surface of the ovary. The oestrogen then stimulates the endometrium (the lining of the womb), promoting the growth of new blood vessels and mucus-producing cells (hence the name proliferative, meaning reproduction and growth). At the end of this stage ovulation occurs: a mature Graafian follicle ruptures releasing a single egg which then travels along the Fallopian tube to the uterus.

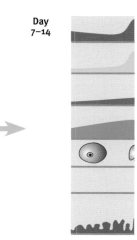

Day 7–14

Proliferative

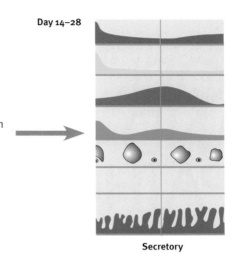

Day 14–28

Secretory

THIRD (SECRETORY) PHASE

This lasts for approximately 14 days. Luteinising hormone (LH), secreted in the anterior lobe of the pituitary gland, stimulates the ruptured follicle lining to grow into corpus luteum – a temporary structure formed by the effect of this hormone on the ruptured ovarian follicle. The corpus luteum produces progesterone thus stimulating the endometrium to retain fluid and produce mucus, which makes it easier for sperm to pass through the reproductive tract. After ovulation, the egg can only be fertilised during the next 12-48 hours. If it is not fertilised, the menstrual phase begins.

As soon as progesterone levels drop (a result of the collapse of the corpus luteum and endometrium), the pituitary gland starts the production of FSH again, and thus stimulates the ovaries to produce another follicle and then another ovum. The cycle begins again.

WHEN DOES THE MENSTRUAL CYCLE STOP HAPPENING?

Once the menarche (start of menstruation) has passed, menstruation only stops in three instances:

- Amenorrhoea (see Diseases and Disorders section for more information)
- Pregnancy (see Pregnancy section for more information)
- Menopause

MENOPAUSE (CLIMACTERIC)

A woman can, technically speaking, bear children as long as she is menstruating. This reproductive period lasts about 35 years, until the ova (egg) supply is exhausted. Women are born with a certain number of eggs. When these run out, the menopause begins. The average age for

• DID YOU KNOW?

The menstrual cycle gets its name from the word menses which is the plural of month in Latin.

menopause to begin is 45-55 and it takes an average of five years to complete (though it can last ten). During this period the hormonal changes that began with puberty will be reversed. For example the ovaries will gradually stop responding to FSH and LH, the hormones that provoked changes in puberty, and thus produce less oestrogen and progesterone. The reduction in these hormones causes irregular menstrual cycles (before menstruation stops completely), shrunken breasts, less hair growth on the body, flushes, sweats, palpitations, atrophied sex organs and possibly unpredictable behaviour. Many of these symptoms of the menopause can be alleviated by use of Hormone Replacement Therapy (HRT).

YOU NOW KNOW

The endocrine system's structure and function. The final section explains some of the diseases which affect it.

TOPIC 4: DISEASES AND DISORDERS (PATHOLOGIES)

ADDISON'S SYNDROME

Cause: hyposecretion of adrenocortical hormones (sex, growth and salt regulation hormones).
Effects: muscular atrophy and weakness; hypotension; gastric problems like vomiting, changes in skin pigmentation, irregular menstrual cycle and dehydration.

AMENORRHOEA

Cause: can be caused by hypersecretion of testosterone (in females), stress; radical weight loss, anaemia.
Effect: absence of menstruation.

CUSHING'S SYNDROME

Cause: hypersecretion of adrenocortical hormones (sex, growth and salt regulation hormones) i.e. the opposite of Addison's syndrome.
Effects: muscular atrophy and weakness, hypertension, moon-shaped face, redistribution of body fat, sometimes mental illness, osteoporosis.

PRE-MENSTRUAL SYNDROME

Cause: onset of menstruation; usually occurs about one week before.
Effects: depression, irritability, bloating, swollen and tender breast tissue, restlessness.

POLYCYSTIC OVARIAN SYNDROME

(also known as Stein-Leventhal syndrome)
Cause: not known.
Effects: irregular menstrual cycle, due to stimulation, multiple growth of follicular ovarian cysts and sometimes infertility, enlarged ovaries and often high levels of oestrogen; 50% of patients are obese and become hirsute; age range of sufferers is usually 16-30.

STRESS

Stress is a threat to the body and the body responds to it like any other danger – the adrenal medulla releases adrenaline and noradrenaline to help us with the fight or flight response. The physical manifestations of the arrival of adrenaline in the body are faster heart rate and breathing, sweating (hence sweaty palms when we are frightened or nervous), a glucose rush from the liver and heightened senses (like hearing and sight). Prolonged stress may cause amenorrhoea in women and low production of sperm in men.

DIABETES MELLITUS
TYPE 1

Cause: Auto-immune disease results in pancreas being unable to produce insulin
Effects: Symptoms include high blood glucose level, excessive thirst, high urine output, tiredness and weight loss. Cannot be cured but can be controlled by regular (2-4/day) insulin injections.

TYPE 2

Cause: The body cells do not respond properly to insulin and the pancreas may not produce enough. Linked closely to obesity.
Effects: Symptoms are as Type 1, but may not be as obvious and take longer to develop. Can be controlled by a healthy diet and physical activity. Tablets or insulin injections may also be required.

GOITRE

An abnormally enlarged thyroid gland; can result from underproduction or overproduction of hormone or from a deficiency of iodine in the diet.

GRAVE'S DISEASE

Is an auto-immune disease. It most commonly

affects the thyroid, causing it to grow to twice its size or more, be overactive, with related hyperthyroid symptoms such as increased heartbeat, muscle weakness, disturbed sleep and irritability.

HYPERTHYROIDISM (THYROTOXICOSIS)

An overactive thyroid gland; a glandular disorder resulting from an overproduction of thyroid hormones.

HYPOTHYROIDISM

An underactive thyroid gland; a glandular disorder resulting from insufficient production of thyroid hormones.

INSOMNIA

An inability to sleep; chronic sleeplessness.

MYXOEDEMA

Hypothyroidism marked by dry skin and swellings around lips and nose as well as mental deterioration.

ACROMEGALY

Enlargement of bones of hands, feet and face; often accompanied by headache, muscle pain and emotional disturbances; caused by overproduction of growth hormone by the anterior pituitary gland (due to a tumour).

GIGANTISM

Excessive size; usually caused by excessive secretion of growth hormone from the pituitary gland.

HYPERPARATHYROIDISM

Excessive secretion of parathyroid hormone resulting in abnormally high levels of calcium in the blood; can affect many systems of the body (especially causing bone resorption and osteoporosis).

HYPOPARATHYROIDISM

Inadequate secretion of parathyroid hormone resulting in abnormally low levels of calcium in the blood.

INTERRELATIONSHIPS

Endocrine system links to:

Nervous: works very closely with the nervous system to provide homeostasis – balance in the body. The pituitary gland (endocrine) has an infinite link to the hypothalamus (nervous system/brain) both of which exert great control over the body.

Circulatory: hormones are secreted and carried in the bloodstream to the various target organs.

Digestive: digestion is reliant upon hormones secreted in the stomach, small intestines and pancreas.

Reproductive: governs the reproductive system particularly in females as it controls the menstrual cycle and the release of hormones during pregnancy and childbirth.

Summary

The endocrine system

- consists of ductless glands
- produces hormones which affect behaviour and function
- plays a major role in growth, puberty, the reproductive cycle (menstruation, production of sperm, pregnancy, menopause), responses to stress, kidney and digestive functions.

DON'T FORGET
TO LOGIN TO GAIN ACCESS TO YOUR **FREE** MULTI-MEDIA LEARNING RESOURCES

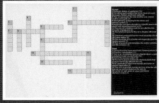

☐ Test your knowledge with crosswords

☐ Test your knowledge with fill in the gaps

☐ Test your knowledge with interactive animations and diagrams

To login to use these resources visit

www.emspublishing.co.uk/anatomy and follow the onscreen instructions.

AN INTRODUCTORY GUIDE TO

Anatomy
&Physiology

09

The Reproductive system

The reproductive system enables humans to reproduce.

The Reproductive system

Unlike many of the other anatomical systems in the body, the organs in this system differ completely in men and women. In men, they include the prostate gland, testes, testicular vessels, penis and scrotum and in women they include the ovaries, Fallopian tubes, uterus, cervix, vagina and labia. In both sexes, the pelvic girdle is the bony cavity which protects the organs.

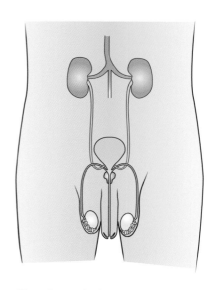

The male reproductive system

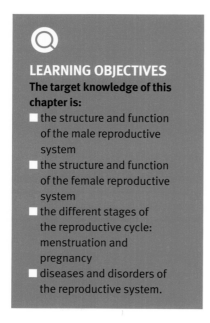

LEARNING OBJECTIVES
The target knowledge of this chapter is:
- the structure and function of the male reproductive system
- the structure and function of the female reproductive system
- the different stages of the reproductive cycle: menstruation and pregnancy
- diseases and disorders of the reproductive system.

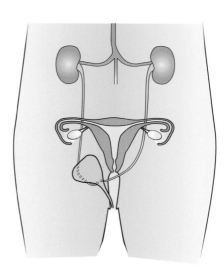

The female reproductive system

TOPIC 1: MALE REPRODUCTIVE SYSTEM

The male reproductive system is more visible than the female system, with most of the organs outside the body. This, as you will discover, is for a very good reason.

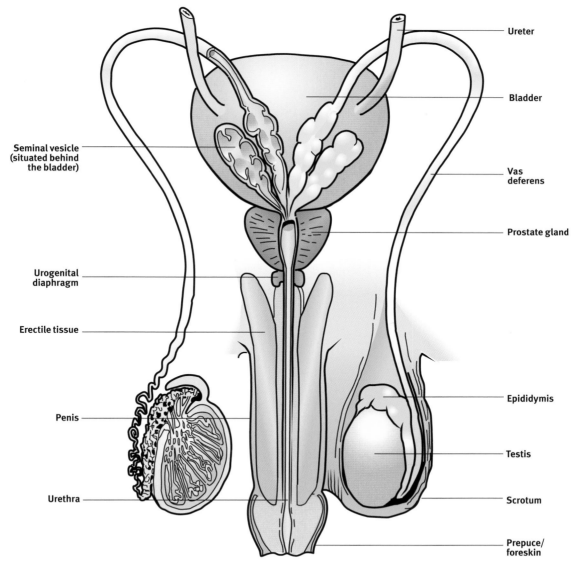

Ureter

Bladder

Seminal vesicle (situated behind the bladder)

Vas deferens

Prostate gland

Urogenital diaphragm

Erectile tissue

Epididymis

Penis

Testis

Urethra

Scrotum

Prepuce/ foreskin

Posterior view

WHAT IS THE PELVIC GIRDLE?

The pelvic girdle is the bony cavity which forms a protective basin for the reproductive organs. Both men and women have one, although it is wider in women to allow for the passage of a baby in childbirth.

Structure: the pelvis is a circle of bones, consisting of the two hip,
or innominate bones (each one combining three bones fused together: ilium, ischium and pubis) and, anteriorly, the symphysis pubis, the cartilaginous link between the left and right sides of the girdle. Posteriorly, the sacrum forms the back of the girdle.

Functions: the pelvic girdle protects the internal organs of the reproductive system, as well as the bladder and rectum. It supports the spine and provides attachments for the muscles of the lower back, abdomen and thighs.

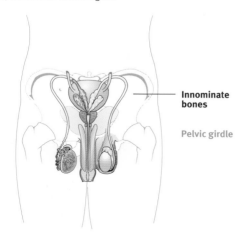

Innominate bones

Pelvic girdle

WHAT IS THE PROSTATE GLAND?

Structure: the prostate is a small gland situated between the bladder and the rectum. It surrounds the beginning of the urethra (known as the prostatic urethra).

Functions: the prostate's position, at the start of the urethra, is important because it produces two secretions carried in semen. One secretion helps keep the lining of the urethra moist and the other is part of the seminal fluids, which help semen to travel along the urethra and into the female.

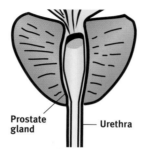

Prostate gland

Urethra

WHAT ARE THE TESTES?

The testes (testis or testicle singular) are the male gonads or glands.

Structure: testes are two glands contained within a sac of skin and muscle called the scrotum. They develop in the abdomen before descending into the scrotum just before birth.

Functions: the testes produce spermatozoa (also known as sperm) and the male sex hormone testosterone which is responsible for male sexual characteristics. Spermatozoa develop in the testes, and are also stored there because they must be kept at a slightly lower temperature than the average body temperature (35°C).

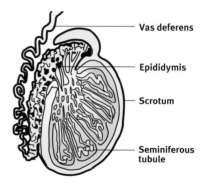

Vas deferens

Epididymis

Scrotum

Seminiferous tubule

WHAT ARE THE TESTICULAR VESSELS?

The testicular vessels are the epididymis and the vas deferens, two tubes which form the passageway from the testes to the urethra.

EPIDIDYMIS

Structure: the epididymis is a tightly coiled tube. It opens from the top of each testis, continues down along the side of the gland then straightens out into the vas deferens.

Functions: to store and transport sperm as well as acting as a site where immature sperm can develop.

VAS DEFERENS

Structure: a duct with muscular walls leading from the epididymis to the urethra.

Function: the vas deferens acts as a passageway for the transfer of sperm from the storage site of the epididymis to the prostatic urethra and eventually to the penis. This occurs during sexual activity. By contracting its muscular walls the vas deferens pushes the sperm forward.

SCROTUM

One of two external sex organs in the male, the scrotum is a sac which contains the testes, epididymis and vas deferens. It hangs behind the penis.

Structure: a sac made of an outer layer of skin and an inner layer of muscle. A membrane divides it into two halves, one for each testis.

Functions: to support and protect the testes as well as maintain the correct temperature for them. The testes are kept outside the body in order to keep them at a slightly lower temperature than the body. However, if the temperature in the scrotum drops, it reacts by contracting its muscular walls, thus moving itself and the testes closer to the body and thus raising the temperature of the glands. If the temperature is too high, the muscles relax, moving the scrotum and testes away from the body and thus lowering the temperature.

PENIS

The penis is the main external sex organ of the male. It has three important parts: erectile tissue bodies, the foreskin and the urethra.

Structure: the penis consists of three bodies of spongy, erectile tissue all running lengthways. Two of these run side by side above the urethra, a tube that runs through the centre of the penis and acts as a duct for urine and semen. The third lies underneath them, forming a tube containing the urethra which becomes the tip of the penis, known as the 'glans'. This tissue is full of blood vessels. Surrounding the glans is the prepuce, or foreskin, a loose double fold of skin which protects the glans. The foreskin is sometimes removed either to prevent infection or for religious reasons.

Cross-section of the penis

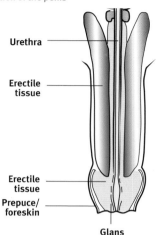

Urethra

Erectile tissue

Erectile tissue

Prepuce/ foreskin

Glans

Functions: the penis has a double role –
- organ of excretion. It carries urine from the bladder for excretion.
- organ of reproduction. During sexual activity the penis becomes erect. This 'erection' is caused by an increase in the amount of blood circulating in the vessels of the spongy tissues. These tissues then swell up causing the penis to enlarge. Eventually, the tissues become rigid which allows penetration into the vagina of the female and safe delivery of the semen during intercourse.

WHAT IS A SPERM?

Structure: sperm look like microscopic tadpoles. Each one consists of a head (the male sex cell), a middle section and a tail, which helps to propel the sperm along the vagina and into the uterus. The head is a nucleus that contains 23 chromosomes whereas the tail is a flagellum, a projection resembling a thread, which moves backwards and forwards enabling the sperm to 'swim' to its destination.

Function: sperm fertilises the ova (singular: ovum) that the female reproductive system produces. Ova, or eggs, are the female sex cells. The head of the sperm, carrying the important genetic information in the form of chromosomes, inserts itself into the ovum and the tail, which is no longer needed, breaks down. Although semen (the fluid ejaculated during intercourse) contains millions

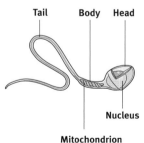

Tail   Body   Head

Nucleus

Mitochondrion

A sperm cell

of sperm, only one is needed to fertilise an ovum. Once fertilised, the ovum usually grows and develops into a baby.

WHAT IS SEMEN?

Semen is the fluid discharged from the penis during sexual intercourse. It contains sperm and secretions from the prostate gland and seminal vesicle (a small structure behind the bladder).

YOU NOW KNOW
All the names and functions of the different organs in the male reproductive system. The next section explains the female reproductive system.

DID YOU KNOW?
When sexual activity takes place, the body's reflexes stop urine from entering the urethra.

TOPIC 2: FEMALE REPRODUCTIVE SYSTEM

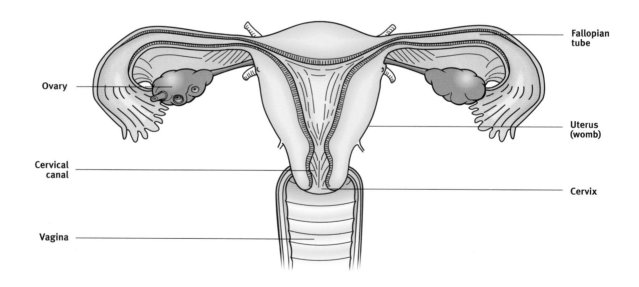

- Fallopian tube
- Ovary
- Uterus (womb)
- Cervical canal
- Cervix
- Vagina

The female reproductive system

This system is hidden inside the body, apart from the entrance to the vagina and the vulva. Just like the male system, the organs within the body are contained and protected by the pelvic girdle. This bony cavity has the same structure in men and women but is wider in the female, in order to allow room for the passage of a baby.

WHAT IS THE UTERUS?

The centre of the female reproductive system is the uterus, also known as the womb. It is here that a fertilised ovum grows into a baby. The top end opens out into the Fallopian tubes (which lead to the ovaries) and the bottom end, or cervix, opens into the vagina and forms the birth canal.

Structure: the uterus is a muscular, hollow organ that sits at a right angle to the vagina and connects with the Fallopian tubes. It is the size and shape of an upside-down pear, about 7.5cm long and 5cm wide and expands during pregnancy to accommodate the foetus. The lining of the uterus consists of layers of tissues which respond to hormonal secretions. These layers thicken every month ready to act as a nourishing bed for the fertilised ovum.

Function: the uterus is the place where the foetus grows and develops. Every month it prepares itself for a possible pregnancy and if there is no fertilised ovum, menstruation occurs (see Menstrual Cycle on page 90).

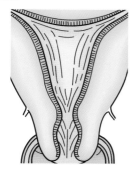

The uterus

WHAT IS THE CERVIX?
Structure: the cervix is the narrow neck of the uterus which opens into the vagina. Usually it is the width of a pencil lead but during childbirth it dilates to allow the passage of the baby.

Function: the cervix forms the first part of the birth canal. The dilation of the cervix is a measurement used to determine how soon childbirth will begin.

WHAT ARE THE OVARIES?
The ovaries are the female gonads or glands.

Structure: the ovaries are glands. They are approximately the size and shape of almonds and they are positioned either side of the uterus, just below the Fallopian tubes.

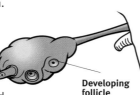

Developing follicle

The ovary

Function: the ovaries secrete the hormones responsible for female sexual characteristics

(progesterone and oestrogen) as well as storing female sex cells called ova or eggs (singular: ovum). Unlike sperm, ova exist in the body at birth, but in an immature and undeveloped form in follicles. After puberty one of these follicles will develop and rupture, releasing an ovum every month. This is known as ovulation (see Menstrual Cycle).

WHAT IS A FOLLICLE?
These are small structures on the surface of the ovary, which are known as Graafian follicles when they mature. They contain fluid and an egg or ovum. As soon as an ovum is mature and ready to be fertilised, the follicle splits, releasing the ovum which then travels along the Fallopian tube to the uterus.

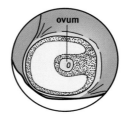

Mature follicle

WHAT ARE THE FALLOPIAN TUBES?
Structure: the Fallopian tubes are funnel-shaped tubes which start at the top of the uterus and continue along to the ovaries. They are named after the Italian anatomist who discovered them.

Functions: the Fallopian tubes are a passageway from the ovaries to the uterus for the ovum, as well as the site of fertilisation. Sperm swim up these tubes to reach the ovum.

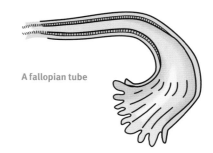

A fallopian tube

WHAT IS THE VAGINA?
Structure: the vagina is a muscular passage leading from the cervix to the vulva. It connects the internal sex organs with those on the outside of the body. During sexual activity the blood vessels in the vaginal walls fill with blood causing them to swell and become engorged.

Functions: the vagina connects the cervix to the vulva, and thus to the outside of the body. It serves as a passageway for menstrual blood, forms part of the birth canal during labour and is the site of penetration during intercourse.

WHAT IS THE VULVA?

The external organs of the female reproductive system are known collectively as the vulva. They include the mons pubis, the labia majora and minora and the clitoris.

The vulva

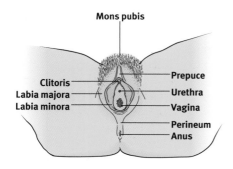

Mons pubis: a protective pad of fat over the symphysis pubis which is covered in hair after puberty.

Labia majora: two large folds of fatty tissue which run lengthways either side of the vulva from the mons pubis to the perineum (skin and tissues between the sex organs and the anus). They protect the entrance to the vagina and urethra.

Labia minora: two smaller folds of skin within the labia majora which surround the clitoris and form a hood (prepuce) to protect it.

Clitoris: a very small, sensitive organ which contains erectile tissue like the penis. It is situated just below the mons pubis. During sexual activity the erectile tissues fill with blood and swell.

THE BREASTS

The breasts are accessory organs to the reproductive system. Although not directly involved in the process of reproduction, they develop during pregnancy ready for their function as milk-secreting glands.

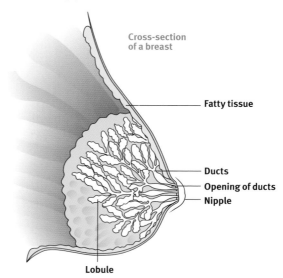

Cross-section of a breast

Structure: the breasts are glands which sit on the front of the female chest (men also have breasts, but they are undeveloped). Their size varies considerably. Each breast is circular and convex, with a central, raised nipple. Breasts consist of adipose and areolar tissue supported by fascia. The tissue forms lobes, subdivided into lobules, which open into several ducts. These ducts open on the surface of the nipple. During pregnancy the lobules develop and produce milk. Hormones cause the breasts to grow during puberty and then activate the secretion of milk during pregnancy.

Function: to secrete milk post-pregnancy.

Q

YOU NOW KNOW

You now know the structure and function of both male and female reproductive systems. The next section explains how reproduction works.

TOPIC 3: PREGNANCY

There are six main stages of pregnancy.

FERTILISATION

Post-ovulation, the ovum enters the Fallopian tube in the direction of the uterus. It reaches the centre of the tube in around 30 minutes. If sperm (in semen) have been deposited in the vagina within 24 hours of ovulation, there is a three day window in which fertilisation may occur. Several hundred sperm (out of the many million deposited) will have swum through the uterus and into the Fallopian tubes in the search for an ovum. Only one sperm is needed to fertilise an ovum. The sperm penetrates the ovum's membrane and enters the ovum. This is fertilisation.

POST-FERTILISATION

The tail of the sperm breaks down and its head or nucleus grows. The nucleus of the sperm and the nucleus of the ovum fuse to make a single nucleus. Within this new nucleus, the male and female chromosomes join up forming the zygote, the first cell of a new baby.

CELL DIVISION

Once the zygote has formed, it undergoes a process of mitotic cell division, dividing into two, then four, then eight cells and so on until a ball of cells, called a morula, is formed. After five days this develops into a blastocyst (a multi-celled structure) which enters the uterus and implants in the endometrium of the uterus on the seventh day (post-fertilisation).

● DID YOU KNOW?

The female body is capable of producing 35 children in an average lifetime!

FORMATION OF EMBRYO

By day 24 the blastocyst has formed an amniotic cavity (a fluid-filled sac) containing an embryo that looks a little like a seahorse. The endometrium and part of the blastocyst mesh and develop into the placenta, the baby's support system (which allows the passage of nutrients, oxygen and waste to and from baby and mother).

DEVELOPMENT OF FOETUS

The embryo is known as the foetus from eight weeks. It develops in the amniotic cavity. The fluid protects the baby from shocks and pressure and allows it to grow unhindered.

BIRTH (PARTURITION)

Just before birth, the membrane of the amniotic cavity breaks and the amniotic fluid is released via the vagina. Childbirth usually occurs in the 40th week after fertilisation.

YOU NOW KNOW

You now know the names and functions of the male and female reproductive systems, how menstruation and reproduction occur. The final section explains some of the diseases and disorders of the reproductive system.

TOPIC 4: DISEASES AND DISORDERS (PATHOLOGIES

ECTOPIC PREGNANCY

This is a pregnancy which occurs outside the uterus. A fertilised ovum may develop inside the Fallopian tube instead of travelling to the uterus. There is a danger of haemorrhage and death.

AMENORRHOEA

Causes: can be caused by hypersecretion of testosterone in females, other hormonal imbalances, stress, radical weight loss, anaemia or excessive exercise.
Effect: absence of menstruation.

DYSMENORRHOEA

Causes: spasm or congestion of the uterus, imbalance in hormones or emotional disturbances.
Effect: extremely difficult and painful menstruation.

PRE-MENSTRUAL SYNDROME

Cause: onset of menstruation; usually occurs about one week before.
Effect: depression, irritability, bloating and water retention, swollen and tender breast tissue (mastalgia), restlessness.

POLYCYSTIC OVARIAN SYNDROME

(also known as Stein-Leventhal syndrome)
Cause: hyposecretion of female sex hormones (luteinising hormone).
Effect: irregular menstrual cycle, multiple growth of follicular ovarian cysts and sometimes infertility, enlarged ovaries, 50% of patients are obese and become hirsute (hairy); age range of sufferers is usually 16-30.

CANCER

Cancer is the development of malignant cells. It can occur in breasts, ovaries, the cervix, testes and/or prostate gland.

CHLAMYDIA

A sexually transmitted infection caused by bacteria of the genus Chlamydia; may cause genital inflammation, discharge, pelvic pain and fever.

ENDOMETRIOSIS

The presence of endometrium elsewhere than in the lining of the uterus; causes premenstrual pain and dysmenorrheal.

FIBROIDS

A benign tumour of the uterus that is comprised of either fibrous connective tissue or muscle.

HYSTERECTOMY

An operation in which the uterus is removed.

MENSTRUAL DISORDERS

Menorrhagia - abnormally heavy or prolonged menstruation; can be a symptom of uterine tumours and can lead to anaemia if prolonged.

PROSTATITIS

Inflammation of the prostate gland characterized by perineal pain, irregular urination and (if severe) chills and fever.

MENOPAUSE

The time in a woman's life in which the menstrual cycle ends.

VULVOVAGINAL CANDIDIASIS (THRUSH)

A yeast infection of the vagina.

BENIGN PROSTATIC ENLARGEMENT/ HYPERPLASIA
An abnormal increase in tissue growth caused by excessive cell division.

FRIGIDITY
A sexual unresponsiveness (especially of women) and inability to achieve orgasm during intercourse.

IMPOTENCE
An inability (usually of the male) to copulate.

INFERTILITY
This primarily refers to the biological inability of a person to contribute to conception. Infertility may also refer to the state of a woman who is unable to carry a pregnancy to full term.

OVARIAN CYSTS
Are fluid-filled sacs that can form on the ovary when one or more of the egg-containing follicles mature, but do not release the egg into the fallopian tube.

PELVIC INFLAMMATORY DISEASE
An inflammation of the female pelvic organs (especially the Fallopian tubes) caused by infection by any of several micro-organisms.

PRE-ECLAMPSIA
A condition in pregnancy characterized by abrupt hypertension (a sharp rise in blood pressure), albuminuria (leakage of large amounts of the protein albumin into the urine) and oedema (swelling) of the hands, feet and face. Pre-eclampsia is the most common complication of pregnancy.

PROLAPSE
The slipping or falling out of place of an organ e.g. the uterus/vagina.

GONORRHOEA
A common venereal disease caused by the bacterium Neisseria gonorrhoeae; symptoms are painful urination and pain around the urethra.

SYPHILLIS
A sexually transmitted disease caused by the spirochetal bacterium.

TRICHOMONAS
Commonly called "trick." It is caused by a single-celled organism that is a member of the protozoa family of micro-organisms. When this organism infects the vagina it can cause a frothy, greenish-yellow discharge.

VAGINITIS
Any inflammation of the vagina, usually referring to an infection due to bacteria, yeast, or other pathogens that result in discomfort, itching, and/or abnormal discharge.

TOXIC SHOCK SYNDROME
(TSS) is a very rare but potentially fatal illness caused by a bacterial toxin.

INTERRELATIONSHIPS
Reproductive links to:
Endocrine: hormones from the endocrine system govern the reproductive system particularly in females.
Nervous: sexual stimulus is relayed by nerve impulses.

Summary
The reproductive system
- is different and complementary in men and women
- is dedicated to the reproduction of the species.

DON'T FORGET
TO LOGIN TO GAIN ACCESS TO YOUR **FREE** MULTI-MEDIA LEARNING RESOURCES

☐ Test your knowledge with crosswords

☐ Test your knowledge with fill in the gaps

☐ Test your knowledge with interactive animations and diagrams

To login to use these resources visit

www.emspublishing.co.uk/anatomy and follow the onscreen instructions.

AN INTRODUCTORY GUIDE TO

Anatomy
& Physiology

The Digestive system

The alimentary canal (gastrointestinal tract) is composed of the mouth, oesophagus, stomach, small and large intestine.

The Digestive system

Without food, water and oxygen, human beings could not survive. The digestive system is the set of organs which transform whatever we eat into substances that can be used in the body for energy, growth and repair. Once the food has been broken down by various chemical processes, and the nutrients removed, the rest is excreted as waste. The whole process involves many different organs and sometimes takes several hours.

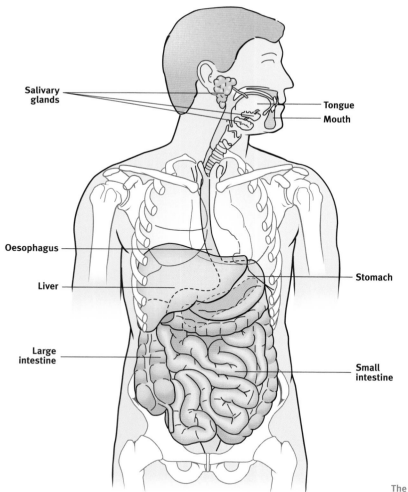

Salivary glands
Tongue
Mouth
Oesophagus
Liver
Stomach
Large intestine
Small intestine

The digestive system

LEARNING OBJECTIVES
The target knowledge of this chapter is:
- the structure of the digestive system
- the function of the digestive system
- the four stages of digestion
- the chemistry of digestion
- the function of enzymes
- diseases and disorders of the digestive system.

TOPIC 1: DIGESTION

WHAT IS DIGESTION?

The breakdown and transformation of solid and liquid food into microscopic substances. These substances are then transported by the blood into different areas of the body. **There are four stages of digestion:**

Mouth: ingestion (the taking in of food or liquid into the body), chewing and swallowing; start of starch digestion

Stomach: mixing and protein digestion

Small intestine: carbohydrate and fat digestion; absorption

Large intestine: waste and excretion.

Section 1: the mouth

WHERE DOES DIGESTION START?

In the mouth where the action of teeth and saliva combine in the first stage of breakdown, chewing and partially digesting the food so that it will pass more easily along the oesophagus. The ball of food that leaves the mouth is known as a bolus.

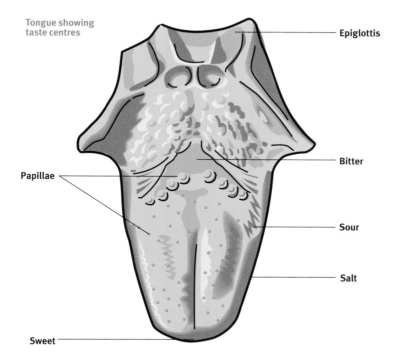

Tongue showing taste centres

Epiglottis

Bitter

Papillae

Sour

Salt

Sweet

WHAT IS SALIVA?

Saliva is a liquid secreted by three pairs of salivary glands: the parotid gland (situated below the ear), the submandibular gland and the sublingual gland (both situated below the tongue). It contains water, mucus and the enzyme salivary amylase.

Saliva has three functions:

- to lubricate the food with mucus, making it easier to swallow
- to start digestion: it contains the enzyme salivary amylase, which acts on cooked starch turning it into shorter polysaccharides
- to keep the mouth and teeth clean.

WHAT IS AN ENZYME?

If you think about the food you eat, and the difference in size between it and the microscopic cells and tissues that it will feed and support in your body, it is easy to understand why a digestive system that breaks food down into different units is needed. Enzymes are an important part of the process. If the digestive system is a conveyor belt, enzymes are the machines and workers which slowly change whatever is on the belt to make it smaller and smaller so that, eventually, it can be carried around the body in blood. They are made of protein and act as catalysts i.e. they make chemical changes happen in other substances, whilst themselves remaining unchanged. They act on food, changing it into smaller particles.

WHAT IS THE TONGUE?

Structure: the tongue is a muscular organ, covered with a membrane. It is held in place by attachments to the mandible (lower jaw) and the hyoid bone. Tiny projections known as papillae cover the top, increasing its surface area and producing a rough texture. Sensory nerve endings in the papillae form what we commonly know as taste buds.

Functions: the tongue has three digestive functions — taste, chewing and swallowing:
- **taste:** the tongue is covered with thousands of taste buds which are sensitive to salt, sweet, sour and bitter chemicals in food and drink. They
  help us enjoy what we eat and drink and act as the first line of defence, warning us when food, drink or foreign matter are off or inedible.
- **chewing:** the tongue aids chewing by moving food around the mouth, pushing it between the teeth and covering it with saliva, which contains enzymes that start the digestive process. The food is turned into a partially digested mass known as a bolus.
- **swallowing:** when the food is ready to travel to the stomach, the tongue pushes it to the back of the mouth.

HOW DOES FOOD GET FROM THE MOUTH TO THE STOMACH?

Via the action of swallowing and through the portion of the gastrointestinal tract known as the oesophagus. The tongue pushes the bolus to the back of the mouth, towards the pharynx, a muscular tube behind the mouth. The food passes into the pharynx and down to the oesophagus. The epiglottis, a small flap of cartilage which forms part of the larynx (the windpipe) moves upwards and forwards, blocking the entrance to the larynx. This stops the food from 'going down the wrong way' and prevents choking.

WHAT IS THE OESOPHAGUS?

Structure: the oesophagus is a muscular tube which leads from the pharynx, at the back of the mouth, to the stomach, the first main organ of digestion.

Function: to carry chewed food from the pharynx to the stomach. Food moves along it by a muscular contraction known as peristalsis. The muscle fibres contract and relax which acts like a wave on the tube, pushing the bolus forwards. The lining of the oesophagus secretes mucus to ease and lubricate the passage of food.

Section 2: the stomach

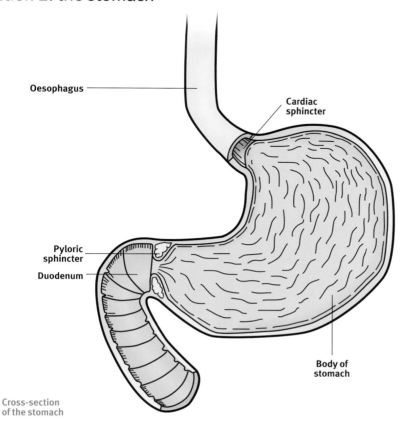

Oesophagus

Cardiac sphincter

Pyloric sphincter

Duodenum

Body of stomach

Cross-section of the stomach

• DID YOU KNOW?

Food may stay in your stomach for as little as 30 minutes or as long as four hours, depending on what it is. Carbohydrate meals are the quickest to leave the stomach because they are not digested until the small intestine.

WHAT IS THE STOMACH?

Structure: the stomach is a J-shaped, elastic organ which expands and contracts depending on what is in it. Food enters it from the oesophagus via the cardiac sphincter, a valve that stops back flow of the stomach's contents, and leaves it through the pyloric sphincter into the duodenum, the first part of the small intestine. The wall of the stomach is a combination of layers of muscle fibre with an inner mucous membrane. The latter has lots of folds, called rugae. When the stomach is full they stretch out, enabling expansion, then they contract when it empties.

WHAT DOES IT DO?

Functions:
- digests proteins through the action of enzymes
- churns food with gastric juices
- helps to lubricate the food by producing mucus (from the mucous membrane)
- absorbs alcohol
- kills bacteria by producing hydrochloric acid.
- storage of food prior to it passing to the small intestine

GASTRIC JUICES CONTAIN:
- **hydrochloric acid:** neutralises bacteria and activates pepsin
- **rennin:** enzyme that curdles milk protein (only in infants)
- **pepsin:** enzyme that acts on proteins turning them into polypeptides.

At this stage proteins have been partially digested and, along with the carbohydrates such as starch which were partially digested in the mouth, they have to wait until the small intestine to complete digestion.

THE CHEMISTRY OF DIGESTION

The whole digestive process is a combination of different chemical reactions that act on the food we eat, reducing it to the building blocks of nutrients for absorption and use by the body. Every piece of food we eat is composed of fats, carbohydrates and proteins. These must be broken down into their relative chemical compounds in order for the body to use them i.e. by the time the bread you eat reaches your muscles as energy it has been chewed, churned, liquefied and the starch changed to useable glucose. The following shows the main chemical reactions and breakdowns at different stages of digestion.

WHAT ARE PROTEINS?

Proteins foods include dairy products, meat, fish and beans. They are made up of interlinked polypeptide chains and are the building material for the body. In order to be used by the body they must be broken down into their smaller components – amino acids. There are approximately 20 amino acids classified by whether they are essential (those the body cannot make, that must therefore be supplied in the diet) and non-essential (those the body can make).

Proteins are broken down in the body by the following processes:
■ In the stomach, the enzyme pepsin begins the digestion of proteins in the stomach by breaking them down into large polypeptides.
■ In the small intestine, enzymes from the pancreas, including trypsin and chymotrypsin, break the large polypeptides into smaller chains.
■ Finally, still in the small intestine, enzymes from the intestine, including aminopeptidase, breaks up the small polypeptides into individual amino acids ready for absorption.

WHAT ARE FATS?

Fats are classified into saturated, monounsaturated or polyunsaturated categories. Saturated fats can be found in dairy products and meat. Monounsaturated fats can be found in olive oil and avocados. Polyunsaturated fats can be found in sunflower oil and oily fish. Some polyunsaturated fats cannot be made by the body

and are therefore also classified as essential fats and must be consumed in the diet. In order to be used by the body, fats must be broken down to fatty acids and glycerol.

Fats are broken down in the body by the following processes:
■ In the small intestine, fat are emulsified by bile salts from the liver (i.e. turned into liquid form and carried in another liquid – bile)
■ In the small intestine, lipase from the pancreas breaks down emulsified fats into fatty acids and glycerol ready for absorption

WHAT ARE CARBOHYDRATES?

Carbohydrates are classified as monosaccharides, disaccharides or polysaccharides. Monosaccharides include fructose in fruit. Disaccharides include lactose in milk. Polysaccharides include starch and fibre in cereals, potatoes and other plant sources, and glycogen in meat. All carbohydrates are broken down to monosaccharides for absorption and all eventually become glucose to supply the body with energy.

Carbohydrates are broken down in the body by the following processes:
■ In the mouth, salivary amylase begins the breakdown of polysaccharides
■ In the small intestine, intestinal amylase breaks down polysaccharides to disaccharides
■ In the small intestine, maltase, lactase and sucrase convert disaccharides to monosaccharides ready for absorption.

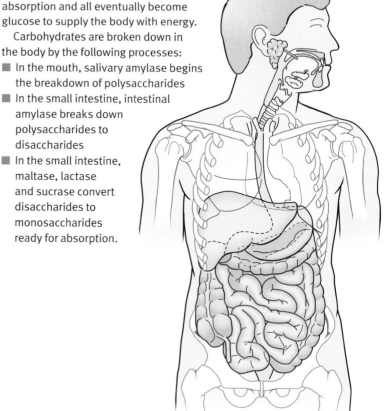

Section 3: the small intestine

WHAT IS THE SMALL INTESTINE?

The small intestine, ironically, is not that small. It is seven metres long and divided into three different parts: the duodenum, the jejunum and the ileum. The walls have several layers, including a muscular layer, a layer containing blood vessels, lymph vessels and nerves and an inner mucous membrane. The inner wall is covered with villi, tiny finger-like projections which increase the surface area for absorption and contain a network of blood and lymph vessels.

WHAT DOES THE SMALL INTESTINE DO?

Completion of the chemical digestion of food and the subsequent absorption of nutrients takes place in the small intestine.

Nutrients are absorbed through the villi into the blood and lymph vessels. Hardly any food is absorbed elsewhere in the digestive system.

HOW DOES DIGESTION AND ABSORPTION TAKE PLACE IN THE SMALL INTESTINE?

1 peristaltic movements mix food with intestinal and pancreatic juices as well as bile. The movements push the food against the villi. Intestinal juices are composed of enzymes:
- maltase, sucrase and lactase which split disaccharides into monosaccharides
- enterokinase which activates trypsin in pancreatic juice

● DID YOU KNOW?

90% of absorption takes place in the small intestine whereas only 10% takes place in the stomach and large intestine.

- peptidases which split polypeptides into amino acids
2 a number of hormones in the small intestine help digestion by stimulating the production of pancreatic or intestinal juices and regulating acidity levels, for example cholecystokinin (CCK)
3 absorption: digested food is absorbed by either active transport or diffusion
- Most nutrients, including amino acids and sugars, are absorbed by active transport through the walls of the villi where they enter the bloodstream and are carried to the liver in the hepatic portal vein.
- Fats, fatty acids and glycerol diffuse into the lacteals (lymphatic capillaries). They are called lacteals because the fat passes into them in suspension, causing the lymph to look milky.

OTHER FUNCTIONS OF THE SMALL INTESTINE

To protect the digestive system from infection. It is the only section of the digestive system with a direct link to the protective lymphatic system.

Cross-section of wall of small intestine

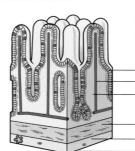

- Mucous membrane
- Lacteal (lymphatic vessel)
- Submucous layer
- Circular muscle
- Longitudinal muscle
- Peritoneum

ORGAN	SECRETION	ACTION
Mouth Salivary glands	Salivary amylase	Converts starch into shorter chain polysaccharides
Stomach	Rennin Hydrochloric acid Pepsin	Coagulates milk into curds (in infants) Neutralises bacteria Coagulates proteins into peptones (any of various water-soluble protein derivatives obtained by partial hydrolysis of a protein by an acid or enzyme during digestion)
Duodenum	1: Pancreatic juice ■ trypsin ■ lipase ■ amylase 2: Bile	Converts peptones into shorter chain polypeptides Converts fats into fatty acids and glycerol Converts polysaccharides into disaccharides Emulsifies fats
Small intestine (from the villi)	Intestinal juice ■ maltase ■ sucrase ■ lactase ■ enterokinase ■ peptidases	Convert disaccharides into monosaccharides Activates trypsin in pancreatic juice Convert polypeptides into amino acids

Section 4: the large intestine and waste

WHAT IS THE LARGE INTESTINE?

The large intestine deals with waste. It is about 1.5m long and sits draped around the small intestine, in an arch shape. It consists of the caecum, appendix, colon, rectum, anal canal and anus.

Functions: to reabsorb water and nutrients from digestive waste and to get rid of waste. Whatever remains of the food, once it has been through the processes of mixing, conversion and absorption carried out in the stomach and small intestine, is passed into the large intestine. Any remaining nutrients are removed and the result is faeces.

FAECES

Faeces are the unwanted leftovers from food, combined with cellulose (roughage which is indigestible, found in foods like vegetables and bran), dead blood cells, bacteria (both living and dead), fatty acids and mucus, used to help move the faeces through the large intestine. The colour comes from the dead blood cells and bilirubin, a bile pigment.

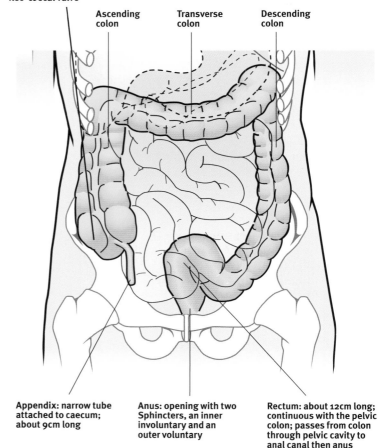

Caecum: a small pouch; the ileum empties its contents into the caecum through the ileo-cæcal valve

The large intestine

Ascending colon

Transverse colon

Descending colon

Appendix: narrow tube attached to caecum; about 9cm long

Anus: opening with two Sphincters, an inner involuntary and an outer voluntary

Rectum: about 12cm long; continuous with the pelvic colon; passes from colon through pelvic cavity to anal canal then anus

Summary
Of large intestine's functions

- Absorption of nutrients, vitamins, salt or water left in digestive waste.
- Secretion of mucus to help passage of faeces.
- Storage of faeces in rectum (short-term because the arrival of faeces in rectum tells brain of need to defecate).
- Micro-organism/bacteria activity: many bacteria live in the large intestine. Though they can cause disease they are harmless in the colon and may even be useful.
- Defecation: a 'mass movement' pushes waste along the transverse colon, often stimulated by food arriving in the stomach. It is a reflex but humans have control of it. If the reflex is ignored, more water will be absorbed from the faeces which may cause constipation.

TOPIC 2:
ACCESSORY ORGANS

There are several other organs involved in the digestive process: the tongue, teeth and salivary glands, liver, pancreas and gall bladder. They are known as accessory organs because, although they do not form part of the gastrointestinal tract, they help the digestive process by breaking down foodstuffs and the toxins/ waste produced during digestion. The role of the tongue, teeth and salivary glands has been mentioned earlier in the chapter.

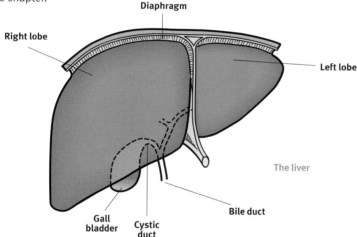

Diaphragm

Right lobe

Left lobe

The liver

Gall bladder

Cystic duct

Bile duct

WHAT IS THE LIVER?

Structure: the largest gland in the body, the liver sits at the top of the abdomen, just below the diaphragm and just above and to the right of the medial line. It is vital because it performs many essential functions.

Functions: the liver is vital for cleansing and storage as well as production. It:
removes
- toxins from drugs, alcohol, and harmful substances
- nitrogen from amino acids.
stores
- vitamins A, B12, D, E, K
- glycogen (a compound that stores energy)
- iron, from the breakdown of red blood cells and food
- fats.
produces
- heat (the liver is the body's radiator, producing more heat than any other organ as a result of its various functions)
- vitamin A (from carotene, found in green-leafed vegetables and carrots)
- Vitamin D
- heparin
- plasma proteins: albumin, globulin, prothrombin, fibrinogen
- bile
- uric acid and urea, from breakdown of red blood cells and de-amination of amino acids.
converts
- stored (saturated) fat into other fat products (like cholesterol)
- glycogen to glucose, when energy is needed
- glucose back to glycogen, in presence of insulin
- metabolises protein.

THE LIVER IN HISTORY

Like parts of the circulation, parts of the digestive system have always been seen as very important throughout history, both for what they do and what they represent. This is especially true with the liver. For example in ancient Rome, animals were sacrificed for their livers before battles. The organs were then used to predict what might happen. For example, a pale liver was bad news and predicted defeat whereas a healthy red liver meant the conditions were favourable for victory. The liquid secreted by the liver, bile, was thought to be one of four body fluids known as humours which determined personality. Black bile (or melancholy) meant a person was sad and choler (or yellow bile) meant they were irritable. A coward's liver was thought to be bloodless, which is why someone cowardly is lily-livered.

WHAT IS THE GALL BLADDER?

Structure: a pear-shaped sac attached by the cystic and bile ducts to the posterior of the liver. Whenever there is excess bile secreted by the liver which can't be used immediately for digestion, the bile passes first along the bile duct then along the cystic duct to the gall bladder where it will be stored until needed.

Functions:
- reservoir for bile (from liver)
- secretes mucus to add to bile
- absorbs water from bile, making it more concentrated
- contracts in order to empty bile into duodenum.

WHAT IS THE PANCREAS?

Structure: the pancreas is a gland situated behind the stomach, between the duodenum and the spleen. It delivers pancreatic juices to the duodenum through the pancreatic duct. The cells of the pancreas are divided into the islets of Langerhans (which produce insulin and glucagon) and a network of alveoli (small sac-like cavities). The alveoli are lined with cells that produce enzymes.

Functions: the pancreas works with both the digestive and the endocrine systems. It produces enzymes to break down food, the hormone insulin which regulates the blood sugar level after eating by causing the conversion of glucose to glycogen for storage in the liver and muscles, and the hormone glucagon which converts glycogen back to glucose.

Pancreatic juices contain:
- lipase (fat digestion)
- amylase (starch digestion)
- trypsin (protein digestion).

WHAT IS INSULIN

Insulin is a hormone secreted by specialised cells in the pancreas known as the islets of Langerhans. It regulates blood sugar level. When we eat, the blood sugar level rises. The sugar in the blood is in the form of glucose. Insulin helps cells absorb glucose and turns any excess glucose into glycogen, an insoluble sugar which is stored in the liver until the body needs it. Thus the blood sugar level drops. A lack of insulin causes diabetes mellitus. Type 1 diabetes is caused by auto-immune damage to the pancreas resulting in low or no insulin production. Type 2 diabetes is strongly linked to obesity and although insulin may still be produced it is unable to work properly in the body (insulin resistance). In either type, glucose cannot be properly absorbed into the body resulting in the following symptoms – a dangerously high level of blood sugar, the loss of glucose through excretion, thirstiness and excessive urine production.

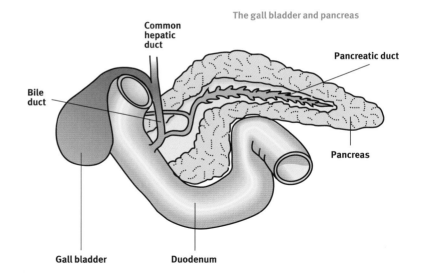

The gall bladder and pancreas

Common hepatic duct

Pancreatic duct

Bile duct

Pancreas

Gall bladder

Duodenum

WHAT IS BILE?

Structure: a thick liquid produced in the liver as a result of the breakdown of red blood cells. It contains salts, bile pigments, acids and water.

Functions: emulsifying fats, stimulating peristalsis and creating alkaline conditions in the small intestine.

TOPIC 3: DISEASES AND DISORDERS (PATHOLOGIES

ANOREXIA
Anorexia is a loss of appetite. Anorexia nervosa is a psychological condition which often affects teenage girls and young women. The sufferers have a fear of gaining weight or being fat and refuse to eat very much or stop eating altogether. It can be severely debilitating and sometimes fatal.

APPENDICITIS
Acute inflammation of the appendix, usually treated by removal of the organ.

BULIMIA
Bulimia is an insatiable hunger during binging episodes coupled with compensatory evacuation methods such as self-induced vomiting and excessive use of laxatives. Bulimia nervosa is a psychological condition which often affects teenage girls and young women, and increasingly young men.

CIRRHOSIS
Chronic damage to an organ causing hardening. Several types of cirrhosis exist but the most common is cirrhosis of the liver, which is frequently caused by excessive alcohol consumption.

CONSTIPATION
Infrequent or uncomfortable bowel movements, causing hard faeces to block the rectum. Caused by lack of fibre in the diet, lack of fluids and lack of exercise. Sometimes caused by stress.

GALL STONES
Stones formed from residues of bile pigments, cholesterol and calcium salts, found in the gall bladder.

HEARTBURN
Burning sensation in oesophagus or throat, caused by back flow and regurgitation of acidic stomach contents.

HERNIA
A rupture, in which an organ pushes through the surface of the structures which normally hold it in.

JAUNDICE
Excessive levels of bile pigments in the blood cause skin to turn yellow. Caused by malfunctioning gall bladder or obstructed flow of bile.

IRRITABLE BOWEL SYNDROME
No exact cause is yet known for irritable bowel syndrome (sometimes referred to as IBS), though stress and low-fibre, high fat diets are said to contribute. Symptoms include stomach and bowel pain and alternate bouts of diarrhoea and constipation.

STRESS
The most common effect of stress on the digestive system is ulcers. Anxiety and lack of relaxation cause overproduction of gastric juices and if they have nothing to work on they will start to attack the lining of the stomach or other structures. In short, the stomach starts digesting itself!

ULCER
Erosion in the walls of the digestive system, often caused by too much acid.

COELIAC'S DISEASE
Is a common bowel condition that is caused by intolerance to a protein called gluten.

DIARRHOEA
Frequent and watery bowel movements.

FLATULENCE
A state of excessive gas in the alimentary canal.

GINGIVITIS
Inflammation of the gums.

HICCOUGHS
Is the spasmodic contraction of the diaphragm that repeats several times per minute.
Indigestion (Dyspepsia)
A disorder of digestive function characterized by discomfort, heartburn or nausea.

NAUSEA
Is the sensation of unease and discomfort in the stomach with an urge to vomit.

OBESITY
Is a medical condition in which excess body fat has accumulated to the extent that it may have an adverse effect on health, leading to reduced life expectancy.

CANDIDA
A fungus, called Candida albicans, which causes yeast infections like thrush in the mouth, throat, intestines and other parts of the body.

COLITIS
An inflammation of the large intestine (the colon).

COLITIS/ULCERATIVE COLITIS
Is a form of inflammatory bowel disease (IBD). It is a form of colitis, a disease of the intestine, specifically the large intestine or colon, which includes characteristic ulcers, or open sores in the colon.

CROHN'S DISEASE
A disease of the small intestine that often spreads to the colon. Crohn's disease is characterized by diarrhoea, cramping and loss of appetite and weight, with local abscesses and scarring.

DIVERTICULOSIS
A condition of the large intestines characterized by the development of weakness in the intestinal wall that permits herniation or outpouching of the intestinal lining. Diverticulosis usually develops as a result of inadequate dietary fibre.

DIVERTICULITIS
An inflammation of a diverticulum in the digestive tract (especially the colon); characterized by painful abdominal cramping, fever and constipation.

ENTERITIS
An inflammation of the intestine (especially the small intestine) usually characterized by diarrhoea.

GASTRITIS
An inflammation of the lining of the stomach which is characterized by nausea, loss of appetite and discomfort after eating.

INFLAMED GALL BLADDER
An inflammation of the gall bladder.

PERNICIOUS ANAEMIA
A chronic progressive anaemia of older adults, thought to be caused by impaired absorption of vitamin B-12 due to the absence of intrinsic factor.

ULCER
Oesophageal – An ulceration of the oesophagus.

INTERRELATIONSHIPS
Digestive system links to:
All systems: provides nutrition to the whole body.
Circulatory: the circulatory system transports nutrients from the digestive system to every system of the body.
Endocrine: the endocrine system secretes certain hormones, which help metabolism.
Lymphatic: lymphatic vessels are found in the lacteals of the villi in the small intestine and help with the absorption of fats.
Muscular: the digestive system supplies glucose for energy to the muscular system: sphincter muscles contract along the alimentary canal to push food along – known as peristalsis.
Nervous: all the organs of the digestive system are stimulated by nerve impulses.

Summary
The digestive system
- transforms food and drink into nutrients and waste
- consists of every process from eating (ingestion) to excretion
- relies on chemicals (enzymes) to carry out the break down of food.

The Respiratory system

The respiratory system consists of the nose, lungs, diaphragm and the air passages, such as the trachea, which connect them.

The Respiratory system

The respiratory system is the body's breathing equipment. Similar to the digestive system, it takes substances from outside the body (gases, particularly oxygen), circulates them through the body to cells and tissues, then excretes the excess and waste. Oxygen is the respiratory system's 'food' and carbon dioxide is its 'waste'. Breathing is the most fundamental action of the human body: we cannot live without it for more than a couple of minutes.

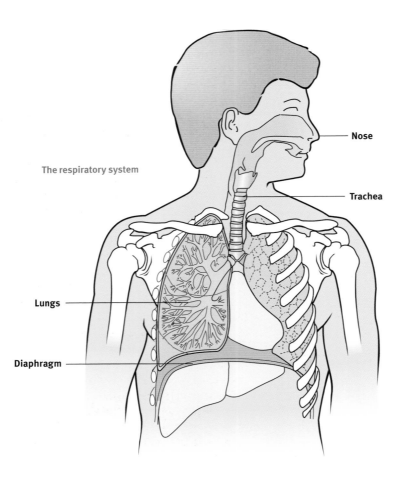

The respiratory system

Nose

Trachea

Lungs

Diaphragm

LEARNING OBJECTIVES
The target knowledge of this chapter is:
- the structure of the respiratory system
- the function of the respiratory system
- what is external respiration
- what is internal respiration
- how the nervous system controls breathing
- diseases and disorders of the respiratory system.

TOPIC 1: STRUCTURE

Section 1: how oxygen enters the body: the passage of air from nose to lungs

WHAT IS BREATHING?
Breathing, or external respiration, is the inhalation and exhalation of air and the gases it contains.

HOW DO WE BREATHE?
Through the nose and the system of passageways and organs with which it connects. The nose is the only organ of respiration that we can see. The following section explains the structure and function of the organs of the respiratory system.

WHAT IS THE NOSE?
The nose is an organ on the face. It acts as the first passageway for air entering the body.

Structure: the nose is made of cartilage and two nasal bones. It is covered with skin, both inside and out and lined with a mucous membrane that is ciliated i.e. it has microscopic hairs. The two nostrils lead into a bony nasal cavity, which has two chambers, divided by a nasal septum. The septum is made of cartilage. Thus the outside of the nose which we can see, is mostly made of cartilage whereas the inside of the nose is mostly made of bone. The nasal cavity connects to the paranasal sinuses, hollow spaces inside the bones surrounding the nose which are full of air and are also lined with mucous membrane.

Functions: the nose is the first organ that air enters. It has three functions:
- to work as the organ of smell
- to moisten and warm the air entering the nostrils
- to filter dust, bacteria, and other foreign matter from the air using the mucous membrane and its hairs. The mucus collects any dirt and bacteria and prevents it from passing into the lungs. The cilia push the mucus into the throat. It is then swallowed and travels to the stomach where any bacteria are neutralised by gastric acids.

PHARYNX
Once air has been filtered, moistened and warmed in the nose it travels to the pharynx, a tube which leads from the back of the nose and mouth and divides into the oesophagus (posteriorly) and larynx (anteriorly). It works as part of both the digestive and respiratory systems.

Structure: the pharynx is about 12.5cm long and made of muscular and fibrous tissue. At the back of the section of the pharynx which connects to the nose are small masses of lymphoid tissue which form the pharyngeal tonsils, or adenoids. Like the palatine tonsils (at the junction of the mouth and throat) the pharyngeal tonsils filter bacteria.

Function: it acts as an air passage and also warms and moistens the air.

Upper respiratory tract

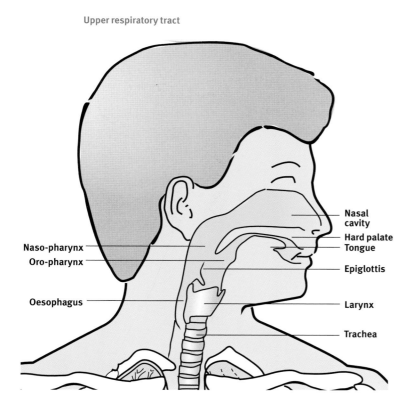

Nasal cavity
Hard palate
Tongue
Epiglottis
Larynx
Trachea
Naso-pharynx
Oro-pharynx
Oesophagus

LARYNX

From the pharynx, air travels down to the larynx (also known as the voice box).

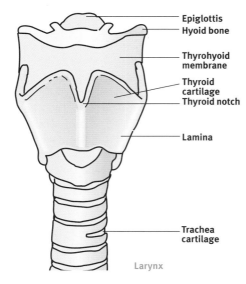

Larynx

Epiglottis
Hyoid bone
Thyrohyoid membrane
Thyroid cartilage
Thyroid notch
Lamina
Trachea cartilage

Structure: the larynx is a tube positioned between the tongue at the back of the mouth and the trachea (the tube leading to the lungs). It is made of rings of cartilage, attached to each other by membranes and ligaments. The thyroid cartilage at the top of the larynx, which is larger in men than in women, forms the Adam's apple which is often visible in the throat.

Function: the larynx is a passageway for air between the pharynx and trachea. It filters bacteria, helps in voice production and warms and moistens the air.

TRACHEA

From the larynx, air travels to the trachea.

Structure: the trachea is a continuation of the larynx. It is a tube about 10cm long which runs from the front of the neck to the chest where it divides into two bronchi, tubes which lead to the lungs. The trachea is made of incomplete rings of hyaline cartilage (anteriorly) and involuntary muscle and connective tissue (posteriorly). It is lined with ciliated epithelium which contains mucus-secreting goblet cells.

Function: the trachea is a passageway for air between the larynx and bronchi. The goblet secretory cells in the lining secrete mucus which collects any foreign matter or bacteria and the cilia then push this up to the larynx.

BRONCHI

The bronchi are the branches of the respiratory tube which transport air in and out of each lung.

Structure: bronchi (singular: bronchus) connect the trachea to the lungs. There are two of them, one on the left and one on the right which enter the lungs at the hilum, a concave depression, where they subdivide into different branches for different lobes of the lungs. Like the trachea, they are made of hyaline cartilage, involuntary muscle and connective tissue and are lined with ciliated epithelium.

Function: to pass air from the trachea into the bronchioles, and thus to the lungs.

The bronchi

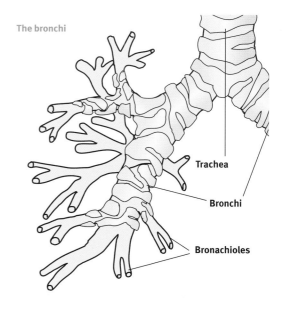

Trachea
Bronchi
Bronachioles

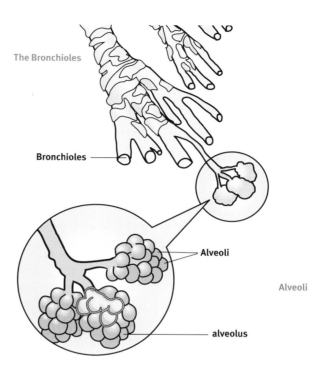

The Bronchioles

Bronchioles

Alveoli

Alveoli

alveolus

BRONCHIOLES

The final and finest tubes in the passage of air from the nose to the lungs are the bronchioles.

Structure: bronchioles are made of muscular, fibrous and elastic tissue. They become progressively smaller as they spread further into the lungs until they are no more than a single layer of flattened epithelial cells (just like blood capillaries). These microscopic tubes are called terminal bronchioles.

Function: bronchioles take air to the alveoli of the lungs.

LUNGS

The two lungs are the centre of the respiratory system. It is in these two spongy organs that gases enter and exit the blood.

Structure: the lungs are positioned either side of the heart; the left lung is divided into two lobes, the superior and inferior lobes, whereas the right lung is divided into three, the superior, middle and inferior. Lobes are subdivided into lobules. Lung tissue is made of bronchioles, alveoli, blood vessels, nerves, connective tissue and elastic tissue. They are covered in a special membrane called the pleura.

Function: lungs allow the exchange of gases into and out of the blood.

PLEURA

Structure: the pleura is a serous membrane that surrounds each lung. It has two layers, the inner, visceral layer which sticks to the lung tissue and covers the surface and the outer, parietal layer which sticks to the chest wall and the top of the diaphragm. The two layers are separated by a space called the pleural cavity which is filled with a serous fluid.

Function: the pleural cavity prevents friction between the two layers during respiration.

ALVEOLI

The exchange of gases in the lungs takes place in tiny sacs called alveoli (singular: alveolus) at the end of the terminal bronchioles.

Structure: alveoli are made of a thin layer of squamous epithelial cells and are surrounded by a capillary network.

Function: to exchange gases between the circulatory and respiratory systems. The pulmonary artery delivers deoxygenated blood to the capillary network which is then oxygenated by contact with the air in the alveoli. The oxygenated blood then leaves the lungs via the capillary network and the pulmonary veins and travels to the heart to be pumped around the body.

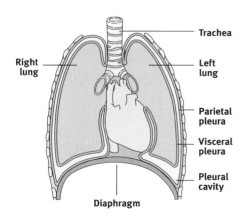

The lungs

Trachea

Right lung

Left lung

Parietal pleura

Visceral pleura

Pleural cavity

Diaphragm

YOU NOW KNOW
The names, structures and functions of all the organs and passageways which transmit air from outside the body into the lungs. The next section explains the mechanism of breathing.

Section two: how breathing works – internal and external respiration

MECHANISM OF RESPIRATION

Although all of these separate tubes and passageways have individual functions, it is their function as a whole that is important i.e. to allow us, and every cell in our body, to breathe. The entrance and exit of air in and out of the body is a process known as breathing, whereas the entrance and exit of oxygen and carbon dioxide in and out of cells is known as gaseous exchange.

WHAT IS EXTERNAL RESPIRATION?

External respiration is the breathing in and out of air, and the diffusion of oxygen from the alveoli into the blood and carbon dioxide from the blood to the alveoli. In order to understand how the gases pass from one tissue to the next it is important to know the following physical law:

gases diffuse from a higher pressure to a lower pressure until equal pressure is achieved.

Diffusion occurs when a strong concentration of a gas comes into contact with a weak concentration of the same gas. The dissolved gas molecules will move from the strong concentration to the weak concentration until the concentration is equal on both sides. In the case of oxygen and carbon dioxide this occurs through the capillary and alveoli walls. The oxygen in the alveoli is under more pressure than the venous, deoxygenated blood in the capillaries so the oxygen passes from the alveoli (high pressure) into the capillaries (low pressure). Once the pressure in both is the same, the exchange stops. The carbon dioxide in the blood is under more pressure than the carbon dioxide in the alveoli so it diffuses through the capillary walls to the alveoli. The blood is thus oxygenated and its waste removed and it now travels back to the heart ready to be pumped round the body. The lungs then expel the carbon dioxide through the process of exhalation.

WHAT IS INTERNAL RESPIRATION?

Internal respiration is the diffusion of oxygen from the blood to the body cells, and of carbon dioxide from the body cells to the blood.

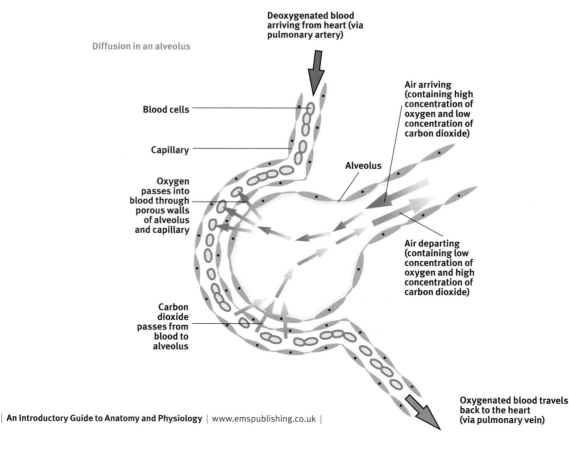

Diffusion in an alveolus

Deoxygenated blood arriving from heart (via pulmonary artery)

Air arriving (containing high concentration of oxygen and low concentration of carbon dioxide)

Blood cells

Capillary

Alveolus

Oxygen passes into blood through porous walls of alveolus and capillary

Air departing (containing low concentration of oxygen and high concentration of carbon dioxide)

Carbon dioxide passes from blood to alveolus

Oxygenated blood travels back to the heart (via pulmonary vein)

Once blood has been oxygenated in the lungs it travels back to the heart and is then pumped round the body. When blood reaches the various cells of the body, oxygen is again transferred by diffusion: the pressure of the oxygen in the blood is high whereas the pressure of the oxygen in the cells is low, so the oxygen passes into the cells. The amount of oxygen delivered depends on how busy the cell is. For example, more oxygen will be delivered to a muscle cell when it is exercising than when it is resting. The blood delivers its oxygen and collects the carbon dioxide (pressure in the blood is lower than in the cells so the carbon dioxide passes into the blood), carrying it back to the lungs where it will be delivered to the alveoli and then exhaled.

HOW DOES BLOOD TRAVEL TO AND FROM THE LUNGS?

Via the pulmonary circulation which is the movement of blood from the heart to the lungs and back.

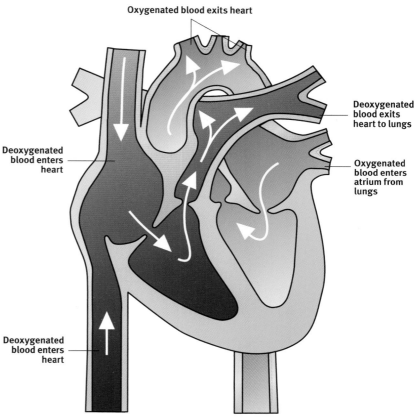

Oxygenated blood exits heart

Deoxygenated blood exits heart to lungs

Deoxygenated blood enters heart

Oxygenated blood enters atrium from lungs

Deoxygenated blood enters heart

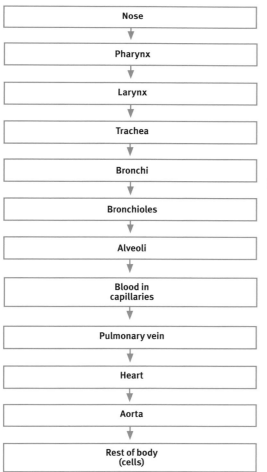

Nose
Pharynx
Larynx
Trachea
Bronchi
Bronchioles
Alveoli
Blood in capillaries
Pulmonary vein
Heart
Aorta
Rest of body (cells)

Oxygen's route into the body

● DID YOU KNOW?

Think of internal respiration as a postal service delivering and collecting gases instead of letters. Oxygen is sent around the body, carbon dioxide is collected.

HOW DOES AIR GET INTO THE BODY IN THE FIRST PLACE?

Through the same gaseous pressure principle. Air enters the respiratory system (this is known as inspiration or inhalation) when the pressure is lower inside the lungs and leaves the lungs when the pressure in the atmosphere around the body is lower (known as expiration or exhalation). But it is the action of the muscles involved in respiration that make these changes in pressure, and the movement of air, happen. The main muscle involved in the mechanics of respiration is the diaphragm which is helped by the intercostal muscles (positioned between the ribs).

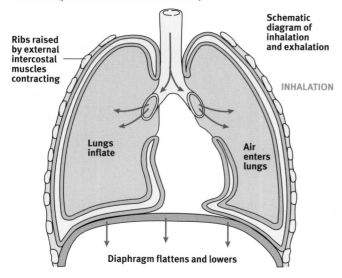

Schematic diagram of inhalation and exhalation

INHALATION

Ribs raised by external intercostal muscles contracting

Lungs inflate

Air enters lungs

Diaphragm flattens and lowers

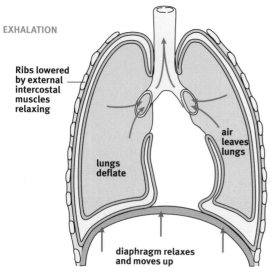

EXHALATION

Ribs lowered by external intercostal muscles relaxing

lungs deflate

air leaves lungs

diaphragm relaxes and moves up

WHAT IS THE DIAPHRAGM?

The diaphragm is a large muscle. It is positioned between the chest and abdomen and separates them from each other.

Structure: the diaphragm is made of a central sheet of tendon with muscle fibres towards the edges and it has three origins – posterior, lateral and anterior. When relaxed it is a dome shape; when contracted it flattens out.

Functions:

■ inspiration/inhalation: when the diaphragm contracts, it flattens out and since it forms the bottom of the chest cavity, this cavity then increases in size and volume. This lowers the pressure inside the chest. Air is thus sucked in because the pressure is lower inside the body than outside.

■ expiration/exhalation: when the diaphragm relaxes it becomes a dome shape and pushes up the chest cavity, thus reducing the cavity's size and volume and increasing the pressure. Air rushes out because the pressure is lower outside.

■ the diaphragm also helps with expulsive body actions:
  – micturition (urine excretion)
  – defecation (faeces expulsion)
  – parturition (giving birth).

WHAT ARE THE INTERCOSTAL MUSCLES?

Intercostal muscles are between the ribs. These muscles aid the diaphragm in respiration. During inspiration the external intercostal muscles contract at the same time as the diaphragm, lifting the rib cage up and outwards. The flattened and lowered diaphragm and the raised ribs cause an increase in the size of the chest cavity. During expiration, the external intercostals relax allowing the ribs to fall down and inwards, helping to decrease the size of the chest cavity. Nerve impulses delivered by the intercostal nerves tell the muscles when to contract and relax.

HOW DOES THE BODY KNOW WHEN TO BREATHE?

Nerve cells called chemoreceptors, found in the aorta and carotid arteries (i.e. arteries which are very close to the heart) send impulses to the respiratory centre in the medulla oblongata of the brain with messages about the low levels of oxygen and high levels of carbon dioxide. When the level of carbon dioxide is too high and the level of oxygen too low a nerve impulse is sent to the diaphragm telling it to contract, thus causing inhalation. This is especially important during exercise and illness.

THE BRAIN'S ROLE IN BREATHING

Two centres of the brain are involved – the respiratory centre in the medulla oblongata and the pons Varolii:

- the respiratory centre stimulates inspiration and controls the depth of breathing and its regularity
- the pons Varolii stops inspiration thus provoking expiration. When the respiratory centre tells the diaphragm to contract, air is sucked into the lungs, stimulating nerve cells called stretch receptors found in the lung tissue. These receptors send impulses to the pons Varolii which then sends impulses to the diaphragm telling it to relax, thus provoking expiration.

WHAT DOES AIR CONTAIN

Air that comes into the body contains approximately 21% oxygen and 0.04% carbon dioxide whereas air that leaves the body contains approximately 15% oxygen and 4% carbon dioxide. Thus, the air we exhale contains 100 times more carbon dioxide and 6% less oxygen than the air we inhale.

N.B. It is important to remember that breathing is not an intermittent process! The body does not stop breathing when the correct levels of oxygen and carbon dioxide are established, although breathing slows down and speeds up depending on our level of activity and health. Cells and tissues need to breathe all the time because every bodily function and movement requires oxygen and produces carbon dioxide. Breathing is a necessary and (in a healthy person) automatic function which continues throughout life.

YOU NOW KNOW

the structure and function of the respiratory system and how it is controlled by the nervous system. The final section of the chapter outlines the diseases and disorders of the respiratory system.

TOPIC 2: DISEASES AND DISORDERS (PATHOLOGIES)

BRONCHITIS
Inflammation of the bronchial tubes which causes coughing, shortness of breath and fatigue. Causes include smoking and infections.

EMPHYSEMA
Alveoli stretch and lose their elasticity. This prevents effective breathing, causing cough, shortness of breath, and wheezing.

PLEURISY
Inflammation of the pleural lining; fluid may develop in pleura. Causes localised chest pain, shortness of breath, cough.

PNEUMONIA
Inflammation of lung tissue caused by infection. The lungs fill with fluid. Causes cough, fever, fatigue, headache and chest pain can be fatal.

TUBERCULOSIS

Disease caused by bacteria, inhaled or eaten (in infected meat or milk). Symptoms include cough, night sweats and fever. BCG injections are used to vaccinate against it.

ASTHMA

Difficulty in exhalation, coughing and wheezing. Often caused by allergies.

RHINITIS

Stuffy, congested nose and sinuses. Caused by cold, flu, hay fever and sinus infections.

HAY FEVER

Allergic rhinitis; caused by allergy to certain pollens; symptoms include sneezing, runny nose and eyes and sometimes swelling/itching.

SINUSITIS

Inflammation of sinuses, often following respiratory infection; causes headaches and facial pain.

STRESS

Stress causes breathing rate to increase.

COMMON COLD

A mild viral infection involving the nose and respiratory passages (but not the lungs).

COUGH

A sudden noisy expulsion of air from the lungs that clears the air passages.

INFLUENZA

An acute contagious disease of the upper airways and lungs, caused by a virus, which rapidly spreads.

LARYNGITIS

An inflammation of the mucous membrane of the larynx; characterized by hoarseness or loss of voice and coughing.

PHARYNGITIS

A sore throat: inflammation of the pharynx.

PULMONARY EMBOLISM

A blockage of the pulmonary artery by foreign matter or by a blood clot.

TONSILLITIS

Is an infection of the tonsils and will often, but not necessarily, cause a sore throat and fever.

COR PULMONALE

Enlargement of the right ventricle of the heart due to disease of the lungs or of the pulmonary blood vessels.

CHRONIC OBSTRUCTIVE AIRWAYS DISEASE (COPD)

Refers to chronic bronchitis and emphysema, a pair of two commonly co-existing diseases of the lungs in which the airways become narrowed.

CYSTIC FIBROSIS

The most common congenital disease; the child's lungs, intestines and pancreas become clogged with thick mucus; caused by defect in a single gene; no cure is known.

HYPERVENTILATION

An increased depth and rate of breathing, greater than is demanded by the body needs; can cause dizziness and tingling of the fingers and toes and chest pain if continued.

LUNG CANCER

Is a disease of uncontrolled cell growth in tissues of the lung or carcinoma of the lungs; one of the commonest forms of cancer.

PERTUSSIS

Whooping cough: a disease of the respiratory mucous membrane.

PNEUMOTHORAX

An abnormal presence of air in the pleural cavity resulting in the collapse of the lung; may be spontaneous (due to injury to the chest) or induced (as a treatment for tuberculosis).

PULMONARY FIBROSIS

A chronic lung inflammation with progressive scarring of the alveolar walls that can lead to death.

SARCOIDOSIS

A chronic disease of unknown cause marked by the formation of nodules in the lungs, liver, lymph glands and salivary glands.

SEVERE ACUTE RESPIRATORY SYNDROME (SARS)

A respiratory disease of unknown etiology that apparently originated in mainland China in 2003; characterized by fever and coughing or difficulty breathing or hypoxia; can be fatal.

SNORING

Is the vibration of respiratory structures and the resulting sound, due to obstructed air movement during breathing while sleeping.

INTERRELATIONSHIPS
Respiratory system links to:
Circulatory: the circulation transports oxygen from the respiratory system to every cell of the body and transports carbon dioxide to the respiratory system to be exhaled.
Nervous: respiration is closely controlled by the nervous system, which indicates when inhalation or exhalation should happen. Chemoreceptors in the main arteries stimulate the nervous response of the respiratory system to begin the process of inhaling oxygen when required.
Muscular: the intercostal muscles and diaphragm are fundamental to the process of respiration.

Summary
The respiratory system

- is a system for the exchange of gases from outside to inside the body and vice versa
- is controlled by the nervous system

DON'T FORGET
TO LOGIN TO GAIN ACCESS TO YOUR **FREE** MULTI-MEDIA LEARNING RESOURCES

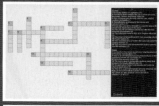

☐ Test your knowledge with crosswords

☐ Test your knowledge with fill in the gaps

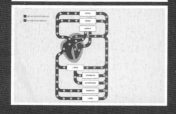

☐ Test your knowledge with interactive animations and diagrams

To login to use these resources visit
www.emspublishing.co.uk/anatomy and follow the onscreen instructions.

AN INTRODUCTORY GUIDE TO
Anatomy & Physiology

The Urinary system

The urinary system filters blood and produces urine. It consists of the kidneys, ureters, bladder and urethra.

The Urinary system

The urinary system is one of the human body's waste disposal units and its filtration unit. Composed of the kidneys, ureters (tubes connecting kidneys to the bladder), bladder and urethra, this system helps to empty the body of potentially harmful waste substances, like urea and alcohol. It does so through filtration and excretion.

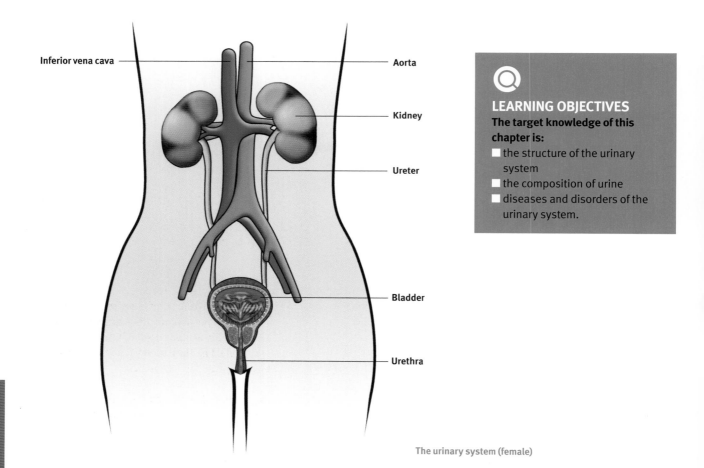

Inferior vena cava

Aorta

Kidney

Ureter

Bladder

Urethra

The urinary system (female)

LEARNING OBJECTIVES
The target knowledge of this chapter is:
- the structure of the urinary system
- the composition of urine
- diseases and disorders of the urinary system.

TOPIC 1: STRUCTURE

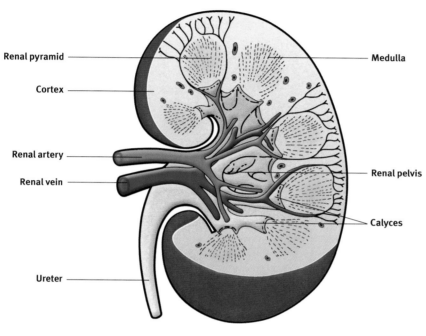

Renal pyramid

Cortex

Renal artery

Renal vein

Ureter

Medulla

Renal pelvis

Calyces

Cross-section
of kidney

WHAT IS A KIDNEY?

A kidney is a bean-shaped organ, about 11cm
long. Humans have two of them, positioned on the
posterior wall of the abdomen, either side of the
spine, in the upper lumbar part of the back. On its
way through the body about a quarter of the total
blood in circulation passes through the kidneys
in order to be filtered of toxic substances before
re-circulating.

Structure: a kidney's structure has two distinct
parts – the cortex on the outside and the medulla
on the inside. The medulla leads into an area called
the pelvis (sometimes called the renal pelvis). The
concave centre of the kidney is known as the hilum

and it is at this point that blood vessels, lymphatic
vessels, nerves and the ureter enter the organ.
Kidney tissue is made up of over a million twisted
tubes called nephrons, which do the kidneys' work
of filtration and excretion.

Functions: to filter the blood, reabsorb useful
materials needed by the body and form urine.

WHAT IS THE RENAL PELVIS?

Structure: the renal pelvis is a funnel-shaped
cavity which connects the medulla to the ureter.

Function: it collects urine from the tubules in the
medulla and passes it into the ureter.

WHAT ARE URETERS?
The tubes which connect the kidneys to the bladder.

Function: to take urine from the kidneys to the bladder. The presence of urine inside them stimulates a mechanical contraction which propels the fluid forwards.

WHAT IS THE BLADDER?
Structure: sometimes called the urinary bladder this is a sac-like organ in the pelvic cavity.

Function: a reservoir for urine. When about 200ml of urine has been collected the presence of the liquid stimulates the autonomic nerve endings in the bladder wall and the walls contract. The bladder has an internal sphincter which relaxes when the walls contract, thus opening and emptying the urine into the urethra.

WHAT IS THE URETHRA?
Structure: a narrow tube passing from the bladder to the outside of the body.
It has an external sphincter which is voluntarily controlled by the central nervous system. It is shorter in women, thus making them more susceptible to infection.

Function: to take urine from inside the body (the bladder) to outside. In men, the urethra is also the passage for semen.

YOU NOW KNOW
the names of all the different parts of the urinary system and their individual functions. The next section explains the filtration of blood and the production of urine.

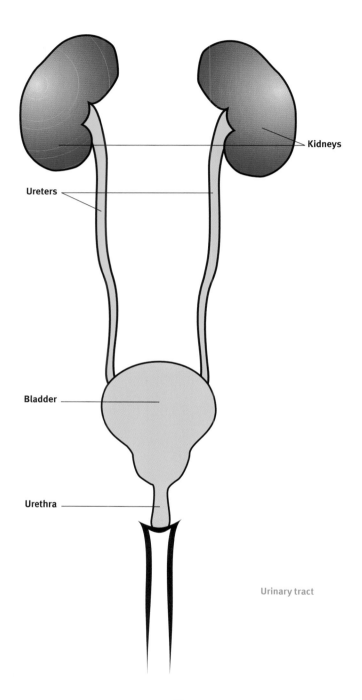

Kidneys

Ureters

Bladder

Urethra

Urinary tract

● DID YOU KNOW?
Eight large glasses per day is the recommended intake of water for a healthy body.

TOPIC 2: FUNCTIONS

The three stages of filtration and urine production

1) Filtration in the Bowman's capsule

Blood enters the kidneys via the afferent arterioles. These tiny blood vessels become the glomerulus, a tangle of capillaries surrounded by the glomerular capsule, also known as the Bowman's capsule. The blood in the capillaries is under pressure and since the capillary walls are permeable to water and other substances these pass through into the capsule, whilst blood cells and protein remain in the blood vessel. The Bowman's capsule thus serves as the collection point for the waste products carried in the blood. However, at this point the capsule has also collected other substances which are not waste and these will be reabsorbed as they pass through the nephron.

2) Re-absorption in the convoluted tubules

Once the filtered substances have been collected by the capsule they are passed into a system of twisted tubes, known as convoluted tubules. The tubes of the nephron which lead away from the Bowman's capsule are known as the proximal convoluted tubules. These straighten out into a long loop, called the Loop of Henle, which passes into the medulla and back to the cortex. Finally, there is another series of twists called the distal convoluted tubules. Reabsorption takes place in the tubules. Cells in the lining of the tubules are able to absorb any water, glucose, salts and ions which the body needs that must not be disposed of as waste. Only 1% of the liquid filtered into the Bowman's capsule is actually excreted as urine. The rest is re-absorbed.

3) Collection in the pelvic calyces

The nephron straightens out into a collecting tube in the medulla. These collecting tubes form masses called pyramids of the medulla, the tops of which stick up into the renal pelvis. The branches of the pelvis, or calyces, connect with the tops of these pyramids and collect the waste liquid, funneling it back into the pelvis, from where it will empty into the ureter.

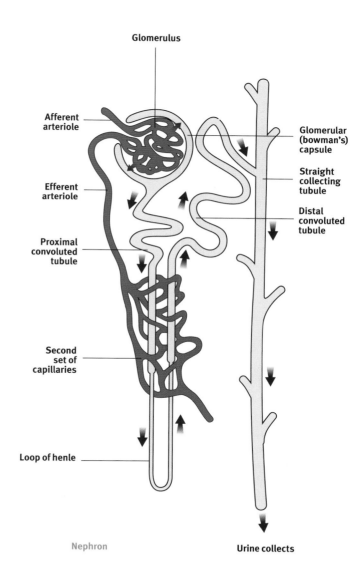

Glomerulus

Afferent arteriole

Efferent arteriole

Proximal convoluted tubule

Second set of capillaries

Loop of henle

Glomerular (bowman's) capsule

Straight collecting tubule

Distal convoluted tubule

Nephron

Urine collects

WHAT IS EXCRETED: COMPOSITION OF URINE

The liquid that results from the processes of filtration and reabsorption is known as urine. This amber-coloured liquid is composed of 96% water, 2% urea, and 2% other substances, such as ammonia, sodium, potassium, phosphates, chlorides, sulphates and excess vitamins. The salts must be excreted in order to maintain the correct balance of fluids and electrolytes in the body. The colour of urine comes from bilirubin, a bile pigment. Normal urine is acidic, but this varies depending on diet and other factors.

URINE PRODUCTION

About 1.5 litres of urine is produced every 24 hours, which is only a small percentage compared to the amount of liquid filtered from the blood in the glomerulus. Urine production is increased by liquid intake and cold weather and decreased by drinking less and any activity or state that increases sweating (hot weather, exercise). Humans need a minimum of 0.5 litres of water per day for waste removal.

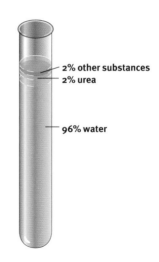

2% other substances
2% urea
96% water

Composition of urine

● DID YOU KNOW?

Since 96% of urine is composed of water it is no surprise that a common English expression for urination is to pass water.

YOU NOW KNOW
the urinary system works. The following section explains some of the diseases that affect it.

TOPIC 3: DISEASES AND DISORDERS

CYSTITIS

Inflammation of the bladder, causing pain when urinating. Sometimes caused by infections. Very common in women due in part to the shorter length of the female urethra.

KIDNEY STONES

Deposits of substances found in urine which form solid stones within the renal pelvis, bladder or ureters. Extremely painful and often removed by surgery.

NEPHRITIS OR BRIGHT'S DISEASE

Inflammation of the kidney, resulting from causes other than infection. Often used to refer to a wide range of different inflammatory disorders.

DIABETES INSIPIDUS

Impaired ADH production by the pituitary gland, or response to it by the kidneys. Causes excessive urine production so toxins in the body become too concentrated.

GLOMERULONEPHRITIS

A type of glomerular kidney disease in which the kidneys' filters become inflamed and scarred, and slowly lose their ability to remove wastes and excess fluid from the blood to make urine.

PYELONEPHRITIS

Inflammation of the kidney and its pelvis caused by bacterial infection.

URINARY TRACT INFECTIONS

Is a bacterial infection that affects any part of the urinary tract.

URETHRITIS

Inflammation of the urethra; results in painful urination.

DYSURIA

Painful or difficult urination, most frequently caused by infection or inflammation.

ENURESIS

An inability to control the flow of urine and involuntary urination. This can also be known as bed wetting.

INCONTINENCE

An involuntary urination or defecation.

NEPHROBLASTOMA

A tumour of the kidneys that typically occurs in children.

RENAL FAILURE

An inability of the kidneys to excrete waste resulting in a situation in which the kidneys fail to function adequately.

RENAL COLIC

Is a type of pain commonly caused by the obstruction to the flow of urine, often caused by kidney stones.

URAEMIA

An accumulation in the blood of nitrogenous waste products (urea) that are usually excreted in the urine.

INTERRELATIONSHIPS

Urinary system links to:

Circulatory: the kidneys purify all the blood in the body.

Endocrine: the kidneys produce the enzyme renin which helps to regulate blood pressure as part of a system involving hormones.

Skeletal: the kidneys help to stimulate the production of bone marrow in the long bones.

Skin: the urinary system removes waste by excretion and therefore links to the other excretory system — the skin.

Summary

The urinary system

- filters blood of potentially harmful substances
- produces urine through the processes of filtration and re-absorption
- excretes waste (urine).

DON'T FORGET
TO LOGIN TO GAIN ACCESS TO YOUR **FREE** MULTI-MEDIA LEARNING RESOURCES

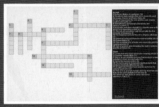

☐ Test your knowledge with crosswords

☐ Test your knowledge with fill in the gaps

☐ Test your knowledge with interactive animations and diagrams ·

To login to use these resources visit

www.emspublishing.co.uk/anatomy and follow the onscreen instructions.

AN INTRODUCTORY GUIDE TO
Anatomy & Physiology

13

Nails

Nails

The fingernail, or nail plate, serves to protect the end of the fingertip and to enhance the sensitivity of the nerves in the fingertip. The nail we see is itself a plate of translucent keratin, but it is part of a system that continually replenishes the nail plate, and protects and seals the system from infection and the environment.

TOPIC 1: STRUCTURE AND FUNCTION

THE COMPONENTS OF THE NAIL SYSTEM

The nail system that lies beneath the nail has six main components, each with a specific purpose, and each shown in the diagram (right).
These are the:

- free edge
- hyponychium
- peronychium (lateral nail fold)
- eponychium (cuticle)
- nail plate
- cuticle
- nail bed
- nail folds
- matrix
- mantle
- lunula
- nail wall

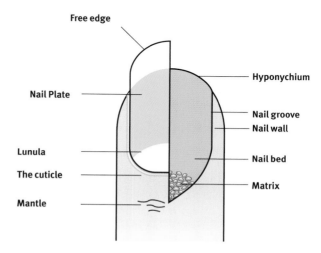

The structure of the nail

Free edge

The free edge of the nail is the part extending beyond the end of the skin of the fingertip.

Hyponychium

The hyponychium forms a seal between the free edge of the nail and the skin of the fingertip.

Peronychium

The paronychial edge or peronichium is the skin that overlaps the sides of the nail. The peronichium is the site of paronicia infections, hangnails and ingrowing nails.

Eponychium

The eponychium forms a seal between the skin and the nail plate that protects the underlying matrix from infection.

Nail plate

What we commonly call the fingernail is actually the nail plate, a protective shield of translucent keratin for the nail bed beneath. Grooves in the

underneath of the plate help to hold it to the nail bed. While the nail plate is actually translucent, the blood vessels beneath it give it a pink appearance.

Cuticle

It protects the matrix from infection.

Nail bed

As the matrix produces new cells, pushing the nail forward, the nail moves along the nail bed, which adds cells to the underside of the nail, thickening and strengthening it as it grows. The nail bed contains the blood vessels (which, seen through the translucent nail plate, give the nail its colour), the nerves that provide sensation and melanocytes. The nail bed lies directly beneath the nail plate. Both have grooves which dovetail into each other, holding the nail plate in place as it grows forward.

Nail folds

The nail folds are the folds in the skin which protect the matrix, and in which the edges of the nail plate sit. The root of the nail is protected by the proximinal nail fold, and the edges by the lateral nail folds.

Matrix

The matrix is where the cells of the nail plate and nail bed are produced. It lies mostly beneath the nail and the nail bed with only the tip of the root visible through the nail plate as the lunula. The matrix produces keratin cells for the nail plate and bed, pushing older cells forward along the finger or toe as it does so.

Mantle

Deep fold of skin at the base of the nail before the cuticle.

Lunula

The half moon on our fingernails, or lunula, is actually the visible front end of the germinal matrix extending underneath the nail plate. The prominence of the lunula varies from person to person, and is normally most visible on the thumbnails. The shape of the lunula is reflected in the natural shape of the free edge of the nail.

Nail wall

The folds of skin which overlap the sides of the nail plate for protection.

HOW THE NAIL GROWS

Nail growth rate varies, but may be up to 3 mm per week for fingernails and 1 mm for toenails, with the whole fingernail being replaced two or three times per year, and the toenail every year to 18 months. The growth rate peaks in our early teens and then reduces with age, but it may increase again during pregnancy, the summer, or while we sleep.

FACTORS AFFECTING NAIL GROWTH

Nail growth and health can be affected by a range of factors, including:

- **Health** – the shape, integrity and colour of the nail can be affected by diseases of the lung, heart, kidney, liver or thyroid.

- **Age** – the growth rate of both fingernails and toenails slows as we get older, and the protein in the nail becomes more brittle and prone to splitting.

- **Diet** – while serious vitamin or mineral deficiencies may affect the nails, diet does not generally cause abnormal nail changes, except in cases of severe malnutrition.

- **Medication** – medication may affect the rate at which fast-growing cells in the body reproduce

- **Climate** – blood increases in hotter climates thereby increasing nail growth.

- **Damage** – if the matrix is damaged nail growth can be affected or retarded.

- **Lifestyle** – environmental factors, eg hands in water, or chemical solutions.

YOU NOW KNOW
- the components of the nail system
- how the nail grows

TOPIC 2:
NAIL CONDITIONS, DISEASES AND DISORDERS

There are many specific nail conditions, some of which are localised to the nails, while others may be related to more general medical conditions. You need to be able to recognise them and to know which ones are contraindicated for treatments.

Salon Name
Client Consultation Form – *Manicure and Pedicure Treatments*

Client Name: Date:
Address:

                                                 Profession:
e-mail: Tel. No: Day
                                                          Eve

PERSONAL DETAILS:
Age group: Under 20☐ 20–30☐ 30–40☐ 40–50☐ 50–60☐ 60+☐
Lifestyle: Active☐ Sedentary☐
Last visit to the doctor:
GP Address:
No. of children (if applicable):
Date of last period (If applicable):

DISEASES AND DISORDERS *(select where/if appropriate):*

Transverse ridges ☐	Leuconychia ☐
Vertical ridges ☐	Flaking ☐
Beau's lines ☐	Onychorrhexis ☐
Blue nails ☐	Pitting ☐
Psoriasis ☐	Pterygium ☐
Tinea Ungium ☐	Onychia ☐
Tinea Pedis ☐	Hang nail ☐
Paronychia (Whitlow) ☐	Lamella dystrophy ☐
Sepsis ☐	Onychomycosis ☐

Onychatrophia ☐
Onychauxis ☐
Onychgryposis ☐
Onychocryptosis ☐
Koilonychia ☐
Onychophagy ☐
Koilonychia ☐
Warts ☐

CONTRAINDICATIONS REQUIRING MEDICAL PERMISSION – in circumstances where medical permission cannot be obtained clients must give their informed consent in writing prior to treatment *(select if/where appropriate):*

Haemophilia ☐	Recent operations affecting the area ☐
Any condition being treated by a GP, dermatologist or another practitioner ☐	Diabetes ☐
	Inflamed nerve ☐
Acute Arthritis ☐	Undiagnosed pain ☐
Medical oedema ☐	Acute rheumatism ☐
Nervous/Psychotic conditions ☐	

CONTRAINDICATIONS THAT RESTRICT TREATMENT *(select where/if appropriate):*

Fever ☐	Recent fractures (minimum 3 months) ☐
Contagious or infectious diseases ☐	Sunburn ☐
Diarrhoea and vomiting ☐	Repetitive strain injury ☐
Under the influence of recreational drugs or alcohol ☐	Carpal Tunnel Syndrome ☐
	Severely bitten or damaged nails ☐
Any known allergies ☐	Nail separation ☐
Undiagnosed lumps and bumps ☐	Eczema ☐
Inflammation ☐	Psoriasis ☐
Cuts ☐	Verucca ☐
Severe bruising ☐	Loss of skin sensation ☐
Abrasions ☐	Chilblains ☐
Scar tissue (2 years for major operation and 6 months for a small scar) ☐	Corns ☐

NAIL TEST *(select where/if appropriate):*
Moisture content: Excellent ☐ Good ☐ Fair ☐ Poor ☐
Cuticle condition: Excellent ☐ Good ☐ Fair ☐ Poor ☐
Skin condition: Dehydrated ☐ Dry ☐ Normal ☐
Skins healing ability: Excellent ☐ Good ☐ Fair ☐ Poor ☐
Circulation: Good ☐ Normal ☐ Poor ☐

FINDING OUT ABOUT NAIL CONDITIONS

Nail conditions are not always immediately obvious. Your starting points to finding out about your client's nails are:

- your client's consultation card (if your client has been before)
- communicating with your client
- preliminary visual check and initial cleanse.

If you have treated the client before, check the client's record card for any existing conditions and previous treatments before your client arrives. The record card must be updated on each visit, with any new observations, as existing conditions can change and new ones arise.

Wipe the hands with sanitiser, and remove any enamel before checking for contraindications.

WHAT TO LOOK OUT FOR

Onychosis is the technical term for a nail disease. Pronounce the 'onych' part of the technical terms 'on-eek'. It comes from the Greek for nail or claw.

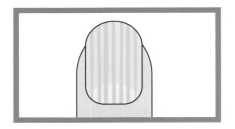

Ridges and furrows

Superficial ridges (corrugations) – possibly the result of age (with thickening of nails) or illness

Longitudinal (vertical ridges) – possibly associated with ill health

Single ridges – result of trauma, constant picking or ill health

Single transverse (horizontal) furrow (Beau's lines) – possibly the result of ill health.

Deep furrows – possibly the result of dermatitis (see below) or ill health Ridges and furrows can generally be buffed to make them smoother.

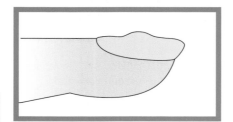

PITTING

Pitting is a sign of an underlying problem, such as dermatitis or psoriasis (see below), which can be a contraindication; if severe, suggest that your client seeks medical attention.

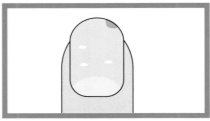

WHITE SPOTS (LEUCONYCHIA)

This is a common condition generally caused by an injury to the nail matrix, allowing an air pocket to form. The nails can be treated gently to avoid further injury.

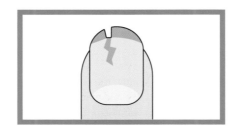

BRITTLE NAILS (ONYCHORRHEXIS)

Poor blood supply, caused by anaemia, illness or use of over-strong detergents removing natural oils, has dried the nails making them brittle, with a tendency to break easily. Regular use of cuticle cream, manicures, moisturiser and good diet should help this condition.

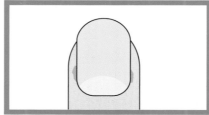

HANG NAIL

The cuticle has split as it has adhered to the nail plate and cannot continue to move forward with the growth of the nail, causing the cuticle to split leaving it prone to infection. Cut the torn cuticle carefully with cuticle clippers, and soften

with cuticle cream/oil. Suggest regular manicures to the client as these will help prevent recurrence.

DISCOLOURED NAILS

Blue nail – may be caused by poor circulation, anaemia or a heart problem. Using massage cream and finger exercises should help circulation.

Black nail – usually the result of heavy bruising. If particularly severe, the nail plate may detach from the nail bed, but a new nail usually grows to replace it. Treat very gently, avoiding pressure. If severe, avoid the nail until a new nail is in place.

Stained – nails can be stained by several things, including nicotine, dark nail enamels and hair dyes. Advise your client about the possible cause of the staining and buff nails regularly to reduce stains and encourage new nail growth.
Discolouration due to ringworm – see below.

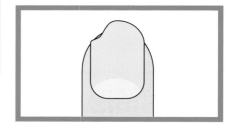

FLAKING (LAMELLA DYSTROPHY)

Flaking can be due to biting, incorrect or severe hand and nail treatments, lengthy exposure to hot water or harsh chemicals, or to general ill health. Keeping the nails short, moisturising and regular manicure with home-care advice should cure this condition.

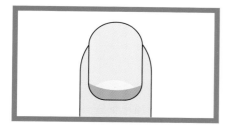

OVERGROWTH OF THE CUTICLE (PTERYGIUM)

The cuticle has a hardened growth which has grown over and stuck to the nail plate. Treat by softening the cuticle with oil or paraffin wax, then gently pushing it back and removing the excess cuticle carefully with nail clippers. Regular massage and manicures should prevent the condition recurring.

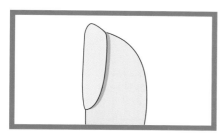

EXCESSIVE THICKENING (ONYCHAUXIS OR CLAW NAIL)

The nail plate has thickened and in some cases discoloured, usually due to internal disorders, infection, damage below the nail, or to constant rubbing (for instance by a badly fitting shoe). If not infected, the nail may be filed smooth, buffed and shaped as usual. Infections are contraindications to treatment and your client should seek medical advice.

ENLARGED NAIL WITH INCREASED CURVE (ONYCHOGRYPHOSIS)

Similar to claw nail; the nail plate has thickened and curved over due to an increase in the horny cells of the nail plate. This is a common complaint in older people, especially if combined with

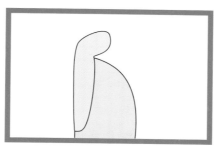

ill-fitting shoes or neglect. It should be treated by a chiropodist or advise medical attention.

NAIL IS BECOMING SMALLER (ONYCHATROPHIA)

As it becomes smaller, the nail becomes opaque and ridged and sometimes wastes away completely. It is usually caused by injury under the nail, nervous disorders or disease and manicures are not advised. The nail should be protected from products such as detergents. Advise your client to seek medical advice.

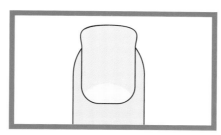

SPOON-SHAPED NAIL (KOILONYCHIA)

An abnormal growth causes the nail to splay at the sides, with a depression in the middle. It can be hereditary or due to a type of anaemia or overactive thyroid. If possible, the underlying cause should be treated medically.

INGROWING NAILS (ONYCHOCRYPTOSIS)

Most often affecting the big toe, the side

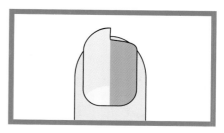

of the nail plate grows into the flesh of the nail wall. Ingrowing nails are usually caused by incorrect cutting or filing too far down the sides, ill-fitting shoes or neglect. They can be very painful and inflamed with swelling and pus. If infected, do not treat, advise medical treatment.

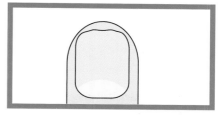

BITTEN NAILS (ONYCHOPHAGY)

Nail biting reduces the size of the nail so it eventually has no free edge. The nails look ragged and the fingertips sore, increasing chances of infection or hangnails. Regular manicure treatments can help by softening the cuticles, filing the nail edges smooth (if there is enough edge to file) and buffing to encourage growth. However, the condition will only clear up when the biting stops.

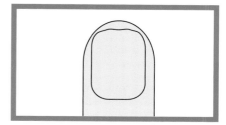

ONYCHOPTOSIS

Onychoptosis is identified as a condition where the nail may occasionally shed and/or come off. It may affect one or more nails and may occur after certain diseases, fever, system upset or medication.

TOPIC 3:
CONTRAINDICATIONS AND INFECTION

In addition to the nail conditions above, some of which may become infectious, there are diseases which are specific to hands, feet and nails which may be contraindicated.

Contraindications requiring medical permission – in circumstances where medical permission cannot be obtained clients must give their informed consent in writing prior to the treatment

- Haemophilia
- Any condition already being treated by a GP, dermatologist or another practitioner
- Medical oedema
- Arthritis
- Nervous/Psychotic conditions
- Recent operations of the hands or feet
- Diabetes
- Inflamed nerve
- Undiagnosed pain
- Acute rheumatism

CONTRAINDICATIONS THAT RESTRICT TREATMENT

- Any form of infection, disease or fever
- Under the influence of recreational drugs or alcohol
- Diarrhoea and vomiting
- Any known allergies
- Undiagnosed lumps and bumps
- Inflammation
- Cuts
- Severe bruising
- Abrasions
- Scar tissues (2 years for major operation and 6 months for a small scar)
- Recent fractures

• KEY POINT

All infections are contraindicated

(minimum 3 months)
- Sunburn
- Repetitive strain injury
- Carpal tunnel
- Severely bitten/damaged nails
- Nail separation
- Eczema
- Psoriasis
- Verrucas
- Corns
- Chill blains
- Loss of skin sensation

It is important to be able to recognise the different infections that can affect hands and feet:

ONYCHIA

A bacterial or fungal infection usually caused by a damaged cuticle being infected by biting or thumb sucking, frequent use of detergents or immersion in water. It can be very red and sore. Give advice about prevention and seeking medical treatment. Ringworm and athletes foot (onychomycosis/tinea unguium and tinea pedis)

Fungal infections are the most common form of toe and finger nail infection. Highly infectious ringworm first appears as a yellow-brown discolouration at the free edge. This condition is caused by a fungus attacking the nail plate and bed through the free edge but it can spread to the nail root. The nail thickens and becomes furrowed and spongy and sometimes completely detached. Medical advice is essential. Athletes foot (tinea pedis) is another highly contagious form of ringworm, in which the skin between and under the toes becomes swollen, white and waterlogged. It is contraindicated for manicure/pedicure.

PARONYCHIA (WHITLOW)

A bacterial infection of the skin around the nail, which becomes swollen, red and inflamed. Usually caused by broken skin, rough treatment or injury to the cuticle/nail fold, or exposure to unsterile manicure tools or harsh chemicals. A long-term infection may result in the nail becoming deformed. Medical advice should be sought.

WARTS AND VERRUCAS

Warts are caused by a virus and generally appear on the hands and fingers, especially where there are hangnails. They appear as raised patches, and are sometimes discoloured and rough. A viral wart infection of the nail fold and nail bed is called periungium viral warts.
Verrucas are compressed warts on the feet. Both warts and verrucas are contagious and contraindicated to manicure/pedicure.

CORNS

Corns generally appear over the joints in the toes or on the soles of the feet. They have a central core surrounded by thick skin which thickens further when rubbed, putting painful pressure on nerve endings. The client should be referred to a chiropodist for specialised treatment.

PSORIASIS

Psoriasis is characterised by small red patches covered in silvery scales. It can affect the skin around and under the nails. It may itch but if rubbed it can start to bleed and then is open to infection. The cause is unknown it can appear at any age and may be inherited or could be triggered by stress or illness. It is not contagious. It is contraindicated if the lesions are open and weeping.

ECZEMA AND DERMATITIS

Possibly hereditary or due to allergic reactions, the skin appears very dry and red, it may crack and flake and is usually itchy. Clients may be allergic to the lanolin in creams, the resins in nail hardeners and polishes and some ingredients in nail extensions. Take careful notes of any contra-actions.

YOU NOW KNOW
- nail conditions and how to find out about them
- nail contraindications and infections

DON'T FORGET
TO LOGIN TO GAIN ACCESS TO YOUR **FREE** MULTI-MEDIA LEARNING RESOURCES

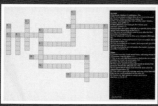

☐ Test your knowledge with crosswords

☐ Test your knowledge with fill in the gaps

☐ Test your knowledge with interactive animations and diagrams

To login to use these resources visit

www.emspublishing.co.uk/anatomy and follow the onscreen instructions.

AN INTRODUCTORY GUIDE TO

Anatomy & Physiology

Hair

TOPIC 1:
THE STRUCTURE AND FUNCTION OF HAIR

Hair grows in follicles which are in the dermis, the layer of skin beneath the epidermis. See Chapter 1 for more details of the skin and its structure. The dermis is connected to the blood and lymph supply as well as the nerves. It is made up of connective tissue, containing sweat glands, sebaceous glands and hair follicles.

HAIR FOLLICLES

The hair follicles travel through the epidermis and the dermis. The erector pili muscles are attached to each hair and help with temperature control of the body by pulling the hair upright and trapping a layer of air – goose pimples to keep the body warm (vasoconstriction).

SEBACEOUS GLANDS

Associated with each hair follicle is a sebaceous gland. These produce sebum, a fatty acid which keeps the skin moist and lubricates the hair shaft. When sweat and sebum combine on the surface of the skin they form the acid mantle, a protective shield which helps to control bacteria levels, prevents infections and disease, and acts as a natural moisturiser. The pH balance of the skin is 4.5 –5.6 and this acid environment helps to prevent bacterial growth.

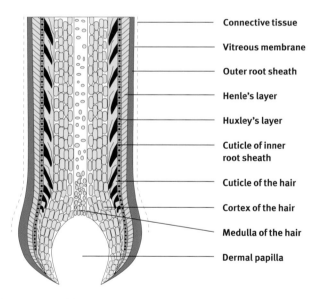

Connective tissue

Vitreous membrane

Outer root sheath

Henle's layer

Huxley's layer

Cuticle of inner root sheath

Cuticle of the hair

Cortex of the hair

Medulla of the hair

Dermal papilla

Cross-section of the hair in the follicle

The hair consists of three different layers:

- **The Cuticle** – is the outer layer which consists of overlapping, transparent keratin scales.
- **The Cortex** – middle layer consists of elongated cells which contain the pigment melanin, this is what gives the hair its colour.
- **The Medulla** – is the centre of the hair and is composed of loosely connected keratinised cells.

The layers of the follicle consist of the following:

- **The Inner Root Sheath** – which includes the Cuticle which interlocks with the cuticle of the hair, Huxley's layer which is 2 or more cells thick and the Henle's layer which is one cell thick.
- **The Outer Root Sheath** – this forms the follicle wall and is a continuation of the growing layer of the epidermis of the skin.
- **Vitreous Membrane** – this separates the connective tissue from the outer root sheath.

- **Connective Tissue** – This surrounds both the follicle and the sebaceous gland providing both the sensory supply and blood supply.
  The Dermal papilla supplies the follicle with the blood and nourishment required for growth.

TYPES OF HAIR

The hair growing on a human body can be one of three different types, depending on how old the person is and where the hair is growing.

■ Lanugo hair

About six months before a child is born, it begins to develop a coat of fine, soft, downy hair all over its body. These hairs begin growing at the same time, and grow at the same rate. The lanugo hair is normally shed one month before the child is born, but premature babies may be born still covered in lanugo hair.

The follicles that produce vellus hairs have no sebaceous glands, and are distributed over most of the body, with the exception of the soles of the feet, palms of the hands, the lips and nipples. Pale in colour, vellus hairs themselves only grow to one to two centimetres in length.

HAIR GROWTH CYCLE

The hair that we so often describe as 'growing' is actually mostly dead. The hair grows at its base, the hair bulb, in the follicle, and the hair we see above about a centimetre from the skin is in fact a dead shaft of keratin. The hair will grow from its base in the follicle for many years, and then falls out. The follicle rests for a while, and then resumes production of a new hair. This hair growth cycle has three stages, called the Anagen, Catogen and Telogen.

■ Terminal hairs

What we normally think of as hair is called terminal hair, and is produced by hair follicles with sebaceous glands. It grows on the head, areas of the face, underarms and the pubic area. Congenital tendencies to baldness may result in terminal hairs becoming shorter and thinner, so that they resemble vellus hairs.

■ Anagen

The anagen, or growing, phase can last from two to seven years, during which time the hair grows vigorously, at a rate of about a centimetre per month, although the hair can grow more quickly in the summer. Untrimmed, each of our hairs would grow to about a metre long before falling out! During the anagen phase, the hair bulb generates the pigment melanin, which gives our hair its colour. The length of the anagen stage of the cycle is an inherited characteristic.

■ Catagen

The anagen phase is followed by a phase of two to four weeks when the follicle rests. This phase is called the catagen, or intermediate, phase. The bulb produces neither hair cells nor pigment, and shrinks slightly, becoming less deep.

■ Telogen

In the telogen phase a new hair begins to grow in the hair follicle. As it does so, the old hair will be shed as we brush or wash our hair. By the end of the telogen phase, which lasts about three months, the old hair has been shed, and a new one is growing from the follicle and out of the skin, ready to begin its own anagen phase.

FACTORS THAT AFFECT THE HAIR GROWTH CYCLE

A range of factors can affect hair growth. These factors may be hormonal, dietary, environmental or, as we saw when discussing the hair growth cycle, they may be hereditary.

■ Hormonal factors

As we will see in the next topic on the endocrine system, there are a variety of hormonal factors that affect the hair growth cycle. As the state of the endocrine system changes as an individual grows, and varies according to stress, menstrual cycles, etc., the hair growth cycle is also affected.

Changes in androgen (male hormone) levels particularly affect the hair, and affect the rate of hair growth and the thickness of the hairs.

Female hormone levels (oestrogens) slow hair growth and extend the growing phase of the hair growth cycle.

As a result, hair growth can be affected in

DIET AND ENVIRONMENTAL FACTORS

Hair growth can be affected by both general diet, and specific dietary deficiencies. A very poor diet can lead to hair loss, through its effect on the endocrine system, and the changes of hormone levels that it induces. This can be seen in people who go on crash diets, or those who suffer from anorexia. Problems may also be caused by factors as varied as anaemia, alcohol consumption, or a lack of Vitamin B or zinc in a diet.

several ways by the balance of androgens and oestrogen in the blood. At the time of puberty the rise in androgen levels is responsible for the hair on the body changing into recognisable terminal hair, and the development of underarm and pubic hair. Later in life, changes in hormone levels will increase face, chest, nose and ear hair growth. In women, hair growth can be affected by hormonal changes during pregnancy, when they have high levels of oestrogen. and during the menopause when the oestrogen levels reduce.

Other hormones can also affect the hair, e.g. thyroid hormone accelerating hair growth.

YOU NOW KNOW
- the structure and function of hair
- the types of hair
- the hair growth cycle
- the factors that affect the hair growth cycle.

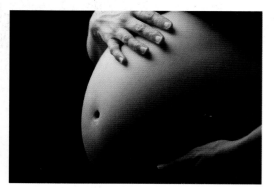

Ears, nose and eyes

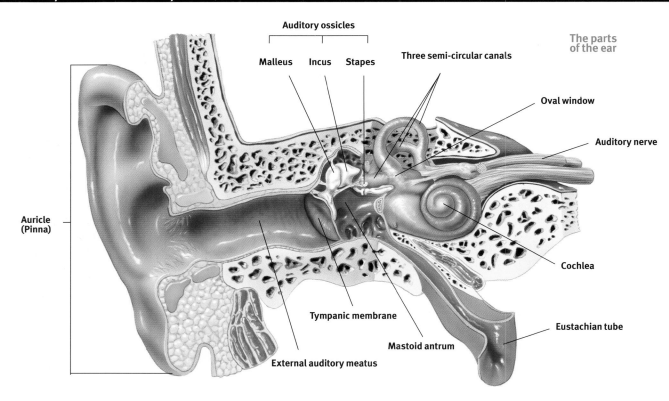

Auditory ossicles

Malleus   Incus   Stapes

Three semi-circular canals

The parts of the ear

Oval window

Auditory nerve

Auricle (Pinna)

Cochlea

Tympanic membrane

Mastoid antrum

Eustachian tube

External auditory meatus

TOPIC 1: THE EAR

The ears provide hearing and maintain body balance. The ear structure has three parts - the outer ear, the middle ear and the inner ear.

THE OUTER EAR

The outer ear is the visible part of the ear. It protects the inner structures from damage. The External auditory meatus (auditory canal) is lined with ceruminous glands and hairs, which filter out dust and foreign particles. The outer ear is also the passage for sound waves. The tympanic membrane (eardrum) separates the auditory canal from the middle ear.

THE MIDDLE EAR

The middle ear is found within a cavity in the temporal bone. It has minute bones known as auditory ossicles that transmit sounds from the tympanic membrane to the inner ear.

THE INNER EAR

The inner ear is responsible for hearing and balance. Within the inner ear structures, the vibrations of sound waves are translated into nerve impulses. Structures within the inner ear, the semicircular canals and vestibule, help to maintain posture and balance.

THE EUSTACHIAN TUBE

The Eustachian tube connects the middle ear to the throat. It maintains the atmospheric pressure of air within the ear, enabling the eardrum to vibrate as the sound waves reach it. This is vital for hearing.

The ears are complex, sensitive organs and are susceptible to damage in many ways. Loud noise or trauma many damage the sensitive receptors in the ears, causing hearing loss. Viral or bacterial infections may cuase disorders such as Otitis media. Problems with the inner ear can cause conditions such as Menieres disease, tinnitus, vertigo or labrynthitis, which affect the balance and health of the client.

TOPIC 2: THE NOSE

STRUCTURE

Most of the nose is concerned with breathing: inhaling air into the body and exhaling it from the body. However, it is also the organ of smell and thus very important in a therapy based on the power of aromas! At the top of the nose there are two areas of pigmented tissue known as olfactory membranes. They contain the olfactory, or smell-sensing cells, which have fine hair-like protrusions called cilia. The olfactory cells connect to nerves in an area known as the olfactory plexus. Once triggered, these nerves send messages along the olfactory nerves to the brain, particularly the limbic system. This area of the brain deals with memory, emotions, our basic instincts and mechanical functions.

FUNCTION

When odor molecules pass over the olfactory cells, it is thought that these cells trigger receptor areas which send an impulse via the olfactory plexus and nerves to the brain. Here the information is processed and interpreted (i.e. is it a new smell, a nice smell, a smell with positive or negative associations?). Depending on the interpretation, the brain sends messages to other parts of the body to elicit a response (e.g. if dislike is the message the person will stop sniffing the bottle, possibly grimace, and turn away from the smell).

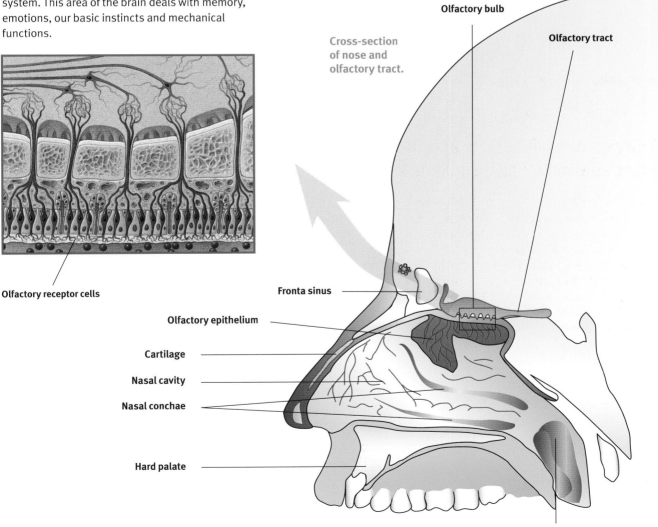

Cross-section of nose and olfactory tract.

Olfactory bulb

Olfactory tract

Olfactory receptor cells

Fronta sinus

Olfactory epithelium

Cartilage

Nasal cavity

Nasal conchae

Hard palate

Naso-pharynx

TOPIC 3: THE EYE

THE EYES

The eyes are the organs of sight. They are positioned separately, but function generally as a pair, assisting in the maintenance of balance.

The eyelids are layers of tissue above and below the front of the eye. They protect the eyes through blinking (20-30 times per minute) and the eyelashes that line the edges of the eyelids filter and trap substances such as dust. Sebaceous and mucous secretions lubricate the eyelids. Lacrimal glands secrete a fluid that keeps the surface of the eye moist and prevents the cornea from drying out. If a foreign body enters the eye,

extra fluid is produced to wash away the particle. Parasympathetic stimulation of these glands causes crying, when large amounts of fluid are produced.

The eyes have a fibrous outer layer known as the sclera or white of eye. At the front of the eye this is covered by a thin mucous membrane, the conjunctiva. The conjunctiva also lines the inside of the eyelids and helps prevents damage and drying of the eye through mucous secretions. Light enters the eye through a transparent dome, the cornea, and it is focused onto the retina at the back of the eye. It passes through the cornea, the

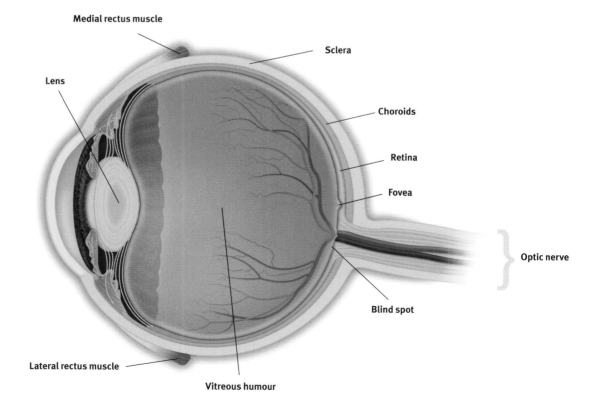

Cross section of the eye

pupil and the iris. The iris is the coloured disc in the centre of the eye, and it controls the amount of light entering through dilation or contraction of the pupil, which appears as a black dot in the middle. The pupil dilates when the light is low and contracts when the light is bright, permitting or restricting the passage of light through the opening. The lens of the eye sits behind the pupil and refracts (bends) light reflected by objects. The ciliary muscles control the thickness of the lens, refracting light and allowing the eyes to focus. The lens becomes thicker to focus on objects nearby and thinner to focus on objects in the distance. The retina forms the inner layer of the eye wall. It contains light sensitive cells (photoreceptors). Near the centre of the retina is the macula,

which is highly sensitive and contains millions of photoreceptors called rods and cones. The photoreceptors permit the conversion of light rays into nerve impulses. In the centre of the retina is a small dimple, the fovea, which provides sharpest vision and is the location of most colour perception At the nasal side of the macula, the nerve fibres gather to form the optic nerve, one of the cranial nerves. This nerve leaves the eye through an area known as the blind spot. The blind spot has no light sensitive cells. The eyeball is divided into two sections, each one filled with fluid. These fluids maintain the internal pressure and shape of the eyeball. Aqueous humour fills the space between the cornea and the lens, providing nourishment to the tissues.

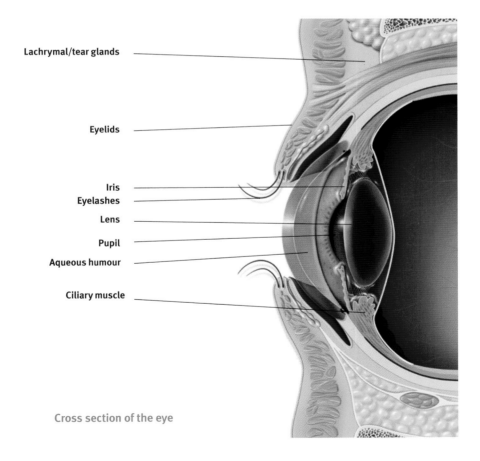

Lachrymal/tear glands

Eyelids

Iris
Eyelashes
Lens
Pupil
Aqueous humour

Ciliary muscle

Cross section of the eye

TOPIC 4: DISEASES AND DISORDERS (PATHOLOGIES)

THE EAR

Deafness - Partial or complete loss of hearing.

Labrynthitis - Is an inflammation of the inner ear which can cause balance disorders.

Meniere's disease - Is a disorder of the inner ear that can affect hearing and balance. It is characterized by episodes of dizziness and tinnitus and progressive hearing loss, usually in one ear.

Motion sickness – Is the state of being dizzy or nauseated because of the motions that occur while travelling in or on a moving vehicle.

Otitis media – Is an acute or chronic inflammation of the middle ear.

Tinnitus – Is a ringing or booming sensation in one or both ears; a symptom of an ear infection.

Vertigo – Is dizziness: a reeling sensation; a feeling that you are about to fall.

THE EYE

Blepharitis - Inflammation of the eyelids characterized by redness, swelling and dried crusts.

Cataracts - An eye disease that involves the clouding or opacification of the natural lens of the eye.

Conjunctivitis - An inflammation of the eye's outer membrane, which causes redness, swelling, itching and watering in one or both eyes and is contagious.

Corneal ulcer - Is an inflammatory or, more seriously, infective condition of the cornea, involving disruption of its epithelial layer with involvement of the corneal stroma.

Glaucoma - An eye disease that damages the optic nerve and impairs vision (sometimes progressing to blindness).

16

Teeth

TOPIC 1: FUNCTIONS OF THE TEETH

Teeth come in 4 different types, each type has a different function. Incisors and Canine teeth are for cutting and are used for bitting off pieces of food. The Chewing of food is done by the premolar and molar teeth using their flat surfaces.

Babies are born with both sets of teeth, the temporary or deciduous teeth and the permanent teeth in the immature form within the mandible and maxilla.

TOPIC 2: STRUCTURE OF A TOOTH

All 32 permanent teeth are embedded in the alveoli or sockets of the alveolar ridges of the mandible and the maxilla. Although the shapes of the teeth types may differ, their essential structure consists of:

THE CROWN
The crown of the tooth is the part that you can see above your gum line. The part of the tooth that is covered by enamel is called the "anatomical crown."

THE ROOT
The root is the part of the tooth that extends into the upper or lower jawbones. Different types of teeth have different root formations. Some, such as incisors and canine teeth, have a single root. Molars may have one, two or three roots depending on their type and location in the mouth. At the end of each root is a small opening called the apical foramen. Blood vessels and nerves pass through this opening to enter the tooth.

THE NECK
The Neck is the narrowed region where the crown meets the root

All teeth are made from:

ENAMEL
The crown of the tooth is covered in a hard outer shell of enamel. Although enamel is able to cope with the stress of chewing, biting and grinding, it is quite brittle and is prone to chipping and cracking. The care and protection of the teeth is important as once enamel is broken, it can not be healed as with broken bones.

CEMENTUM
Cementum covers the root of the tooth and is neither as white nor as hard as enamel is. Cementum helps to hold the tooth in place with tiny fibers in the jawbone.

DENTIN
Dentin makes up most of the tooth and is a bone-like substance that is found under the cementum of the root and the enamel of the crown.

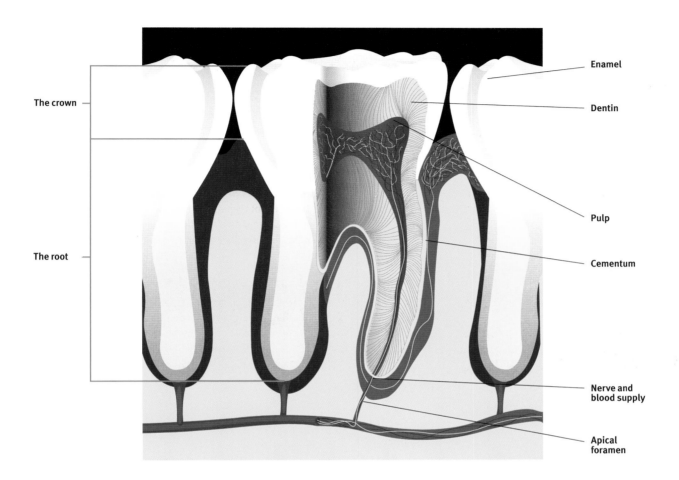

The crown

The root

Enamel

Dentin

Pulp

Cementum

Nerve and
blood supply

Apical
foramen

PULP AND PULP CAVITY

The pulp cavity exists at the core of the tooth beneath the dentin. It is made up of nerves, blood vessels and connective tissue. The tooth is kept alive by the nutrients that are drawn through the blood supply in the 'pulp'. The parts of the pulp that point up towards the points of the teeth (the cusp) are called the pulp horns. The pulp canal, or root canal, is located in the root of the tooth.

PULP CANAL(S) OR ROOT CANAL(S)

The open space inside the root is called the pulp or root canal. The pulp is made of nerves and blood vessels that pass through the root canal and into the tooth. If the pulp becomes infected or inflamed it will not be able to properly feed the tooth and root canal therapy may need to be used to protect the tooth from having to be removed.

● DID YOU KNOW?

There are 20 temporary deciduous teeth, 10 in each jaw. They begin to erupt when the child is about 6 months old.

BLOOD SUPPLY

Maxillary arteries branch through to the teeth and feed most of the arterial blood supply. Venous drainage occurs through a number of veins into the internal jugular veins.

NERVE SUPPLY

Maxillary nerves branch through to the upper teeth to the nerve supply where as the mandibular nerves supply the lower teeth. Both the Maxillary and the mandibular nerves are branches of the trigeminal nerve.

APICAL FORAMEN

There is a small opening at the tip of each root that allows the blood vessels and nerves to enter the tooth, which is called the apical foramen.

TOPIC 3: DISEASES AND DISORDERS

Tooth disorders are nothing to smile about, they include problems such as cavities (also known as tooth decay), infections, and injuries.

PLAQUE

Plaque is a soft and clear substance that can collect as a coating on the surface of the teeth; it comes from the bacteria that live in the mouth. Raw and fibrous foods can be used to scrape off the majority of plaque from the teeth. However, daily diets of processed foods often mean that the plaque is not eliminated as it should be.

CAVITIES

Cavities can cause damage within the structure of the tooth. They are quite common amongst tooth disease and should be treated immediately to avoid a great deal of pain.

GINGIVITIS

Gingivitis can be used as a term to describe non-destructive periodontal disease. The most common form of gingivitis is in response to plaque (also called bacterial biofilms) being left on the tooth's surfaces. It is the most common form of periodontal disease and can also be known as plaque-induced gingivitis. If left untreated, gingivitis can progress into periodontitis. This is a destructive form of periodontal disease.

GUM DISEASE

Periodontal disease is more commonly known as gum disease and is a type of infection that attacks the bones and tissues supporting the teeth. Without treatment, teeth can become painful or even loose, which can result in the tooth being lost altogether.

PERIODONTITIS

Periodontitis is the overarching name for a set of inflammatory diseases that affect the periodontum (the collective name for the tissue that surrounds the teeth). Periodontitis involves progressive loss of the alveolar bone around the teeth. It can lead to loosening or loss of teeth if felt untreated.

HALITOSIS

Halitosis is caused by protein that is broken down by bacteria inside the mouth. When pieces of food get caught between the teeth or in the gums or on the tongue and are not cleaned away properly, as it degrades it can cause a bad smell (or bad breath). However, halitosis can occur as a result of other conditions such as respiratory infections, sinusitis, diabetes and gastrointestinal problems.

DRY MOUTH

Dry mouth (or xerostomia) occurs when the body does not produce enough saliva, leaving the mouth unusually dry. Extended periods of dry mouth can be an indicator of a larger medical condition, or in itself it can cause health problems.

TEETH GRINDING

The unconscious grinding and clenching of the teeth is also known as Bruxism. Teeth grinding usually occurs when an individual is asleep; however, there are a percentage of cases that occur while the person is awake.

TEETH STAINING

Medical experts suggest that human teeth are not supposed to be pure white, and instead their natural colour varies from light yellow to light yellow-red. All teeth become will become darker over time.

● DID YOU KNOW?

The permanent teeth begin to replace the deciduous teeth at around the age of 6, however this process is not completed until around the age of 21.

Index

Index continued

Index continued

Index continued

Index continued

Index continued

Index continued